MANUAL OF MATHEMATICS

GRANINO A. KORN , Ph.D.

Professor of Electrical Engineering
University of Arizona

THERESA M. KORN , M.S.

McGRAW-HILL BOOK COMPANY

New York   *St. Louis*
San Francisco   *Toronto*
London   *Sydney*

This book is for ANNE and JOHN

PREFACE

This small handbook introduces modern mathematical methods and presents comprehensive, connected outlines of basic mathematical subjects for reference and review in a new, concise form.

Each chapter is arranged as a concentrated outline of an entire mathematical subject. Such a presentation is made more manageable and readable through the omission of proofs. Numerous references provide access to textbook material for more detailed study.

The writers have attempted to meet the individual reader's requirements by arranging the subject matter in three levels:

1. The most important formulas and definitions have been collected in easily read tables and boxed groups permitting rapid reference and review.
2. The main text presents in large print a connected review of each subject.
3. More detailed discussions and advanced topics are presented in small print. This arrangement makes it possible to include such material without cluttering the exposition of the main review.

A very extensive index permits the use of the handbook as a short mathematical dictionary.

The material in this manual is largely based on the corresponding sections of our larger "Mathematical Handbook for Scientists and Engineers." Careful editing has reduced the size and cost of this manual, but we have preserved the approach of the larger handbook, which is meant to be a practical and useful reference for professional people.

Chapter 1 begins with a discussion of mathematical models to establish a viewpoint, introduces real and complex numbers, and continues to present the classical material of *basic algebra*, viz., equations, systems of equations, polynomials, and determinants. Chapter 2 outlines *plane and solid analytic geometry*. Chapter 3 deals with *functions, limits,* and *calculus,* including *Fourier analysis* and basic *differential geometry*. Chapter 4 is a review of *vector analysis*.

Chapter 5 introduces *functions of a complex variable* up to the residue theorem and continues to present *Laplace transforms*. Chapter 6 deals with *differential equations*, including the Laplace-transform method, which is basic for engineering analysis, and introductory material on partial differential equations.

As an introduction to the vital topic of system optimization, Chapter 7 presents not only classical *maxima and minima*, but also the simplest methods of the *calculus of variations* and a definition of *linear programming*. Chapter 8, on "modern" algebra, reviews the basic abstract models (groups, rings, fields, vector spaces, and linear algebras) and includes the *matrix algebra* required to represent such models. The chapter closes with a section on *Boolean algebra* and its applications to logic and switching circuits.

Chapter 9 includes reference material on *probability theory*, introduced from a modern axiomatic viewpoint, and material on the elements of *mathematical statistics*. Both topics are essentially indispensable in a modern treatment of mathematical methods. Chapter 10 lists important numerical methods for equation solving, integration, and ordinary differential equations—another important topic in an age of computers. Chapter 11 is a useful *collection of formulas relating to special functions*. Appendixes on *plane geometry*, *plane and spherical trigonometry*, and *combinatorial formulas* have been added for further reference and review. Conveniently arranged tables of Laplace and Fourier transforms, an integral table, and useful numerical tables complete the book.

The writers believe that this volume will give its reader the opportunity to scan a number of mathematical methods and thus to widen his background or correlate his course material with more general developments. The writers earnestly solicit comments and suggestions for improvements, to be addressed to them in care of the publisher.

We are indebted to the Literary Executor of the late Sir Ronald A. Fisher, F.R.S., Cambridge; to Dr. Frank Yates, F.R.S., Rothamsted; and to Messrs. Oliver & Boyd, Ltd., Edinburgh for permission to reprint Tables Nos. III and IV from their book "Statistical Tables for Biological, Agricultural, and Medical Research."

GRANINO A. KORN
THERESA M. KORN

CONTENTS

CHAPTER 3   FUNCTIONS AND LIMITS.   DIFFERENTIAL AND INTEGRAL CALCULUS   59

CHAPTER 4 VECTOR ANALYSIS 101

CHAPTER 5 FUNCTIONS OF A COMPLEX VARIABLE AND LAPLACE TRANSFORMS 120

CHAPTER 6   DIFFERENTIAL EQUATIONS   136

CHAPTER 7   MAXIMA AND MINIMA   157

CHAPTER 8 MODERN ALGEBRA 167

CHAPTER 9 PROBABILITY AND STATISTICS 184

CHAPTER 11   FORMULAS RELATING TO SPECIAL FUNCTIONS 221

APPENDIXES

1 INTRODUCTION. ALGEBRA OF REAL AND COMPLEX NUMBERS

1.1 INTRODUCTION: MATHEMATICAL MODELS

1.1-1 Abstraction and Models. Rational behavior requires decisions, which are frequently described in terms of "operations" on "objects." The complexity of the physical world's phenomena calls for simplified descriptions in terms of verbal or symbolic **models** which "abstract" those properties of objects and operations which are considered essential for the purposes at hand. Different properties may be abstracted for different purposes; for example, a person's life can be described in the form of an epic poem, as a trajectory in space-time, or as a set of tables or graphs relating his body temperature, blood pressure, and bank account to the progress of time. Highly abstract models such as formulas and graphs are often more generally applicable and may be simpler to store and modify than more direct representations such as scale models and photographs.

The properties of a model (say the "laws of nature" described in a physics text) are often so very useful for decision making that one forgets that the model is a construct apart from the real world.   Note, for instance, that branch currents in electrical networks do not add up to zero *because* electrical currents obey Kirchhoff's laws; it would make as much sense to say that a flea has six legs *because* it is so pictured in biology books.   Models (or "theories") must be selected, tested, and, when necessary, modified by recourse to observations or experiments (**scientific method**).   Models can and often should be discarded on the basis of new experimental evidence, or simply when other models prove more convenient or useful (e.g., replacement of Bohr's atomic theory by quantum mechanics).

1.1-2   Mathematical   Models.   Descriptive   and   Constructive Definitions.
Mathematics, in its general sense, is the art and science of defining and manipulating symbolic models, which may or may not represent real situations.   A **mathematical model** involves a class of undefined (abstract, symbolic) **mathematical objects,** such as numbers or vectors, and **relations** between these objects.   A mathematical relation is a hypothetical rule which associates two or more of the undefined objects (see also Secs. 8.1-1 to 8.1-6).   Many relations are described in terms of **mathematical operations** associating one or more objects (**operand, operands**) with another object or set of objects (**result**).   The abstract model, with its unspecified objects, relations, and operations, is *defined* by a self-consistent set of rules (**defining postulates**) which introduce the operations to be employed and state general relations among their results (**descriptive definition** of a mathematical model in terms of its properties).

A **constructive definition** introduces a mathematical model in terms of previously defined mathematical concepts (e.g., definition of vector or matrix addition in terms of numerical addition, Secs. 4.2-2 and 8.2-3).   The logical consistency of a descriptive definition is usually demonstrated by the construction or exhibition of an example which satisfies the defining postulates (**existence proof**).   Note carefully that the existence of mathematical problem solutions is *not* ensured by the existence of corresponding physical phenomena; existence proofs check the validity of *models*.

A mathematical model will reproduce suitably chosen features of a physical situation if it is possible to establish **rules of correspondence** relating specific physical objects and relationships to corresponding mathematical objects and relationships. It may also be instructive and/or enjoyable to construct mathematical models which do not match any counterpart in the physical world. The most generally familiar mathematical models are more or less directly abstracted from physical experience (counting, ordering, comparing, measuring).

1.1-3 Representation of Models. Two mathematical models are **isomorphic** if and only if there exists a one-to-one reciprocal correspondence between the objects of the two models such that corresponding objects satisfy corresponding relations in each model. Isomorphic models can thus "represent" one another, and this can be a very great convenience. In particular, objects and operations of more general mathematical models are often labeled with sets of real numbers which may be related to the results of physical measurements. The resulting **representations** of mathematical models in terms of numerical operations are not unique, but depend on the scheme of measurements (**frame of reference, coordinate system**) used to label objects with numbers (e.g., analytic geometry, Sec. 2.1-1).

1.1-4 Algebra and Algebras. The word *algebra* has three loosely related meanings.

1. The theory of "algebraic" operations, i.e., operations involving a finite number of "binary" operations (usually called addition and/or multiplication) defined for a specific model, e.g., *algebra of real numbers, vector algebra, matrix algebra.* Such an algebra is necessarily also concerned with the solution of equations.
2. A mathematical model of a type defined by algebraic operations, e.g., a *linear algebra* (Sec. 8.1-6), a *Boolean algebra* (Sec. 8.3-1).
3. A general subject encompassing such algebras, e.g., *elementary algebra, modern algebra, abstract algebra.*

1.2 NUMBERS AND BASIC OPERATIONS

1.2-1 Operations with Real Numbers. The remainder of this chapter deals with the algebra of real and complex numbers, i.e., with the study of those relations between real and complex numbers which involve a finite number of additions and multiplications (see also Sec. 1.1-4). This is considered to include the solution of equations based on such relations, even though actual exact numerical solutions may require infinite numbers of additions and/or multiplications.   The definitions and relations presented in this chapter serve as basic tools in many more general mathematical models.

Addition and multiplication of real numbers satisfy the following rules.

$a + b$ and ab are real numbers (or algebraic numbers, rational numbers, integers, positive integers) if this is true for a and b (CLOSURE)
$a + b = b + a$ $ab = ba$ (COMMUTATIVE LAWS)
$a + (b + c) = (a + b) + c = a + b + c$
$\qquad\qquad a(bc) = (ab)c = abc$ (ASSOCIATIVE LAWS)   (1.2-1)
$a \cdot 1 = a$ (MULTIPLICATIVE IDENTITY)
$a(b + c) = ab + ac$ (DISTRIBUTIVE LAW)
$a + c = b + c$ implies $a = b$
$ca = cb, c \neq 0$ implies $a = b$ (CANCELLATION LAWS)

The real number 0 (**zero, additive identity**) has the properties

$$a + 0 = a \qquad a \cdot 0 = 0 \qquad\qquad\qquad (1.2\text{-}2)$$

for every real a.

The (unique) **additive inverse** $-a$ and the (unique) **multiplicative inverse (reciprocal)** $a^{-1} = 1/a$ of a real number a are respectively defined by

$$a + (-a) = a - a = 0 \qquad aa^{-1} = 1 \qquad (a \neq 0) \qquad (1.2\text{-}3)$$

Division by 0 is not admissible.

1.2-2   The Real-number System.   In addition to the "algebraic" properties (1), the class of the **positive integers** 1, 2, . . . has the properties of being **simply ordered** (n is "greater than" m or $n > m$ if and only if $n = m + x$, where x is a positive integer) and **well-ordered** (every nonempty set of positive integers has a smallest element).   *A set of positive integers containing* (1) 1 *and the "successor"* $n + 1$ *of each of its elements n, or* (2) *all integers less than n for any n, contains all positive integers (Principle of Finite Induction).*

The properties of positive integers may be alternately defined by *Peano's Five Axioms,* viz., (1) 1 is a positive integer, (2) each positive integer n has a unique successor $S(n)$, (3) $S(n) \neq 1$, (4) $S(n) = S(m)$ implies $n = m$, (5) the principle of finite induction holds.   Addition and multiplication satisfying the rules (1) are defined by the "recursive" definitions $n + 1 = S(n)$, $n + S(m) = S(n + m)$; $n \cdot 1 = n, n \cdot S(m) = n \cdot m + n$.

Operations on the elements $m - n$ of the **class of all integers** (positive, negative, or zero) are interpreted as operations on corresponding pairs (m, n) of positive integers m, n such that $(m - n) + n = m$, where 0, defined by $n + 0 = n$, corresponds to (n, n), for all n. An integer is **negative** if and only if it is neither positive nor zero. The study of the properties of integers is called **arithmetic.**

Operations on **rational numbers** m/n $(n \neq 0)$ are interpreted as operations on corresponding pairs (m, n) of integers m, n such that $(m/n)n = m$. m/n is positive if and only if mn is positive.

Real **algebraic** (including rational and **irrational**) **numbers,** corresponding to (real) roots of algebraic equations with integral coefficients (Sec. 1.4-2) and real **transcendental numbers,** for which no such correspondence exists, may be introduced in terms of limiting processes involving rational numbers (*Dedekind cuts,* Ref. 6).

The class of all rational numbers comprises the roots of all linear equations (Sec. 1.4-5) with rational coefficients, and includes the integers. The class of all real algebraic numbers comprises the real roots of all algebraic equations (Sec. 1.4-2) with algebraic coefficients, including the rational numbers. The class of all real numbers contains the real roots of all equations involving a finite or infinite number of additions and multiplications of real numbers and includes real algebraic and transcendental numbers.

A real number a is greater than the real number b $(a > b, b < a)$ if and only if $a = b + x$, where x is a positive real number.

1.2-3   *Equality and Identity.* An equation $a = b$ implies $b = a$ (*symmetry* of the equality relation), and $a + c = b + c$, $ac = bc$ [in general, $f(a) = f(b)$ if $f(a)$ stands for an operation having a unique result]. $a = b$ and $b = c$ together imply $a = c$ (*transitivity* of the equality relation). $ab \neq 0$ implies $a \neq 0$, $b \neq 0$.

In general, an equation involving operations on a quantity x or on several quantities x_1, x_2, . . . will hold only for special values of x or special sets of values x_1, x_2, . . . (see also Sec. 1.4-1). *If it is desired to stress the fact* that an equation holds for *all* values of x or of x_1, x_2, . . . within certain ranges of interest, the identity symbol $\equiv$ may be used instead of the equality symbol $=$ [***Example:*** $(x - 1)(x + 1) \equiv x^2 - 1$], and/or the ranges of the variables in question may be indicated on the right of the equation. $a \equiv b$ (better $a \overset{\Delta}{\equiv} b$) is also used with the meaning "a is defined as equal to b."

1.2-4   *Absolute Values.* The **absolute value** $|a|$ of a real number a is defined as equal to a if $a \geq 0$ and equal to $-a$ if $a < 0$. Note

$$|a| \geq 0 \qquad\qquad |a| = 0 \text{ implies } a = 0 \qquad\qquad (1.2\text{-}4)$$

$$\big||a| - |b|\big| \leq |a + b| \leq |a| + |b| \qquad \big||a| - |b|\big| \leq |a - b| \leq |a| + |b|$$

$$|ab| = |a|\,|b| \qquad \left|\frac{a}{b}\right| = \frac{|a|}{|b|} \qquad (b \neq 0) \qquad (1.2\text{-}5)$$

$$|a| \leq A \text{ and } |b| \leq B \text{ implies } |a| + |b| \leq A + B \text{ and } |ab| \leq AB$$

1.2-5   *Powers and Roots.*   The **n**th **power** of any real number (**base**) a is defined as the product of n factors equal to a, where the **exponent** n is a positive integer.   Powers involving exponents p, q other than positive integers are defined so that

$$a^p a^q = a^{p+q} \qquad (a^p)^q = a^{pq}$$

$$a^{-p} = \frac{1}{a^p} \qquad a^0 = 1 \qquad (a \neq 0) \tag{1.2-6}$$

where $x = a^{1/p} \equiv \sqrt[p]{a}$ (**p**th **root** of the **radicand** a) is a solution of the equation $x^p = a$.   In general, $\sqrt[p]{a}$ is not unique; if a is a positive real number, we shall define $\sqrt[p]{a}$ specifically as the positive real value of $a^{1/p}$, although this is also written as $+\sqrt[p]{a}$ or $\underset{+}{\sqrt[p]{a}}$.   Thus, the positive value of $\pm\sqrt[2]{a}$ (**square root** of $a > 0$) is written $\sqrt{a}$ or $\underset{+}{\sqrt{a}}$.   For $q \neq 0$,

$$\frac{a^p}{a^q} = a^{p-q} \qquad a^{\frac{p}{q}} = \sqrt[q]{a^p} = (\sqrt[q]{a})^p \qquad \sqrt[p]{\sqrt[q]{a}} = \sqrt[pq]{a}$$

$$(ab)^p = a^p b^p \qquad \sqrt[p]{ab} = \sqrt[p]{a}\sqrt[p]{b} \tag{1.2-7}$$

$$\left(\frac{a}{b}\right)^p = \frac{a^p}{b^p} \qquad \sqrt{\frac{a}{b}} = \frac{\sqrt[p]{a}}{\sqrt[p]{b}} \qquad (b \neq 0)$$

1.2-6   *Logarithms.*   The **logarithm** $x = \log_c a$ to the **base** $c > 0$ ($c \neq 1$) of the number (**numerus**) $a > 0$ may be defined as the solution of the equation

$$c^x = a \qquad \text{or} \qquad c^{\log_c a} = a \tag{1.2-8}$$

(see also Sec. 11.1-10). $\log_c a$ may be a transcendental number (Sec. 1.2-1).   Note

$$\log_c c = 1 \qquad \log_c c^p = p \qquad \log_c 1 = 0$$
$$\log_c (ab) = \log_c a + \log_c b \qquad \text{(\small LOGARITHMIC PROPERTY)}$$
$$\log_c \left(\frac{a}{b}\right) = \log_c a - \log_c b \tag{1.2-9}$$
$$\log_c (a^p) = p \log_c a \qquad \log_c (\sqrt[p]{a}) = \frac{1}{p} \log_c a \qquad (p \neq 0)$$

$$\log_{c'} a = \log_c a \log_{c'} c = \frac{\log_c a}{\log_c c'} \quad \log_{c'} c = \frac{1}{\log_c c'} \quad (c' \neq 1)$$

(CHANGE OF BASE)   (1.2-10)

Of particular interest are the "common" logarithms to the base 10 and the *natural (Napierian) logarithms* to the base

$$e = \lim_{n \to \infty} \left(1 + \frac{1}{n}\right)^n = 2.71828182 \cdots \qquad (1.2\text{-}11)$$

e is a transcendental number. $\log_e a$ may be written ln a, log a, or log nat a. $\log_{10} a$ is sometimes written log a. Note

$$\log_e a = \frac{\log_{10} a}{\log_{10} e} = \log_e 10 \log_{10} a = (2.30259 \cdots) \log_{10} a$$

$$\log_{10} a = \frac{\log_e a}{\log_e 10} = \log_{10} e \log_e a = (0.43429 \cdots) \log_e a$$

(1.2-12)

1.2-7 Complex Numbers. **Complex numbers** (sometimes called imaginary numbers) are not numbers in the elementary sense used in connection with counting or measuring; they constitute a new class of mathematical objects defined by the properties described below.

Each complex number c may be made to correspond to a unique pair (a, b) of real numbers a, b, and conversely. The sum and product of two complex numbers $c_1 \leftrightarrow (a_1, b_1)$ and $c_2 \leftrightarrow (a_2, b_2)$ are defined as $c_1 + c_2 \leftrightarrow (a_1 + a_2, b_1 + b_2)$ and $c_1 c_2 \leftrightarrow (a_1 a_2 - b_1 b_2, a_1 b_2 + a_2 b_1)$, respectively. The real numbers a are "embedded" in this class of complex numbers as the pairs $(a, 0)$. The **unit imaginary number*** i defined as $i \leftrightarrow (0, 1)$ satisfies the relations

$$i^2 = (-i)^2 = -1 \quad i = \sqrt{-1} \quad -i = -\sqrt{-1} \quad (1.2\text{-}13)$$

Each complex number $c \leftrightarrow (a, b)$ may be written as the sum $c = a + ib$ of a real number $a \leftrightarrow (a, 0)$ and a **pure imaginary number** $ib \leftrightarrow (0, b)$. The real numbers $a = \text{Re}\ (c)$ and $b = \text{Im}\ (c)$ are respectively called the **real part** of c and the **imaginary part** of c. Two complex numbers $c = a + ib$ and $c^* = a - ib$ having equal real parts and equal and opposite imaginary parts are called **complex conjugates.**

Two complex numbers $c_1 = a_1 + ib_1$ and $c_2 = a_2 + ib_2$ are **equal** if

---

* Many engineers (especially electrical engineers) write j instead of i.

and only if their respective real and imaginary parts are equal, i.e., $c_1 = c_2$ if and only if $a_1 = a_2$, $b_1 = b_2$. $c = a + ib = 0$ implies $a = b = 0$.
ADDITION AND MULTIPLICATION OF COMPLEX NUMBERS SATISFIES ALL RULES OF SEC. 1.2-1, with

$$i^2 = -1 \qquad i^3 = -i \qquad i^4 = 1 \qquad i^{4n+1} = i$$
$$i^{4n+2} = -1 \qquad i^{4n+3} = -i \qquad (n = 0, 1, 2, \ldots) \qquad (1.2\text{-}14)$$

$$
\begin{aligned}
&c_1 \pm c_2 = (a_1 \pm a_2) + i(b_1 \pm b_2) \\
&c_1 c_2 = (a_1 a_2 - b_1 b_2) + i(a_1 b_2 + a_2 b_1) \\
&\frac{c_1}{c_2} = \frac{a_1 + ib_1}{a_2 + ib_2} = \frac{(a_1 a_2 + b_1 b_2) + i(a_2 b_1 - a_1 b_2)}{a_2{}^2 + b_2{}^2} \qquad (c_2 \neq 0) \\
&(c_1 + c_2)^* = c_1^* + c_2^* \qquad (c_1 c_2)^* = c_1^* c_2^* \\
&\left(\frac{c_1}{c_2}\right)^* = \frac{c_1^*}{c_2^*} \qquad (c_2 \neq 0) \qquad (c^*)^* = c \\
&a = \mathrm{Re}\,(c) = \frac{(c + c^*)}{2} \qquad b = \mathrm{Im}\,(c) = \frac{(c - c^*)}{2i}
\end{aligned}
\qquad (1.2\text{-}15)
$$

Complex numbers $z = x + iy$ are conveniently represented as points $(z) \equiv (x, y)$ or corresponding position vectors (Sec. 2.5-2) in the **Argand** or **Gauss plane** (Fig. 1.2-1).   The (rectangular cartesian,

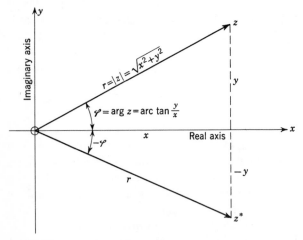

Fig. 1.2-1 Representation of complex numbers as points or position vectors. The x and the y axis are called the real axis and the imaginary axis, respectively.

Sec. 2.2-1) x axis and y axis are referred to as the **real axis** and **imaginary axis,** respectively. The abscissa and ordinate of each point (z) respectively represent the real part x and the imaginary part y of z. The corresponding polar coordinates (Sec. 2.2-4) r, φ are, respectively, the **absolute value (norm, modulus) and the argument (amplitude)** of the complex number z:

$$r = |z| = \sqrt[+]{x^2 + y^2} = \sqrt[+]{zz^*} = |z^*|$$
$$\varphi = \arg(z) = \arctan(y/x) = -\arg(z^*)$$
$$x = r\cos\varphi \qquad y = r\sin\varphi \qquad\qquad (1.2\text{-}16)$$
$$z = x + iy = r(\cos\varphi + i\sin\varphi) = re^{i\varphi}$$

Addition of complex numbers corresponds to addition of the corresponding position vectors. Given $z_1 = r_1(\cos\varphi_1 + i\sin\varphi_1)$, $z_2 = r_2(\cos\varphi_2 + i\sin\varphi_2)$,

$$z_1 z_2 = r_1 r_2 [\cos(\varphi_1 + \varphi_2) + i\sin(\varphi_1 + \varphi_2)]$$
$$\frac{z_1}{z_2} = \frac{r_1}{r_2}[\cos(\varphi_1 - \varphi_2) + i\sin(\varphi_1 - \varphi_2)] \qquad (z_2 \neq 0)$$
$$z^p = r^p(\cos\varphi + i\sin\varphi)^p = r^p[\cos(p\varphi) + i\sin(p\varphi)]$$

(DE MOIVRE'S THEOREM)   (1.2-17)

ALL FORMULAS OF SECS. 1.2-2 TO 1.2-6 HOLD FOR COMPLEX NUMBERS.

Note

$$\left.\begin{array}{l} \sqrt[n]{1} = \cos\dfrac{2k\pi}{n} + i\sin\dfrac{2k\pi}{n} \\[2ex] \sqrt[n]{-1} = \cos\dfrac{(2k+1)\pi}{n} + i\sin\dfrac{(2k+1)\pi}{n} \end{array}\right\} \begin{array}{l} (n = 1, 2, \ldots; \\ k = 0, 1, 2, \ldots, n-1) \\ (n\ values) \end{array} \quad (1.2\text{-}18)$$

In particular,

$$\sqrt{1} = \pm 1 \qquad \sqrt{-1} = \pm i \qquad\qquad\qquad\qquad (1.2\text{-}19)$$

$$\sqrt[3]{1} = \begin{cases} 1 \\ \cos 120° + i\sin 120° = \tfrac{1}{2}(-1 + i\sqrt{3}) \\ \cos 120° - i\sin 120° = \tfrac{1}{2}(-1 - i\sqrt{3}) \end{cases}$$
$$\qquad\qquad\qquad\qquad\qquad\qquad\qquad\qquad\qquad (1.2\text{-}20)$$
$$\sqrt[3]{-1} = \begin{cases} \cos 60° + i\sin 60° = \tfrac{1}{2}(1 + i\sqrt{3}) \\ -1 \\ \cos 60° - i\sin 60° = \tfrac{1}{2}(1 - i\sqrt{3}) \end{cases}$$

1.2-8   The Binomial Theorem and Related Formulas. The basic addition and multiplication rules for real and complex numbers a, b,

c, . . . imply the following relations, which are useful for simplifying complicated expressions.

$$(a \pm b)^2 = a^2 \pm 2ab + b^2$$
$$(a \pm b)^3 = a^3 \pm 3a^2b + 3ab^2 \pm b^3$$
$$(a \pm b)^4 = a^4 \pm 4a^3b + 6a^2b^2 \pm 4ab^3 + b^4$$
$$\cdots \cdots \cdots \cdots \cdots \cdots \cdots$$

$$(a + b)^n = \sum_{j=0}^{n} \binom{n}{j} a^j b^{n-j} \qquad (n = 1, 2, \ldots) \qquad (1.2\text{-}21)$$

with $\quad \dbinom{n}{j} = \dfrac{n!}{j!(n-j)!}$

$$(j = 0, 1, 2, \ldots \le n = 0, 1, 2, \ldots)$$

(*Binomial Theorem* for integral exponents n; see also Sec. 11.1-11.)   The **factorial** $n!$ of any integer $n \ge 0$ is defined by

$$0! = 1 \qquad n! = 1 \cdot 2 \cdot 3 \cdots (n-1)n$$

The quantities $\dbinom{n}{j}$ are called **binomial coefficients.**

Note also

$$(a + b + c)^2 = a^2 + b^2 + c^2 + 2ab + 2ac + 2bc \qquad (1.2\text{-}22)$$

$$(a^2 - b^2) = (a + b)(a - b)$$
$$(a^2 + b^2) = (a + ib)(a - ib) \qquad\qquad (1.2\text{-}23)$$

$$a^n - b^n = (a - b)(a^{n-1} + a^{n-2}b + \cdots + ab^{n-2} + b^{n-1})$$
$$(n = 1, 2, \ldots) \qquad (1.2\text{-}24)$$

If n is an *even* positive integer,

$$a^n - b^n = (a + b)(a^{n-1} - a^{n-2}b + \cdots + ab^{n-2} - b^{n-1}) \qquad (1.2\text{-}25)$$

If n is an *odd* positive integer,

$$a^n + b^n = (a + b)(a^{n-1} - a^{n-2}b + \cdots - ab^{n-2} + b^{n-1}) \qquad (1.2\text{-}26)$$

Note also

$$a^4 + a^2b^2 + b^4 = (a^2 + ab + b^2)(a^2 - ab + b^2) \qquad (1.2\text{-}27)$$

1.2-9   *Polynomials and Symmetric Functions.*   (*a*) A **polynomial in** (**integral rational function** of) the quantities $x_1, x_2, \ldots, x_n$ is a sum involving a finite number of terms of the form $ax_1^{k_1}x_2^{k_2} \cdots x_n^{k_n}$, where each k_j is a nonnegative integer.   The largest value of $k_1 + k_2 + \cdots + k_n$ occurring in any term is the **degree** of the polynomial.   A polynomial is **homogeneous** if and only if all its terms are of the same degree.

(*b*) A polynomial in x_1, x_2, . . . , x_n (and more generally, any function of x_1, x_2, . . . , x_n) is (**completely**) **symmetric** if and only if its value is unchanged by permutations of the x_1, x_2, . . . , x_n for any set of values x_1, x_2, . . . , x_n. The **elementary symmetric functions** S_1, S_2, . . . , S_n of x_1, x_2, . . . , x_n are the polynomials

$$\begin{aligned} S_1 &\equiv x_1 + x_2 + \cdots + x_n & S_2 &\equiv x_1 x_2 + x_1 x_3 + \cdots \\ S_3 &\equiv x_1 x_2 x_3 + x_1 x_2 x_4 + \cdots & \cdots \quad S_n &\equiv x_1 x_2 \cdots x_n \end{aligned} \tag{1.2-28}$$

where S_k is the sum of all $\dfrac{n!}{(n-k)!k!}$ products combining k factors x_j without repetition of subscripts (see also Table C-2). *Every polynomial symmetric in* x_1, x_2, . . . , x_n *can be rewritten as a unique polynomial in* S_1, S_2, . . . , S_n; the coefficients in the new polynomial are algebraic sums of integral multiples of the given coefficients.

Every polynomial symmetric in x_1, x_2, . . . , x_n *can also be expressed as a polynomial in a finite number of the symmetric functions*

$$s_0 \equiv n \qquad s_1 \equiv \sum_{i=1}^{n} x_i \qquad s_2 \equiv \sum_{i=1}^{n} x_i^2 \qquad \cdots \qquad s_k \equiv \sum_{i=1}^{n} x_i^k \tag{1.2-29}$$

The symmetric functions (28) and (29) are related by *Newton's formulas*

$$(-1)^k k S_k + (-1)^{k-1} S_{k-1} s_1 + (-1)^{k-2} S_{k-2} s_2 + \cdots = 0 \qquad (k = 1, 2, \ldots) \tag{1.2-30}$$

where one defines $S_k = 0$ for $k > n$ and $k < 0$, and $S_0 = 1$ (see also Sec. 1.4-3).

1.2-10 *Arithmetic Progression.* If a_0 is the first term and d is the *common difference* between successive terms a_j, then

$$a_j = a_0 + jd \qquad (j = 0, 1, 2, \ldots)$$

$$s_n = \sum_{j=0}^{n} a_j = \frac{n+1}{2}(2a_0 + nd) = \frac{n+1}{2}(a_0 + a_n) \tag{1.2-31}$$

1.2-11 *Geometric Progression.* If a_0 is the first term and r is the *common ratio* of successive terms, then (see Sec. 11.1-11 for infinite geometric series),

$$a_j = a_0 r^j \qquad (j = 0, 1, 2, \ldots)$$

$$s_n = \sum_{j=0}^{n} a_j = \sum_{j=0}^{n} a_0 r^j = a_0 \frac{1 - r^{n+1}}{1 - r} = \frac{a_0 - a_n r}{1 - r} \tag{1.2-32}$$

1.3 DETERMINANTS

1.3-1 Definition. The **determinant**

$$D = \det[a_{ik}] = \begin{vmatrix} a_{11} & a_{12} & \cdots & a_{1n} \\ a_{21} & a_{22} & \cdots & a_{2n} \\ \cdot & \cdot & \cdots & \cdot \\ a_{n1} & a_{n2} & \cdots & a_{nn} \end{vmatrix} \tag{1.3-1}$$

of the square array (matrix, Sec. 8.2-1) of n^2 (real or complex) numbers (**elements**) a_{ik} is the sum of the $n!$ terms $(-1)^r a_{1k_1} a_{2k_2} \cdots a_{nk_n}$ each corresponding to one of the $n!$ different ordered sets $k_1, k_2, \ldots, k_n$ obtained by r interchanges of elements from the set $1, 2, \ldots, n$. The number n is the **order** of the determinant (1). Actual computation of a determinant in terms of its elements is simplified by the use of Secs. 1.3-2 and 1.3-3.

1.3-2   *Minors and Cofactors.   Expansion in Terms of Cofactors.*
The (complementary) **minor** D_{ik} of the element a_{ik} in the nth-order determinant (1) is the $(n-1)^{\text{st}}$-order determinant obtained from (1) on erasing the ith row and the kth column. The **cofactor** A_{ik} of the element a_{ik} is the coefficient of a_{ik} in the expansion of D, or

$$\mathrm{A}_{ik} = (-1)^{i+k} D_{ik} = \frac{\partial D}{\partial a_{ik}} \tag{1.3-2}$$

A determinant D may be represented in terms of the elements and cofactors of any one row or column as follows:

$$D = \det[a_{ik}] = \sum_{i=1}^{n} a_{ij}\mathrm{A}_{ij} = \sum_{k=1}^{n} a_{jk}\mathrm{A}_{jk} \qquad (j = 1, 2, \ldots, n)$$

(SIMPLE LAPLACE DEVELOPMENT) $\qquad\qquad\qquad\qquad$ (1.3-3)

Note also that

$$\sum_{i=1}^{n} a_{ij}\mathrm{A}_{ih} = \sum_{k=1}^{n} a_{jk}\mathrm{A}_{hk} = 0 \qquad (j \neq h) \tag{1.3-4}$$

1.3-3   *Examples: Second- and Third-order Determinants*

$$\begin{vmatrix} a_{11} & a_{12} \\ a_{21} & a_{22} \end{vmatrix} = a_{11}a_{22} - a_{21}a_{12} \tag{1.3-5}$$

$$\begin{vmatrix} a_{11} & a_{12} & a_{13} \\ a_{21} & a_{22} & a_{23} \\ a_{31} & a_{32} & a_{33} \end{vmatrix} = a_{11}a_{22}a_{33} - a_{11}a_{23}a_{32} + a_{12}a_{23}a_{31} - a_{13}a_{22}a_{31} + a_{13}a_{21}a_{32} - a_{12}a_{21}a_{33}$$

$$= a_{11}(a_{22}a_{33} - a_{32}a_{23}) - a_{21}(a_{12}a_{33} - a_{32}a_{13}) + a_{31}(a_{12}a_{23} - a_{22}a_{13})$$
$$= a_{11}(a_{22}a_{33} - a_{32}a_{23}) - a_{12}(a_{21}a_{33} - a_{31}a_{23}) + a_{13}(a_{21}a_{32} - a_{31}a_{22})$$
$$\text{etc.} \tag{1.3-6}$$

$$D = \begin{vmatrix} 2 & 2 & 3 \\ 1 & -4 & 1 \\ 3 & 4 & 2 \end{vmatrix} = 26$$

1.3-4   *Miscellaneous Theorems.*   (a) *The value D of a determinant (1) is not changed by any of the following operations:*

1. *The rows are written as columns, and the columns as rows [interchange of i and k in Eq. (1)].*
2. *An even number of interchanges of any two rows or two columns.*
3. *Addition of the elements of any row (or column), all multiplied, if desired, by the same parameter α, to the respective corresponding elements of another row (or column, respectively).*

Examples:

$$
\begin{vmatrix}
a_{11} & a_{12} & \cdots & a_{1n} \\
a_{21} & a_{22} & \cdots & a_{2n} \\
\cdot & \cdot & & \cdot \\
a_{n1} & a_{n2} & \cdots & a_{nn}
\end{vmatrix}
=
\begin{vmatrix}
a_{11} & a_{21} & \cdots & a_{n1} \\
a_{12} & a_{22} & \cdots & a_{n2} \\
\cdot & \cdot & & \cdot \\
a_{1n} & a_{2n} & \cdots & a_{nn}
\end{vmatrix}
$$

$$
=
\begin{vmatrix}
a_{11} + \alpha a_{12} & a_{12} & \cdots & a_{1n} \\
a_{21} + \alpha a_{22} & a_{22} & \cdots & a_{2n} \\
\cdot & \cdot & & \cdot \\
a_{n1} + \alpha a_{n2} & a_{n2} & \cdots & a_{nn}
\end{vmatrix}
\tag{1.3-7}
$$

(b) *An odd number of interchanges of any two rows or two columns is equivalent to multiplication of the determinant by -1.*

(c) *Multiplication of all the elements of any one row or column by a factor α is equivalent to multiplication of the determinant by α.*

(d) *If the elements of the jth row (or column) of an nth-order determinant D are represented as sums $\sum_{r=1}^{m} c_{r1}, \sum_{r=1}^{m} c_{r2}, \ldots, \sum_{r=1}^{m} c_{rn}$, D is equal to the sum $\sum_{r=1}^{m} D_r$ of m n^{th}-order determinants D_r. The elements of each D_r are identical with those of D, except for the elements of the jth row (or column, respectively), which are $c_{r1}, c_{r2}, \ldots, c_{rn}$.*

Example:

$$
\begin{vmatrix}
a_{11} + b_{11} & a_{12} + b_{12} & \cdots & a_{1n} + b_{1n} \\
a_{21} & a_{22} & \cdots & a_{2n} \\
\cdot & \cdot & & \cdot \\
a_{n1} & a_{n2} & \cdots & a_{nn}
\end{vmatrix}
$$

$$
=
\begin{vmatrix}
a_{11} & a_{12} & \cdots & a_{1n} \\
a_{21} & a_{22} & \cdots & a_{2n} \\
\cdot & \cdot & & \cdot \\
a_{n1} & a_{n2} & \cdots & a_{nn}
\end{vmatrix}
+
\begin{vmatrix}
b_{11} & b_{12} & \cdots & b_{1n} \\
a_{21} & a_{22} & \cdots & a_{2n} \\
\cdot & \cdot & & \cdot \\
a_{n1} & a_{n2} & \cdots & a_{nn}
\end{vmatrix}
\tag{1.3-8}
$$

(e) *A determinant is equal to zero if*

1. *All elements of any row or column are zero.*
2. *Corresponding elements of any two rows or columns are equal, or proportional with the same proportionality factor.*

1.3-5   *Multiplication of Determinants* (see also Sec. 8.2-3).   The
product of two n^{th}-order determinants $\det [a_{ik}]$ and $\det [b_{ik}]$ is

$$\det [a_{ik}] \det [b_{ik}] = \det \left[\sum_{j=1}^{n} a_{ij}b_{jk} \right] = \det \left[\sum_{j=1}^{n} a_{ji}b_{kj} \right]$$

$$= \det \left[\sum_{j=1}^{n} a_{ij}b_{kj} \right] = \det \left[\sum_{j=1}^{n} a_{ji}b_{jk} \right] \qquad (1.3\text{-}9)$$

1.4   ALGEBRAIC EQUATIONS: GENERAL THEOREMS

1.4-1   *Solution of an Equation.   Roots.*   To **solve an equation**

$$f(x) = 0 \qquad\qquad\qquad (1.4\text{-}1)$$

for the unknown x means to find values of x [**roots** of Eq. (1), **zeros**
of $f(x)$] which satisfy the given equation. $x = x_1$ is a **root (zero) of
order (multiplicity)** m (**multiple** root if $m > 1$) if and only if, for
$x = x_1$, $f(x)/(x - x_1)^{m-1} = 0$ and $f(x)/(x - x_1)^{m} \neq 0$.   A **complete
solution** of Eq. (1) specifies all roots together with their orders.   Solutions may be verified by substitution.

1.4-2   *Algebraic Equations.*   An equation (1) of the form

$$f(x) = a_0 x^n + a_1 x^{n-1} + \cdots + a_{n-1}x + a_n = 0 \qquad (a_0 \neq 0) \qquad (1.4\text{-}2)$$

where the **coefficients** a_i are real or complex numbers, is called an
algebraic equation of degree n **in the unknown** x. $f(x)$ is a
polynomial of degree n in x (see also Sec. 1.2-9). a_n is the **absolute
term** of the polynomial (2).

   *An algebraic equation of degree n has exactly n roots if a root of order
m is counted as m roots (Fundamental Theorem of Algebra).*

   Numbers expressible as roots of algebraic equations with real integral coefficients are algebraic numbers (in general complex, with rational and/or irrational
real and imaginary parts); if the coefficients are algebraic, the roots are still algebraic
(see also Sec. 1.2-1).   General formulas for the roots of algebraic equations in terms
of the coefficients and involving only a finite number of additions, subtractions,
multiplications, divisions, and root extractions exist *only* for equations of degree one
(**linear equations,** Sec. 1.4-5a), two (**quadratic equations,** Sec. 1.4-5b), three
(**cubic equations,** Sec. 1.4-6), and four (**quartic equations,** Sec. 1.4-7).

1.4-3   Relations between Roots and Coefficients. The symmetric functions S_k and s_k (Sec. 1.2-9) of the roots $x_1, x_2, \ldots, x_n$ of an algebraic equation (2) are related to the coefficients $a_0, a_1, \ldots, a_n$ as follows:

$$\frac{a_k}{a_0} = (-1)^k S_k \qquad (k = 0, 1, 2, \ldots, n) \tag{1.4-3}$$

$$ka_k + a_{k-1}s_1 + a_{k-2}s_2 + \cdots + a_0 s_k = 0 \qquad (k = 1, 2, \ldots) \tag{1.4-4}$$

where one defines $a_k = 0$ for $k > n$ and $k < 0$. The equations (4) are another version of *Newton's formulas* (1.2-30).

1.4-4   Real Algebraic Equations and Their Roots. An algebraic equation (2) is called **real** if and only if all coefficients a_i are real; the corresponding real polynomial $f(x)$ is real for all real values of x. The following theorems are useful for determining the general location of roots (e.g., prior to numerical solution, Sec. 10.1-1; see also Sec. 5.3-5).

In theorems (*b*) through (*f*), a root of order m is counted as m roots.

(*a*) COMPLEX ROOTS. *Complex roots of real algebraic equations occur in pairs of complex conjugates* (Sec. 1.2-7). *A real algebraic equation of odd degree must have at least one real root.*

(*b*) ROUTH-HURWITZ CRITERION. *The number of roots with positive real parts of a real algebraic equation* (2) *is equal to the number of sign changes (disregard vanishing terms) in either one of the sequences*

$$T_0, T_1, \frac{T_2}{T_1}, \frac{T_3}{T_2}, \ldots, \frac{T_n}{T_{n-1}} \tag{1.4-5}$$

or $\quad T_0, T_1, T_1 T_2, T_2 T_3, \ldots, T_{n-1} T_{n-2}, a_n$

where $\quad T_0 = a_0 > 0 \qquad T_1 = a_1 \qquad T_2 = \begin{vmatrix} a_1 & a_0 \\ a_3 & a_2 \end{vmatrix}$

$$T_3 = \begin{vmatrix} a_1 & a_0 & 0 \\ a_3 & a_2 & a_1 \\ a_5 & a_4 & a_3 \end{vmatrix} \qquad T_4 = \begin{vmatrix} a_1 & a_0 & 0 & 0 \\ a_3 & a_2 & a_1 & a_0 \\ a_5 & a_4 & a_3 & a_2 \\ a_7 & a_6 & a_5 & a_4 \end{vmatrix} \quad \cdots \tag{1.4-6}$$

Given $a_0 > 0$, all roots have negative real parts if and only if $T_0, T_1, T_2, \ldots, T_n$ are all positive. This is true if and only if all a_i and either all even-numbered T_k or all odd-numbered T_k are positive (Liénard-Chipart Test).

ALTERNATIVE FORMULATION. *All the roots of a real n^{th}-degree equation* (2) *have negative real parts if and only if this is true for the $(n-1)^{\text{st}}$-degree equation*

$$a_0' x^{n-1} + a_1' x^{n-2} + a_2' x^{n-3} + a_3' x^{n-4} + \cdots \equiv a_1 x^{n-1} + a_2 x^{n-2}$$
$$+ a_3 x^{n-3} + a_4 x^{n-4} + \cdots - \frac{a_0}{a_1} a_3 x^{n-2} - \frac{a_0}{a_1} a_5 x^{n-4} - \cdots = 0$$

This theorem may be applied repeatedly and yields a simple recursion scheme. *The number of roots with negative real parts is precisely equal to the number of negative multipliers* $-a_0{}^{(j)}/a_1{}^{(j)}$ ($j = 0, 1, 2, \ldots, n-1$; $a_0{}^{(0)} = a_0 > 0$, $a_1{}^{(0)} = a_1$) *encountered in successive applications of the theorem.* The method becomes more complicated if one of the $a_1{}^{(j)}$ vanishes (see Ref. 6, which also indicates an extension to complex equations).

(*c*) LOCATION OF REAL ROOTS: DESCARTES'S RULE OF SIGNS. *The number of positive real roots of a real algebraic equation* (2) *either is equal to the number* N_a *of sign changes in the sequence* a_0, a_1, $\ldots$, a_n *of coefficients, where vanishing terms are disregarded, or is less than* N_a *by a positive even integer.* Application of this theorem to $f(-x)$ yields a similar theorem for negative real roots.

(*d*) LOCATION OF REAL ROOTS: AN UPPER BOUND FOR THE REAL ROOTS. *If the first* k *coefficients* a_0, a_1, $\ldots$, a_{k-1} *in a real algebraic equation* (2) *are nonnegative* (a_k *is the first negative coefficient*) *then all real roots of Eq.* (2) *are smaller than* $1 + \sqrt[k]{q/a_0}$, *where* q *is the absolute value of the negative coefficient greatest in absolute value.* Application of this theorem to $f(-x)$ may similarly yield a lower bound of the real roots.

(*e*) LOCATION OF REAL ROOTS: ROLLE'S THEOREM (see also Sec. 3.7-1). *The derivative* (Sec. 3.5-1) $f'(x)$ *of a real polynomial* $f(x)$ *has an odd number of real zeros between two consecutive real zeros of* $f(x)$.

$f(x) = 0$ has no real root or one real root between two consecutive real roots a, b of $f'(x) = 0$ if $f(a) \neq 0$ and $f(b) \neq 0$ have equal or opposite signs, respectively. At most, one real root of $f(x) = 0$ is greater than the greatest root or smaller than the smallest root of $f'(x) = 0$.

(*f*) LOCATION OF REAL ROOTS: BUDAN'S THEOREM. *For any real algebraic equation* (2), *let* $N(x)$ *be the number of sign changes in the sequence of derivatives* (Sec. 3.5-1) $f(x)$, $f'(x)$, $f''(x)$, $\ldots$, $f^{(n)}(x)$, *if vanishing terms are disregarded. Then either the number of real roots of Eq.* (2) *located between two real numbers* a *and* $b > a$ *not themselves roots of Eq.* (2) *is* $N(a) - N(b)$, *or it is less than* $N(a) - N(b)$ *by a positive even integer.*

The number of real roots of Eq. (2) located between a and b is odd or even if $f(a)$ and $f(b)$ have opposite or equal signs, respectively.

(*g*) LOCATION OF REAL ROOTS: STURM'S METHOD. *Given a real algebraic equation* (2) *without multiple roots, let* $N(x)$ *be the number of sign changes* (disregard vanishing terms) *in the sequence of functions*

$$f_0 = f(x) = g_0(x)f_1(x) - f_2(x)$$
$$f_1 = f'(x) = g_1(x)f_2(x) - f_3(x) \qquad (1.4\text{-}7)$$
$$f_2(x) = g_2(x)f_3(x) - f_4(x) \quad \cdots$$

where for $i > 1$ each $f_i(x)$ is (-1) times the remainder (Sec. 1.5-2) obtained on dividing $f_{i-2}(x)$ by $f_{i-1}(x)$; $f_n(x) \neq 0$ is a constant. Then the number of real roots of Eq. (2) located between two real numbers a and $b > a$ not themselves roots of Eq. (2) is equal to $N(a) - N(b)$.

Sturm's method applies even if, for convenience in computation, a function $f_i(x)$ in the above process is replaced by $F_i(x) = f_i(x)/k(x)$, where $k(x)$ is a positive constant or a polynomial in x positive for $a \leq x \leq b$, and the remaining functions are based on $F_i(x)$ instead of on $f_i(x)$. Similar operations may be performed again on any of the $F_j(x)$, etc.

If $f(x)$ has *multiple roots*, $f(x)$ and $f'(x)$ have a common divisor (Sec. 1.5-3); in this case, $f_n(x)$ is not a constant, and $N(a) - N(b)$ is the number of real roots between a and b, where each multiple root is counted *only once*.

1.4-5 Solution of Linear and Quadratic Equations.   (*a*) LINEAR EQUATIONS.

The solution of the general equation of the first degree (**linear equation**)

$$ax = b \quad \text{or} \quad ax - b = 0 \quad (a \neq 0) \qquad (1.4\text{-}8)$$

is $x = \dfrac{b}{a}$ (1.4-9)

(*b*) QUADRATIC EQUATIONS.   The **quadratic equation**

$$ax^2 + bx + c = 0 \quad (a \neq 0) \qquad (1.4\text{-}10)$$

has the roots

$$x_{1,2} = \frac{-b \pm \sqrt{b^2 - 4ac}}{2a} \qquad (1.4\text{-}11)$$

The roots x_1 and x_2 are real and different, real and equal, or complex conjugates if the **discriminant** $D = b^2 - 4ac$ is, respectively, positive, zero, or negative. Note $x_1 + x_2 = -b/a$, $x_1 x_2 = c/a$.

Example: $x^2 + 4x + 13 = 0$ has the complex conjugate roots

$$x_1 = \frac{-4 + \sqrt{16 - 52}}{2} = -2 + 3i \qquad x_2 = \frac{-4 - \sqrt{16 - 52}}{2} = -2 - 3i$$

1.4-6 Cubic Equations.   (*a*) CARDAN'S SOLUTION.   The **cubic equation**

$$x^3 + ax^2 + bx + c = 0 \qquad (1.4\text{-}12)$$

is transformed to the "reduced" form

$$y^3 + py + q = 0 \qquad p = -\frac{a^2}{3} + b \qquad q = 2\left(\frac{a}{3}\right)^3 - \frac{ab}{3} + c \qquad (1.4\text{-}13)$$

through the substitution $x = y - a/3$. The roots y_1, y_2, y_3 of the "reduced" cubic equation (13) are

$$\left.\begin{array}{l} y_1 = A + B \qquad y_{2,3} = -\dfrac{A+B}{2} \pm i\dfrac{A-B}{2}\sqrt{3} \\[2mm] \text{with}\quad A = \sqrt[3]{-\dfrac{q}{2} + \sqrt{Q}} \qquad B = \sqrt[3]{-\dfrac{q}{2} - \sqrt{Q}} \qquad Q = \left(\dfrac{p}{3}\right)^3 + \left(\dfrac{q}{2}\right)^2 \end{array}\right\} \quad (1.4\text{-}14)$$

where the real values of the cube roots are used. *The cubic equation has one real root and two conjugate complex roots, three real roots of which at least two are equal, or three different real roots, if Q is positive, zero, or negative, respectively.* In the latter case ("irreducible" case), the method of Sec. 1.4-6b may be used.

(b) TRIGONOMETRIC SOLUTION. If $Q < 0$ ("irreducible" case),

$$\left.\begin{array}{l} y_1 = 2\sqrt[+]{-p/3}\,\cos(\alpha/3) \qquad y_{2,3} = -2\sqrt[+]{-p/3}\,\cos(\alpha/3 \pm 60°) \\[2mm] \text{with}\quad \cos\alpha = -\dfrac{q}{2\sqrt[+]{-(p/3)^3}} \end{array}\right\} \quad (1.4\text{-}15)$$

If $Q \geq 0$, $p > 0$,

$$\left.\begin{array}{l} y_1 = -2\sqrt[+]{p/3}\,\cot 2\alpha \qquad y_{2,3} = \sqrt[+]{p/3}\,(\cot 2\alpha \pm i\sqrt{3}\,\operatorname{cosec} 2\alpha) \\[2mm] \text{with}\quad \tan\alpha = \sqrt[3]{\tan(\beta/2)} \quad (|\alpha| \leq 45°) \\[2mm] \qquad\quad\ \tan\beta = 2\sqrt[+]{(p/3)^3}/q \quad (|\beta| \leq 90°) \end{array}\right\} \quad (1.4\text{-}16a)$$

(c) If $Q \geq 0$, $p < 0$,

$$\left.\begin{array}{l} y_1 = -2\sqrt[+]{-p/3}\,\operatorname{cosec} 2\alpha \\[2mm] y_{2,3} = \sqrt[+]{-p/3}\,(\operatorname{cosec} 2\alpha \pm i\sqrt{3}\,\cot 2\alpha) \\[2mm] \text{with}\quad \tan\alpha = \sqrt[3]{\tan(\beta/2)} \quad (|\alpha| \leq 45°) \\[2mm] \qquad\quad\ \sin\beta = 2\sqrt[+]{(-p/3)^3}/q \quad (|\beta| \leq 90°) \end{array}\right\} \quad (1.4\text{-}16b)$$

The real value of the cube root is used.

1.4-7   *Quartic Equations.* (a) DESCARTES-EULER SOLUTION. The **quartic equation (biquadratic equation)**

$$x^4 + ax^3 + bx^2 + cx + d = 0 \qquad (1.4\text{-}17)$$

is transformed to the "reduced" form

$$y^4 + py^2 + qy + r = 0 \qquad (1.4\text{-}18)$$

through the substitution $x = y - a/4$. The roots y_1, y_2, y_3, y_4 of the "reduced" quartic equation (18) are the four sums

$$\pm \sqrt{z_1} \pm \sqrt{z_2} \pm \sqrt{z_3} \tag{1.4-19}$$

with the signs of the square roots chosen so that

$$\sqrt{z_1}\,\sqrt{z_2}\,\sqrt{z_3} = -q/8 \tag{1.4-20}$$

where z_1, z_2, z_3 are the roots of the cubic equation

$$z^3 + \frac{p}{2}z^2 + \frac{p^2 - 4r}{16}z - \frac{q^2}{64} = 0 \tag{1.4-21}$$

(b) FERRARI'S SOLUTION. Given any root y_1 of the **resolvent cubic equation** corresponding to Eq. (17),

$$y^3 - by^2 + (ac - 4d)y - a^2d + 4bd - c^2 = 0 \tag{1.4-22}$$

the four roots of the quartic equation (17) are given as roots of the two quadratic equations

$$x^2 + \frac{a}{2}x + \frac{y_1}{2} = \pm \sqrt{\left(\frac{a^2}{4} - b + y_1\right)x^2 + \left(\frac{a}{2}y_1 - c\right)x + \frac{y_1^2}{4} - d} \tag{1.4-23}$$

The radicand on the right is a perfect square.

1.5 FACTORING OF POLYNOMIALS AND QUOTIENTS OF POLYNOMIALS. PARTIAL FRACTIONS

1.5-1 Factoring of a Polynomial. If a polynomial $F(x)$ can be represented as a product of polynomials $f_1(x)$, $f_2(x)$, . . . , $f_s(x)$, these polynomials are called **factors** (**divisors**) of $F(x)$. If $x = x_1$ is a zero of order m of any factor $f_i(x)$, it is also a zero of order $M \geq m$ of $F(x)$. *Every (real or complex) polynomial $f(x)$ of degree n in x can be expressed as a product of a constant and n linear factors $(x - \alpha_k)$ in one and only one way, namely,*

$$f(x) \equiv a_0 x^n + a_1 x^{n-1} + \cdots + a_{n-1}x + a_n$$
$$\equiv a_0 \prod_{k=1}^{n} (x - x_k) \tag{1.5-1}$$

where the x_k are the zeros of $f(x)$; a zero x_k of order m_k (Sec. 1.4-2) contributes m_k factors $(x - x_k)$ (Factor Theorem). Pairs of factors $[x - (a_k + i\omega_k)]$, $[x - (a_k - i\omega_k)]$ corresponding to pairs of complex conjugate roots (see also Sec. 1.4-4a) $x_k = a_k + i\omega_k$, $x_k = a_k - i\omega_k$ may be combined into real quadratic factors $[(x - a_k)^2 + \omega_k^2]$.

1.5-2 Quotients of Polynomials. Remainder. Long Division. The quotient $F(x)/f(x)$ of a polynomial $F(x)$ of degree N and a polynomial $f(x)$ of degree $n < N$ may be expressed in the form

$$\frac{F(x)}{f(x)} \equiv \frac{A_0 x^N + A_1 x^{N-1} + \cdots + A_N}{a_0 x^n + a_1 x^{n-1} + \cdots + a_n}$$

$$\equiv (b_0 x^{N-n} + b_1 x^{N-n-1} + \cdots + b_{N-n}) + \frac{r_1(x)}{f(x)} \qquad (1.5\text{-}2)$$

where the **remainder** $r_1(x)$ is a polynomial of degree smaller than n. The coefficients b_k and the remainder $r_1(x)$ are uniquely determined, e.g., by the process of **long division** (**division algorithm**) indicated in Fig. 1.5-1.

In Fig. 1.5-1, each product $b_0 f(x)$, $b_1 f(x)$, . . . is subtracted in turn, with the coefficients b_0, b_1, . . . chosen so as to eliminate the respective coefficients of x^N, x^{N-1}, . . . in successive differences until the remainder is reached.   The remainder $r_1(x)$ vanishes if and only if $f(x)$ is a divisor (Sec. 1.5-1) of $F(x)$.

The remainder obtained on dividing any polynomial $f(x)$ by $(x - c)$ is equal to $f(c)$ (Remainder Theorem).

1.5-3   *Common Divisors and Common Roots of Two Polynomials.* If a polynomial $g(x)$ is a **common divisor (factor)** of $F(x)$ and $f(x)$, its zeros are common zeros of $F(x)$ and $f(x)$.   In the quotient (2), any common divisor may be factored out and canceled as with numerical fractions.

The *greatest common divisor* (common factor of greatest degree) of $F(x)$ and $f(x)$ is uniquely defined except for a constant factor and may be obtained as follows: Divide $r_1(x)$ into $f(x)$; divide the resulting remainder $r_2(x)$ into $r_1(x)$, and continue until some remainder, $r_k(x)$, say, vanishes.   Then any constant multiple of $r_{k-1}(x)$ is the desired greatest common divisor.

1.5-4   *Expansion in Partial Fractions.* Any quotient $g(x)/f(x)$ of a polynomial $g(x)$ of degree m and a polynomial $f(x)$ of degree $n > m$ without common roots can be expressed as a sum of n **partial fractions** corresponding to the roots x_k (of respective orders m_k) of $f(x) = 0$ as follows:

$$\frac{g(x)}{f(x)} = \sum_k \sum_{j=1}^{m_k} \frac{b_{kj}}{(x - x_k)^i}$$

$$= \sum_k \left[\frac{b_{k1}}{(x - x_k)} + \frac{b_{k2}}{(x - x_k)^2} + \cdots + \frac{b_{km_k}}{(x - x_k)^{m_k}} \right] \qquad (1.5\text{-}3)$$

The coefficients b_{kj} are obtained by one of the following methods, or by a combination of these methods:

$$
\begin{array}{l}
\quad (A_0x^N + \quad A_1x^{N-1} + \qquad\qquad A_2x^{N-2} + \cdots) \div (a_0x^n + a_1x^{n-1} + a_2x^{n-2} + \cdots) = \dfrac{A_0}{a_0}x^{N-n} + \left(\dfrac{A_1}{a_0} - A_0\dfrac{a_1}{a_0{}^2}\right)x^{N-n-1} + \cdots + r_1(x) \\
\underline{-\left(A_0x^N + A_0\dfrac{a_1}{a_0}x^{N-1} + \qquad A_0\dfrac{a_2}{a_0}x^{N-2} + \cdots\right)} \\
\quad \left(A_1 - A_0\dfrac{a_1}{a_0}\right)x^{N-1} + \left(A_2 - A_0\dfrac{a_2}{a_0}\right)x^{N-2} + \cdots \\
\quad \cdots\cdots\cdots\cdots\cdots\cdots\cdots\cdots\cdots\cdots\cdots \text{ etc.}
\end{array}
$$

Examples:

1.
$$
\begin{array}{l}
\qquad (2x^3 - 4x^2 - 2x + 3) \div (x - 2) = 2x^2 - 2 - \dfrac{1}{x - 2} \\
\underline{-(2x^3 - 4x^2)} \\
\qquad\qquad -2x + 3 \\
\qquad\quad \underline{-(-2x + 4)} \\
\qquad\qquad\quad -1
\end{array}
$$

2.
$$
\begin{array}{l}
\qquad (x^4 - x^2 + ax - a^4 + a^2 + b) \div (x^2 - a^2) = x^2 + (a^2 - 1) + \dfrac{ax + b}{x^2 - a^2} \\
\underline{-(x^4 - a^2x^2)} \\
\qquad (a^2 - 1)x^2 + ax - (a^2 - 1)a^2 + b \\
\quad \underline{-[(a^2 - 1)x^2 \qquad - (a^2 - 1)a^2]} \\
\qquad\qquad\quad ax \qquad\qquad + b
\end{array}
$$

Fig. 1.5-1 Long division.

1. If $m_k = 1$ (x_k is a simple root), then $b_{k1} = g(x_k)/f'(x_k)$.
2. Multiply both sides of Eq. (3) by $f(x)$ and equate coefficients of equal powers of x on both sides.
3. Multiply both sides of Eq. (3) by $f(x)$ and differentiate successively. Let $\varphi_k(x) = f(x)/(x - x_k)^{m_k}$. Then obtain $b_{km_k}, b_{km_k-1}, \ldots$ successively from

$$g(x_k) = b_{km_k}\varphi_k(x_k)$$
$$g'(x_k) = b_{km_k}\varphi_k'(x_k) + b_{km_k-1}\varphi_k(x_k)$$
$$g''(x_k) = b_{km_k}\varphi_k''(x_k) + 2b_{km_k-1}\varphi_k'(x_k) + 2b_{km_k-2}\varphi_k(x_k)$$
$$\cdot \; \cdot \; \cdot \; \cdot \; \cdot \; \cdot \; \cdot \; \cdot \; \cdot \; \cdot \; \cdot \; \cdot \; \cdot \; \cdot \; \cdot \; \cdot \; \cdot \; \cdot \; \cdot$$
$$g^{(m_k-1)}(x_k) = b_{km_k}\varphi_k^{(m_k-1)}(x_k) + m_k b_{km_k-1}\varphi_k^{(m_k-2)}(x_k)$$
$$+ m_k b_{km_k-2}(m_k - 1)\varphi_k^{(m_k-3)}(x_k) + \cdots + m_k! b_{k_1}\varphi_k(x_k)$$

The partial fractions corresponding to any pair of complex conjugate roots $a_k + i\omega_k$, $a_k - i\omega_k$ of order m_k are usually combined into

$$c_{k1}\frac{x + d_{k1}}{[(x - a_k)^2 + \omega_k^2]} + c_{k2}\frac{x + d_{k2}}{[(x - a_k)^2 + \omega_k^2]^2}$$
$$+ \cdots + c_{km_k}\frac{x + d_{km_k}}{[(x - a_k)^2 + \omega_k^2]^{m_k}} \qquad (1.5\text{-}4)$$

The coefficients c_{kj} and d_{kj} may be determined directly by method 2 above. If $g(x)$ and $f(x)$ are real polynomials, all coefficients b_{kj}, c_{kj}, d_{kj} in the resulting partial-fraction expansion are real.

Every rational function of x (Sec. 3.3-2) can be represented as a sum of a polynomial and a finite set of partial fractions. Partial-fraction expansions are important in connection with integration (Sec. 3.6-5c) and integral transforms (Sec. 5.4-8).

Examples:

$$\frac{1}{(a + bx)(f + gx)} \equiv \frac{1}{fb - ag}\left(\frac{b}{a + bx} - \frac{g}{f + gx}\right)$$
$$\frac{1}{(x + a)(x + b)(x + c)} \equiv \frac{A}{x + a} + \frac{B}{x + b} + \frac{C}{x + c}$$

with $A = \dfrac{1}{(b - a)(c - a)}$ $B = \dfrac{1}{(a - b)(c - b)}$ $C = \dfrac{1}{(a - c)(b - c)}$

$$\frac{1}{(x + a)(x + b)(x + c)(x + d)} \equiv \frac{A}{x + a} + \frac{B}{x + b} + \frac{C}{x + c} + \frac{D}{x + d}$$

with $A = \dfrac{1}{(b - a)(c - a)(d - a)}$ $B = \dfrac{1}{(a - b)(c - b)(d - b)}$ $\cdots$

$$\frac{1}{(a + bx^2)(f + gx^2)} \equiv \frac{1}{fb - ag} \cdot \left(\frac{b}{a + bx^2} - \frac{g}{f + gx^2}\right)$$

1.6 SYSTEMS OF SIMULTANEOUS EQUATIONS

1.6-1 *Simultaneous Equations.*

To solve a suitable set (system) of simultaneous equations

$$f_i(x_1, x_2, \ldots) = 0 \qquad (i = 1, 2, \ldots) \tag{1.6-1}$$

for the unknowns $x_1, x_2, \ldots$ means to determine a set of values of $x_1, x_2, \ldots$ which satisfy the equations (1) simultaneously. The solution is complete if all such sets are found. One can frequently *eliminate* successive unknowns x_j from a system (1), e.g., by solving one equation for x_j and substituting the resulting expression in the remaining equations. The number of equations and unknowns is thus reduced until a single equation remains to be solved for a single unknown. The procedure is then repeated to yield a second unknown, etc. Solutions may be verified by substitution.

1.6-2 *Simultaneous Linear Equations: Cramer's Rule.*

Consider a set (system) of n linear equations in n unknowns $x_1, x_2, \ldots, x_n$

$$\begin{aligned}
a_{11}x_1 + a_{12}x_2 + \cdots + a_{1n}x_n &= b_1 \\
a_{21}x_1 + a_{22}x_2 + \cdots + a_{2n}x_n &= b_2 \\
\cdots \cdots \cdots \cdots \cdots \cdots \cdots \cdots \cdots & \\
a_{n1}x_1 + a_{n2}x_2 + \cdots + a_{nn}x_n &= b_n
\end{aligned} \quad \text{or} \quad \sum_{k=1}^{n} a_{ik}x_k = b_i \qquad (i = 1, 2, \ldots, n) \tag{1.6-2}$$

such that at least one of the absolute terms b_i is different from zero. If the **system determinant**

$$D = \det [a_{ik}] = \begin{vmatrix} a_{11} & a_{12} & \cdots & a_{1n} \\ a_{21} & a_{22} & \cdots & a_{2n} \\ \cdots & \cdots & \cdots & \cdots \\ a_{n1} & a_{n2} & \cdots & a_{nn} \end{vmatrix} \tag{1.6-3}$$

differs from zero, the system (2) has the unique solution

$$x_k = \frac{D_k}{D} \qquad (k = 1, 2, \ldots, n) \qquad \text{(CRAMER'S RULE)} \tag{1.6-4}$$

where D_k is the determinant obtained on replacing the respective elements $a_{1k}, a_{2k}, \ldots, a_{nk}$ in the kth column of D by $b_1, b_2, \ldots, b_n$, or

$$D_k = \sum_{i=1}^{n} A_{ik}b_i \qquad (k = 1, 2, \ldots, n) \tag{1.6-5}$$

where A_{ik} is the cofactor (Sec. 1.3-2) of a_{ik} in the determinant D.

Example: For the system

$$x_1 + x_2 + 3x_3 = -9$$
$$\tfrac{1}{2}x_1 - 2x_2 + x_3 = 2$$
$$3x_1 + 4x_2 + 4x_3 = -14$$

$$D = \begin{vmatrix} 1 & 1 & 3 \\ \tfrac{1}{2} & -2 & 1 \\ 3 & 4 & 4 \end{vmatrix} = 13$$

$$D_1 = \begin{vmatrix} -9 & 1 & 3 \\ 2 & -2 & 1 \\ -14 & 4 & 4 \end{vmatrix} = 26 \qquad x_1 = 2$$

$$D_2 = \begin{vmatrix} 1 & -9 & 3 \\ \tfrac{1}{2} & 2 & 1 \\ 3 & -14 & 4 \end{vmatrix} = -26 \qquad x_2 = -2$$

$$D_3 = \begin{vmatrix} 1 & 1 & -9 \\ \tfrac{1}{2} & -2 & 2 \\ 3 & 4 & -14 \end{vmatrix} = -39 \qquad x_3 = -3$$

1.6-3 Simultaneous Linear Equations: General Theory. *The system of m linear equations in n unknowns x_1, x_2, . . . , x_n,*

$$\sum_{k=1}^{n} a_{ik}x_k = b_i \qquad (i = 1, 2, \ldots, m) \tag{1.6-6}$$

possesses a solution if and only if the matrices

$$\begin{bmatrix} a_{11} & a_{12} & \cdots & a_{1n} \\ a_{21} & a_{22} & \cdots & a_{2n} \\ \cdot & \cdot & \cdot & \cdot \\ a_{m1} & a_{m2} & \cdots & a_{mn} \end{bmatrix} \quad \begin{bmatrix} a_{11} & a_{12} & \cdots & a_{1n} & b_1 \\ a_{21} & a_{22} & \cdots & a_{2n} & b_2 \\ \cdot & \cdot & \cdot & \cdot & \cdot \\ a_{m1} & a_{m2} & \cdots & a_{mn} & b_m \end{bmatrix} \tag{1.6-7}$$

(**system matrix** *and* **augmented matrix**) *are of equal rank* (Sec. 8.2-6).   Otherwise the equations are *inconsistent*.

The unique solution of Sec. 1.6-2 applies if $r = m = n$.   If both matrices (7) are of rank $r < m$, the equations (6) are *linearly dependent;* $m - r$ equations can be expressed as linear combinations of the remaining r equations and are satisfied by their solution.   The r independent equations determine r unknowns as linear functions of the remaining $n - r$ unknowns, which are left arbitrary.

1.6-4 Simultaneous Linear Equations: n Homogeneous Equations in n Unknowns.   In particular, *a system of n homogeneous linear equations in n unknowns,*

$$\sum_{k=1}^{n} a_{ik}x_k = 0 \qquad (i = 1, 2, \ldots, n) \tag{1.6-8}$$

has a solution different from the trivial solution $x_1 = x_2 = \cdots = x_n = 0$ *if and only if* $D = \det [a_{ik}] = 0$ (see also Sec. 1.6-2).

In this case, there exist exactly $n - r$ linearly independent solutions $x_1{}^{(1)}$, $x_2{}^{(1)}$, . . . , $x_n{}^{(1)}$; $x_1{}^{(2)}$, $x_2{}^{(2)}$, . . . , $x_n{}^{(2)}$; . . . ; $x_1{}^{(n-r)}$, $x_2{}^{(n-r)}$, . . . , $x_n{}^{(n-r)}$, where r is the rank of the system matrix (Sec. 1.6-3). The most general solution is, then,

$$x_i = \sum_{j=1}^{n-r} c_j x_i{}^{(i)} \qquad (i = 1, 2, \ldots, n) \tag{1.6-9}$$

where the c_j *are arbitrary constants.*

In the important special case where $r = n - 1$

$$x_1 = cA_{k1} \qquad x_2 = cA_{k2} \qquad \cdots \qquad x_n = cA_{kn} \tag{1.6-10}$$

is a solution for any arbitrary constant c, *so that all ratios* x_i/x_k *are uniquely determined;* the solutions (10) obtained for different values of k are identical.

References and Bibliography *(see also the bibliography for Chap. 8)*

1. Aitken, A. C.: *Determinants and Matrices*, 8th ed., Interscience, New York, 1956.
2. Birkhoff, G., and S. MacLane: *A Survey of Modern Algebra*, 3d ed., Macmillan, New York, 1965.
3. Dickson, L. E.: *New First Course in the Theory of Equations*, Wiley, New York, 1939.
4. Kemeny, J. G., et al.: *Introduction to Finite Mathematics*, Prentice-Hall, Englewood Cliffs, N.J., 1957.
5. Korn, G. A., and T. M. Korn: *Mathematical Handbook for Scientists and Engineers*, McGraw-Hill, New York, 1961.
6. Landau, E.: *The Foundation of Analysis*, Chelsea, New York, 1948.
7. Middlemiss, R. R.: *College Algebra*, McGraw-Hill, New York, 1952.
8. Uspensky, J. V.: *Theory of Equations*, McGraw-Hill, New York, 1948.

Additional background material

9. Cohen, L. W., et al.: *The Structure of the Real Number System*, Van Nostrand, Princeton, N.J., 1963.
10. Feferman, S.: *The Number Systems: Foundations of Algebra and Analysis*, Addison-Wesley, Reading, Mass., 1964.
11. Landin, J., and N. T. Hamilton: *Set Theory: The Structure of Arithmetic*, Allyn and Bacon, Boston, Mass., 1961.
12. Struik, D. J.: *A Concise History of Mathematics*, 2d ed., Dover, New York, 1948.

2 ANALYTIC GEOMETRY

2.1 INTRODUCTION

2.1-1 Analytic Geometry. A *geometry* is a mathematical model involving relations between objects referred to as *points*. Each geometry is defined by a self-consistent set of *defining postulates*, which may or may not be chosen so as to make the model correspond to physical space relationships. The study of such models is also called geometry. *Analytic geometry* represents each point by an ordered set of numbers (**coordinates**), so that relations between points are represented by relations between coordinates.

This chapter introduces its subject matter in the manner of most elementary courses: the concepts of euclidean geometry are assumed to be known and are simply translated into analytical language. The differential geometry of curves and surfaces is outlined in Secs. 3.12-1 to 3.12-5.

2.2 PLANE ANALYTIC GEOMETRY: BASIC CONCEPTS

2.2-1 Cartesian Coordinate Systems. A plane **cartesian coordinate system** (cartesian reference system) associates a unique ordered
pair of real numbers (**cartesian coordinates**), the **abscissa** x and the
ordinate y, with every point $P \equiv (x, y)$ in the finite portion of the euclidean plane by reference to a pair of directed straight lines (**coordinate
axes**) OX, OY intersecting at the **origin** O (Fig. 2.2-1a). The parallel
to OY through P intersects the x **axis** OX at the point P'. Similarly,
the parallel to OX through P intersects the y **axis** OY at P''. The
directed distances $OP' = x$ (positive in the positive x axis direction) and
$OP'' = y$ (positive in the positive y axis direction) are the cartesian
coordinates of the point $P \equiv (x, y)$.

x and y may or may not be measured with equal scales. In a general (oblique) cartesian coordinate system, the angle $XOY = \omega$ between
the coordinate axes may be between 0 and 180 deg (**right-handed
cartesian coordinate systems**) or between 0 and —180 deg (**left-
handed cartesian coordinate systems**).

In a **right-handed rectangular cartesian coordinate system,**
the directions of the coordinate axes are chosen so that a rotation of 90
deg in the positive (counterclockwise) sense would make the positive x
axis OX coincide with the positive y axis OY (Fig. 2.2-1b). The coordinates x and y are thus equal to the respective directed distances
between the y axis and the point P, and between the x axis and the
point P.

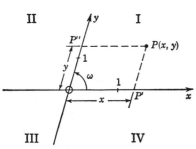

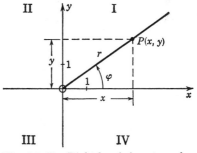

Fig. 2.2-1a Right-handed oblique cartesian coordinate system. The points
marked "1" define the coordinate scales
used. Note the quadrant designations
I, II, III, IV.

Fig. 2.2-1b Right-handed rectangular
cartesian coordinate system and polar-
coordinate system.

THROUGHOUT THE REMAINDER OF THIS CHAPTER, ALL CARTESIAN COORDINATES x, y REFER TO RIGHT-HANDED RECTANGULAR CARTESIAN COORDINATE SYSTEMS, AND EQUAL SCALE UNITS OF UNIT LENGTH ARE USED TO MEASURE x AND y.

2.2-2 Basic Relations. In terms of rectangular cartesian coordinates:

1. The **distance** d between the points $P_1 \equiv (x_1, y_1)$ and $P_2 \equiv (x_2, y_2)$ is

$$d = \sqrt{(x_2 - x_1)^2 + (y_2 - y_1)^2} \qquad (2.2\text{-}1)$$

2. The oblique **angle** γ between two directed straight-line segments $\overrightarrow{P_1P_2}$ and $\overrightarrow{P_3P_4}$ is given by

$$\cos \gamma = \frac{(x_2 - x_1)(x_4 - x_3) + (y_2 - y_1)(y_4 - y_3)}{\sqrt{(x_2 - x_1)^2 + (y_2 - y_1)^2} \sqrt{(x_4 - x_3)^2 + (y_4 - y_3)^2}} \qquad (2.2\text{-}2)$$

where the coordinates of the points P_1, P_2, P_3, P_4 are denoted by the respective corresponding subscripts.

The **direction cosines** $\cos \alpha_x$ and $\cos \alpha_y$ of a directed line segment $\overrightarrow{P_1P_2}$ are the cosines of the angles α_x and $\alpha_y = 90 \deg - \alpha_x$, respectively.

$$\cos \alpha_x = \frac{x_2 - x_1}{\sqrt{(x_2 - x_1)^2 + (y_2 - y_1)^2}}$$

$$\qquad (2.2\text{-}3)$$

$$\cos \alpha_y = \sin \alpha_x = \frac{y_2 - y_1}{\sqrt{(x_2 - x_1)^2 + (y_2 - y_1)^2}}$$

3. The coordinates x, y of **the point** P **dividing the directed line segment between the points** $P_1 \equiv (x_1, y_1)$ **and** $P_2 \equiv (x_2, y_2)$ **in the ratio** $\overrightarrow{P_1P} : \overrightarrow{PP_2} = m:n = \mu:1$ are

$$x = \frac{mx_2 + nx_1}{m + n} = \frac{x_1 + \mu x_2}{1 + \mu} \qquad y = \frac{my_2 + ny_1}{m + n} = \frac{y_1 + \mu y_2}{1 + \mu}$$
$$(-\infty \leq \mu \leq \infty) \qquad (2.2\text{-}4)$$

Specifically, the coordinates of the **mid-point** of P_1P_2 are

$$x = \frac{x_1 + x_2}{2} \qquad y = \frac{y_1 + y_2}{2} \qquad (2.2\text{-}5)$$

4. The **area** S **of the triangle with the vertices** $P_1 \equiv (x_1, y_1)$, $P_2 \equiv (x_2, y_2)$, $P_3 \equiv (x_3, y_3)$ is

$$S = \tfrac{1}{2}\begin{vmatrix} x_1 & y_1 & 1 \\ x_2 & y_2 & 1 \\ x_3 & y_3 & 1 \end{vmatrix} = \tfrac{1}{2}[x_1(y_2 - y_3) + x_2(y_3 - y_1) + x_3(y_1 - y_2)]$$

(2.2-6)

This expression is positive if the circumference $P_1P_2P_3$ runs around the inside of the triangle in a positive (counterclockwise) direction. Specifically, if $x_3 = y_3 = 0$,

$$S = \tfrac{1}{2}\begin{vmatrix} x_1 & x_2 \\ y_1 & y_2 \end{vmatrix} = \tfrac{1}{2}(x_1y_2 - x_2y_1)$$

(2.2-7)

2.2-3 Translation and Rotation of the Coordinate Axes. (*a*) Let x, y be the coordinates of any point P with respect to a right-handed rectangular cartesian reference system. Let $\bar{x}$, $\bar{y}$ be the coordinates of the same point P with respect to a second right-handed rectangular cartesian reference system whose axes have the same directions as those of the x, y system, and whose origin has the coordinates $x = x_0$ and $y = y_0$ in the x, y system. If equal scales are used to measure the coordinates in both systems, the coordinates $\bar{x}$, $\bar{y}$ are related to the coordinates x, y by the *transformation equations* (see also Fig. 2.2-2*a* and Chap. 8)

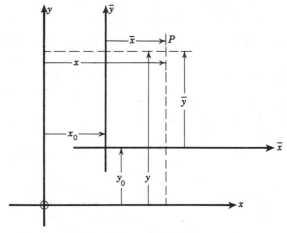

Fig. 2.2-2a   Translation of coordinate axes.

$$\bar{x} = x - x_0 \qquad \bar{y} = y - y_0$$

or

$$x = \bar{x} + x_0 \qquad y = \bar{y} + y_0$$

(2.2-8)

The equations (8) permit a second interpretation. If $\bar{x}$, $\bar{y}$ are considered as coordinates referred *to the x, y system* of axes, then the point defined by $\bar{x}$, $\bar{y}$ is *translated* by a direct amount $-x_0$ in the x axis direction and by a directed amount $-y_0$ in the y axis direction with respect to the point (x, y). Transformations of this type applied to each point x, y of a plane curve may be used to indicate the translation of the entire curve.

(*b*) Let x, y be the coordinates of any point P with respect to a right-handed rectangular cartesian reference system. Let $\bar{x}$, $\bar{y}$ be the coordinates of the same point P with respect to a second right-handed rectangular cartesian reference system having the same origin O and rotated with respect to the x, y system so that the angle $XO\bar{X}$ between the x axis OX and $\bar{x}$ axis $O\bar{X}$ is equal to ϑ measured in radians in the positive (counterclockwise) sense. If equal scales are used to measure all four coordinates x, y, $\bar{x}$, $\bar{y}$, the coordinates $\bar{x}$, $\bar{y}$ are related to the coordinates x, y by the transformation equations (see also Fig. 2.2-2*b*)

$$\bar{x} = x \cos \vartheta + y \sin \vartheta \qquad \bar{y} = -x \sin \vartheta + y \cos \vartheta$$

or

$$x = \bar{x} \cos \vartheta - \bar{y} \sin \vartheta \qquad y = \bar{x} \sin \vartheta + \bar{y} \cos \vartheta$$

(2.2-9)

A second interpretation of the transformation (9) is the definition of a point $(\bar{x}, \bar{y})$ rotated about the origin by an angle $-\vartheta$ with respect to the point (x, y).

(*c*) If the origin of the $\bar{x}$, $\bar{y}$ system in Sec. 2.2-3*b* is not the same as the origin of the x, y system but has the coordinates $x = x_0$ and $y = y_0$ in the x, y system, the transformation equations become

$$\bar{x} = (x - x_0) \cos \vartheta + (y - y_0) \sin \vartheta$$
$$\bar{y} = -(x - x_0) \sin \vartheta + (y - y_0) \cos \vartheta$$

or

$$x = x_0 + \bar{x} \cos \vartheta - \bar{y} \sin \vartheta$$
$$y = y_0 + \bar{x} \sin \vartheta + \bar{y} \cos \vartheta$$

(2.2-10)

2.2-4 *Polar Coordinates.* A **plane polar-coordinate system** associates ordered pairs of numbers r, φ (**polar coordinates**) with each point P of the plane by reference to a directed straight line (x axis in

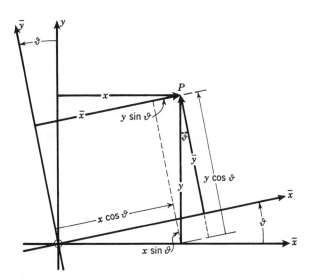

Fig. 2.2-2b   Rotation of coordinate axes.

Fig. 2.2-1b), the **polar axis.**   Each point P has the polar coordinates r, defined as the directed distance OP, and φ, defined as the angle XOP measured in radians in the counterclockwise sense between OX and OP. The point O is called the **pole** of the polar-coordinate system; r is the **radius vector** of the point P.

Negative values of the angle φ are measured in the clockwise sense from the polar axis.   Points (r, φ) are by definition identical to the points $(-r, \varphi \pm 180 \text{ deg})$; this convention associates points of the plane with pairs of numbers (r, φ) with negative as well as positive radius vectors r.

NOTE: Unlike a cartesian coordinate system, a polar-coordinate system does not establish a reciprocal one-to-one correspondence between the pairs of numbers (r, φ) and the points of the plane.   The ambiguities involved may, however, be properly taken into account in most applications.

If the pole and the polar axis of a polar-coordinate system coincide with the origin and the x axis, respectively, of a right-handed rectangular cartesian coordinate system (Fig. 2.2-1b), then the following transformation equations relate the polar coordinates (r, φ) and the rectangular cartesian coordinates (x, y) of corresponding points if equal scales are used for the measurement of r, x, and y:

$$x = r \cos \varphi \qquad y = r \sin \varphi$$

$$|r| = \sqrt{x^2 + y^2} \qquad \varphi = \arctan \frac{y}{x} \qquad (2.2\text{-}11)$$

In terms of polar coordinates (r, φ)

1. The **distance** d between the points (r_1, φ_1) and (r_2, φ_2) is

$$d = \sqrt{r_1{}^2 + r_2{}^2 - 2r_1r_2 \cos (\varphi_2 - \varphi_1)} \qquad (2.2\text{-}12)$$

2. The **area** S **of the triangle** with the vertices $P_1 \equiv (r_1, \varphi_1)$, $P_2 \equiv (r_2, \varphi_2)$, and $P_3 \equiv (r_3, \varphi_3)$ is

$$S = \tfrac{1}{2}[r_1r_2 \sin (\varphi_2 - \varphi_1) + r_2r_3 \sin (\varphi_3 - \varphi_2) + r_1r_3 \sin (\varphi_1 - \varphi_3)] \qquad (2.2\text{-}13)$$

2.2-5 Representation of Curves. (a) EQUATION OF A CURVE. A relation of the form

$$\varphi(x, y) = 0 \qquad \text{or} \qquad y = f(x) \qquad (2.2\text{-}14)$$

is, in general, satisfied only by the coordinates x, y of points belonging to a special set defined by the given relation.   In most cases of interest, the point set will be a *curve* (see also Sec. 2.5-8).   Conversely, a given curve will be represented by a suitable equation (14), which must be satisfied by the coordinates of all points (x, y) on the curve.   Note that a curve may have more than one branch.

The curves corresponding to the equations

$$\varphi(x, y) = 0 \qquad \lambda\varphi(x, y) = 0$$

where λ is a constant different from zero, are identical.

(b) PARAMETRIC REPRESENTATION OF CURVES.   A plane curve can also be represented by two equations

$$x = x(t) \qquad y = y(t) \qquad (2.2\text{-}15)$$

where t is a variable parameter.

(c) INTERSECTION OF TWO CURVES.   Pairs of coordinates x, y which simultaneously satisfy the equations of two curves

$$\varphi_1(x, y) = 0 \qquad \varphi_2(x, y) = 0 \qquad (2.2\text{-}16)$$

represent the *points of intersection* of the two curves.   In particular, if the equation $\varphi(x, 0) = 0$ has one or more real roots x, the latter are the abscissas of the intersections of the curve $\varphi(x, y) = 0$ with the x axis.

For any real number λ, the equation

$$\varphi_1(x, y) + \lambda\varphi_2(x, y) = 0 \qquad (2.2\text{-}17)$$

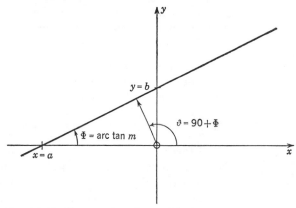

Fig. 2.2-3   The equation of a straight line.

describes a curve passing through all points of intersection (real and imaginary) of the two curves (16).

2.2-6   *The Straight Line.*   (*a*) Every equation of the form

$$Ax + By + C = 0 \tag{2.2-18}$$

where A and B must not vanish simultaneously, represents a *straight line*, and every straight line corresponds to a linear equation (18).

The following special forms of the equation of a straight line are of particular interest (Figs. 2.2-3 and 2.2-4):

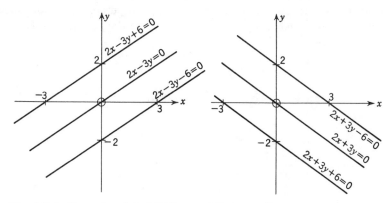

Fig. 2.2-4   Examples of straight lines and their equations.

1. **Slope-intercept form.** Straight line at an angle Φ with the positive x axis and intercepting the y axis at $y = b$:

$$y = mx + b \qquad m = \tan \Phi$$

m is the **slope** of the straight line.

2. **Two-intercept form.** Straight line intercepting the x axis at $x = a$ and the y axis at $y = b$:

$$\frac{x}{a} + \frac{y}{b} - 1 = 0$$

3. **Normal form.** Let p be the length of the directed perpendicular from the origin onto a straight line; let ϑ be the angle between the positive x axis and the directed perpendicular, measured in the positive (counterclockwise) sense. Then the equation of the straight line is

$$x \cos \vartheta + y \sin \vartheta - p = 0$$

4. **Point-slope form.** Straight line through the point (x_1, y_1) and having the slope m:

$$y - y_1 = m(x - x_1)$$

5. **Two-point form.** Straight line through the (noncoincident) points $P_1 \equiv (x_1, y_1)$ and $P_2 \equiv (x_2, y_2)$:

$$\frac{y - y_1}{y_2 - y_1} = \frac{x - x_1}{x_2 - x_1} \qquad \text{or} \qquad \begin{vmatrix} x & y & 1 \\ x_1 & y_1 & 1 \\ x_2 & y_2 & 1 \end{vmatrix} = 0$$

When the equation of a straight line is given in the general form (18), the intercepts a and b, the slope m, the perpendicular distance p from the origin, $\cos \vartheta$, and $\sin \vartheta$ are related to the parameters A, B, and C as follows:

$$a = -\frac{C}{A} \qquad b = -\frac{C}{B}$$

$$m = \tan \Phi = -\frac{A}{B} \qquad \Phi = \vartheta - 90 \text{ deg} \tag{2.2-19}$$

$$p = -\frac{C}{\pm \sqrt{A^2 + B^2}}$$

$$\cos \vartheta = \frac{A}{\pm \sqrt{A^2 + B^2}} \tag{2.2-20}$$

$$\sin \vartheta = \frac{B}{\pm \sqrt{A^2 + B^2}}$$

In order to avoid ambiguity, one chooses the sign of $\pm\sqrt{A^2 + B^2}$ in Eqs. (20) so that $p > 0$.

(*b*) In terms of a variable parameter t, the rectangular cartesian coordinates x and y of a point on any straight line may be expressed in the form

$$x = c_1 t + c_2 \qquad y = k_1 t + k_2 \qquad\qquad (2.2\text{-}21)$$

with

$$m = \frac{k_1}{c_1} \qquad a = \frac{k_1 c_2 - k_2 c_1}{k_1} \qquad b = \frac{k_2 c_1 - k_1 c_2}{c_1} \qquad (2.2\text{-}22)$$

(*c*) In terms of *polar coordinates* r, φ, the equation of any straight line may be expressed in the form

$$r(A \cos \varphi + B \sin \varphi) + C = 0 \qquad\qquad (2.2\text{-}23)$$

$$\text{or} \quad r \cos (\varphi - \vartheta) = p \qquad\qquad\qquad\qquad (2.2\text{-}24)$$

2.2-7   Relations Involving Points and Straight Lines.   (*a*) The *directed distance d from the straight line* (18) *to a point* (x_0, y_0) *is*

$$d = \frac{A x_0 + B y_0 + C}{\pm\sqrt{A^2 + B^2}} \qquad\qquad (2.2\text{-}25)$$

where the sign of $\pm\sqrt{A^2 + B^2}$ is chosen to be opposite to that of C. d is positive if the straight line lies between the origin and the point (x_0, y_0).

Three points (x_1, y_1), (x_2, y_2), *and* (x_3, y_3) *are on a straight line if and only if*

$$\begin{vmatrix} x_1 & y_1 & 1 \\ x_2 & y_2 & 1 \\ x_3 & y_3 & 1 \end{vmatrix} = 0 \qquad\qquad (2.2\text{-}26)$$

(*b*) *Two straight lines*

$$A_1 x + B_1 y + C_1 = 0 \qquad \text{or} \qquad y = m_1 x + b_1$$
$$\text{and} \quad A_2 x + B_2 y + C_2 = 0 \qquad \text{or} \qquad y = m_2 x + b_2 \qquad (2.2\text{-}27)$$

intersect in the point

$$x = \frac{B_1 C_2 - B_2 C_1}{A_1 B_2 - A_2 B_1} = \frac{b_1 - b_2}{m_2 - m_1}$$
$$y = \frac{C_1 A_2 - C_2 A_1}{A_1 B_2 - A_2 B_1} = \frac{m_2 b_1 - m_1 b_2}{m_2 - m_1} \qquad (2.2\text{-}28)$$

Either *angle* γ_{12} (measured counterclockwise) *from the first to the second straight line* (27) *is given by*

$$\tan \gamma_{12} = \frac{A_1 B_2 - A_2 B_1}{A_1 A_2 + B_1 B_2} = \frac{m_2 - m_1}{m_1 m_2 + 1} \qquad (2.2\text{-}29)$$

The straight lines (27) are *parallel* if

$$A_1 B_2 - A_2 B_1 = 0 \qquad \text{or} \qquad m_1 = m_2 \qquad (2.2\text{-}30)$$

and *perpendicular* if

$$A_1 A_2 + B_1 B_2 = 0 \qquad \text{or} \qquad m_2 = -\frac{1}{m_1} \qquad (2.2\text{-}31)$$

The equation of *every straight line passing through the point of intersection of two straight lines* will be of the form

$$\lambda_1 (A_1 x + B_1 y + C_1) + \lambda_2 (A_2 x + B_2 y + C_2) = 0 \qquad (2.2\text{-}32)$$

where λ_1 and λ_2 are not both equal to zero.

Conversely, every equation of the form (32) describes a straight line passing through the point of intersection. If the straight lines (27) are parallel, Eq. (32) represents a straight line parallel to the two. *If the straight lines are given in the normal form*, the straight lines corresponding to $\lambda_2/\lambda_1 = 1$ and $\lambda_2/\lambda_1 = -1$ *bisect the angles* between the given straight lines.

2.3 SECOND-ORDER CURVES (CONIC SECTIONS)

2.3-1 *General Second-degree Equation. Classification of Conics.*
The **second-order curves** or **conic sections** (**conics**) are represented by the **general second-degree equation**

$$a_{11}x^2 + 2a_{12}xy + a_{22}y^2 + 2a_{13}x + 2a_{23}y + a_{33} = 0$$

or

$$(a_{11}x + a_{12}y + a_{13})x + (a_{21}x + a_{22}y + a_{23})y$$
$$+ (a_{31}x + a_{32}y + a_{33}) = 0 \qquad (2.3\text{-}1)$$

with

$$a_{ik} = a_{ki} \qquad (i, k = 1, 2, 3)$$

For any equation (1), the three quantities

$$I = a_{11} + a_{22} \qquad D = A_{33} = \begin{vmatrix} a_{11} & a_{12} \\ a_{21} & a_{22} \end{vmatrix} \qquad A = \begin{vmatrix} a_{11} & a_{12} & a_{13} \\ a_{21} & a_{22} & a_{23} \\ a_{31} & a_{32} & a_{33} \end{vmatrix}$$

$$(2.3\text{-}2)$$

and the *sign* of the quantity

$$A' = \begin{vmatrix} a_{22} & a_{23} \\ a_{32} & a_{33} \end{vmatrix} + \begin{vmatrix} a_{11} & a_{13} \\ a_{31} & a_{33} \end{vmatrix} \qquad (2.3\text{-}3)$$

are *invariants* with respect to the translation and rotation transformations (2.2-8), (2.2-9), and (2.2-10). Such invariants define properties of the conic which do not depend on its position and permit classification of the corresponding curves in accordance with Table 2.3-1.

Table 2.3-1   *Classification of conic sections (conics)*

			Proper conics $A \neq 0$	Improper (degenerate) conics $A = 0$
Central conics $D \neq 0$	$D > 0$	$\dfrac{A}{I} < 0$	Real ellipse (circle if $I^2 = 4D$ or $a_{11} = a_{22}, a_{12} = 0$)	
		$\dfrac{A}{I} > 0$	No real locus (imaginary ellipse)	
		$\dfrac{A}{I} = 0$		Point in finite portion of plane (point ellipse; real intersection of two imaginary straight lines)
	$D < 0$		Hyperbola	Two real straight lines inter- secting in finite portion of plane (degenerate hyperbola)
Noncentral conics $D = 0$	$A' > 0$		Parabola	No real locus (imaginary parallels)
	$A' < 0$			Two real parallel straight lines
	$A' = 0$			One real straight line (coincident parallels)

Examples:

$x^2 + 2y^2 - 2x + 12y + 18 = 0$ represents an *ellipse.*
$xy - 2x - y - 8 = 0$ represents a *hyperbola.*
$x^2 - 10y = 0$ represents a *parabola.*
$2x^2 - y^2 - xy - x - 2y - 1 = 0$ represents *two intersecting straight lines.*

2.3-2 Transformation of the Equation of a Conic to Standard Form.

Rotation of the coordinate axes through an angle ϑ such that

$$\tan 2\vartheta = \frac{2a_{12}}{a_{11} - a_{22}} \tag{2.3-4}$$

combined with a suitable translation of the origin (Sec. 2.2-3) reduces the equation of each proper conic (Table 2.3-1) to one of the *standard* or *type forms* (sometimes called *canonical forms*)

$$\frac{x^2}{a^2} + \frac{y^2}{b^2} = 1 \qquad \text{(ELLIPSE)} \tag{2.3-5a}$$

$$\frac{x^2}{a^2} - \frac{y^2}{b^2} = 1 \qquad \text{(HYPERBOLA)} \tag{2.3-5b}$$

$$y^2 = 4px \qquad \text{(PARABOLA)} \tag{2.3-5c}$$

Table 2.3-2 *Special formulas relating to ellipses, hyperbolas, and parabolas represented in standard form* (*see also Fig. 2.3-1*)

No.		Ellipse	Hyperbola	Parabola
1	Equation in standard form	$\dfrac{x^2}{a^2} + \dfrac{y^2}{b^2} = 1$	$\dfrac{x^2}{a^2} - \dfrac{y^2}{b^2} = 1$	$y^2 = 4px$
2	Eccentricity	$\epsilon = \sqrt{1 - \dfrac{b^2}{a^2}} < 1$	$\epsilon = \sqrt{1 + \dfrac{b^2}{a^2}} > 1$	$\epsilon = 1$
3	Focus or foci	$(a\epsilon, 0) \quad (-a\epsilon, 0)$	$(a\epsilon, 0) \quad (-a\epsilon, 0)$	$(p, 0)$
4	Equation(s) of directrix or directrices	$x = \dfrac{a}{\epsilon} \quad x = -\dfrac{a}{\epsilon}$	$x = \dfrac{a}{\epsilon} \quad x = -\dfrac{a}{\epsilon}$	$x = -p$
5	Latus rectum	$\lvert 4p \rvert = \dfrac{2b^2}{a}$	$\lvert 4p \rvert = \dfrac{2b^2}{a}$	$4p$
6	Focal radius or radii of a point (x_1, y_1) on the curve	$r_1 = a + x_1\epsilon$ $r_2 = a - x_1\epsilon$ *Note:* $r_1 + r_2 = 2a$	$r_1 = a + x_1\epsilon$ $r_2 = -a + x_1\epsilon$ *Note:* $r_1 - r_2 = 2a$	$r = x_1 + p$
7	Equation of diameter* conjugate to chords of slope m	$y = -\dfrac{b^2}{a^2 m}x$	$y = \dfrac{b^2}{a^2 m}x$	$y = \dfrac{2p}{m}$
8	Area of segment between the vertex convex to the left and a chord through (x_1, y_1) and $(x_1, -y_1)$	$\dfrac{\pi}{2}ab + \dfrac{b}{a}\left(x_1\sqrt{a^2 - x_1{}^2} + a^2 \arcsin\dfrac{x_1}{a}\right)$	$x_1 y_1 - ab \log_e\left(\dfrac{x_1}{a} + \dfrac{y_1}{b}\right)$	$\tfrac{4}{3}x_1 y_1$
9	Equation in terms of polar coordinates r, φ (Fig. 2.3-1)	$r^2 = \dfrac{b^2}{1 - \epsilon^2 \cos^2 \varphi}$	$r^2 = \dfrac{-b^2}{1 - \epsilon^2 \cos^2 \varphi}$	$r = \dfrac{4p \cos \varphi}{1 - \cos^2 \varphi}$

* That is, the locus of the midpoints of these chords.

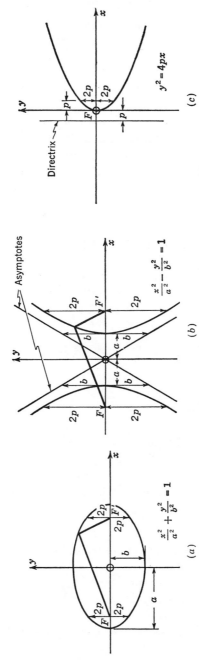

Fig. **2.3-1** Graphs of ellipse, hyperbola, and parabola in standard form (Sec. 2.3-2), showing foci, axes, and length of the latus rectum (Sec. 2.3-3) for each curve.

39

The equations of *improper (degenerate) conics* (Table 2.3-1) are similarly transformed to the standard forms

$$\frac{x^2}{a^2} + \frac{y^2}{b^2} = 0 \text{ (POINT)} \qquad \frac{x^2}{a^2} - \frac{y^2}{b^2} = 0 \text{ (INTERSECTING STRAIGHT LINES)}$$
$$\left.\begin{array}{l}\\ \frac{x^2}{a^2} = 1 \text{ (PARALLEL STRAIGHT LINES)} \qquad x^2 = 0 \text{ (ONE STRAIGHT LINE)}\end{array}\right\} \quad (2.3\text{-}6)$$

2.3-3 Definitions of Proper Conics in Terms of Loci.

Once the equation of any proper conic is reduced to its standard form (5), a simple translation may be used to introduce a new system of coordinates x, y such that the equation of the conic appears in the form

$$y^2 = 4px - (1 - \epsilon^2)x^2 \qquad (2.3\text{-}7)$$

The conic passes through the origin of the new x, y system; the x axis is a *symmetry axis* (principal axis) of the conic.

*Equation (7) describes a proper conic as the locus of a point which moves so that the ratio $\epsilon \geq 0$ (**eccentricity**) of its distances from a fixed point (**focus**) and from a fixed line (**directrix**) is a constant. The conic will be an ellipse if $\epsilon < 1$ and, specifically, a circle if $\epsilon = 0$. The conic will be a hyperbola if $\epsilon > 1$, and a parabola if $\epsilon = 1$.*

The equation of the *directrix* of the conic represented by Eq. (7) is

$$x = -\frac{2p}{\epsilon(1 + \epsilon)} \qquad (2.3\text{-}8)$$

The coordinates x and y of the *focus* are

$$x = \frac{2p}{1 + \epsilon} \qquad y = 0 \qquad (2.3\text{-}9)$$

The directrix is perpendicular to the symmetry axis. The latter passes through the focus and also through the **vertex** $x = y = 0$ of the conic. The distance between the focus and the directrix is equal to $2p/\epsilon$.

In the case of a *central conic* (ellipse or hyperbola), the straight line

$$x = \frac{2p}{1 - \epsilon^2} = a \qquad (2.3\text{-}10)$$

is a symmetry axis (principal axis) of the conic, so that two foci and two directrices can be defined.

The **latus rectum** of a proper conic is defined as the length of a chord through the focus and perpendicular to the symmetry axis and is equal to $|4p|$.

If the focus of a proper conic is chosen as the pole and the symmetry axis as the polar axis of a polar-coordinate system, the equation of the conic in terms of the polar coordinates r, φ is

$$r = \frac{2p}{1 + \epsilon \cos \varphi} \qquad\qquad (2.3\text{-}11)$$

NOTE: *All types of improper as well as of proper conics may be obtained as the intersections of a right circular cone with a plane for various inclinations of the plane with respect to the cone.* If the conic is a pair of (distinct, coincident, or imaginary) parallel straight lines (see also Table 2.3-1), then the cone must be regarded as degenerated into a *cylinder*, unless the plane is tangent to the cone.

2.3-4   The Circle.   The *general form of the equation of a circle* in rectangular cartesian coordinates is

$$x^2 + y^2 + Ax + By + C = 0$$

or

$$(x - x_0)^2 + (y - y_0)^2 = R^2 \qquad\qquad (2.3\text{-}12)$$

with

$$2x_0 = -A \qquad 2y_0 = -B$$
$$R^2 = \tfrac{1}{4}(A^2 + B^2 - 4C) > 0$$

The point (x_0, y_0) is the center of the circle, and R is its radius. The circle (12) touches the x axis or the y axis if $4C = A^2$ or $4C = B^2$, respectively. The *equation of a circle about the origin* is

$$x^2 + y^2 = R^2 \qquad\qquad (2.3\text{-}13)$$

The *equation of the circle through three noncollinear points* (x_1, y_1), (x_2, y_2), (x_3, y_3) is

$$\begin{vmatrix} x^2 + y^2 & x & y & 1 \\ x_1^2 + y_1^2 & x_1 & y_1 & 1 \\ x_2^2 + y_2^2 & x_2 & y_2 & 1 \\ x_3^2 + y_3^2 & x_3 & y_3 & 1 \end{vmatrix} = 0 \qquad\qquad (2.3\text{-}14)$$

Equation (14) is a necessary and sufficient condition that the four points (x, y), (x_1, y_1), (x_2, y_2), (x_3, y_3) lie on a circle.

2.4   HIGHER PLANE CURVES

2.4-1   *Examples of Algebraic Curves* (*Fig. 2.4-1*)

    (*a*) NEIL'S PARABOLA: $y = ax^{3/2}$

    (*b*) WITCH OF AGNESI: $x^2y = 4a^2(2a - y)$

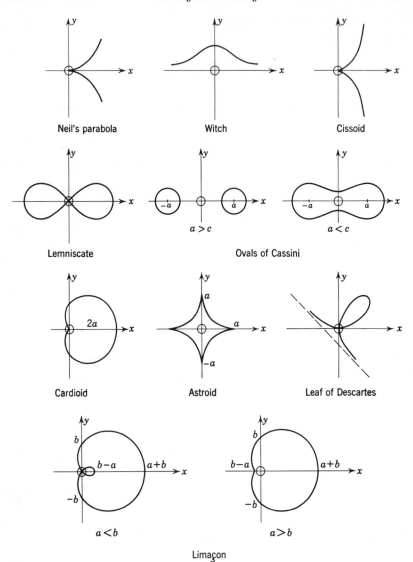

Fig. 2.4-1 Examples of algebraic curves (Sec. 2.4-1).

(c) CONCHOID OF NICOMEDES:

$$(x^2 + y^2)(x - a)^2 = x^2b^2$$

(d) CISSOID OF DIOCLES:

$$y^2(a - x) = x^3 \qquad \text{or} \qquad r = a\left(\frac{1}{\cos\varphi} - \cos\varphi\right)$$

(e) LEMNISCATE OF BERNOULLI:

$$(x^2 + y^2)^2 - a^2(x^2 - y^2) = 0 \qquad \text{or} \qquad r^2(r^2 - a^2\cos 2\varphi) = 0$$

(f) OVALS OF CASSINI: $(x^2 + y^2 + a^2)^2 - 4a^2x^2 = c^4$
(locus of points for which the product of the distances from $(-a, 0)$ and $(a, 0)$ is equal to c^2)

(g) STROPHOID: $x^3 + x(a^2 + y^2) = 2a(y^2 + x^2)$

(h) CRUCIFORM: $x^2y^2 = a^2(x^2 + y^2) \qquad \text{or} \qquad r = \dfrac{2a}{\sin 2\varphi}$

(i) CARDIOID:

$$(x^2 + y^2 - ax)^2 = a^2(x^2 + y^2) \qquad \text{or} \qquad r = a(1 + \cos\varphi)$$

(j) TRISECTRIX:

$$y^2 = \frac{x^3(3a - x)}{a + x} \qquad \text{or} \qquad r = a\left(4\cos\varphi - \frac{1}{\cos\varphi}\right)$$

(k) ASTROID: $x^{2/3} + y^{2/3} = a^{2/3}$

(l) LEAF OF DESCARTES: $x^3 + y^3 = 3axy$

(m) LIMAÇON OF PASCAL: $r = b - a\cos\varphi$

(n) LITUUS: $r^2\varphi = a^2$

2.4-2 Examples of Transcendental Curves *(Fig. 2.4-2)*

(a) CATENARY: $y = \dfrac{a}{2}\left(e^{\frac{x}{a}} + e^{-\frac{x}{a}}\right)$

(b) (LINEAR) SPIRAL OF ARCHIMEDES: $r = a\varphi$

(c) PARABOLIC SPIRAL: $r^2 = 4p\varphi$

(d) LOGARITHMIC SPIRAL: $r = ae^{b\varphi}$

(e) The locus of a point (x, y) at the distance a_1 from the center of a circle of radius a rolling on the x axis is a **cycloid** and may be represented by

$$x = at - a_1\sin t \qquad y = a - a_1\cos t \qquad\qquad (2.4\text{-}1)$$

if the point (x, y) rolls with the circle.

(f) The locus of a point (x, y) at the distance a_1 from the center of a circle of radius a rolling on the outside of the circle $x^2 + y^2 = b^2$ is an **epicycloid** and may be represented by

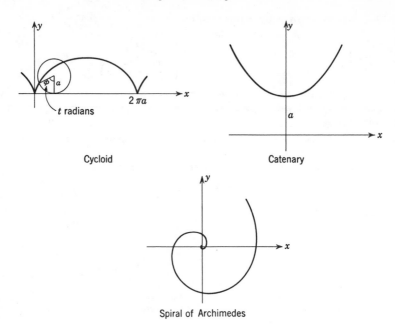

Fig. 2.4-2 Some transcendental curves (Sec. 2.4-2).

$$x = (a + b) \sin \frac{at}{b} - a_1 \sin \frac{a + b}{b} t$$

$$y = (a + b) \cos \frac{at}{b} - a_1 \cos \frac{a + b}{b} t \tag{2.4-2}$$

if the point (x, y) rolls with the circle.

(g) The locus of a point (x, y) at the distance a_1 from the center of a circle of radius a rolling on the inside of the circle $x^2 + y^2 = b^2$ is a **hypocycloid** and may be represented by

$$x = (b - a) \sin \frac{at}{b} - a_1 \sin \frac{b - a}{b} t$$

$$y = (b - a) \cos \frac{at}{b} + a_1 \cos \frac{b - a}{b} t \tag{2.4-3}$$

if the point (x, y) rolls with the circle.

(h) A **tractrix** may be represented by

$$x = a \left(\cos t + \log_e \tan \frac{t}{2} \right) \qquad y = a \sin t \tag{2.4-4}$$

2.5 SOLID ANALYTIC GEOMETRY: BASIC CONCEPTS

2.5-1 Cartesian Coordinate Systems. A **cartesian reference system** or **cartesian coordinate system** associates a unique set of three real numbers (**cartesian coordinates**) x, y, z with every point $P \equiv (x, y, z)$ by reference to three noncoplanar directed straight lines (**cartesian coordinate axes**) intersecting at the **origin** O. Specifically, a **rectangular** cartesian coordinate system has mutually perpendicular coordinate axes, and the coordinates x, y, z of a point P are equal to the directed distances, measured on suitable scales, between the origin and the yz plane, the xz plane, and the xy plane, respectively. The rectangular cartesian coordinate system OX, OY, OZ is **right-handed** if and only if the rotation needed to turn the x axis OX into the y-axis direction OY through an angle $\sphericalangle XOY < 180$ deg would propel a right-handed screw in the direction of the positive z axis.

In a **rectangular** cartesian coordinate system, the coordinate axes are mutually perpendicular (Fig. 2.5-1). The coordinates x, y, z of a point P are equal to the directed distances, measured on suitable scales, between the origin and the yz plane, the xz plane, and the xy plane, respectively.

THROUGHOUT THIS HANDBOOK ALL COORDINATE VALUES x, y, z REFER TO RIGHT-HANDED RECTANGULAR CARTESIAN COORDINATE SYSTEMS, AND EQUAL SCALE UNITS OF UNIT LENGTH ARE USED FOR MEASURING x, y, AND z.

2.5-2 Position Vectors. Given the vector notation introduced in Chap. 4, each point $P \equiv (x, y, z) \equiv (\mathbf{r})$ may be represented uniquely by the **position vector**

$$\mathbf{r} = \mathbf{i}x + \mathbf{j}y + \mathbf{k}z \equiv (x, y, z) \qquad (2.5\text{-}1)$$

which may be represented geometrically by the translation $\overrightarrow{OP}$. The base vectors $\mathbf{i}$, $\mathbf{j}$, $\mathbf{k}$ are unit vectors directed along the x, y, z axes, respectively, of the right-handed rectangular cartesian coordinate system used (see also Secs. 4.1-1 and 4.2-3).

2.5-3 Cylindrical and Spherical Coordinate Systems. Figure 2.5-1 also illustrates **cylindrical coordinates** r', φ, z and **spherical coordinates** r, ϑ, φ (**radius vector, colatitude,** and **longitude**) defined so that

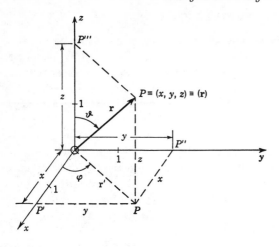

Fig. 2.5-1 Right-handed rectangular cartesian coordinate system, cylindrical coordinate system, and spherical coordinate system.

$$r' = \sqrt[+]{x^2 + y^2} \qquad\qquad x = r' \cos \varphi$$

$$\varphi = \arctan \frac{y}{x} \qquad\qquad y = r' \sin \varphi \qquad (2.5\text{-}2)$$

$$z = z$$

$$r = \sqrt[+]{x^2 + y^2 + z^2} \qquad\qquad x = r \sin \vartheta \cos \varphi$$

$$\vartheta = \arccos \frac{z}{\sqrt{x^2 + y^2 + z^2}} \qquad y = r \sin \vartheta \sin \varphi \qquad (2.5\text{-}3)$$

$$\varphi = \arctan \frac{y}{x} \qquad\qquad z = r \cos \vartheta$$

2.5-4 Basic Relations. Direction Cosines. (*a*) The **distance** d between the points P_1 and P_2 specified by

$$P_1 \equiv (x_1, y_1, z_1) \equiv (\mathbf{r}_1)$$
$$P_2 \equiv (x_2, y_2, z_2) \equiv (\mathbf{r}_2)$$

is

$$\boxed{\begin{aligned} d &= \sqrt{(x_2 - x_1)^2 + (y_2 - y_1)^2 + (z_2 - z_1)^2} \\ &= \sqrt{(\mathbf{r}_2 - \mathbf{r}_1) \cdot (\mathbf{r}_2 - \mathbf{r}_1)} = |\mathbf{r}_2 - \mathbf{r}_1| \end{aligned}} \qquad (2.5\text{-}4)$$

(*b*) The coordinates and the position vector of the **midpoint** of the line segment P_1P_2 are given by

$$x = \frac{x_1 + x_2}{2} \qquad y = \frac{y_1 + y_2}{2} \qquad z = \frac{z_1 + z_2}{2} \qquad \mathbf{r} = \frac{\mathbf{r}_1 + \mathbf{r}_2}{2}$$

$$(2.5\text{-}5)$$

(*c*) The **direction cosines** $\cos \alpha_x$, $\cos \alpha_y$, $\cos \alpha_z$ **of the directed line segment** $\overrightarrow{P_1P_2}$ are the cosines of the angles α_x, α_y, α_z between $\overrightarrow{P_1P_2}$ and the positive x, y, and z axis, respectively:

$$\cos \alpha_x = \frac{x_2 - x_1}{\sqrt{(x_2 - x_1)^2 + (y_2 - y_1)^2 + (z_2 - z_1)^2}}$$

$$\cos \alpha_y = \frac{y_2 - y_1}{\sqrt{(x_2 - x_1)^2 + (y_2 - y_1)^2 + (z_2 - z_1)^2}} \qquad (2.5\text{-}6)$$

$$\cos \alpha_z = \frac{z_2 - z_1}{\sqrt{(x_2 - x_1)^2 + (y_2 - y_1)^2 + (z_2 - z_1)^2}}$$

with

$$\cos^2 \alpha_x + \cos^2 \alpha_y + \cos^2 \alpha_z = 1 \qquad (2.5\text{-}7)$$

The direction cosines of the directed line segment $\overrightarrow{P_2P_1}$ are $-\cos \alpha_x$, $-\cos \alpha_y$, $-\cos \alpha_z$.

(*d*) Any set of three numbers a_x, a_y, a_z proportional (with the same proportionality constant) to the direction cosines $\cos \alpha_x$, $\cos \alpha_y$, $\cos \alpha_z$ are called **direction numbers** of the line in question, and

$$\cos \alpha_x = \frac{a_x}{\pm \sqrt{a_x^2 + a_y^2 + a_z^2}}$$

$$\cos \alpha_y = \frac{a_y}{\pm \sqrt{a_x^2 + a_y^2 + a_z^2}} \qquad (2.5\text{-}8)$$

$$\cos \alpha_z = \frac{a_z}{\pm \sqrt{a_x^2 + a_y^2 + a_z^2}}$$

where the sign of the square root is taken to be the same in all three equations; its choice fixes the positive direction of the line. The components of any vector **a** (Sec. 4.2-3) having the same direction as either $\overrightarrow{P_1P_2}$ or $\overrightarrow{P_2P_1}$ are direction numbers of $\overrightarrow{P_1P_2}$. (***Example:*** $x_2 - x_1$, $y_2 - y_1, z_2 - z_1$.) The direction cosines of $\overrightarrow{P_1P_2}$ are the components of a unit vector directed along $\overrightarrow{P_1P_2}$.

(*e*) The angle γ between two line segments having the respective direction cosines $\cos \alpha_x$, $\cos \alpha_y$, $\cos \alpha_z$ and $\cos \alpha'_x$, $\cos \alpha'_y$, $\cos \alpha'_z$ or the respective direction numbers a_x, a_y, a_z and a'_x, a'_y, a'_z is given by

$$\cos \gamma = \cos \alpha_x \cos \alpha'_x + \cos \alpha_y \cos \alpha'_y + \cos \alpha_z \cos \alpha'_z$$

$$= \frac{a_x a'_x + a_y a'_y + a_z a'_z}{\sqrt{a_x{}^2 + a_y{}^2 + a_z{}^2} \sqrt{a_x'^2 + a_y'^2 + a_z'^2}} \tag{2.5-9}$$

2.5-5 *Translation and Rotation of Rectangular Cartesian Coordinate Systems.* (*a*) TRANSLATION OF COORDINATE AXES.
Let x, y, z be the coordinates of any point P with respect to a right-handed rectangular cartesian reference system. Let $\bar{x}$, $\bar{y}$, $\bar{z}$ be the coordinates of the same point P with respect to a second right-handed rectangular cartesian reference system whose axes have the same directions as the corresponding axes of the x, y, z system, and whose origin has the coordinates $x = x_0$, $y = y_0$, $z = z_0$ in the x, y, z system. If equal scales are used to measure the coordinates in both systems, the coordinates $\bar{x}$, $\bar{y}$, $\bar{z}$ are related to the coordinates x, y, z by the *transformation equations*

$$\begin{array}{ll} \bar{x} = x - x_0 & x = \bar{x} + x_0 \\ \bar{y} = y - y_0 & y = \bar{y} + y_0 \\ \bar{z} = z - z_0 & z = \bar{z} + z_0 \end{array} \tag{2.5-10}$$

(*b*) ROTATION OF COORDINATE AXES. Given any point $P \equiv (x, y, z)$, let $\bar{x}$, $\bar{y}$, $\bar{z}$ be the coordinates of the same point with respect to a second right-handed rectangular cartesian reference system having the same origin O as the x, y, z system and oriented with respect to the latter so that

The $\bar{x}$ axis has the direction cosines t_{11}, t_{21}, t_{31}.
The $\bar{y}$ axis has the direction cosines t_{12}, t_{22}, t_{32}.
The $\bar{z}$ axis has the direction cosines t_{13}, t_{23}, t_{33}.

Then in the $\bar{x}$, $\bar{y}$, $\bar{z}$ system

The x axis has the direction cosines t_{11}, t_{12}, t_{13}.
The y axis has the direction cosines t_{21}, t_{22}, t_{23}.
The z axis has the direction cosines t_{31}, t_{32}, t_{33}.

If equal scales are used to measure x, y, z, $\bar{x}$, $\bar{y}$, and $\bar{z}$, the transformation equations relating the coordinates $\bar{x}$, $\bar{y}$, $\bar{z}$ to the coordinates x, y, z are

$$
\begin{aligned}
\bar{x} &= t_{11}x + t_{21}y + t_{31}z & x &= t_{11}\bar{x} + t_{12}\bar{y} + t_{13}\bar{z} \\
\bar{y} &= t_{12}x + t_{22}y + t_{32}z \quad \text{or} & y &= t_{21}\bar{x} + t_{22}\bar{y} + t_{23}\bar{z} \quad (2.5\text{-}11) \\
\bar{z} &= t_{13}x + t_{23}y + t_{33}z & z &= t_{31}\bar{x} + t_{32}\bar{y} + t_{33}\bar{z}
\end{aligned}
$$

NOTE: The transformations (11) are *orthogonal; each t_{ik} equals the cofactor of t_{ki} in the determinant*

$$\det [t_{ik}] = 1 \tag{2.5-12}$$

(Sec. 1.3-2), and

$$\sum_{j=1}^{3} t_{ij}t_{jk} = \sum_{j=1}^{3} t_{ji}t_{kj} = \begin{cases} 1 \text{ if } i = k \\ 0 \text{ if } i \neq k \end{cases} \tag{2.5-13}$$

(*c*) SIMULTANEOUS TRANSLATION AND ROTATION. If the origin of the $\bar{x}$, $\bar{y}$, $\bar{z}$ system is not that of the x, y, z system but has the coordinates $x = x_0$, $y = y_0$, $z = z_0$ in the x, y, z system, the transformation equations become

$$
\begin{aligned}
\bar{x} &= t_{11}(x - x_0) + t_{21}(y - y_0) + t_{31}(z - z_0) \\
\bar{y} &= t_{12}(x - x_0) + t_{22}(y - y_0) + t_{32}(z - z_0) \\
\bar{z} &= t_{13}(x - x_0) + t_{23}(y - y_0) + t_{33}(z - z_0)
\end{aligned}
$$

or $\qquad\qquad\qquad\qquad\qquad\qquad\qquad\qquad\qquad\qquad\qquad (2.5\text{-}14)$

$$
\begin{aligned}
x &= t_{11}\bar{x} + t_{12}\bar{y} + t_{13}\bar{z} + x_0 \\
y &= t_{21}\bar{x} + t_{22}\bar{y} + t_{23}\bar{z} + y_0 \\
z &= t_{31}\bar{x} + t_{32}\bar{y} + t_{33}\bar{z} + z_0
\end{aligned}
$$

where the direction cosines t_{ik} satisfy the relations (12) and (13).

The equations (14) relate the coordinates of a point in *any* two right-handed rectangular cartesian reference systems if the same scales are used for all coordinate measurements.

(*d*) ALTERNATIVE INTERPRETATION OF COORDINATE TRANSFORMATIONS. The transformation equations (14) [of which (10) and (11) are special cases] may also be interpreted as *defining a new point P having the coordinates* $\bar{x}$, $\bar{y}$, $\bar{z}$ *in the x, y, z system* and obtained by successive translation and rotation of the original point *P*.

2.5-6 Representation of Curves.

A **continuous curve** in three-dimensional euclidean space is a set of points $(x, y, z) \equiv (\mathbf{r})$ whose coordinates satisfy a system of parametric equations

$$\begin{aligned} x &= x(t) \\ y &= y(t) \quad \text{or} \quad \mathbf{r} = \mathbf{r}(t) \quad (-\infty \leq t_1 \leq t \leq t_2 \leq \infty) \\ z &= z(t) \end{aligned}$$

(2.5-15)

where $x(t)$, $y(t)$, $z(t)$ are continuous functions of the real parameter t throughout the closed interval $[t_1, t_2]$ (**parametric representation of a curve**). Alternatively, a curve may be defined by an equivalent set of two equations

$$\varphi_1(x, y, z) = 0 \qquad \varphi_2(x, y, z) = 0 \tag{2.5-16}$$

A curve can have more than one branch; branches may or may not be connected.

A **simple curve** (simple arc, simple segment) is a (portion of a) continuous curve consisting of a single branch without multiple points, so that the functions (16) are single-valued, and

$$x(\tau_1) = x(\tau_2) \qquad y(\tau_1) = y(\tau_2) \qquad z(\tau_1) = z(\tau_2) \tag{2.5-17}$$

are not satisfied by any pair of values $\tau_1 \neq \tau_2$ of t in the closed interval $[t_1, t_2]$. A **simple closed curve** is a continuous curve without multiple points except for a common initial and terminal point; i.e., the only solutions of Eqs. (17) in the closed interval $[t_1, t_2]$ are $\tau_1 = t_1$, $\tau_2 = t_2$. A **regular arc** is a continuous curve which can be represented in terms of some parameter t so that every point of the curve is a **regular point** where $x(t)$, $y(t)$, $z(t)$ have unique continuous derivatives (Sec. 4.5-1) not all equal to zero. A **regular** (**piecewise smooth**) **curve** is a simple curve or a simple closed curve composed of a finite number of regular arcs.

NOTE: Analogous definitions apply to curves in the plane.

2.5-7 Representation of Surfaces.

The coordinates of each point $(x, y, z) \equiv (\mathbf{r})$ on a **continuous surface** in three-dimensional euclidean space satisfy a set of parametric equations

$$x = x(u, v) \quad y = y(u, v) \quad z = z(u, v) \quad \text{or} \quad \mathbf{r} = \mathbf{r}(u, v)$$

(2.5-18)

for suitable ranges of the real parameters u, v; the functions (18) are continuous (*parametric representation of a surface*). A surface can also be defined by an equation

$$\varphi(x, y, z) = 0 \quad \text{or} \quad z = f(x, y) \tag{2.5-19}$$

A surface can have more than one sheet; sheets may or may not be connected. *The surfaces corresponding to the equations*

$$\varphi(x, y, z) = 0 \quad \text{and} \quad \lambda\varphi(x, y, z) = 0 \tag{2.5-20}$$

are identical for any constant λ different from zero.

2.5-8   Surfaces and Curves. The **intersection** of two surfaces

$$\varphi_1(x, y, z) = 0 \quad \varphi_2(x, y, z) = 0 \tag{2.5-21}$$

is the curve whose points (x, y, z) satisfy both equations (21). The line of intersection can have more than one branch; or it may degenerate into a set of points where the two surfaces touch.

For any pair of real numbers λ_1, λ_2 not simultaneously equal to zero, the equation

$$\lambda_1\varphi_1(x, y, z) + \lambda_2\varphi_2(x, y, z) = 0 \tag{2.5-22}$$

corresponds to a surface passing through all points of the curve of intersection of the two surfaces (21), if that curve exists.

2.6   PLANES AND STRAIGHT LINES

2.6-1   Equation of a Plane. (*a*) Given a right-handed rectangular cartesian coordinate system, an equation *linear* in x, y, z, i.e., a relation of the general form

$$\boxed{Ax + By + Cz + D = 0 \quad \text{or} \quad \mathbf{A} \cdot \mathbf{r} + D = 0 \tag{2.6-1}}$$

where A, B, and C must not all vanish simultaneously, represents a **plane**; conversely, every plane situated in the finite portion of space can be represented by a linear equation of the form (1).

A, B, C are direction numbers (Sec. 2.5-4) of the (positive or negative; see below) *normal* to the plane; the vector $\mathbf{A} \equiv (A, B, C)$ is directed along the normal. The special case $D = 0$ corresponds to a plane through the origin.

(*b*) The following *special forms* of the equation of the plane are of interest:

1. **Intercept form.** Plane intercepting the x axis at $x = a$, the y axis at $y = b$, and the z axis at $z = c$:

$$\frac{x}{a} + \frac{y}{b} + \frac{z}{c} - 1 = 0$$

2. **Normal form.** Let $p > 0$ be the length of the directed perpendicular between the origin and a plane; let $\cos \alpha_x$, $\cos \alpha_y$, $\cos \alpha_z$ be the direction cosines (Sec. 2.5-4) of this directed perpendicular, which is taken to be the **positive normal** to the plane. Then the equation of the plane is

$$x \cos \alpha_x + y \cos \alpha_y + z \cos \alpha_z - p = 0$$

3. **Point-direction form.** Plane through the point $(x_1, y_1, z_1) \equiv (\mathbf{r}_1)$; the normal has the direction numbers A, B, C:

$$A(x - x_1) + B(y - y_1) + C(z - z_1) = 0$$

or

$$\mathbf{A} \cdot (\mathbf{r} - \mathbf{r}_1) = 0$$

4. **Three-point form.** Plane through the three points $P_1 \equiv (x_1, y_1, z_1) \equiv (\mathbf{r}_1)$, $P_2 \equiv (x_2, y_2, z_2) \equiv (\mathbf{r}_2)$, $P_3 \equiv (x_3, y_3, z_3) \equiv (\mathbf{r}_3)$, which must not lie in a straight line:

$$\begin{vmatrix} x & y & z & 1 \\ x_1 & y_1 & z_1 & 1 \\ x_2 & y_2 & z_2 & 1 \\ x_3 & y_3 & z_3 & 1 \end{vmatrix} = 0 \quad \text{or} \quad [(\mathbf{r} - \mathbf{r}_1)(\mathbf{r} - \mathbf{r}_2)(\mathbf{r} - \mathbf{r}_3)] = 0$$

or

$$\begin{vmatrix} y_1 & z_1 & 1 \\ y_2 & z_2 & 1 \\ y_3 & z_3 & 1 \end{vmatrix} x + \begin{vmatrix} z_1 & x_1 & 1 \\ z_2 & x_2 & 1 \\ z_3 & x_3 & 1 \end{vmatrix} y$$

$$+ \begin{vmatrix} x_1 & y_1 & 1 \\ x_2 & y_2 & 1 \\ x_3 & y_3 & 1 \end{vmatrix} z - \begin{vmatrix} x_1 & y_1 & z_1 \\ x_2 & y_2 & z_2 \\ x_3 & y_3 & z_3 \end{vmatrix} = 0$$

(c) When the equation of a plane is given in the general form (1), the quantities $a, b, c, p, \cos \alpha_x, \cos \alpha_y, \cos \alpha_z$ defined above are related to the parameters A, B, C, D as follows:

$$a = -\frac{D}{A} \qquad b = -\frac{D}{B} \qquad c = -\frac{D}{C} \tag{2.6-2}$$

$$
\left.
\begin{aligned}
\cos \alpha_x &= \frac{A}{(A^2 + B^2 + C^2)^{1/2}} \\[2mm]
\cos \alpha_y &= \frac{B}{(A^2 + B^2 + C^2)^{1/2}} \\[2mm]
\cos \alpha_z &= \frac{C}{(A^2 + B^2 + C^2)^{1/2}} \\[2mm]
p &= -\frac{D}{(A^2 + B^2 + C^2)^{1/2}}
\end{aligned}
\right\} \tag{2.6-3}
$$

where the sign of the square root is chosen so that $p > 0$.

(*d*) The parametric representation (Sec. 2.5-7) of any plane has the form

$$
\begin{aligned}
x &= x_1 + a_x u + b_x v \\
y &= y_1 + a_y u + b_y v \\
z &= z_1 + a_z u + b_z v
\end{aligned} \tag{2.6-4}
$$

or

$$\mathbf{r} = \mathbf{r}_1 + u\mathbf{a} + v\mathbf{b}$$

2.6-2 *Equations of the Straight Line.* (*a*) Two linearly independent linear equations

$$
\begin{aligned}
\varphi_1(x, y, z) &\equiv A_1 x + B_1 y + C_1 z + D_1 = 0 \\
\varphi_2(x, y, z) &\equiv A_2 x + B_2 y + C_2 z + D_2 = 0
\end{aligned}
$$

or

$$\mathbf{A}_1 \cdot \mathbf{r} + D_1 = 0 \qquad \mathbf{A}_2 \cdot \mathbf{r} + D_2 = 0 \tag{2.6-5}$$

with

$$(\mathbf{A}_1 \times \mathbf{A}_2 \neq 0)$$

represent a **straight line** (intersection of two planes, Sec. 2.5-8). Conversely, every straight line situated in the finite portion of space can be represented in the form (5). Equation (5) represents a straight line through the origin if and only if $D_1 = D_2 = 0$ (see Secs. 4.2-5 and 4.2-6 for definitions of vector dot and cross products).

(*b*) The following *special forms* of the equations of a straight line are of interest:

---

1. **Two-point form.** Straight line through the points (x_1, y_1, z_1) and (x_2, y_2, z_2):

$$\frac{x - x_1}{x_2 - x_1} = \frac{y - y_1}{y_2 - y_1} = \frac{z - z_1}{z_2 - z_1}$$

2. **Point-direction form** or **symmetric form.** Straight line with direction numbers a_x, a_y, a_z (Sec. 2.5-4) through the point $(x_1, x_2, x_3) \equiv (\mathbf{r}_1)$ (see also Sec. 2.5-4):

$$\frac{x - x_1}{a_x} = \frac{y - y_1}{a_y} = \frac{z - z_1}{a_z} \qquad \text{or} \qquad (\mathbf{r} - \mathbf{r}_1) = \mathbf{a}t$$

(*c*) The quantities

$$
\begin{aligned}
a_x &= B_1C_2 - B_2C_1 \\
a_y &= C_1A_2 - C_2A_1 \\
a_z &= A_1B_2 - A_2B_1
\end{aligned}
\qquad
\begin{aligned}
&\text{(\scriptsize RECTANGULAR} \\
&\text{\scriptsize CARTESIAN COMPONENTS} \\
&\text{\scriptsize OF } \mathbf{a} = \mathbf{A}_1 \times \mathbf{A}_2)
\end{aligned}
\qquad (2.6\text{-}6)
$$

are direction numbers (Sec. 2.5-4) of the straight line described by Eq. (5) [*direction numbers of the line of intersection of the two planes* (5)].

(*d*) The rectangular cartesian coordinates x, y, z of a point on a straight line satisfy the parametric equations

$$x = x_1 + a_x t \qquad y = y_1 + a_y t \qquad z = z_1 + a_z t$$

or $\quad \mathbf{r} = \mathbf{r}_1 + t\mathbf{a}$

$$(2.6\text{-}7)$$

[*straight line through the point* $(\mathbf{r}_1)$ *in the direction of the vector* $\mathbf{a}$].

2.6-3 Formulas for Angles and Distances. (*a*) *The angle γ_1 between two straight lines* having the direction cosines $\cos \alpha_x$, $\cos \alpha_y$, $\cos \alpha_z$ and $\cos \alpha'_x$, $\cos \alpha'_y$, $\cos \alpha'_z$ is given by

$$\cos \gamma_1 = \cos \alpha_x \cos \alpha'_x + \cos \alpha_y \cos \alpha'_y + \cos \alpha_z \cos \alpha'_z \qquad (2.6\text{-}8)$$

The two straight lines are *parallel* if $\cos \gamma_1 = 1$ and *mutually perpendicular* if $\cos \gamma_1 = 0$.

(*b*) *The angle γ_2 between* (*the normals of*) *two planes* $Ax + By + Cz + D = 0$ and $A'x + B'y + C'z + D' = 0$ or $\mathbf{A} \cdot \mathbf{r} + D = 0$ and $\mathbf{A}' \cdot \mathbf{r} + D' = 0$ is given by

$$\cos \gamma_2 = \frac{AA' + BB' + CC'}{\sqrt{A^2 + B^2 + C^2} \sqrt{A'^2 + B'^2 + C'^2}} = \frac{\mathbf{A} \cdot \mathbf{A}}{|\mathbf{A}| \, |\mathbf{A}'|} \qquad (2.6\text{-}9)$$

(c) The angle γ_3 between the straight line

$$\frac{x - x_1}{\cos \alpha_x} = \frac{y - y_1}{\cos \alpha_y} = \frac{z - z_1}{\cos \alpha_z}$$

and (its projection on) the plane $Ax + By + Cz + D = 0$ is given by

$$\sin \gamma_3 = \frac{A \cos \alpha_x + B \cos \alpha_y + C \cos \alpha_z}{(A^2 + B^2 + C^2)^{\frac{1}{2}}} \tag{2.6-10}$$

(d) *Distance d_0 between the point* $(x_0, y_0, z_0) = (\mathbf{r}_0)$ *and the plane* $Ax + By + Cz + D = 0$ *or* $\mathbf{A} \cdot \mathbf{r} + D = 0$:

$$d_0 = \frac{Ax_0 + By_0 + Cz_0 + D}{(A^2 + B^2 + C^2)^{\frac{1}{2}}} = \frac{\mathbf{A} \cdot \mathbf{r}_0 + D}{\pm |\mathbf{A}|} \tag{2.6-11}$$

where the sign of the square root is chosen to be opposite to that of D. d_0 is positive if the plane lies between the origin and the point (x_0, y_0, z_0).

(e) *Distance d_0' between the point* $(x_0, y_0, z_0) = (\mathbf{r}_0)$ *and the straight line* $(x - x_1)/\cos \alpha_x = (y - y_1)/\cos \alpha_y = (z - z_1)/\cos \alpha_z$:

$$d_0' = + \{(x_0 - x_1)^2 + (y_0 - y_1)^2 + (z_0 - z_1)^2$$
$$- [(x_0 - x_1) \cos \alpha_x + (y_0 - y_1) \cos \alpha_y + (z_0 - z_1) \cos \alpha_z]^2\}^{\frac{1}{2}} \tag{2.6-12}$$

2.6-4 Special Conditions. (a) *Three points* (x_1, y_1, z_1), (x_2, y_2, z_2), (x_3, y_3, z_3) *lie on a straight line* (*are* **collinear**) *if and only if*

$$\frac{x_3 - x_1}{x_2 - x_1} = \frac{y_3 - y_1}{y_2 - y_1} = \frac{z_3 - z_1}{z_2 - z_1} \tag{2.6-13}$$

or

$$\begin{vmatrix} y_1 & z_1 & 1 \\ y_2 & z_2 & 1 \\ y_3 & z_3 & 1 \end{vmatrix} = \begin{vmatrix} z_1 & x_1 & 1 \\ z_2 & x_2 & 1 \\ z_3 & x_3 & 1 \end{vmatrix} = \begin{vmatrix} x_1 & y_1 & 1 \\ x_2 & y_2 & 1 \\ x_3 & y_3 & 1 \end{vmatrix} = 0 \tag{2.6-14}$$

(b) *Four points* (x_1, y_1, z_1), (x_2, y_2, z_2), (x_3, y_3, z_3), (x_4, y_4, z_4) *lie in a plane if and only if*

$$\begin{vmatrix} x_1 & y_1 & z_1 & 1 \\ x_2 & y_2 & z_2 & 1 \\ x_3 & y_3 & z_3 & 1 \\ x_4 & y_4 & z_4 & 1 \end{vmatrix} = 0 \quad \text{or} \quad [(\mathbf{r}_2 - \mathbf{r}_1)(\mathbf{r}_3 - \mathbf{r}_1)(\mathbf{r}_4 - \mathbf{r}_1)] = 0 \tag{2.6-15}$$

(c) *Three planes* $Ax + By + Cz + D = 0$, $A'x + B'y + C'z + D' = 0$, $A''x + B''y + C''z + D'' = 0$ *intersect in a straight line if*

$$\begin{vmatrix} A & B & C \\ A' & B' & C' \\ A'' & B'' & C'' \end{vmatrix} = 0 \tag{2.6-16}$$

(d) Note the *principle of duality: to every theorem involving only the relative positions of points, planes, and straight lines, there corresponds another theorem obtained by interchanging the terms "point" and "plane" in the original theorem.*

2.7 QUADRIC SURFACES

2.7-1 General Second-degree Equation. Representation of Quadric Surfaces in Standard Form.
For every general second-degree equation

$$a_{11}x^2 + a_{22}y^2 + a_{33}z^2 + 2a_{12}xy + 2a_{13}xz + 2a_{23}yz$$
$$+ 2a_{14}x + 2a_{24}y + 2a_{34}z + a_{44} = 0 \qquad (2.7\text{-}1)$$

Table 2.7-1 *Equations (in standard or type form) and principal properties of proper quadric surfaces*

Surface (see also Fig. 2.7-1)	Equation in standard or type form	Section by plane	Remarks
(Real) **ellipsoid** [*ellipsoid of revolution (spheroid)* if two principal diameters are equal and (*a*) smaller than the third (*prolate spheroid*) or (*b*) greater than the third (*oblate spheroid*); *sphere* if $a^2 = b^2 = c^2$]	$\dfrac{x^2}{a^2} + \dfrac{y^2}{b^2} + \dfrac{z^2}{c^2} = 1$	Real or imaginary **ellipse; point** (tangent plane)	Vertices at $(\pm a, 0, 0)$ if $a^2 > b^2, a^2 > c^2$; principal diameters have the lengths $2a, 2b, 2c$
Hyperboloid of one sheet (*of revolution* if $a^2 = b^2$)	$\dfrac{x^2}{a^2} + \dfrac{y^2}{b^2} - \dfrac{z^2}{c^2} = 1$	**Hyperbola, parabola,** or **ellipse** corresponding to plane parallel to two generators, one generator, or no generator, respectively, of the asymptotic cone	Doubly ruled surface; contains two families of straight lines (generators) $\dfrac{x}{a} + \dfrac{z}{c} = \lambda\left(1 + \dfrac{y}{b}\right),$ $\lambda\left(\dfrac{x}{a} - \dfrac{z}{c}\right) = 1 - \dfrac{y}{b}$ and $\dfrac{x}{a} + \dfrac{z}{c} = \mu\left(1 - \dfrac{y}{b}\right),$ $\mu\left(\dfrac{x}{a} - \dfrac{z}{c}\right) = 1 + \dfrac{y}{b}$ Locus of a straight line intersecting three given straight lines. Asymptotic cone (inside the surface) $x^2/a^2 + y^2/b^2 - z^2/c^2 = 0$
Hyperboloid of two sheets (*of revolution* if $b^2 = c^2$)	$\dfrac{x^2}{a^2} - \dfrac{y^2}{b^2} - \dfrac{z^2}{c^2} = 1$		Vertices at $(\pm a, 0, 0)$; distance between vertices is $2a$ Asymptotic cone (outside the surface) $\dfrac{x^2}{a^2} - \dfrac{y^2}{b^2} - \dfrac{z^2}{c^2} = 0$
Elliptic paraboloid (*of revolution* if $a^2 = b^2$)	$\dfrac{x^2}{a^2} + \dfrac{y^2}{b^2} = z$	**Parabola** (diametral plane); real or imaginary **ellipse; point** (tangent plane)	Vertex at origin
Hyperbolic paraboloid	$\dfrac{x^2}{a^2} - \dfrac{y^2}{b^2} = z$	**Parabola** (diametral plane), **hyperbola**	Saddle point at origin. Doubly ruled surface; contains two families of straight lines $\dfrac{x}{a} + \dfrac{y}{b} = \lambda, \dfrac{x}{a} - \dfrac{y}{b} = \dfrac{z}{\lambda}$ and $\dfrac{x}{a} - \dfrac{y}{b} = \mu, \dfrac{x}{a} + \dfrac{y}{b} = \dfrac{z}{\mu}$

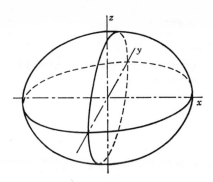

Ellipsoid: $\dfrac{x^2}{a^2} + \dfrac{y^2}{b^2} + \dfrac{z^2}{c^2} = 1$

(a)

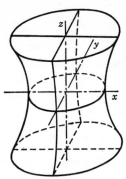

Hyperboloid of one sheet: $\dfrac{x^2}{a^2} + \dfrac{y^2}{b^2} - \dfrac{z^2}{c^2} = 1$

(b)

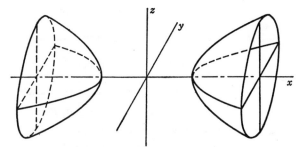

Hyperboloid of two sheets: $\dfrac{x^2}{a^2} - \dfrac{y^2}{b^2} - \dfrac{z^2}{c^2} = 1$

(c)

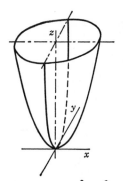

Elliptic paraboloid: $\dfrac{x^2}{a^2} + \dfrac{y^2}{b^2} = z$

(d)

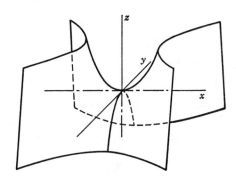

Hyperbolic paraboloid: $\dfrac{x^2}{a^2} - \dfrac{y^2}{b^2} = z$

(e)

Fig. 2.7-1 Proper quadric surfaces.

a suitable rotation and/or translation of coordinate axes (Sec. 2.5-5) will produce the equation of one of the **proper quadrics** listed in Table 2.7-1 if and only if the fourth-order determinant det $[a_{ik}]$ differs from zero; otherwise, it is possible to obtain the equation of an **improper quadric,** viz.,

$$\frac{x^2}{a^2} + \frac{y^2}{b^2} + \frac{z^2}{c^2} = 0 \qquad \text{(POINT)}$$

$$\frac{x^2}{a^2} + \frac{y^2}{b^2} - \frac{z^2}{c^2} = 0 \qquad \text{(ELLIPTIC CONE; circular if } a^2 = b^2\text{)}$$

$$\frac{x^2}{a^2} + \frac{y^2}{b^2} = 1 \qquad \text{(ELLIPTIC CYLINDER; circular if } a^2 = b^2\text{)}$$

$$\frac{x^2}{a^2} - \frac{y^2}{b^2} = 1 \qquad \text{(HYPERBOLIC CYLINDER)}$$

$$\frac{x^2}{a^2} + \frac{y^2}{b^2} = 0 \qquad \text{(STRAIGHT LINE)} \qquad (2.7\text{-}2)$$

$$\frac{x^2}{a^2} - \frac{y^2}{b^2} = 0 \qquad \text{(TWO INTERSECTING PLANES)}$$

$$\frac{x^2}{a^2} = y \qquad \text{(PARABOLIC CYLINDER)}$$

$$\frac{x^2}{a^2} = 1 \qquad \text{(TWO PARALLEL PLANES)}$$

$$x^2 = 0 \qquad \text{(ONE REAL PLANE)}$$

Figure 2.7-1 shows the five proper quadric surfaces. See Ref. 2 for the choice of transformation, and for the classification of quadrics in terms of the given coefficients a_{ik}.

2.7-2　The Sphere.　The *equation of a sphere* of radius r about the point (x_1, y_1, z_1) is

$$(x - x_1)^2 + (y - y_1)^2 + (z - z_1)^2 = r^2 \qquad \text{or} \qquad |\mathbf{r} - \mathbf{r}_1| = r \qquad (2.7\text{-}3)$$

The most general form of the equation of a sphere is

$$A(x^2 + y^2 + z^2) + 2Bx + 2Cy + 2Dz + E = 0 \qquad (A \neq 0) \qquad (2.7\text{-}4)$$

References and Bibliography

1. Cell, J. W.: *Analytic Geometry*, 3d ed., Wiley, New York, 1960.
2. Middlemiss, R. R.: *Analytic Geometry*, McGraw-Hill, New York, 1955.
3. Purcell, E. J.: *Analytic Geometry*, Appleton-Century-Crofts, New York, 1958.
4. Smith, E. S., et al.: *Analytic Geometry*, Wiley, New York, 1954.

Additional background material

5. Coxeter, H. S. M.: *Introduction to Geometry*, Wiley, New York, 1961.
6. Klein, F.: *Famous Problems of Elementary Geometry*, 2d ed., Dover, New York, 1956.

3 FUNCTIONS AND LIMITS. DIFFERENTIAL AND INTEGRAL CALCULUS

3.1 INTRODUCTION

3.1-1 Survey. This chapter is primarily concerned with numerical *functions of real variables.* Such functions furnish "analytical" descriptions of relationships between objects labeled with sets of real numbers. The introduction of *limits of functions* (Secs. 3.4-1 to 3.4-6) permits one to define new mathematical operations (limiting processes), such as addition and multiplications of infinite numbers of terms, differentiation, and integration. Limiting processes are also used to derive numerical approximations.

The *differential calculus* (Secs. 3.5-1 to 3.5-4) describes relations between small changes of suitable variables. The *integral calculus* (Secs. 3.6-1 to 3.6-5) yields measures for overall or average properties of a set of objects and furnishes techniques for adding many small changes. Sections 3.8-1 to 3.9-2 outline the properties of *infinite series*, and Secs. 3.10-1 to 3.11-3 deal with the representation of functions by *power series*, *Fourier series*, and *Fourier integrals*.

3.2 FUNCTIONS

3.2-1   Functions and Variables.   (*a*) Given a *rule of correspondence* which associates a real or complex number

$$y = f(x) \tag{3.2-1}$$

with each given real or complex number x of a set S_x, y is called a (numerical) **function** $y = y(x) = f(x)$ of the **argument** x.   Equation (1) specifies a **value** (or values) $y = Y = f(X)$ of the variable y corresponding to each suitable value $x = X$ of the variable x.   If the relation (1) is primarily intended to describe the dependence of y on x, x is called the **independent variable,** and y is called the **dependent variable.**

The term "variable x" essentially refers to a *set* of values X, and Eq. (1) symbolizes a set of correspondences relating values X of X and values $Y = f(X)$ of y. In order to conform with the notation employed in most textbooks, the symbol x will be used to denote both the *variable x* and a *value of the variable x* whenever this notation does not result in ambiguities.

If one interprets x and y as plane cartesian coordinates (Sec. 2.2-2), a real function $y = f(x)$ of a real variable x is often represented by a curve (**graph** of y vs. x).

(*b*)   A function

$$y = f(x_1, x_2, \ldots, x_n) \tag{3.2-2}$$

of n variables $x_1, x_2, \ldots, x_n$ similarly associates values of a (dependent) variable y with ordered sets of values of the (independent) variables $x_1, x_2, \ldots, x_n$.

(*c*)   In most applications, the variables x, y or $x_1, x_2, \ldots, x_n, y$ label physical objects or quantities, so that *suitable relations* (1) *or* (2) *describe physical relationships*. (***Example:*** $y = x_1 x_2$ if x_1, x_2, and y respectively label the voltage, current, and power in a simple electric circuit.)

(*d*)   The set S_x of values of x (or of sets of values of $x_1, x_2, \ldots, x_n$) for which the relationship (1) or (2) is defined is the **domain of definition** of the function $f(x)$ or $f(x_1, x_2, \ldots, x_n)$.   The corresponding set S_y of values of y is the **range** of the function.

(*e*)   A **sequence** of real or complex numbers $s_0, s_1, s_2, \ldots$ represents a function $s_n = s_n(n)$ defined on the set of nonnegative integers n.

3.2-2   Functions with Special Properties.   (*a*) A function is **single-valued** wherever a single function value corresponds to the value of the argument.   A function is **multiple-valued** wherever two or more function values correspond to the value of the argument.   The function $y(x)$ has an **inverse function** $x(y)$ if $y = y(x)$ implies $x = x(y)$.   [NOTE:

Many authors define *every* function as single-valued, so that, for example, $\sqrt{x}$ and $-\sqrt{x}$ are *two* functions.]

(*b*) A function $f(x)$ of a real or complex variable x is **even** if and only if $f(-x) \equiv f(x)$; **odd** if and only if $f(-x) \equiv -f(x)$; **periodic** with the **period** T if and only if $f(t + T) \equiv f(t)$; (weakly) **monotonic** on a set of values of x if it does not decrease or increase with increasing x on that set.

(*c*) $y = f(x)$ is an **algebraic function** of x if and only if x and y satisfy a relation of the form $F(x, y) = 0$, where $F(x, y)$ is a polynomial in x and y (Sec. 1.2-9). In particular, $y = f(x)$ is a **rational** (**rational algebraic**) **function** of x if $f(x)$ is a polynomial (**integral rational function**) or a quotient of two polynomials (**fractional rational function**). y is a **linear function** of x if $y = ax + b$.

3.3 POINT SETS, INTERVALS, AND REGIONS

3.3-1 Introduction. When discussing the properties of a function $f(x)$ of a real variable x, one is often required to specify a *set of values* of x such that $f(x)$ is defined and satisfies given conditions. Note that either functions or sets may be described in this manner. It is customary to refer to the values of a real variable x (or to objects labeled by values of x) as *points* (x) of a line, and to sets of such real numbers as **linear point sets**.

Properties of a function $f(x_1, x_2, \ldots, x_n)$ of n real variables $x_1, x_2, \ldots, x_n$ are similarly related to sets of "points" $(x_1, x_2, \ldots, x_n)$ in an n-dimensional "space" which comprises all points $(x_1, x_2, \ldots, x_n)$ under consideration.

The use of geometrical language is prompted by the *Cantor-Dedekind axiom of continuity*, which *postulates* the existence of a one-to-one reciprocal correspondence between the real numbers and the points of a straight line. This "coordinate axiom" is compatible with the properties of real numbers as well as with the postulates defining euclidean and other geometries.

3.3-2 Properties of Sets. (*a*) ALGEBRA OF SETS (CLASSES). An object (point) P contained in a set (class) S is an **element** of S ($P \in S$). A set S_1 is a **subset** of another set S_2 (S_1 is **contained in** S_2, $S_1 \subset S_2$) if and only if each element of S_1 is an element of S_2. S_1 and S_2 are **equal** ($S_1 = S_2$) if and only if both contain the same elements, i.e., if and only if $S_1 \subset S_2$ and $S_2 \subset S_1$. The **empty set** 0 is, by definition, a subset of every set S.   A **proper subset** (**proper part**) of S is a nonempty subset of S not equal to S.   The **union** (**join, logical sum**) $S_1 \cup S_2$ (or $S_1 + S_2$) is the set of all elements contained in *either S_1 or S_2, or both.*   The **intersection** (**meet, logical product**) $S_1 \cap S_2$ (or $S_1 S_2$) of S_1 and S_2 is the set of all elements contained in *both S_1 and S_2.* The **complement** of a set S with respect to a set I containing S is the set of all elements of I *not* contained in S.   *The subsets of any set (class) I constitute a Boolean algebra (Sec. 8.3-1) under the operations of logical addition and multiplication.*

(b) CARDINAL NUMBERS AND COUNTABILITY.   Two sets S_1 and S_2 have the same **cardinal number** if and only if there exists a reciprocal one-to-one correspondence between their respective elements. S is an **infinite set** if it has the same cardinal number as one of its proper subsets; otherwise, S is a **finite set.**

A finite or infinite set S is **countable** (**enumerable, denumerable**) if and only if it is possible to establish a reciprocal one-to-one correspondence between its elements and those of a set of real integers.   *Every finite set is countable;* the cardinal number of a finite set is identical with the number of its elements.   *Every subset of a countable set is countable. The union of a countable set of countable sets is a countable set.*

3.3-3 Bounds.   (a) A real number M is an **upper bound** or a **lower bound** of a set S_y of real numbers y if and only if, respectively, $y \le M$ or $y \ge M$ for all y in S_y.   A set of real or complex numbers is **bounded** (has an **absolute bound**) if the set of their absolute values has an upper bound; otherwise the set is **unbounded.**

Every (nonempty) set S_y of real numbers y having an upper bound has a **least upper bound** (**l.u.b.**) sup y, and every (nonempty) set of real numbers y having a lower bound has a **greatest lower bound** (**g.l.b.**) inf y.   If S_y is finite, sup y is necessarily equal to the **maximum** value max y actually assumed by a number y in S_y, and inf y is equal to the **minimum** min y.

Example: The set of all real numbers less than 1 has the least upper bound 1, but no maximum.

(b) A real or complex function $y = f(x)$ or $y = f(x_1, x_2, \ldots, x_n)$ is **bounded** on a set S of "points" (x) or $(x_1, x_2, \ldots, x_n)$ if and only if the corresponding set S_y of function values y is bounded.   Similarly, a real function $y = f(x)$ or $y = f(x_1, x_2, \ldots, x_n)$ has an **upper bound,**

lower bound, least upper bound, greatest lower bound, (absolute) **maximum,** and/or (absolute) **minimum** on a set S of "points" (x) or $(x_1, x_2, \ldots, x_n)$ if this is true of the corresponding set S_y of function values y.

3.3-4 *Intervals.* Given a real variable x, the set of all values of x (points) such that

1. $a < x < b$ is the **bounded open interval** (a, b).
2. $a < x$ is the **unbounded open interval** (a, ∞).
3. $x < a$ is the **unbounded open interval** $(-\infty, a)$.
4. $a \leq x \leq b$ is the **bounded closed interval** $[a, b]$.

Sets of points (x) such that $a \leq x < b$, $a < x \leq b$, $a \leq x$, $x \leq a$ may be referred to as **semiclosed intervals.** Every interval I_1 contained in another interval I_2 is a **subinterval** of I_2.

3.3-5 *Definition of Neighborhoods.* (a) Given any finite real number a, an (open) **δ-neighborhood of the point** $(x = a)$ **in the space of real numbers** is any open interval $(a - \delta, a + \delta)$ containing $x = a$; or the set of all points (x) such that $|x - a| < \delta$ for some positive real number δ. Every set of points (x) containing a δ-neighborhood of $(x = a)$ is a **neighborhood** of the point $(x = a)$.

(b) Every set containing all points (x) such that $x > M$ for some real number M is a **neighborhood of plus infinity** $(+\infty)$ **in the space of real numbers;** every set containing all points (x) such that $x < N$ for some real number N is a **neighborhood of minus infinity** $(-\infty)$ **in the space of real numbers.**

(c) In a space whose "points" are (described as) ordered sets $(x_1, x_2, \ldots, x_n)$ of real numbers, one may define an (open) δ-neighborhood of the point $(a_1, a_2, \ldots, a_n)$, where $a_1, a_2, \ldots, a_n$ are finite, as the set of all points $(x_1, x_2, \ldots, x_n)$ such that $|x_1 - a_1| < \delta$, $|x_2 - a_2| < \delta$, $\ldots$, and $|x_n - a_n| < \delta$ for some positive real number δ; every point set containing a δ-neighborhood of $(a_1, a_2, \ldots, a_n)$ is a neighborhood of this point.

3.3-6 *Open and Closed Sets and Regions.* (a) A point P is a **limit point (cluster point, accumulation point)** of the point set S if and only if every neighborhood of P contains points of S other than P itself. A limit point P is an **interior point** of S if and only if S is a neighborhood of P; otherwise, P is a **boundary point** of S. A point P is an **isolated point** of S if and only if P has a neighborhood in which P is the only point belonging to S.

A point set S is

An **open set** if and only if it contains only interior points.

A **closed set** if and only if it contains all its limit points; a finite set is closed.

A **discrete** (**isolated**) **set** if and only if it contains isolated points; *every discrete set is countable.*

(*b*) In the euclidean plane or space, a **simply connected open region** D is an open set of points such that every closed curve in D can be continuously contracted into a point without leaving D. If a region is not simply connected, it is said to be **multiply connected.** A point P is on the **boundary** of the region D if every neighborhood of P contains points in D and points not in D; the boundary of a simply connected open region is a simple surface or simple closed surface. Connected regions in D are **subregions** of D. An open region and its boundary or boundaries constitute a **closed region.** A region of a euclidean plane or space is **bounded** if and only if all its points can be described by bounded cartesian coordinates.

3.4 LIMITS, CONTINUOUS FUNCTIONS, AND RELATED TOPICS

3.4-1 Limits of Functions and Sequences. (*a*) A single-valued function $f(x)$ has (approaches, converges to, tends to)

1. A (*necessarily finite and unique*) **limit** $\lim_{x \to a} f(x) = L$ *as x approaches a finite value $x = a$* $[f(x) \to L$ as $x \to a]$ if and only if for each positive real number ϵ there exists a real number $\delta > 0$ such that $0 < |x - a| < \delta$ implies that $f(x)$ is defined and $|f(x) - L| < \epsilon$.

2. A (necessarily finite and unique) limit $\lim_{x \to \infty} f(x) = L$ *as x increases indefinitely* [*increases without bound, tends to infinity;* $f(x) \to L$ as $x \to \infty$] if and only if for each positive real number ϵ there exists a real number N such that $x > N$ implies that $f(x)$ is defined and $|f(x) - L| < \epsilon$.

(*b*) A *sequence* of numbers $s_0,\ s_1,\ s_2,\ \ldots\ [\equiv s(n)]$ converges to a (necessarily finite and unique) limit $\lim_{n \to \infty} s_n = S$ if and only if for each positive real number ϵ there exists a real integer N such that $n > N$ implies $|s_n - S| < \epsilon$.

(*c*) A real function $f(x)$ **increases indefinitely (increases without bound, tends to infinity)**

1. *As* x *approaches a finite value* $x = a$ [$f(x) \to \infty$ as $x \to a$; some authors write $\lim_{x \to a} f(x) = \infty$] if and only if for each positive real number M there exists a real number $\delta > 0$ such that $0 < |x - a| < \delta$ implies that $f(x)$ is defined, and $f(x) > M$.

2. *As* x *increases indefinitely* [$f(x) \to \infty$ as $x \to \infty$; some authors write $\lim_{x \to \infty} f(x) = \infty$] if and only if for each real number M there exists a real number N such that $x > N$ implies that $f(x)$ is defined and $f(x) > M$.

These definitions apply, in particular, to indefinitely increasing sequences. A real variable x or $f(x)$ **decreases indefinitely** [$x \to -\infty$ or $f(x) \to -\infty$] if, respectively, $-x \to \infty$, or $-f(x) \to \infty$. Section 3.4-1 specifies the mathematical meaning of *infinity* in the context of the *real-number system*.

3.4-2   *Operations with Limits.*   If the limits in question exist,

$$
\begin{aligned}
&\lim_{x \to a} [f(x) + g(x)] = \lim_{x \to a} f(x) + \lim_{x \to a} g(x) \\
&\lim_{x \to a} [\alpha f(x)] = \alpha \lim_{x \to a} f(x) \\
&\lim_{x \to a} [f(x)g(x)] = \lim_{x \to a} f(x) \lim_{x \to a} g(x) \\
&\lim_{x \to a} \frac{f(x)}{g(x)} = \frac{\lim_{x \to a} f(x)}{\lim_{x \to a} g(x)} \qquad [\lim_{x \to a} g(x) \neq 0]
\end{aligned}
\qquad (3.4\text{-}1)
$$

a may be finite or infinite; these rules also apply to limits of sequences.

3.4-3   *Asymptotic Relations between Two Functions* (*see also Sec. 3.8-2*).
Given two real or complex functions $f(x)$, $g(x)$ of a real or complex variable x, one writes

1. $f(x) = O[g(x)]$ {$f(x)$ is $O[g(x)]$, $f(x)$ is **of the order of** $g(x)$} as $x \to a$ if and only if there exists a neighborhood of $x = a$ such that $|f(x)/g(x)|$ is bounded.

2. $f(x) \sim g(x)$ [$f(x)$ is **asymptotically proportional** to $g(x)$] as $x \to a$ if and only if $\lim_{x \to a} [f(x)/g(x)]$ exists and differs from zero.

3. $f(x) \simeq g(x)$ [$f(x)$ is **asymptotically equal** to $g(x)$] as $x \to a$ if and only if $\lim_{x \to a} [f(x)/g(x)] = 1$; this implies that *the percentage difference between $f(x)$ and $g(x)$ converges to zero* as $x \to a$.

4. $f(x) = o[g(x)]$ as $x \to a$ if and only if $\lim_{x \to a} [f(x)/g(x)] = 0$. This may often be read "$f(x)$ becomes negligible compared with $g(x)$ as $x \to a$."

In each of the above definitions, a may be finite or infinite.   Functions **of order 1, 2,** . . . and functions **of exponential order** are functions of the order of x, x^2, . . . , and e^x as $x \to \infty$; functions **of order -1, -2,** . . . are functions of the order of x^{-1}, x^{-2}, . . . as $x \to 0$.

Asymptotic relations often yield estimates or approximations of $f(x)$ in terms of $g(x)$ in a neighborhood of $x = a$; note that $f(x) \simeq g(x)$ implies that the fractional error $\dfrac{f(x) - g(x)}{f(x)}$ decreases in absolute value as $x \to a$.   One writes

$$f(x) = \varphi(x) + O[g(x)] \quad\quad if \quad\quad f(x) - \varphi(x) = O[g(x)]$$
$$\text{and} \quad f(x) = \varphi(x) + o[g(x)] \quad\quad if \quad\quad f(x) - \varphi(x) = o[g(x)]$$

3.4-4   *Uniform Convergence.*   (a) A single-valued function $f(x_1, x_2)$ **converges uniformly on a set S of values of x_2**

1. To the (*necessarily finite and unique*) function $\lim\limits_{x_1 \to a} f(x_1, x_2) = L(x_2)$ if and only if for each positive real number ϵ there exists a real number $\delta > 0$ such that $0 < |x_1 - a| < \delta$ implies that $f(x_1, x_2)$ is defined and $|f(x_1, x_2) - L(x_2)| < \epsilon$ *for all x_2 in S* (δ is independent of x_2).

2. To the (necessarily finite and unique) function $\lim\limits_{x_1 \to \infty} f(x_1, x_2) = L(x_2)$ if and only if for each positive real number ϵ there exists a real number N such that $x_1 > N$ implies that $f(x_1, x_2)$ is defined and $|f(x_1, x_2) - L(x_2)| < \epsilon$ *for all x_2 in S.*

(b) A *sequence of functions* $s_0(x)$, $s_1(x)$, $s_2(x)$, . . . converges uniformly on a set S of values of x to the (necessarily finite and unique) function

$$\lim_{n \to \infty} s_n(x) = s(x)$$

if and only if for each positive real number ϵ there exists a real integer N such that $n > N$ implies $|s_n(x) - s(x)| < \epsilon$ *for all x in S.*

3.4-5   *Continuous Functions.*   (a) A single-valued function $f(x)$ defined throughout a neighborhood of $x = a$ is **continuous at $x = a$** [**at the point** $(x = a)$] if and only if $\lim\limits_{x \to a} f(x)$ exists and equals $f(a)$, i.e., if and only if for every positive real number ϵ there exists a real number $\delta > 0$ such that $|x - a| < \delta$ implies $|f(x) - f(a)| < \epsilon$.

Similarly, a single-valued function $f(x_1, x_2, \ldots, x_n)$ defined throughout a neighborhood of the point $(a_1, a_2, \ldots, a_n)$ is continuous at $(a_1, a_2, \ldots, a_n)$ if and only if

$$\lim_{\substack{x_1 \to a_1,\ x_2 \to a_2, \\ \ldots,\ x_n \to a_n}} f(x_1, x_2, \ldots, x_n) = f(a_1, a_2, \ldots, a_n)$$

A single-valued function $f(x_1, x_2, \ldots, x_n)$ is **continuous in x_1** at the point $(a_1, a_2, \ldots, a_n)$ if and only if $f(x_1, a_2, \ldots, a_n)$ is continuous for $x_1 = a_1$.   A function continuous in x_1, x_2, . . . , and x_n separately at $(a_1, a_2, . . . , a_n)$ is *not* necessarily continuous at $(a_1, a_2, . . . , a_n)$.

(*b*) A function is **continuous on a set of points** (e.g., an interval or region) if and only if it is continuous at each point of the set. *A real function continuous on a bounded closed interval* $[a, b]$ *is bounded on* $[a, b]$ *and assumes every value between and including its g.l.b. and its l.u.b. (Sec. 3.3-3) at least once on* $[a, b]$. An analogous theorem holds for a real function of two or more variables continuous on a bounded singly connected closed region.

3.4-6   One-sided (Unilateral) Limits.   Unilateral Continuity.

(*a*) A function $f(x)$ of a real variable x has the (*necessarily finite and unique*) **right-hand limit** $\lim\limits_{x \to a+0} f(x) \equiv \lim\limits_{x \to a+} f(x) \equiv f(a + 0) = L_+$ at $x = a$ if and only if for each positive real number ϵ there exists a real number $\delta > 0$ such that $0 < x - a < \delta$ implies that $f(x)$ is defined, and $|f(x) - L_+| < \epsilon$. $f(x)$ has the **left-hand limit** $\lim\limits_{x \to a-0} f(x) \equiv \lim\limits_{x \to a-} f(x)$ $\equiv f(a - 0) = L_-$ at $x = a$ if and only if for each positive real number ϵ there exists a real number $\delta > 0$ such that $0 < a - x < \delta$ implies that $f(x)$ is defined, and $|f(x) - L_-| < \epsilon$. *If* $\lim\limits_{x \to a} f(x)$ *exists, then*

$$\lim_{x \to a+0} f(x) = \lim_{x \to a-0} f(x) = \lim_{x \to a} f(x)$$

Conversely, $\lim\limits_{x \to a-0} f(x) = \lim\limits_{x \to a+0} f(x)$ *implies the existence of* $\lim\limits_{x \to a} f(x)$.

(*b*) $f(x)$ is **right continuous** or **left continuous** at $x = a$ if $f(a + 0) = f(a)$ or $f(a - 0) = f(a)$, respectively. A **discontinuity of the first kind** of a real function $f(x)$ is a point $x = a$ such that $f(a + 0)$ and $f(a - 0)$ exist; the greatest difference between two of the numbers $f(a)$, $f(a + 0)$, $f(a - 0)$ is the **saltus** of $f(x)$ at such a discontinuity. *The discontinuities of the first kind of* $f(x)$ *constitute a discrete (and thus countable) set* (Sec. 3.3-6a).

(*c*) $f(x)$ is **piecewise continuous** on an interval I if and only if $f(x)$ is continuous throughout I except for a finite number of discontinuities of the first kind.

3.5   DIFFERENTIAL CALCULUS

3.5-1   Derivatives and Differentiation.   (*a*) Let $y = f(x)$ be a real, single-valued function of the real variable x throughout a neighborhood of the point (x). The **(first, first-order) derivative** or **(first-order)**

differential coefficient of $f(x)$ **with respect to** x at the point (x) is the limit

$$\lim_{\Delta x \to 0} \frac{f(x + \Delta x) - f(x)}{\Delta x} \equiv \lim_{\Delta x \to 0} \frac{\Delta y}{\Delta x} \equiv \frac{dy}{dx}$$

$$\equiv \frac{d}{dx} f(x) \equiv f'(x) \equiv y' \qquad (3.5\text{-}1)$$

The function $dy/dx \equiv f'(x)$ is a measure of the *rate of change of y with respect to x* at each point (x) where the limit (1) exists. On a graph of $y = f(x)$, $f'(x)$ corresponds to the *slope of the tangent* (Sec. 3.12-1).

(b) **The second, third,** . . . , n^{th} **derivatives (second-order, third-order,** . . . , n^{th}**-order differential coefficients) of** $y = f(x)$ **with respect to** x at the point (x) are respectively defined as

$$\frac{d}{dx} f'(x) \equiv \frac{d^2 y}{dx^2} \equiv f''(x)$$

$$\frac{d}{dx} f''(x) \equiv \frac{d^3 y}{dx^3} \equiv f'''(x) \qquad (3.5\text{-}2)$$

$$\cdots\cdots\cdots\cdots\cdots\cdots\cdots$$

$$\frac{d}{dx} f^{(n-1)}(x) \equiv \frac{d^n y}{dx^n} \equiv f^{(n)}(x)$$

if the limits in question exist.

Derivatives of a number of frequently used functions are tabulated in Table 3.5-1. Additional derivatives may be obtained through use of the differentiation rules of Table 3.5-2.

3.5-2 *Partial Derivatives.* (a) Let $y = f(x_1, x_2, \ldots, x_n)$ be a real single-valued function of the real variables $x_1, x_2, \ldots, x_n$ in a neighborhood of the point $(x_1, x_2, \ldots, x_n)$. The **(first-order) partial derivative of** $f(x_1, x_2, \ldots, x_n)$ **with respect to** x_1 at the point $(x_1, x_2, \ldots, x_n)$ is the limit

$$\lim_{\Delta x_1 \to 0} \frac{f(x_1 + \Delta x_1, x_2, x_3, \ldots, x_n) - f(x_1, x_2, \ldots, x_n)}{\Delta x_1}$$

$$\equiv \frac{\partial}{\partial x_1} f \equiv \frac{\partial y}{\partial x_1} \equiv f_{x_1}(x_1, x_2, \ldots, x_n) \quad (3.5\text{-}3)$$

The function $\partial y/\partial x_1 \equiv (\partial y/\partial x_1)_{x_1, x_2, \ldots, x_n} \equiv f_{x_1}(x_1, x_2, \ldots, x_n)$ is a measure of the *rate of change of y with respect to x_1 for fixed values of the*

Table 3.5-1 *Derivatives of frequently used functions*

(a)

$f(x)$	$f'(x)$	$f^{(r)}(x)$
x^a	ax^{a-1}	$a(a-1)(a-2) \cdots (a-r+1)x^{a-r}$
e^x	e^x	e^x
a^x	$a^x \log_e a$	$a^x(\log_e a)^r$
$\log_e x$	$\dfrac{1}{x}$	$(-1)^{r-1}(r-1)! \dfrac{1}{x^r}$
$\log_a x$	$\dfrac{1}{x}\log_a e$	$(-1)^{r-1}(r-1)! \dfrac{1}{x^r}\log_a e$
$\sin x$	$\cos x$	$\sin\left(x+\dfrac{\pi r}{2}\right)$
$\cos x$	$-\sin x$	$\cos\left(x+\dfrac{\pi r}{2}\right)$

(b)

$f(x)$	$f'(x)$	$f(x)$	$f'(x)$
$\tan x$	$\dfrac{1}{\cos^2 x}$	$\arcsin x$	$\dfrac{1}{\sqrt{1-x^2}}$
$\cot x$	$-\dfrac{1}{\sin^2 x}$	$\arccos x$	$-\dfrac{1}{\sqrt{1-x^2}}$
$\sec x$	$\dfrac{\sin x}{\cos^2 x}$	$\arctan x$	$\dfrac{1}{1+x^2}$
$\operatorname{cosec} x$	$-\dfrac{\cos x}{\sin^2 x}$	$\operatorname{arccot} x$	$-\dfrac{1}{1+x^2}$
$\sinh x$	$\cosh x$	$\sinh^{-1} x$	$\dfrac{1}{\sqrt{x^2+1}}$
$\cosh x$	$\sinh x$	$\cosh^{-1} x$	$\dfrac{1}{\sqrt{x^2-1}}$
$\tanh x$	$\dfrac{1}{\cosh^2 x}$	$\tanh^{-1} x$	$\dfrac{1}{1-x^2}$
$\coth x$	$-\dfrac{1}{\sinh^2 x}$	$\coth^{-1} x$	$\dfrac{1}{1-x^2}$
$\operatorname{vers} x$	$\sin x$	x^x	$x^x(1+\log_e x)$

remaining independent variables at each point $(x_1, x_2, \ldots, x_n)$ where the limit (3) exists. The partial derivatives $\partial y/\partial x_2$, $\partial y/\partial x_3$, $\ldots$, $\partial y/\partial x_n$ are defined in an analogous manner. *Each partial derivative $\partial y/\partial x_k$ may be found by differentiation of $f(x_1, x_2, \ldots, x_n)$ with respect to x_k while the remaining $n - 1$ independent variables are regarded as constant parameters* [**partial differentiation** of $f(x_1, x_2, \ldots, x_n)$ with respect to x_k].

(b) *Higher-order partial derivatives* of $y = f(x_1, x_2, \ldots, x_n)$ are defined by

$$\frac{\partial^2 y}{\partial x_k{}^2} \equiv f_{x_k x_k} \equiv \frac{\partial}{\partial x_k} \frac{\partial y}{\partial x_k}$$

$$\frac{\partial^2 y}{\partial x_i \, \partial x_k} \equiv f_{x_i x_k} \equiv \frac{\partial}{\partial x_i} \frac{\partial y}{\partial x_k}$$

$$\frac{\partial^3 y}{\partial x_i \, \partial x_j \, \partial x_k} \equiv f_{x_i x_j x_k} \equiv \frac{\partial}{\partial x_i} \frac{\partial^2 y}{\partial x_j \, \partial x_k}$$

$\ldots \ldots \ldots \ldots \ldots \ldots \ldots \ldots \ldots$

if the limits in question exist; in each case, the number of differentiations involved is the **order** of the partial derivative.   Note that

$$\frac{\partial y}{\partial x_i \, \partial x_k} = \frac{\partial y}{\partial x_k \, \partial x_i} \qquad (i \neq k) \tag{3.5-4}$$

if (1) $\partial y/(\partial x_i \, \partial x_k)$ *exists throughout a neighborhood of the point* $(x_1, x_2, \ldots, x_n)$ *and is continuous at* $(x_1, x_2, \ldots, x_n)$*, and* (2) $\partial y/(\partial x_k \, \partial x_i)$ *exists at* $(x_1, x_2, \ldots, x_n)$.

3.5-3 *Differentiation Rules.*

Table 3.5-2 summarizes the most important differentiation rules.   The formulas of Table 3.5-2*a* and *b* apply to *partial differentiation* if $\partial/\partial x_k$ is substituted for d/dx in each case.   Thus, if $u_i = u_i(x_1, x_2, \ldots, x_n)$ $(i = 1, 2, \ldots, m)$,

$$\frac{\partial}{\partial x_k} f(u_1, u_2, \ldots, u_m) = \sum_{i=1}^{m} \frac{\partial f}{\partial u_i} \frac{\partial u_i}{\partial x_k} \qquad (k = 1, 2, \ldots, n)$$

$$\tag{3.5-5}$$

3.5-4 *Jacobians* (see also *Refs. 1 and 3*).

A set of *transformation equations*

$$y_i = y_i(x_1, x_2, \ldots, x_n) \qquad (i = 1, 2, \ldots, n) \tag{3.5-6}$$

Table 3.5-2   *Differentiation rules (existence of continuous derivatives is assumed in each case)*

(a) **Basic Rules**

$$\frac{d}{dx} f[u_1(x),\, u_2(x),\, \ldots,\, u_m(x)] = \frac{\partial f}{\partial u_1}\frac{du_1}{dx} + \frac{\partial f}{\partial u_2}\frac{du_2}{dx} + \cdots + \frac{\partial f}{\partial u_m}\frac{du_m}{dx}$$

$$\frac{d}{dx} f[u(x)] = \frac{df}{du}\frac{du}{dx} \qquad\qquad \frac{d^2}{dx^2} f[u(x)] = \frac{d^2 f}{du^2}\left(\frac{du}{dx}\right)^2 + \frac{df}{du}\frac{d^2 u}{dx^2}$$

(b) **Sums, Products, and Quotients.**   **Logarithmic Differentiation**

$$\frac{d}{dx}[u(x) + v(x)] = \frac{du}{dx} + \frac{dv}{dx} \qquad\qquad \frac{d}{dx}[\alpha u(x)] = \alpha\frac{du}{dx}$$

$$\frac{d}{dx}[u(x)v(x)] = v\frac{du}{dx} + u\frac{dv}{dx} \qquad \frac{d}{dx}\left[\frac{u(x)}{v(x)}\right] = \frac{1}{v^2}\left(v\frac{du}{dx} - u\frac{dv}{dx}\right) \quad [v(x) \neq 0]$$

$$\frac{d}{dx}\log_e y(x) = \frac{y'(x)}{y(x)} \qquad [\text{LOGARITHMIC DERIVATIVE OF } y(x)]$$

NOTE: To differentiate functions of the form $y = \dfrac{u_1(x)u_2(x)\,\cdots}{v_1(x)v_2(x)\,\cdots}$, it may be convenient to find the logarithmic derivative first.

$$\frac{d^r}{dx^r}(\alpha u + \beta v) = \alpha\frac{d^r u}{dx^r} + \beta\frac{d^r v}{dx^r} \qquad\qquad \frac{d^r}{dx^r}(uv) = \sum_{k=0}^{r}\binom{r}{k}\frac{d^{r-k}u}{dx^{r-k}}\frac{d^k v}{dx^k}$$

(c) **Inverse Function Given.**   If $y = y(x)$ has the unique inverse function $x = x(y)$, and $dx/dy \neq 0$,

$$\frac{dy}{dx} = \left(\frac{dx}{dy}\right)^{-1} \qquad\qquad \frac{d^2 y}{dx^2} = -\frac{d^2 x}{dy^2}\Big/\left(\frac{dx}{dy}\right)^3$$

(d) **Implicit Functions.**   If $y = y(x)$ is given implicitly in terms of a suitably differentiable relation $F(x, y) = 0$, where $F_y \neq 0$,

$$\frac{dy}{dx} = -\frac{F_x}{F_y} \qquad\qquad \frac{d^2 y}{dx^2} = -\frac{1}{F_y{}^3}(F_{xx}F_y{}^2 - 2F_{xy}F_x F_y + F_{yy}F_x{}^2)$$

(e) **Function Given in Terms of a Parameter t.**   Given $x = x(t)$, $y = y(t)$ and $\dot{x}(t) \equiv \dfrac{dx}{dt} \neq 0$, $\dot{y}(t) \equiv \dfrac{dy}{dt}$, $\ddot{x}(t) \equiv \dfrac{d^2 x}{dt^2}$, $\ddot{y}(t) \equiv \dfrac{d^2 y}{dt^2}$,

$$\frac{dy}{dx} = \frac{\dot{y}(t)}{\dot{x}(t)} \qquad\qquad \frac{d^2 y}{dx^2} = \frac{\dot{x}(t)\ddot{y}(t) - \ddot{x}(t)\dot{y}(t)}{[\dot{x}(t)]^3}$$

define a reciprocal one-to-one correspondence between sets $(x_1, x_2, \ldots, x_n)$ and $(y_1, y_2, \ldots, y_n)$ throughout a neighborhood of a "point" $(x_1, x_2, \ldots, x_n)$ where the functions (6) are single-valued and continuously differentiable, and where the **Jacobian** or **functional determinant**

$$\frac{\partial(y_1, y_2, \ldots, y_n)}{\partial(x_1, x_2, \ldots, x_n)} \equiv \det\left[\frac{\partial y_i}{\partial x_k}\right] \tag{3.5-7}$$

is different from zero.

Example: Given $x = r \cos \varphi$, $y = r \sin \varphi$, one has

$$\frac{\partial(x, y)}{\partial(r, \varphi)} = \begin{vmatrix} \cos \varphi & -r \sin \varphi \\ \sin \varphi & r \cos \varphi \end{vmatrix} = r$$

which is different from zero unless $r^2 = x^2 + y^2 = 0$.

3.6 INTEGRALS AND INTEGRATION

3.6-1 Definite Integrals (Riemann Integrals).

A real function $f(x)$ bounded on the bounded closed interval $[a, b]$ is **integrable over** (a, b) **in the sense of Riemann** if and only if the sum $\sum\limits_{i=1}^{m} f(\xi_i)(x_i - x_{i-1})$ tends to a unique finite limit I for every sequence of partitions $a = x_0 < \xi_1 < x_1 < \xi_2 < x_2 \cdots < \xi_m < x_m = b$ as $\max |x_i - x_{i-1}| \to 0$. In this case

$$I = \lim_{\max |x_i - x_{i-1}| \to 0} \sum_{i=1}^{m} f(\xi_i)(x_i - x_{i-1}) = \int_a^b f(x)\, dx \qquad (3.6\text{-}1)$$

is the **definite integral of** $f(x)$ **over** (a, b) **in the sense of Riemann (Riemann integral).** $f(x)$ is called the **integrand;** a and b are the **limits of integration.** *Table* 3.6-1 *summarizes important properties of definite integrals.*

$\int_a^b f(x)\, dx$ represents the *area* bounded by the curve $y = f(x)$ (Sec. 3.2-1a) and the x axis between the lines $x = a$ and $x = b$; areas below the x axis are represented by negative numbers.

3.6-2 Improper Integrals.

(a) Given a function $f(x)$ bounded and integrable on every bounded subinterval of (a, b), the concept of a definite integral $\int_a^b f(x)\, dx$ can be extended to apply even if

Table 3.6-1   Properties of integrals

(a) **Elementary Properties.**   *If the integrals exist,*

$$\int_a^b f(x)\,dx = -\int_b^a f(x)\,dx \qquad \int_a^b f(x)\,dx = \int_a^c f(x)\,dx + \int_c^b f(x)\,dx$$

$$\int_a^b [u(x) + v(x)]\,dx = \int_a^b u(x)\,dx + \int_a^b v(x)\,dx \qquad \int_a^b \alpha u(x)\,dx = \alpha \int_a^b u(x)\,dx$$

(b) **Integration by Parts.**   *If $u(x)$ and $v(x)$ are differentiable for $a \leq x \leq b$, and if the integrals exist,*

$$\int_a^b u(x)v'(x)\,dx = u(x)v(x)\Big]_a^b - \int_a^b v(x)u'(x)\,dx$$

or
$$\int_a^b u\,dv = uv\Big]_a^b - \int_a^b v\,du$$

(c) **Change of Variable (Integration by Substitution).**   *If $u = u(x)$ and its inverse function $x = x(u)$ are single-valued and continuously differentiable for $a \leq x \leq b$, and if the integral exists,*

$$\int_a^b f(x)\,dx = \int_{u(a)}^{u(b)} f[(x(u)]\frac{dx}{du}\,du = \int_{u(a)}^{u(b)} f[x(u)]\left(\frac{du}{dx}\right)^{-1}\,du$$

(d) **Differentiation with Respect to a Parameter.**   *If $f(x, \lambda)$, $u(\lambda)$, and $v(\lambda)$ are continuously differentiable with respect to λ,*

$$\frac{\partial}{\partial \lambda}\int_a^b f(x, \lambda)\,dx = \int_a^b \frac{\partial}{\partial \lambda}f(x, \lambda)\,dx$$

$$\frac{\partial}{\partial \lambda}\int_{u(\lambda)}^{v(\lambda)} f(x, \lambda)\,dx = \int_{u(\lambda)}^{v(\lambda)} \frac{\partial}{\partial \lambda}f(x, \lambda)\,dx + f(v, \lambda)\frac{\partial v}{\partial \lambda} - f(u, \lambda)\frac{\partial u}{\partial \lambda}$$

(LEIBNITZ'S RULE)

provided that the integrals exist and, in the case of improper integrals, converge uniformly in a neighborhood of the point (λ).

The second case can often be reduced to the first by a suitable change of variables. Note also

$$\frac{\partial}{\partial \lambda}\int_a^\lambda f(x, \lambda)\,dx = \frac{1}{\lambda - a}\int_a^\lambda \left[f(x, \lambda) + (\lambda - a)\frac{\partial f}{\partial \lambda} + (x - a)\frac{\partial f}{\partial x}\right]\,dx$$

(e) **Inequalities**   *If the integrals exist,*

$$f(x) \leq g(x) \text{ in } (a, b) \text{ implies } \int_a^b f(x)\,dx \leq \int_a^b g(x)\,dx$$

If $|f(x)| \leq M$ on the bounded interval (a, b), the existence of $\int_a^b f(x)\,dx$ implies the existence of $\int_a^b |f(x)|\,dx$, and

$$\left| \int_a^b f(x)\,dx \right| \leq \int_a^b |f(x)|\,dx \leq M(b - a)$$

1. $f(x)$ is unbounded in a neighborhood of a finite limit of integration $x = a$ or $x = b$ (see also Sec. 3.6-2b).
2. The interval (a, b) is unbounded.

Thus, if $f(x)$ is bounded and integrable on every finite interval (a, X) for $a < X < b$, one *defines*

$$\int_a^b f(x) \, dx = \int_a^{b-0} f(x) \, dx = \lim_{X \to b-0} \int_a^X f(x) \, dx \qquad (3.6\text{-}2a)$$

and, in particular, for $b = \infty$,

$$\int_a^\infty f(x) \, dx = \lim_{X \to \infty} \int_a^X f(x) \, dx \qquad (3.6\text{-}2b)$$

Similarly,

$$\int_a^b f(x) \, dx = \int_{a+0}^b f(x) \, dx = \lim_{X \to a+0} \int_X^b f(x) \, dx$$

$$\int_{-\infty}^b f(x) \, dx = \lim_{X \to \infty} \int_{-X}^b f(x) \, dx \qquad (3.6\text{-}2c)$$

Each improper integral defined in this manner exists or **converges** if and only if the limit on the right exists.   An improper integral over $f(x)$ **converges absolutely** if and only if the corresponding improper integral over $|f(x)|$ converges.   *Absolute convergence implies convergence.* A convergent improper integral which does not converge absolutely is **conditionally convergent.**

(b) *The integration rules of Table 3.6-1 apply to suitably convergent improper integrals.*   Given a bounded or unbounded interval (a, b) or $[a, b]$ containing a discrete set of points $x = c_1$, $x = c_2$, . . . such that $f(x)$ is unbounded in a neighborhood of $x = c_i$ ($i = 1, 2, . . .$), $\int_a^b f(x) \, dx$ may be defined as an improper integral equal to a sum of improper integrals (2); e.g.,

$$\int_a^b f(x) \, dx = \lim_{X_1 \to a+0} \int_{X_1}^c f(x) \, dx + \lim_{X_2 \to b-0} \int_c^{X_2} f(x) \, dx$$
$$(a < c < b) \qquad (3.6\text{-}3)$$

$$\int_{-\infty}^\infty f(x) \, dx = \lim_{X_1 \to \infty} \int_{-X_1}^c f(x) \, dx + \lim_{X_2 \to \infty} \int_c^{X_2} f(x) \, dx \qquad (3.6\text{-}4)$$

$$\int_a^b f(x)\,dx = \lim_{X_1 \to c-0} \int_a^{X_1} f(x)\,dx + \lim_{X_2 \to c+0} \int_{X_2}^b f(x)\,dx$$

$$(a < c < b) \qquad (3.6\text{-}5)$$

if the limits exist

(c) An improper integral $\int_a^b f(x, y)\,dx$ **converges uniformly on a set S of values** of y if and only if the corresponding limit (Secs. 3.6-2a and b) converges uniformly on S (Sec. 3.4-4). *If $f(x, y)$ is a continuous function, then $\int_a^b f(x, y)\,dx$ is a continuous function of y in every open interval where the integral converges uniformly (Continuity Theorem).*

(d) Criteria for convergence and uniform convergence of improper integrals are listed in Secs. 3.9-1 to 3.9-3.

3.6-3 Indefinite Integrals. A given single-valued function $f(x)$ has an **indefinite integral** $F(x)$ in $[a, b]$ if and only if there exists a function $F(x)$ such that $F'(x) = f(x)$ in $[a, b]$. In this case $F(x)$ is uniquely defined in $[a, b]$ except for an arbitrary additive constant C (**constant of integration;** see also Sec. 6.1-2); one writes

$$F(x) = \int f(x)\,dx + C \qquad (a \le x \le b) \tag{3.6-6}$$

Note that $F(x) - F(a) \equiv F(x)\Big]_a^x$ is uniquely defined for $a \le x \le b$.

3.6-4 The Fundamental Theorem of the Integral Calculus. *If $f(x)$ is single-valued, bounded, and integrable on $[a, b]$, and there exists a function $F(x)$ such that $F'(x) = f(x)$ for $a \le x \le b$, then*

$$\int_a^x f(\xi)\,d\xi = F(x)\Big]_a^x = F(x) - F(a) \qquad (a \le x \le b) \qquad (3.6\text{-}7)$$

In particular, *if $f(x)$ is continuous in $[a, b]$,*

$$\frac{d}{dx}\int_a^x f(\xi)\,d\xi = f(x) \qquad (a \le x \le b)$$

and Eq. (7) applies.

NOTE: The fundamental theorem of the integral calculus enables one (1) to evaluate definite integrals by reversing the process of differentiation, and (2) to solve differential equations by numerical evaluation of definite integrals.

3.6-5 Integration Methods (*see Table E-2 for examples*). (a) **Integration** is the operation yielding a (definite or indefinite) integral of a given integrand $f(x)$.   Definite integrals may be calculated directly as limits of sums (numerical integration, Secs. 10.3-1 and 10.3-2) or by the calculus of residues (Sec. 5.3-5); more frequently, one attempts to find an indefinite integral which may be inserted into Eq. (7).   To obtain an indefinite integral, one must reduce the given integrand $f(x)$ to a sum of known derivatives with the aid of the "integration rules" listed in Table 3.6-1a, b, c.

The remainder of this section deals with integration methods applicable to special types of integrands. COMPREHENSIVE TABLES OF DEFINITE AND INDEFINITE INTEGRALS ARE PRESENTED IN APPENDIX E.

(b) INTEGRATION OF POLYNOMIALS

$$\int (a_n + a_{n-1}x + a_{n-2}x^2 + \cdots + a_0 x^n)\, dx$$

$$\equiv a_n x + \frac{1}{2} a_{n-1}x^2 + \frac{1}{3} a_{n-2}x^3 + \cdots + \frac{1}{n+1} a_0 x^{n+1} + C$$

$$(3.6\text{-}8)$$

(c) INTEGRATION OF RATIONAL FUNCTIONS.   The methods outlined in Secs. 1.5-2 and 1.5-4 will reduce every rational integrand to the sum of a polynomial and a set of *partial fractions* (1.5-3) and/or (1.5-4).   The partial-fraction terms are integrated successively with the aid of the following formulas:

$$\int \frac{dx}{(x - x_1)^m} \equiv \begin{cases} -\dfrac{1}{(m-1)(x-x_1)^{m-1}} + C & (m \neq 1) \\ \log_e (x - x_1) + C & (m = 1) \end{cases}$$

$$\int \frac{dx}{[(x-a)^2 + \omega^2]} \equiv \frac{1}{\omega} \arctan \frac{x-a}{\omega} + C$$

$$\int \frac{dx}{[(x-a)^2 + \omega^2]^{m+1}} \equiv \frac{x-a}{2m\omega^2 [(x-a)^2 + \omega^2]^m}$$

$$+ \frac{2m-1}{2m\omega^2} \int \frac{dx}{[(x-a)^2 + \omega^2]^m}$$

$$\int \frac{x\, dx}{[(x-a)^2 + \omega^2]^{m+1}} \equiv \frac{a(x-a) - \omega^2}{2m\omega^2 [(x-a)^2 + \omega^2]^m}$$

$$+ \frac{(2m-1)a}{2m\omega^2} \int \frac{dx}{[(x-a)^2 + \omega^2]^m}$$

$$(3.6\text{-}9)$$

(*d*) INTEGRANDS WHICH CAN BE REDUCED TO RATIONAL
FUNCTIONS BY A CHANGE OF VARIABLES (Table 3.6-1*c*).

1. *If the integrand $f(x)$ is a rational function of sin x and cos x, introduce*
   $u = \tan (x/2)$, *so that*

$$\sin x = \frac{2u}{1 + u^2} \qquad \cos x = \frac{1 - u^2}{1 + u^2} \qquad dx = \frac{2du}{1 + u^2}$$

2. *If the integrand $f(x)$ is a rational function of sinh x and cosh x, introduce*
   $u = \tanh (x/2)$, *so that*

$$\sinh x = \frac{2u}{1 - u^2} \qquad \cosh x = \frac{1 + u^2}{1 - u^2} \qquad dx = \frac{2du}{1 - u^2}$$

NOTE: If $f(x)$ is a rational function of $\sin^2 x$, $\cos^2 x$, $\sin x \cos x$, and $\tan x$ (or
of the corresponding hyperbolic functions), one simplifies the calculation by first
introducing $v = x/2$, so that $u = \tan v$ (or $u = \tanh v$).

3. *If the integrand $f(x)$ is a rational function of x and either $\sqrt{1 - x^2}$ or*
   $\sqrt{x^2 - 1}$, *reduce the problem to case 1 or 2 by the respective sub-*
   stitutions $x = \cos v$ or $x = \cosh v$.

4. *If the integrand $f(x)$ is a rational function of x and $\sqrt{x^2 + 1}$, introduce*
   $u = x + \sqrt{x^2 + 1}$, *so that*

$$x = \frac{1}{2} \left(u - \frac{1}{u} \right) \qquad \sqrt{x^2 + 1} = \frac{1}{2} \left(u + \frac{1}{u} \right) \qquad dx = \frac{1}{2} \left(1 + \frac{1}{u^2} \right) du$$

5. *If the integrand $f(x)$ is a rational function of x and $\sqrt{ax^2 + bx + c}$,*
   reduce the problem to case 3 ($b^2 - 4ac < 0$) or to case 4 ($b^2 - 4ac
   > 0) *through the substitution*

$$v = \frac{2ax + b}{\sqrt{|4ac - b^2|}} \qquad x = \frac{v \sqrt{|4ac - b^2|} - b}{2a}$$

6. *If the integrand $f(x)$ is a rational function of x and $u = \sqrt{\dfrac{ax + b}{cx + d}}$,*
   introduce u as a new variable.

7. *If the integrand $f(x)$ is a rational function of x, $\sqrt{ax + b}$, and $\sqrt{cx + d}$,*
   introduce $u = \sqrt{ax + b}$ as a new variable.

Many other substitution methods apply in special cases. Note that the integrals may not be real for all values of x.

(*e*) Integrands of the form $x^n e^{ax}$, $x^n \log_e x$, $x^n \sin x$, $x^n \cos x$
($n \neq -1$); $\sin^m x \cos^n x$ ($n + m \neq 0$); $e^{ax} \sin^n x$, $e^{ax} \cos^n x$ yield to repeated
integration by parts (Table 3.6-1*b*).

3.6-6   Multiple Integrals.   (a) *Let* $f(x, y)$ *be piecewise continuous* (*Sec.* 3.4-6) *on a bounded closed region* D *which is uniquely defined by* $a \le x \le b, g_1(x) \le y \le g_2(x)$ *as well as by* $\alpha \le y \le \beta, \gamma_1(y) \le x \le \gamma_2(y)$, *where* $g_1(x), g_2(x), \gamma_1(y), \gamma_2(y)$ *are piecewise continuous functions.*   Then *Fubini's theorem* states

$$\int_\alpha^\beta dy \int_{\gamma_1(y)}^{\gamma_2(y)} f(x, y) \, dx = \int_\alpha^\beta \left[\int_{\gamma_1(y)}^{\gamma_2(y)} f(x, y) \, dx \right] dy$$

$$= \int_a^b dx \int_{g_1(x)}^{g_2(x)} f(x, y) \, dy$$

$$= \iint_D f(x, y) \, dx \, dy \qquad (3.6\text{-}10)$$

Analogous theorems hold for triple, quadruple, etc., integrals.

The second expression for the integral (10) may be written without the brackets if the meaning of the integration limits is evident.

Example: If D is the region bounded by the circle $x^2 + y^2 = 1$, and $f(x, y) = c =$ constant,

$$\iint_D f(x, y) \, dx \, dy = 4 \int_0^1 \int_0^{\sqrt{1-y^2}} c \, dx \, dy = 4c \int_0^1 \sqrt{1 - y^2} \, dy = \pi c$$

(b) *If* $\int_\alpha^\beta dy \int_a^b f(x, y) \, dx$ *exists and equals* $\int_a^b dx \int_\alpha^\beta f(x, y) \, dy$ *for every* $b > a$, then

$$\int_\alpha^\beta dy \int_a^\infty f(x, y) \, dx = \int_a^\infty dx \int_\alpha^\beta f(x, y) \, dy \qquad (3.6\text{-}11)$$

provided that $\int_a^\infty f(x, y) \, dx$ *converges uniformly for* $\alpha \le y \le \beta$. Similar theorems hold for other improper multiple integrals.

3.6-7   Arc Length of a Rectifiable Curve.   A continuous curve segment is **rectifiable** if and only if every subsegment C_1 in the finite portion of the plane or space has a unique finite **arc length** $s(C_1)$; $s(C_1)$ is the limit of the length of an inscribed polygonal curve as the length of the largest straight-line segment approaches zero.

For a continuous arc C_1 in the euclidean plane or space, described in terms of *rectangular cartesian* coordinates by

$$
\begin{array}{llll}
x = x(t) & y = y(t) & & \text{in the plane} \\
\text{or} \quad x = x(t) & y = y(t) & z = z(t) & \text{in space}
\end{array} \qquad (3.6\text{-}12)
$$

(Secs. 2.2-5b and 2.5-6), the length of an infinitesimal regular arc corresponding to the interval $(t, t + dt)$ is the **element of arc length**

$$ds \equiv \begin{cases} \sqrt{dx^2 + dy^2} \equiv \sqrt{1 + \left(\dfrac{dy}{dx}\right)^2}\, dx \\[2ex] \qquad\equiv \sqrt{\left(\dfrac{dx}{dt}\right)^2 + \left(\dfrac{dy}{dt}\right)^2}\, dt \\[2ex] \qquad\equiv \dfrac{ds}{dt}\, dt \quad \text{in the plane} \\[2ex] \sqrt{dx^2 + dy^2 + dz^2} \\[2ex] \qquad\equiv \sqrt{\left(\dfrac{dx}{dt}\right)^2 + \left(\dfrac{dy}{dt}\right)^2 + \left(\dfrac{dz}{dt}\right)^2}\, dt \\[2ex] \qquad\equiv \dfrac{ds}{dt}\, dt \quad \text{in space} \end{cases} \tag{3.6-13}$$

The sign of ds is assigned arbitrarily, usually so that $ds/dt \geq 0$.

The arc length $s(C_1)$ of a given curve segment C_1 corresponding to a finite interval (t_0, t) is

$$s = s(C_1) = \int_{C_1} ds = \int_{t_0}^{t} \frac{ds}{dt}\, dt = s(t) \tag{3.6-14}$$

The arc length $s(C_1)$ is a geometrical object independent of the coordinate system and the particular parameter t used to describe the curve.

3.6-8 Line Integrals (*see also Secs. 4.4-5 and 4.6-3*). Given a rectifiable arc C described by Eqs. (12) for $a \leq t \leq b$, the **line integral** $\int_C f(x, y, z)\, ds$ over a bounded function $f(x, y, z)$ is defined by

$$\int_C f(x, y, z)\, ds = \lim_{\max \Delta s_i \to 0} \sum_{i=1}^{m} f[x(\tau_i), y(\tau_i), z(\tau_i)]\, \Delta s_i$$

with

$$\Delta s_i = \sqrt{[x(t_i) - x(t_{i-1})]^2 + [y(t_i) - y(t_{i-1})]^2 + [z(t_i) - z(t_{i-1})]^2}$$

$$(a = t_0 < \tau_1 < t_1 < \tau_2 < t_2 < \cdots < \tau_m < t_m = b) \tag{3.6-15a}$$

if the limit exists (see also Sec. 3.6-1). The line integral $(15a)$ can be computed (or directly defined) as an integral over t:

$$\int_C f(x, y, z)\, ds = \int_a^b f[x(t), y(t), z(t)]\, \frac{ds}{dt}\, dt \tag{3.6-15b}$$

where the element of arc length ds is given by Eq. (13).   Omit terms involving z in Eq. (15) for line integrals in the xy plane.   Improper line integrals are defined in the manner of Sec. 3.6-2.

3.7 MEAN-VALUE THEOREMS. VALUES OF INDETERMINATE FORMS

3.7-1 *Mean-value Theorems*.   The following theorems are useful for estimating values and limits of real functions, derivatives, and integrals.

(a) *If $f(x)$ is continuous on $[a, b]$ and continuously differentiable on (a, b) there exists a real number X in (a, b) such that*

$$f(b) - f(a) = f'(X)(b - a) \tag{3.7-1}$$

X is often written as $X = a + \vartheta(b - a)$ $(0 < \vartheta < 1)$.   For $f(a) = f(b) = 0$ the theorem is known as *Rolle's Theorem*.

(b) *If $f(x)$ is continuous on $[a, b]$ there exists a value X of x in (a, b) such that*

$$\int_a^b f(x)\, dx = f(X)(b - a) \tag{3.7-2}$$

(c) *If $f(x)$ and $g(x)$ are continuous on $[a, b]$, and $g(x) \neq 0$ on $[a, b]$, there exists a value X of x in (a, b) such that*

$$\int_a^b f(x)g(x)\, dx = f(X) \int_a^b g(x)\, dx \tag{3.7-3}$$

3.7-2 *Values of Indeterminate Forms* (*see Table 3.7-1 for examples*).
(a) Functions $f(x)$ of the form $u(x)/v(x)$, $u(x)v(x)$, $[u(x)]^{v(x)}$, and $u(x) - v(x)$ are not defined for $x = a$ if $f(a)$ takes the form $0/0, \infty/\infty, 0 \cdot \infty$, $0^0, \infty^0, 1^\infty$, or $\infty - \infty$; but $\lim\limits_{x \to a} f(x)$ may exist.   In such cases, it is often desirable to *define* $f(a) = \lim\limits_{x \to a} f(x)$.

(b) TREATMENT OF $0/0$ AND ∞/∞.   Let $u(a) = v(a) = 0$.   *If there exists a neighborhood of $x = a$ such that* (1) $v(x) \neq 0$, *except for $x = a$, and* (2) $u'(x)$ *and* $v'(x)$ *exist and do not vanish simultaneously, then*

$$\lim_{x \to a} \frac{u(x)}{v(x)} = \lim_{x \to a} \frac{u'(x)}{v'(x)} \tag{3.7-4}$$

whenever the limit on the right exists (L'Hôpital's Rule).

Let $\lim\limits_{x \to a} u(x) = \lim\limits_{x \to a} v(x) = \infty$. *If there exists a neighborhood of $x = a$ such that $x \neq a$ implies* (1) $u(x) \neq 0$, $v(x) \neq 0$, *and* (2) $u'(x)$ *and $v'(x)$ exist and do not vanish simultaneously, then Eq.* (4) *holds whenever the limit on the right exists.*

If $u'(x)/v'(x)$ is itself an indeterminate form, the above method may be applied to $u'(x)/v'(x)$ in turn, so that

$$\lim_{x \to a} \frac{u(x)}{v(x)} = \lim_{x \to a} \frac{u'(x)}{v'(x)} = \lim_{x \to a} \frac{u''(x)}{v''(x)} \tag{3.7-5}$$

If necessary, this process may be continued.

(c) TREATMENT OF $0 \cdot \infty$, 0^0, ∞^0, 1^∞, AND $\infty - \infty$. $u(x)v(x)$, $[u(x)]^{v(x)}$, and $u(x) - v(x)$ can often be reduced to the form $\varphi(x)/\psi(x)$ with the aid of one of the following relations:

$$u(x)v(x) \equiv \frac{u(x)}{1/v(x)} \equiv \frac{v(x)}{1/u(x)}$$

$$[u(x)]^{v(x)} \equiv e^{g(x)} \qquad \left[g(x) \equiv \frac{\log_e u(x)}{1/v(x)} \equiv \frac{v(x)}{1/\log_e u(x)} \right] \tag{3.7-6}$$

$$u(x) - v(x) \equiv \frac{\dfrac{1}{v(x)} - \dfrac{1}{u(x)}}{\dfrac{1}{u(x)} \dfrac{1}{v(x)}} \equiv \log_e g(x) \qquad \left[g(x) \equiv \frac{e^{u(x)}}{e^{v(x)}} \right]$$

so that the methods of Sec. 3.7-2b become applicable.

Table 3.7-1   Some frequently used limits (values of indeterminate forms, Sec. 3.7-2)

$$\lim_{n \to \infty} \left(1 + \frac{1}{n} \right)^n = e \approx 2.71828 \qquad (n = 1, 2, \ldots) \qquad \lim_{x \to 0} (1 + x)^{\frac{1}{x}} = e$$

$$\lim_{x \to 0} \frac{c^x - 1}{x} = \log_e c \qquad\qquad\qquad\qquad\qquad \lim_{x \to 0} x^x = 1$$

$$\lim_{x \to 0} \frac{\sin x}{x} = \lim_{x \to 0} \frac{\tan x}{x} = \lim_{x \to 0} \frac{\sinh x}{x} = \lim_{x \to 0} \frac{\tanh x}{x} = 1$$

$$\lim_{x \to 0} \frac{\sin \omega x}{x} = \omega \qquad (-\infty < \omega < \infty)$$

$$\lim_{x \to 0} x^a \log_e x = \lim_{x \to \infty} x^{-a} \log_e x = \lim_{x \to \infty} x^a e^{-x} = 0 \qquad (a > 0)$$

(*d*) It is often helpful to write $\lim_{x \to a} f(x) = \lim_{\Delta x \to 0} f(a + \Delta x)$ and to isolate terms of the order of Δx by algebraic manipulation or by a Taylor-series expansion (Sec. 3.10-3).

(*e*) The methods of Secs. 3.7-2*a, b, c*, and *d* are readily modified to apply to the *one-sided limits* $\lim_{x \to a-0} f(x)$ and $\lim_{x \to a+0} f(x)$ (Sec. 3.4-6). To find $\lim_{x \to \infty} f(x)$, use $\lim_{x \to \infty} f(x) = \lim_{y \to 0+0} f(1/y)$.

3.8   INFINITE SERIES AND INFINITE PRODUCTS

3.8-1   *Infinite Series.   Convergence* (*see also Sec. 3.4-1*).   An **infinite series** (infinite sum) $a_0 + a_1 + a_2 + \cdots$ of real or complex numbers (terms) $a_0, a_1, a_2, \ldots$ **converges** if and only if the sequence s_0, $s_1, s_2, \ldots$ of the **partial sums** $s_n = \sum_{k=0}^{n} a_k$ has a (necessarily finite and unique) limit s, i.e., if and only if the sequence of the **remainders** $R_{n+1} = s - s_n$ converges to zero.   In this case, s is called the **sum** of the infinite series, and it is permissible to write

$$a_0 + a_1 + a_2 + \cdots = \sum_{k=0}^{\infty} a_k = \lim_{n \to \infty} \sum_{k=0}^{n} a_k = \lim_{n \to \infty} s_n = s$$

$$(3.8\text{-}1)$$

A (necessarily convergent) infinite series $a_0 + a_1 + a_2 + \cdots$ is **absolutely convergent** if and only if the series $|a_0| + |a_1| + |a_2| + \cdots$ converges.   An infinite series which does not converge is **divergent** (**diverges**).   Sections 3.9-1 and 3.9-2 list a number of tests for the convergence of a given infinite series.

3.8-2   *Series of Functions.   Uniform Convergence* (*see also Sec. 3.4-4*).   An infinite series of functions $a_0(x) + a_1(x) + a_2(x) + \cdots$ converges to a function (sum) $s(x)$ for every value of x such that

$$\lim_{n \to \infty} \sum_{k=0}^{n} a_k(x) = s(x)$$

The series **converges uniformly to** $s(x)$ **on a set** S **of values of** x

if and only if the sequence of partial sums $s_n(x) \equiv \sum\limits_{k=0}^{n} a_k(x)$ converges uniformly to $s(x)$ on S.   Section 3.9-2 lists a number of tests for uniform convergence.

3.8-3   *Operations with Convergent Series.*   (a) ADDITION AND MULTIPLICATION BY CONSTANTS.   *If* $\sum\limits_{k=0}^{\infty} a_k$ *and* $\sum\limits_{k=0}^{\infty} b_k$ *are convergent series of real or complex terms, and* α *is a real or complex number, then*

$$\sum_{k=0}^{\infty} a_k + \sum_{k=0}^{\infty} b_k = \sum_{k=0}^{\infty} (a_k + b_k)$$

$$\alpha \sum_{k=0}^{\infty} a_k = \sum_{k=0}^{\infty} \alpha a_k$$

(3.8-2)

In each case, the convergence or absolute convergence of the series on the left implies the same for the series on the right.

(b) REARRANGEMENT OF TERMS.   An **unconditionally convergent** series is a convergent series which converges to the same limit after every rearrangement of its terms; *this is true if and only if the series is absolutely convergent.*   *Every subseries (obtained by omission of terms) of such a series is absolutely convergent.*

3.8-4   *Operations with Infinite Series of Functions.*   (a) ADDITION AND MULTIPLICATION BY BOUNDED FUNCTIONS.   *If* $\sum\limits_{k=0}^{\infty} a_k(x)$ *and* $\sum\limits_{k=0}^{\infty} b_k(x)$ *converge uniformly on a set* S *of values of* x, *the same is true for* $\sum\limits_{k=0}^{\infty} [a_k(x) + b_k(x)]$ *and for* $\sum\limits_{k=0}^{\infty} \varphi(x)a_k(x)$, *where* $\varphi(x)$ *is any function bounded for all* x *in* S.

(b) LIMITS, CONTINUITY, AND INTEGRATION.   *Let* $\sum\limits_{k=0}^{\infty} a_k(x)$ *converge uniformly on a bounded open interval* (a, b) *containing* $x = x_0$ *and* $x = x_1$.   *Then*

1. $$\lim_{x \to x_0} \sum_{k=0}^{\infty} a_k(x) = \sum_{k=0}^{\infty} \lim_{x \to x_0} a_k(x)$$

    $$\lim_{x \to x_0+0} \sum_{k=0}^{\infty} a_k(x) = \sum_{k=0}^{\infty} \lim_{x \to x_0+0} a_k(x)$$

    $$\lim_{x \to x_0-0} \sum_{k=0}^{\infty} a_k(x) = \sum_{k=0}^{\infty} \lim_{x \to x_0-0} a_k(x)$$

    provided that the respective limits $\lim_{x \to x_0} a_k(x)$, $\lim_{x \to x_0+0} a_k(x)$, *or* $\lim_{x \to x_0-0} a_k(x)$ *exist for* $k = 0, 1, 2, \ldots$.

2. $\sum_{k=0}^{\infty} a_k(x)$ *is continuous at* $x = x_0$ *if each* $a_k(x)$ *is continuous at* $x = x_0$.

3. $\sum_{k=0}^{\infty} a_k(x)$ *converges uniformly on the closed interval* $[a, b]$ *and*

    $$\int_{x_1}^{x_0} \sum_{k=0}^{\infty} a_k(x)\, dx = \sum_{k=0}^{\infty} \int_{x_0}^{x_1} a_k(x)\, dx$$

    if each $a_k(x)$ *is continuous throughout* (a, b).

In each of these relations the given conditions imply the convergence of the series on the right.

(c) DIFFERENTIATION.   Let $\sum_{k=0}^{\infty} a_k(x)$ converge for at least one value of x in (a, b).   Then if $a_0'(x)$, $a_1'(x)$, $a_2'(x)$, $\ldots$ *exist and* $\sum_{k=0}^{\infty} a_k'(x)$ *converges uniformly on* (a, b)

$$\frac{d}{dx} \sum_{k=0}^{\infty} a_k(x) = \sum_{k=0}^{\infty} a_k'(x) \qquad (a < x < b) \tag{3.8-3}$$

whenever the derivative on the left exists.   Under the given conditions, this is necessarily true if each $a_k'(x)$ *is continuous on* (a, b).

3.8-5 Infinite Products.   An **infinite product**

$$(1 + a_0)(1 + a_1)(1 + a_2) \cdots = \prod_{k=0}^{\infty} (1 + a_k)$$

of real or complex factors $1 + a_k \neq 0$ **converges** to a limit (**value of the infinite product**) $p = \prod_{k=0}^{\infty} (1 + a_k) \neq 0$ if and only if

$$\lim_{n \to \infty} \prod_{k=0}^{n} (1 + a_k) = p$$

This is true if and only if the infinite series $\sum_{k=0}^{\infty} \log_e (1 + a_k)$ *converges to one of the values of* $\log_e p$ (see also Sec. 11.1-10). If $\lim_{n \to \infty} \prod_{k=0}^{n} (1 + a_k) = 0$ the infinite product is said to **diverge to zero.**

3.9 TESTS FOR THE CONVERGENCE AND UNIFORM CONVERGENCE OF INFINITE SERIES AND IMPROPER INTEGRALS

3.9-1   ***Tests for Convergence of Infinite Series.***   (*a*) A NECESSARY AND SUFFICIENT CONDITION FOR CONVERGENCE.   *A sequence of real or complex numbers* s_0, s_1, s_2, . . . *(e.g., the partial sums of an infinite series, Sec. 3.8-1) converges if and only if for every positive real number* ϵ *there exists a real integer* N *such that* $m > N$, $n > N$ *implies* $|s_n - s_m| < \epsilon$ (*Cauchy's Test* for the convergence of sequences or series).

     (*b*) TESTS FOR SERIES OF REAL POSITIVE TERMS (useful also as *tests for absolute convergence* of real or complex series, Secs. 3.8-1 and 3.8-3).   *An infinite series* $a_0 + a_1 + a_2 + \cdots$ *of real positive terms converges if there exists a real number* N *such that* $n > N$ *implies one or more of the following conditions:*

1. $a_n \leq M_n$ *and/or* $\dfrac{a_{n+1}}{a_n} \leq \dfrac{M_{n+1}}{M_n}$ *where* $M_0 + M_1 + M_2 + \cdots$ *is a convergent comparison series of real positive terms* (*comparison tests for convergence*).

2. *At least one of the quantities*

$$\frac{a_{n+1}}{a_n} \qquad \sqrt[n]{a_n} \qquad n\left(\frac{a_{n+1}}{a_n} - 1\right) + 2$$

$$\left[n\left(\frac{a_{n+1}}{a_n} - 1\right) + 1\right] \log_e n + 2 \qquad (3.9\text{-}1)$$

     has an upper bound $A < 1$.

     The fourth of these four tests is stronger than the third (*Raabe's Test*), which is, in turn, stronger than the first two (*Cauchy's Ratio and Root Tests*).

3. $a_n \leq f(n)$, where $f(x)$ is a real positive decreasing function whose (im-proper) integral $\int_{N+1}^{\infty} f(x)\, dx$ exists (Cauchy's Integral Test for con-vergence; see also Sec. 3.9-3b).

The infinite series $a_0 + a_1 + a_2 + \cdots$ diverges if there exists a real number N such that $n > N$ implies one or more of the following conditions:

1. $a_n \geq d_n$ and/or $\dfrac{a_{n+1}}{a_n} \geq \dfrac{d_{n+1}}{d_n}$, where $d_0 + d_1 + d_2 + \cdots$ is a divergent comparison series of real positive terms (comparison tests for divergence).
2. At least one of the quantities (1) has a lower bound $A \geq 1$.
3. $a_n \geq f(n)$, where $f(x)$ is a real positive decreasing function whose integral $\int_{N+1}^{\infty} f(x)\, dx$ diverges (Cauchy's Integral Test for divergence).

NOTE: The series $\displaystyle\sum_{k=1}^{\infty} \dfrac{1}{k^{\lambda}}$, which converges for real λ if and only if $\lambda > 1$, is useful as a comparison series.

(c) *An infinite series $a_0 + a_1 + a_2 + \cdots$ of real terms converges*

1. *If successive terms are alternatingly positive and negative (alternating series), decrease in absolute value, and $\lim\limits_{n \to \infty} a_n = 0$.*
2. *If the sequence $s_0, s_1, s_2, \ldots$ of the partial sums is bounded and monotonic.*

(d) *Given a decreasing sequence of real positive numbers $\alpha_0, \alpha_1, \alpha_2, \ldots$, the infinite series $\alpha_0 a_0 + \alpha_1 a_1 + \alpha_2 a_2 + \cdots$ converges*

1. *If the series $a_0 + a_1 + a_2 + \cdots$ converges (Abel's Test; see also Sec. 3.9-2c).*
2. *If $\lim\limits_{n \to \infty} \alpha_n = 0$ and $\displaystyle\sum_{k=0}^{n} a_k$ is bounded for all n (Dirichlet's Test).*

3.9-2   Tests for Uniform Convergence of Infinite Series (Sec. 3.8-2).   (a) A NECESSARY AND SUFFICIENT CONDITION FOR UNI-FORM CONVERGENCE.

A sequence $s_0(x), s_1(x), s_2(x), \ldots$ of real or complex functions (e.g., partial sums of an infinite series of functions, Sec. 3.8-2) converges uniformly on a set S of values of x if and only if for every positive real number ϵ there exists a real number N independent of x such *that* $m > N$, $n > N$ *implies* $|s_n(x) - s_m(x)| < \epsilon$ *for all* x *in* S *(Cauchy's Test* for uniform convergence of sequences or series).

(b) *An infinite series* $a_0(x) + a_1(x) + a_2(x) + \cdots$ *of real or complex functions converges uniformly and absolutely on every set* S *of values of* x *such that* $|a_n(x)| \leq M_n$ *for all* n, *where* $M_0 + M_1 + M_2 + \cdots$ *is a convergent comparison series of real positive terms (Weierstrass's Test).* The convergence of the comparison series may be tested in the manner of Sec. 3.9-1b.

(c) *Given a decreasing sequence of real positive terms* α_0, α_1, α_2, . . . , *the infinite series* $\alpha_0 a_0(x) + \alpha_1 a_1(x) + \alpha_2 a_2(x) + \cdots$ *converges uniformly on a set* S *of values of* x

1. *If the infinite series* $a_0(x) + a_1(x) + a_2(x) + \cdots$ *converges uniformly on* S *(Abel's Test;* see also Sec. 3.9-1d).

2. If $\lim\limits_{n \to \infty} \alpha_n = 0$ *and there exists a real number* $A \geq \left| \sum\limits_{k=0}^{n} a_k(x) \right|$ *for all* n *and all* x *in* S *(Dirichlet's Test).*

3.9-3   Tests for Convergence of Improper Integrals *(see also Sec. 3.6-2).* Section 3.9-3 lists convergence criteria for improper integrals of the form $\int_a^\infty f(x)\,dx$ and $\int_a^b f(x)\,dx = \lim\limits_{X \to b-0} \int_a^X f(x)\,dx$. Other improper integrals can be reduced to these forms (Sec. 3.6-2). IT IS ASSUMED THAT $f(x)$ IS BOUNDED AND INTEGRABLE ON EVERY BOUNDED INTERVAL (a, X) WHICH DOES NOT CONTAIN THE UPPER LIMIT OF INTEGRATION.

(a) NECESSARY AND SUFFICIENT CONDITIONS FOR CONVERGENCE (CAUCHY'S TEST). *The improper integral* $\int_a^\infty f(x)\,dx$ *converges if and only if for every positive real number* ϵ *there exists a real number* $M > a$ *such that* $X_2 > X_1 > M$ *implies* $\left| \int_{X_1}^{X_2} f(x)\,dx \right| < \epsilon$.

Similarly, $\int_a^b f(x)\,dx$ *converges if and only if for every positive real number* ϵ *there exists a positive real number* $\delta < b - a$ *such that* $b - X_2 < b - X_1 < \delta$ *implies* $\left| \int_{X_1}^{X_2} f(x)\,dx \right| < \epsilon$.

(b) TESTS FOR IMPROPER INTEGRALS OVER A REAL NONNEGATIVE FUNCTION (useful also as *tests for absolute convergence* of real or complex improper integrals; note that *absolute convergence implies* *convergence).   Given a real function $f(x) \geq 0$ on the interval of integration, the improper integral $\int_a^\infty f(x)\,dx$ or $\int_a^b f(x)\,dx = \lim\limits_{X \to b-0} \int_a^X f(x)\,dx$ converges if and only if $\int_a^X f(x)\,dx$ is bounded for every X in the interval of integration.   In particular, the integral converges if the integration interval contains a real number M such that $x > M$ implies $f(x) \leq g(x)$, where $g(x)$ is a real comparison function such that $\int_a^\infty g(x)\,dx$ $\Big[$ or $\int_a^b g(x)\,dx$, respectively $\Big]$ converges (Comparison Test).*

Similarly, if $\int_a^\infty g(x)\,dx$ or $\int_a^b g(x)\,dx$ diverges, $f(x) \geq g(x)$ implies the divergence of the corresponding integral over $f(x)$.

NOTE: $\int_a^\infty \dfrac{1}{x^\lambda}\,dx$ and $\int_a^b \dfrac{1}{(x-b)^\lambda}\,dx$ converge for $\lambda > 1$ and diverge for $\lambda \leq 1$. The improper integral $\int_a^\infty f(x)\,dx$ converges absolutely if $f(x) = O(1/x^\lambda)$ $(\lambda > 1)$ as $x \to \infty$; $\int_a^b f(x)\,dx$ converges absolutely if $f(x) = O[1/(x-b)^\lambda]$ $(\lambda > 1)$ as $x \to b - 0$.

(c)   The improper integral $\int_a^\infty \alpha(x)f(x)\,dx$ or $\int_a^b \alpha(x)f(x)\,dx$ converges if the corresponding improper integral $\int_a^\infty f(x)\,dx$ or $\int_a^b f(x)\,dx$ converges absolutely, and $\alpha(x)$ is bounded and integrable on every finite subinterval of the interval of integration.

(d)   The improper integral $\int_a^\infty \alpha(x)f(x)\,dx$ converges if, for every $X > a$, $\alpha(X)$ is bounded and monotonic, $f(x)$ is bounded and integrable and has a finite number of sign changes on $[a, X]$, and

1. $\int_a^\infty f(x)\,dx$ *converges (analog of Abel's test, Sec. 3.9-1d) or*

2. $\int_a^X f(x)\,dx$ *is bounded and $\lim\limits_{x \to \infty} \alpha(x) = 0$ (analog of Dirichlet's test, Sec. 3.9-1d).*

3.10   REPRESENTATION OF FUNCTIONS BY INFINITE SERIES AND INTEGRALS.   POWER SERIES AND TAYLOR'S EXPANSION

3.10-1   *Representation of Functions by Infinite Series and Integrals.*   A function $f(x)$ is often represented by a corresponding infinite series $\sum\limits_{k=0}^\infty \alpha_k \varphi_k(x)$ because

1. A sequence of partial sums may yield useful numerical approximations to $f(x)$.
2. It may be possible to describe operations on $f(x)$ in terms of simpler operations on the functions $\varphi_k(x)$ or on the coefficients α_k (transform methods). The functions $\varphi_k(x)$ and the coefficients α_k may have an intuitive (physical) meaning.

Similar advantages apply to representations of functions by (usually improper) integrals $\int_a^b \alpha(\lambda)\varphi(x, \lambda)\,d\lambda$ (see also Sec. 3.11-3c and Chap. 5).

3.10-2 Power Series.   (*a*) A **power series** in the (real or complex) variable x is a series of the form

$$a_0 + a_1 x + a_2 x^2 + \cdots \equiv \sum_{k=0}^{\infty} a_k x^k \qquad (3.10\text{-}1)$$

where the coefficients a_0, a_1, a_2, . . . are real or complex numbers. *Given any power series* (1), *there exists a real number r_c ($0 \leq r_c \leq \infty$) such that the power series converges absolutely and uniformly for $|x| < r_c$ and diverges for $|x| > r_c$. r_c* is called the **radius of convergence** of the power series.

Convergence for $x = x_0$ implies convergence for $|x| < |x_0|$, and divergence for $x = x_0$ implies divergence for $|x| > |x_0|$.

(*b*) *Convergent power series can be added according to Eqs.* (3.8-2). *For $|x| < r_c$, the power series* (1) *is a continuous and repeatedly differentiable function of x; the series may be differentiated and integrated term by term, and the resulting power series have the radius of convergence r_c.*

(*c*) *If there exists a positive real number r such that two power series,*

$\sum\limits_{k=0}^{\infty} a_k x^k$ *and* $\sum\limits_{k=0}^{\infty} b_k x^k$, *converge to the same sum $f(x)$ for all real x such that* $|x| < r$, *then $a_0 = b_0$, $a_1 = b_1$, $a_2 = b_2$, . . .* (*Uniqueness Theorem*).

Example: The *infinite geometric series*

$$a_0 + a_0 x + a_0 x^2 + \cdots \equiv a_0 \sum_{k=0}^{\infty} x^k \equiv a_0 \frac{1}{1 - x} \qquad (|x| < 1)$$

$$(3.10\text{-}2)$$

converges absolutely and uniformly for $|x| < 1$ and diverges for $|x| > 1$.

3.10-3   Taylor's Expansion (*see also Sec. 5.2-2*).   (*a*) *Given a real function $f(x)$ such that $f^{(n)}(x)$ exists for $a \leq x < b$,*

$$\left. \begin{aligned} f(x) &= f(a) + f'(a)(x - a) \\ &\quad + \frac{1}{2!} f''(a)(x - a)^2 + \cdots \\ &\quad + \frac{1}{(n-1)!} f^{(n-1)}(a)(x - a)^{n-1} + R_n(x) \\ \text{with} & \\ |R_n(x)| &\leq \frac{|x - a|^n}{n!} \sup_{a < \xi < x} |f^{(n)}(\xi)| \end{aligned} \right\} \begin{array}{l} (a \leq x < b) \\[2em] (3.10\text{-}3) \end{array}$$

More specifically, *there exists a real number $X = a + \vartheta(x - a)$ such that $a < X < x$ (or $0 < \vartheta < 1$) and*

$$R_n(x) = \int_a^x \int_a^\xi \cdots \int_a^\xi f^{(n)}(\xi) \, d\xi^n = \frac{1}{n!} f^{(n)}(X)(x - a)^n \qquad (a \leq x < b)$$

(LAGRANGE'S REMAINDER FORMULA)   (3.10-4)

X and ϑ depend on a, x, and n (see also Sec. 3.7-1).

(*b*) *Given a function $f(x)$ such that all derivatives $f^{(k)}(x)$ exist and $\lim\limits_{n \to \infty} R_n(x) = 0$ for $a \leq x < b$,*

$$f(x) = \sum_{k=0}^\infty \frac{1}{k!} f^{(k)}(a)(x - a)^k \qquad (a \leq x < b) \qquad (3.10\text{-}5)$$

and *the series converges uniformly to $f(x)$ on every closed subinterval in $a \leq x < b$* [*Taylor-series expansion of $f(x)$ about $x = a$*].

Equation (5) may be written $f(x + \Delta x) = \sum\limits_{k=0}^\infty \frac{1}{k!} f^{(k)}(x) \, \Delta x^k$ with $\Delta x = x - a$.

For $a = 0$, Taylor's series reduces to *MacLaurin's series* $\sum\limits_{k=0}^\infty \frac{1}{k!} f^{(k)}(0) x^k$.

(*c*) Every convergent series expansion of $f(x)$ in powers of $(x - a)$ is necessarily identical with Eq. (5) (Sec. 3.10-2*c*). If $f(x)$ is a rational function, series expansions in powers of x or $1/x$ are often obtained by continued long division. *Refer to Sec. 11.1-11 for examples of power-series expansions.*

Power-series expansions permit term-by-term differentiation and integration (Sec. 3.10-2*b*) and are thus useful for the integration of $f(x)$ and for the solution of differential equations (Sec. 6.1-4*b*).

3.10-4   Multiple Taylor Expansion.   (*a*) *Given a real function $f(x_1, x_2, \ldots, x_n)$ such that all partial derivatives of order m exist and are continuous for $a_i \leq x_i < b_i$ ($i = 1, 2, \ldots, n$), one has*

$$f(x_1, x_2, \ldots, x_n) = f(a_1, a_2, \ldots, a_n) + \sum_{i=1}^{n} \frac{\partial f}{\partial x_i}\bigg]_{a_1, a_2, \ldots, a_n} (x_i - a_i)$$

$$+ \frac{1}{2!} \sum_{i=1}^{n} \sum_{j=1}^{n} \frac{\partial^2 f}{\partial x_i\, \partial x_j}\bigg]_{a_1, a_2, \ldots, a_n} (x_i - a_i)(x_j - a_j)$$

$$+ \cdots + R_m(x_1, x_2, \ldots, x_n)$$

$$(a_i \leq x_i < b_i; i = 1, 2, \ldots, n) \qquad (3.10\text{-}6)$$

The remainder $R_m(x_1, x_2, \ldots, x_n)$ satisfies a relation analogous to Eq. (4).

(b) If all derivatives of $f(x_1, x_2, \ldots, x_n)$ exist and $\lim\limits_{m \to \infty} R_m(x_1, x_2, \ldots, x_n) = 0$ for $a_i \leq x_i < b_i$, then Eq. (6) yields a multiple power-series expansion for $f(x_1, x_2, \ldots, x_n)$ (*multiple Taylor series*).

3.11 FOURIER SERIES AND FOURIER INTEGRALS

3.11-1   Fourier Series.   (a) Fourier series and Fourier integrals are used to represent and/or approximate functions in many important applications, especially in connection with the solution of differential equations.

(b) Given the finite interval of expansion $-T/2 < t < T/2$, the Fourier series generated by a real function $f(t)$ such that $\int_{-T/2}^{T/2} |f(\tau)|\, d\tau$ exists is the infinite trigonometric series

$$\tfrac{1}{2}(a_0) + \sum_{k=1}^{\infty} (a_k \cos k\omega_0 t + b_k \sin k\omega_0 t) \equiv \sum_{k=-\infty}^{\infty} c_k e^{ik\omega_0 t}$$

$$\left(\omega_0 = \frac{2\pi}{T}\right)$$

with

$$a_k = \frac{2}{T} \int_{-T/2}^{T/2} f(\tau) \cos k\omega_0 \tau\, d\tau$$

$$b_k = \frac{2}{T} \int_{-T/2}^{T/2} f(\tau) \sin k\omega_0 \tau\, d\tau \qquad (3.11\text{-}1)$$

$$c_k = c_{-k}^* = \tfrac{1}{2}(a_k - ib_k) = \frac{1}{T} \int_{-T/2}^{T/2} f(\tau)e^{-ik\omega_0 t}\, d\tau$$

$$\left(\omega_0 = \frac{2\pi}{T}; k = 0, 1, 2, \ldots\right)$$

(c) If $\int_{-T/2}^{T/2} [f(\tau)]^2 \, d\tau$ *exists, the Fourier series* (1) *is that trigono-metric series whose coefficients* a_k, b_k *minimize each mean-square error*

$$\frac{1}{T} \int_{-T/2}^{T/2} [f(\tau) - s_n(\tau)]^2 \, d\tau$$

when successive partial sums (*Sec. 3.8-1*)

$$s_0(t) = \tfrac{1}{2}a_0 \qquad s_n(t) \equiv \tfrac{1}{2}a_0 + \sum_{k=1}^{n} \left(a_k \cos k \frac{2\pi t}{T} + b_k \sin k \frac{2\pi t}{T} \right)$$

$$(n = 1, 2, \ldots)$$

are used as approximations to $f(t)$.

If a trigonometric series of the form (1) *converges uniformly to* $f(t)$ *in* $(-T/2, T/2)$, *then its coefficients are necessarily the Fourier coefficients of* $f(t)$ (*Euler's Theorem*).

(d) If $f(t)$ *is a real periodic function* $f(t)$ *with period* T, *the Fourier series* (1) *converges and equals* $f(t)$ *throughout every open interval where* $f(t)$ *is bounded and has a finite number of relative maxima, minima, and discontinuities* (*Dirichlet's conditions*), *provided that one defines* $f(t) = \tfrac{1}{2}[f(t - 0) + f(t + 0)]$ *at each discontinuity.* $f(t)$ *is, then, represented as the sum of*

1. *A constant term* $a_0/2 = c_0$ [*average value* of $f(t)$], *and*
2. *A set of sinusoidal terms* (*sinusoidal components*) *of respective* **frequencies** $\nu_0 = 1/T$ (**fundamental** frequency), $2\nu_0 = 2/T$ (**2nd-harmonic** frequency), $3\nu_0 = 3/T$ (**3rd-harmonic** frequency), ...

The **k**[th]**-harmonic component** $2|c_k| \cos \left(k \dfrac{2\pi t}{T} + \arg c_k \right)$ has the frequency $k\nu_0 = k/T$, the **circular frequency** $k\omega_0 = 2\pi k\nu_0 = 2\pi k/T$, the **amplitude** $2|c_k| = + \sqrt{a_k{}^2 + b_k{}^2}$, and the "phase angle" $\arg c_k = - \arctan (b_k/a_k)$.

Note that

$$<f^2> = \frac{1}{T} \int_{-T/2}^{T/2} [f(\tau)]^2 \, d\tau = \frac{1}{4} a_0{}^2 + \frac{1}{2} \sum_{k=1}^{\infty} (a_k{}^2 + b_k{}^2) = \sum_{k=-\infty}^{\infty} |c_k|^2$$

$$(3.11\text{-}2)$$

whenever the integral on the left exists (*Parseval's Theorem*). Table D-1 of Appendix

D lists the Fourier coefficients and the *mean-square values* (2) for a number of periodic functions.

3.11-2 Fourier Integrals and Fourier Transforms. (a) Let $f(t)$ be a real function such that $\int_{-\infty}^{\infty} |f(\tau)|\, d\tau$ exists. Then

$$f(t) = \int_{-\infty}^{\infty} c(\nu)e^{2\pi i\nu t}\, d\nu \equiv \int_{-\infty}^{\infty} F_F(i\omega)e^{i\omega t}\, \frac{d\omega}{2\pi}$$

$$\equiv \frac{1}{\sqrt{2\pi}} \int_{-\infty}^{\infty} C(\omega)e^{i\omega t}\, d\omega$$

with

$$c(\nu) \equiv \int_{-\infty}^{\infty} f(\tau)e^{-2\pi i\nu}{}_t\, d\tau \equiv F_F(i\omega) \qquad (3.11\text{-}3)$$

$$C(\omega) \equiv \frac{1}{\sqrt{2\pi}} \int_{-\infty}^{\infty} f(\tau)e^{-i\omega\tau}\, d\tau \equiv \frac{1}{\sqrt{2\pi}} F_F(i\omega)$$

$$\equiv \frac{1}{\sqrt{2\pi}} c(\nu) \qquad (\omega = 2\pi\nu)$$

throughout every open interval where $f(t)$ satisfies the Dirichlet conditions of Sec. 3.11-1d, if one defines $f(t) = \frac{1}{2}[f(t-0) + f(t+0)]$ at each discontinuity. The function $c(\nu) \equiv F_F(i\omega)$ $(\omega = 2\pi\nu)$ will be called the **Fourier transform** $\mathfrak{F}[f(t)]$ of $f(t)$. Some authors, especially physicists, refer to $C(\omega) \equiv F_F(i\omega)/\sqrt{2\pi}$ as the Fourier transform of $f(t)$ instead. Table D-2 of Appendix D lists a number of Fourier-transform pairs.

A function $f(t)$ having the Fourier transform $c(\nu)$ will be called an **inverse Fourier transform** $\mathfrak{F}^{-1}[c(\nu)]$ of $c(\nu)$; under the given conditions, Eq. (3) defines $\mathfrak{F}^{-1}[c(\nu)]$ uniquely wherever $f(t)$ is continuous.

Equation (3) may be written in different forms, e.g.,

$$f(t) = \frac{1}{\pi} \int_0^{\infty} d\omega \int_{-\infty}^{\infty} f(\tau) \cos \omega(t - \tau)\, d\tau$$

$$= \sqrt{\frac{2}{\pi}} \int_0^{\infty} |C(\omega)| \cos [\omega t + \arg C(\omega)]\, d\omega$$

$$= 2 \int_0^{\infty} [A(\nu) \cos 2\pi\nu t + B(\nu) \sin 2\pi\nu t]\, d\nu \qquad (\omega = 2\pi\nu) \qquad (3.11\text{-}4)$$

(b) The **Fourier cosine and sine integrals** generated by a real function $f(t)$ whose absolute value $|f(t)|$ is integrable over the interval of expansion $0 < t < \infty$ are respectively defined as

$$2 \int_0^\infty c_C(\nu) \cos 2\pi\nu t \, d\nu \equiv 2 \int_0^\infty F_C(\omega) \cos \omega t \, \frac{d\omega}{2\pi}$$

$$\equiv \sqrt{\frac{2}{\pi}} \int_0^\infty C_C(\omega) \cos \omega t \, d\omega$$

(3.11-5)

$$2 \int_0^\infty c_S(\nu) \sin 2\pi\nu t \, d\nu \equiv 2 \int_0^\infty F_S(\omega) \sin \omega t \, \frac{d\omega}{2\pi}$$

$$\equiv \sqrt{\frac{2}{\pi}} \int_0^\infty C_S(\omega) \sin \omega t \, d\omega$$

with

$$
\left.
\begin{aligned}
c_C(\nu) &\equiv 2 \int_0^\infty f(\tau) \cos 2\pi\nu\tau \, d\tau \\
&\equiv F_C(\omega) \\
C_C(\omega) &\equiv \sqrt{\frac{2}{\pi}} \int_0^\infty f(\tau) \cos \omega\tau \, d\tau \\
&\equiv \frac{1}{\sqrt{2\pi}} F_C(\omega) \equiv \frac{1}{\sqrt{2\pi}} c_C(\nu) \\
c_S(\nu) &\equiv 2 \int_0^\infty f(\tau) \sin 2\pi\nu\tau \, d\tau \\
&\equiv F_S(\omega) \\
C_S(\omega) &\equiv \sqrt{\frac{2}{\pi}} \int_0^\infty f(\tau) \sin \omega\tau \, d\tau \\
&\equiv \frac{1}{\sqrt{2\pi}} F_S(\omega) \equiv \frac{1}{\sqrt{2\pi}} c_S(\nu)
\end{aligned}
\right\} \qquad (\omega = 2\pi\nu)
$$

(3.11-6)

The (real) functions $c_C(\nu) \equiv F_C(\omega) \equiv \mathfrak{F}_C[f(t)]$ and $c_S(\nu) \equiv F_S(\omega) \equiv \mathfrak{F}_S[f(t)]$ will be called, respectively, the **Fourier cosine transform** and the **Fourier sine transform** of $f(t)$. Some authors refer to $C_C(\omega)$ and $C_S(\omega)$ as Fourier cosine and sine transforms, instead.

3.11-3   *Representation of Functions and Operations in Terms of Fourier Coefficients or Fourier Transforms* (*see also Secs. 3.10-1 and 5.4-6*). (*a*) UNIQUENESS THEOREM. A suitably integrable function $f(t)$ uniquely defines its Fourier coefficients or its Fourier transform. Conversely, *a complete set of Fourier coefficients or a Fourier*

Table 3.11-1 **Properties of Fourier transforms**

Let

$$\mathfrak{F}[f(t)] \equiv \int_{-\infty}^{\infty} f(t)e^{-2\pi i\nu t}\,dt \equiv c(\nu) \equiv F_F(i\omega) \equiv \sqrt{2\pi}\,C(\omega) \qquad (\omega = 2\pi\nu)$$

$$f(t) \equiv \int_{-\infty}^{\infty} c(\nu)e^{2\pi i\nu t}\,d\nu \equiv \int_{-\infty}^{\infty} F_F(i\omega)e^{i\omega t}\frac{d\omega}{2\pi} \equiv \frac{1}{\sqrt{2\pi}}\int_{-\infty}^{\infty} C(\omega)e^{i\omega t}\,d\omega$$

and assume that the Fourier transforms in question exist.

(a) $\mathfrak{F}[\alpha f_1(t) + \beta f_2(t)] \equiv \alpha\mathfrak{F}[f_1(t)] + \beta\mathfrak{F}[f_2(t)]$ (LINEARITY)

$\mathfrak{F}[f^*(t)] \equiv c^*(-\nu) \equiv F_F^*(-i\omega)$

$\mathfrak{F}[f(\alpha t)] \equiv \dfrac{1}{\alpha}\,c\left(\dfrac{\nu}{\alpha}\right) \equiv \dfrac{1}{\alpha}\,F_F\left(\dfrac{i\omega}{\alpha}\right)$ (CHANGE OF SCALE, SIMILARITY THEOREM)

$\mathfrak{F}[f(t + \tau)] \equiv e^{2\pi i\nu\tau}c(\nu) \equiv e^{i\omega\tau}F_F(i\omega)$ (SHIFT THEOREM)

(b) CONTINUITY THEOREM. $\mathfrak{F}[f(t, \alpha)] \to \mathfrak{F}[f(t)]$ as $\alpha \to a$ implies $f(t, \alpha) \to f(t)$ wherever $f(t)$ is continuous. Analogous theorems apply to Fourier cosine and sine transforms.

(c) BOREL'S CONVOLUTION THEOREM. $\mathfrak{F}[f_1(t)]\mathfrak{F}[f_2(t)] \equiv \mathfrak{F}[f_1(t) * f_2(t)]$, where

$$f_1(t) * f_2(t) \equiv \int_{-\infty}^{\infty} f_1(\tau)f_2(t - \tau)\,d\tau \equiv \int_{-\infty}^{\infty} f_1(t - \tau)f_2(\tau)\,d\tau$$

$$\mathfrak{F}[f_1(t)f_2(t)] \equiv \int_{-\infty}^{\infty} c_1(\lambda)c_2(\nu - \lambda)\,d\lambda \equiv \int_{-\infty}^{\infty} c_1(\nu - \lambda)c_2(\lambda)\,d\lambda$$

$$\equiv \int_{-\infty}^{\infty} F_{F1}(i\lambda)F_{F2}[i(\omega - \lambda)]\frac{d\lambda}{2\pi}$$

$$\equiv \int_{-8}^{\infty} F_{F1}[i(\omega - \lambda)]F_{F2}(i\lambda)\frac{d\lambda}{2\pi}$$

(d) PARSEVAL'S THEOREM. If $\displaystyle\int_{-\infty}^{\infty} |f_1(t)|^2\,dt$ and $\displaystyle\int_{-\infty}^{\infty} |f_2(t)|^2\,dt$ exist, then

$$\int_{-\infty}^{\infty} \mathfrak{F}^*[f_1(t)]\mathfrak{F}[f_2(t)]\,d\nu = \int_{-\infty}^{\infty} f_1^*(t)f_2(t)\,dt$$

(e) MODULATION THEOREM

$\mathfrak{F}[f(t)e^{i\omega_0 t}] \equiv F_F[i(\omega - \omega_0)] = c(\nu - \nu_0)$

$\mathfrak{F}[f(t)\cos\omega_0 t] \equiv \frac{1}{2}\{F_F[i(\omega - \omega_0)] + F_F[i(\omega + \omega_0)]\}$

$\qquad\qquad \equiv \frac{1}{2}[c(\nu - \nu_0) + c(\nu + \nu_0)]$

$\mathfrak{F}[f(t)\sin\omega_0 t] \equiv \dfrac{1}{2i}\{F_F[i(\omega - \omega_0)] - F_F[i(\omega + \omega_0)]\}$

$\qquad\qquad \equiv \dfrac{1}{2i}[c(\nu - \nu_0) - c(\nu + \nu_0)]$

(f) DIFFERENTIATION THEOREM

$\mathfrak{F}[f^{(r)}(t)] = (2\pi i\nu)^r\mathfrak{F}[f(t)] \qquad (r = 0, 1, 2, \ldots)$

provided that $f^{(r)}(t)$ exists for all t, and that all derivatives of lesser order vanish as $|t| \to \infty$.

transform uniquely defines the corresponding function $f(t)$ at each point of continuity in the interval of expansion.

(*b*) OPERATIONS WITH FOURIER SERIES. *Given $f(t)$ with the Fourier coefficients a_k, b_k, c_k, and $\varphi(t)$ with the Fourier coefficients $\alpha_k, \beta_k, \gamma_k$ for the same interval of expansion, let λ and μ be real constants. Then the function $\lambda f(t) + \mu \varphi(t)$ has the Fourier coefficients $\lambda a_k + \mu \alpha_k$, $\lambda b_k + \mu \beta_k$, $\lambda c_k + \mu \gamma_k$ (term-by-term addition and multiplication by constants).*

Term-by-term integration of a Fourier series over an interval (t_0, t) in the interval of expansion yields a series converging to $\int_{t_0}^{t} f(\tau)\, d\tau$. The theorem holds for all values of t_0 and t if $f(t)$ is periodic with period T.

(*c*) PROPERTIES OF FOURIER TRANSFORMS. Table 3.11-1 lists the most important properties of Fourier transforms (see also Sec. 5.4-6).

3.12 DIFFERENTIAL GEOMETRY

3.12-1   *Tangent and Normal to a Plane Curve.*   (*a*) Given a plane curve C represented by

$$y = f(x) \tag{3.12-1a}$$

or $$\varphi(x, y) = 0 \tag{3.12-1b}$$

or $$x = x(t) \qquad y = y(t) \tag{3.12-1c}$$

(Sec. 2.2-5) in terms of suitably differentiable functions, the **tangent** to C at the point $P_1 \equiv (x_1, y_1)$ is defined as the limit of a straight line (secant) through P_1 and a neighboring point P_2 as P_2 approaches P_1. *The curve* (1) *has a unique tangent described by*

$$y - y_1 = \frac{dy}{dx}\,(x - x_1) \tag{3.12-2a}$$

or $$\frac{\partial \varphi}{\partial x}\,(x - x_1) + \frac{\partial \varphi}{\partial y}\,(y - y_1) = 0 \tag{3.12-2b}$$

or $$x = \frac{dx}{dt}\,(t - t_1) + x_1 \qquad y = \frac{dy}{dt}\,(t - t_1) + y_1 \tag{3.12-2c}$$

at every **regular point** (x_1, y_1) *where it is possible to choose a parameter t so that $x(t)$ and $y(t)$ have unique continuous derivatives not both equal to zero, or, equivalently, where $\varphi(x, y)$ has unique continuous first partial derivatives not both equal to zero.* The *slope* (Sec. 2.2-6) of the tangent (2) is

$$\tan \vartheta = \frac{dy}{dx} = -\frac{\partial \varphi}{\partial x} \Big/ \frac{\partial \varphi}{\partial y} = \frac{dy}{dt} \Big/ \frac{dx}{dt} \tag{3.12-3}$$

(b) The **normal** to the curve (1) at a regular point $P_1 \equiv (x_1, y_1)$ is the straight line through P_1 and perpendicular to the tangent at P_1:

$$y - y_1 = -\frac{1}{dy/dx}(x - x_1) \tag{3.12-4}$$

The direction of the *positive* normal is arbitrarily fixed with respect to the common positive direction of curve and tangent. The positive direction on a curve (1) is arbitrarily fixed by some convention (e.g., direction of increasing t, increasing x, etc).

3.12-2   *Curvature of a Plane Curve.*   The **circle of curvature** (**osculating circle**) of a plane curve C at the point P_1 is the limit of a circle through P_1 and two other distinct points P_2 and P_3 of C as P_2 and P_3 approach P_1. The center of this circle (**center of curvature** of C corresponding to the curve point P_1) is located on the normal to C at P_1. The coordinates of the center of curvature are

$$x_\kappa = x_1 - \frac{dy}{dx}\left[1 + \left(\frac{dy}{dx}\right)^2\right] \Big/ \frac{d^2y}{dx^2} = x_1 - \frac{\dot{y}(\dot{x}^2 + \dot{y}^2)}{\dot{x}\ddot{y} - \dot{y}\ddot{x}}$$
$$y_\kappa = y_1 + \left[1 + \left(\frac{dy}{dx}\right)^2\right] \Big/ \frac{d^2y}{dx^2} = y_1 + \frac{\dot{x}(\dot{x}^2 + \dot{y}^2)}{\dot{x}\ddot{y} - \dot{y}\ddot{x}} \tag{3.12-5}$$

where all derivatives are computed for $x = x_1$ $(t = t_1)$; dots indicate differentiation with respect to t. The radius ρ_κ of the circle of curvature (**radius of curvature** of C at P_1) equals the reciprocal of the **curvature** κ of C at P_1 defined as the rate of turn of the tangent with respect to the arc length s along C (Sec. 3.6-7):

$$\kappa = \frac{1}{\rho_\kappa} = \frac{d\vartheta}{ds} = \frac{d^2y}{dx^2} \Big/ \sqrt{1 + \left(\frac{dy}{dx}\right)^2}^3 = \frac{\dot{x}\ddot{y} - \dot{y}\ddot{x}}{\sqrt{\dot{x}^2 + \dot{y}^2}^3} \tag{3.12-6}$$

where all derivatives are computed for $x = x_1$ $(t = t_1)$. A given curve C is, respectively, *concave* or *convex* in the direction of the positive y axis wherever d^2y/dx^2 and thus κ is positive or negative. Many authors introduce $|\kappa|$ rather than κ as the curvature.

3.12-3   *Curves in Three-dimensional Space* (*see Chap. 4 for vector notation*).   A **regular arc** C is described by

$$\mathbf{r} = \mathbf{r}(t)$$

or $x = x(t)$ $y = y(t)$ $z = z(t)$ $(t_1 \leq t \leq t_2)$ (3.12-7)

where the functions (7) have unique continuous first derivatives and $d\mathbf{r}/dt \neq 0$ for $t_1 \leq t \leq t_2$.   Higher-order derivatives will be assumed to exist as needed.   It is convenient to introduce the *arc length* $s \equiv \displaystyle\int_{t_{1_C}}^{t} ds \equiv \displaystyle\int_{t_{1_C}}^{t} \sqrt{d\mathbf{r} \cdot d\mathbf{r}} \equiv \displaystyle\int_{t_{1_C}}^{t} \sqrt{dx^2 + dy^2 + dz^2}$ (Sec. 3.6-7) as a new parameter; the sign of ds is arbitrarily fixed to determine the *positive direction* of curve and tangents.   Differentiation with respect to s will be indicated by primes, so that, for example,

$$x' \equiv \frac{dx}{ds} \equiv \frac{dx/dt}{ds/dt}$$

3.12-4   The Moving Trihedron (*see Chap. 4 for vector notation*).   (*a*) TANGENT TO A CURVE.   The **tangent** to a regular arc C at the point $P_1 \equiv (\mathbf{r}_1) \equiv (x_1, y_1, z_1)$ is the limit of a straight line (secant)

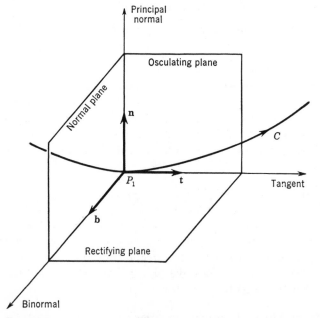

Fig. 3.12-1 The moving trihedron associated with a space curve C.

through P_1 and another point P_2 of C as P_2 approaches P_1. A unique tangent exists at every point of a regular arc. The positive tangent direction coincides with the positive direction of C at P_1.

(b) OSCULATING CIRCLE AND PLANE. PRINCIPAL NORMAL. The **osculating circle** or **circle of curvature** of C at the curve point P_1 is the limit of a circle through P_1 and two other distinct points P_2 and P_3 of C as P_2 and P_3 approach P_1. The plane of this circle (**osculating plane** of C at P_1) contains the tangent to C at P_1. The directed straight line from the curve point P_1 to the center of the osculating circle (**center of curvature**) is perpendicular to the tangent and is called the **principal normal** of C at P_1.

(c) BINORMAL. NORMAL AND RECTIFYING PLANES. The **binormal** of C at P_1 is the directed straight line through P_1 such that *the positive tangent, principal normal, and binormal form a system of right-handed rectangular cartesian axes.* These axes determine the "moving trihedron" comprising the osculating plane and the **normal and rectifying planes** respectively normal to the tangent and to the principal normal of C at P_1 (Fig. 3.12-1).

(d) The unit vectors $\mathbf{t}$, $\mathbf{n}$, and $\mathbf{b}$ respectively directed along the positive tangent, the principal normal, and the binormal are given by

$$\mathbf{t} = \mathbf{r}' \qquad \text{(UNIT TANGENT VECTOR)}$$

$$\mathbf{n} = \frac{\mathbf{r}''}{|\mathbf{r}''|} = \frac{1}{\kappa}\mathbf{r}'' \quad \text{(UNIT PRINCIPAL-NORMAL VECTOR)} \qquad (3.12\text{-}8)$$

$$\mathbf{b} = \mathbf{t} \times \mathbf{n} \qquad \text{(UNIT BINORMAL VECTOR)}$$

at each suitable point of the curve. The vector $\kappa\mathbf{n} = \mathbf{r}''$ is called the **curvature vector;** κ is the *curvature* further discussed in Sec. 3.12-5.

3.12-5 Serret-Frenet Formulas. Curvature and Torsion of a Space Curve. The unit vectors (8) satisfy the relations

$$\mathbf{t}' = \kappa\mathbf{n} \qquad \mathbf{n}' = -\kappa\mathbf{t} + \tau\mathbf{b} \qquad \mathbf{b}' = -\tau\mathbf{n}$$
$$\text{(SERRET-FRENET FORMULAS)}$$

with $(3.12\text{-}9)$

$$\kappa = \frac{1}{\rho_\kappa} = |\mathbf{t}'| = |\mathbf{r}''| \qquad \tau = \frac{1}{\rho_\tau} = \frac{1}{\kappa^2}[\mathbf{r}'\mathbf{r}''\mathbf{r}''']$$

at each curve point P_1. As s increases, the point P_1 moves along the curve C and

1. The tangent rotates about the instantaneous binormal direction at the (positive) angular rate κ (**curvature** of C at P_1).
2. The binormal rotates about the instantaneous tangent direction at the angular rate τ (**torsion** of C at P_1; τ is positive wherever the curve turns in the manner of a right-handed screw).
3. The entire moving trihedron rotates about the instantaneous direction of the **Darboux vector** $\boldsymbol{\Omega} = \tau\mathbf{t} + \kappa\mathbf{b}$ at the (positive) angular rate $|\boldsymbol{\Omega}| = \sqrt{\tau^2 + \kappa^2}$ (**total curvature** of C at P_1).

References and Bibliography

1. Courant, R.: *Differential and Integral Calculus* (2 vols.), Interscience, New York, 1936–1937.
2. Knopp, K.: *Theory and Application of Infinite Series,* Hafner, New York, 1948.
3. Brand, L.: *Advanced Calculus,* Wiley, New York, 1955.
4. Hardy, G. F.: *Pure Mathematics,* Cambridge, New York, 1959.
5. Boas, R. P.: *A Primer of Real Functions,* Wiley, New York, 1960.
6. Widder, D. V.: *Advanced Calculus,* 2d ed., Prentice-Hall, Englewood Cliffs, N.J., 1961.
7. Kuratowski, K. C.: *Introduction to Calculus,* Addison-Wesley, Reading, Mass., 1962.
8. Buck, R. C.: *Advanced Calculus,* 2d ed., McGraw-Hill, New York, 1964.
9. Struik, D. J.: *Differential Geometry,* 2d ed., Addison-Wesley, Reading, Mass., 1961.
10. Guggenheim, H. W.: *Differential Geometry,* McGraw-Hill, New York, 1963.

4 VECTOR ANALYSIS

4.1 INTRODUCTION

4.1-1 Euclidean Vectors. Each class of **euclidean vectors** (e.g., displacements, velocities, forces, magnetic field strengths) permits the definition of operations known as *vector addition* (Sec. 4.2-1), *multiplication of vectors by (real) scalars* (Sec. 4.2-1), and *scalar multiplication of vectors* (Sec. 4.2-5). Each class of (euclidean) vectors commonly encountered in geometry and physics is, moreover, intimately related to the two- or three-dimensional space of euclidean geometry:

1. The vectors of each class permit a reciprocal one-to-one representation by *translations (displacements, directed line segments)* in the geometrical space.
2. In most applications, vectors appear as *functions of position* in geometrical space, so that the vectors are associated with geometrical points (*vector point functions*, Sec. 4.4-1).

Vectors, such as velocities or forces, are usually first introduced in geometrical language as "quantities possessing magnitude and direction" or, somewhat more precisely, as quantities which can be represented by directed line segments subject to a "parallelogram law of addition." Such a geometrical approach, common to most elementary courses, is employed in Secs. 4.2-1 and 4.2-8 to introduce the principal vector operations. Refer to Sec. 8.1-5 for a discussion of vectors from a much more general point of view.

Vector analysis is the study of vector (and scalar) functions. Each vector may be specified by a set of numerical functions (*vector components*) in terms of a suitable reference system (Secs. 4.2-2, 4.2-3, and 4.4-1).

NOTE: The description of a physical situation in terms of vector quantities should not be regarded as merely a kind of shorthand summarizing sets of component equations by single equations, but as an instance of a mathematical model whose essential "building blocks" are not restricted to numbers.

4.2 VECTOR ALGEBRA

4.2-1 Vector Addition and Multiplication of Vectors by (Real) Scalars.

The operation (**vector addition**) of forming the **vector sum** $\mathbf{a} + \mathbf{b}$ of two euclidean vectors $\mathbf{a}$ and $\mathbf{b}$ of a suitable class produces a vector corresponding to the geometrical addition of the corresponding displacements (*parallelogram law*). The **product** of a euclidean vector $\mathbf{a}$ by a real number (**scalar**) α is a vector corresponding to a displacement α times as long as that corresponding to $\mathbf{a}$, with a reversal in direction if α is negative. The *null vector* $\mathbf{0}$ of each class of vectors corresponds to a displacement of length zero, and $\mathbf{a} + \mathbf{0} = \mathbf{a}$. With these geometrical definitions, vector addition and multiplication by scalars satisfy the relations

$$
\begin{aligned}
&\mathbf{a} + \mathbf{b} = \mathbf{b} + \mathbf{a} \\
&\mathbf{a} + (\mathbf{b} + \mathbf{c}) = (\mathbf{a} + \mathbf{b}) + \mathbf{c} = \mathbf{a} + \mathbf{b} + \mathbf{c} \\
&\alpha(\beta\mathbf{a}) = (\alpha\beta)\mathbf{a} \qquad (\alpha + \beta)\mathbf{a} = \alpha\mathbf{a} + \beta\mathbf{a} \\
&\alpha(\mathbf{a} + \mathbf{b}) = \alpha\mathbf{a} + \alpha\mathbf{b} \\
&(1)\mathbf{a} = \mathbf{a} \qquad (-1)\mathbf{a} = -\mathbf{a} \qquad (0)\mathbf{a} = \mathbf{0} \\
&\mathbf{a} - \mathbf{a} = \mathbf{0} \qquad \mathbf{a} + \mathbf{0} = \mathbf{a}
\end{aligned} \tag{4.2-1}
$$

4.2-2 Representation of Vectors in Terms of Base Vectors and Components.

m vectors $\mathbf{a}_1, \mathbf{a}_2, \ldots, \mathbf{a}_m$ are **linearly independent** if and only if $\lambda_1\mathbf{a}_1 + \lambda_2\mathbf{a}_2 + \cdots + \lambda_m\mathbf{a}_m = 0$ implies $\lambda_1 = \lambda_2 = \cdots = \lambda_m = 0$; otherwise the set of vectors is **linearly dependent.** Every vector $\mathbf{a}$ of a **three-dimensional vector space** can be represented as a sum

$$\mathbf{a} = \alpha_1\mathbf{e}_1 + \alpha_2\mathbf{e}_2 + \alpha_3\mathbf{e}_3 \tag{4.2-2}$$

in terms of three linearly independent vectors $\mathbf{e}_1$, $\mathbf{e}_2$, $\mathbf{e}_3$. The coefficients α_1, α_2, α_3 are the **components*** of the vector $\mathbf{a}$ with respect to the **reference system** defined by the **base vectors** $\mathbf{e}_1$, $\mathbf{e}_2$, $\mathbf{e}_3$. Given a suitable reference system, the vectors $\mathbf{a}$, $\mathbf{b}$, . . . are thus represented by the respective ordered sets $(\alpha_1, \alpha_2, \alpha_3)$, $(\beta_1, \beta_2, \beta_3)$, . . . of their components; note that $\mathbf{a} + \mathbf{b}$ and $\alpha\mathbf{a}$ are respectively represented by $(\alpha_1 + \beta_1, \alpha_2 + \beta_2, \alpha_3 + \beta_3)$ and $(\alpha\alpha_1, \alpha\alpha_2, \alpha\alpha_3)$. *Vector relations can, then, be expressed (represented) in terms of corresponding (sets of) relations between vector components.*

Vectors belonging to **two-dimensional vector spaces** (e.g., plane displacements) are similarly represented by sets of *two* components.

4.2-3 Rectangular Cartesian Components of a Vector. Given a right-handed rectangular cartesian coordinate system (Sec. 2.5-1) in the geometrical space, the unit vectors (Sec. 4.2-4) $\mathbf{i}$, $\mathbf{j}$, $\mathbf{k}$ respectively directed along the positive x axis, the positive y axis, and the positive z axis form a convenient system of base vectors at each point. The components a_x, a_y, a_z of a vector

$$\mathbf{a} = a_x\mathbf{i} + a_y\mathbf{j} + a_z\mathbf{k} \tag{4.2-3}$$

are the **(right-handed) rectangular cartesian components** of $\mathbf{a}$.

Note that
$$a_x = \mathbf{a} \cdot \mathbf{i} \qquad a_y = \mathbf{a} \cdot \mathbf{j} \qquad a_z = \mathbf{a} \cdot \mathbf{k}$$
(Sec. 4.2-6) are direction numbers of the vector $\mathbf{a}$; the components $\mathbf{u} \cdot \mathbf{i}$, $\mathbf{u} \cdot \mathbf{j}$, $\mathbf{u} \cdot \mathbf{k}$ of any *unit vector* $\mathbf{u}$ are its direction cosines (Sec. 2.5-4).

4.2-4 Absolute Value (Magnitude, Norm) of a Vector. The **absolute value (magnitude, norm)** $|\mathbf{a}|$ of a euclidean vector $\mathbf{a}$ is a scalar proportional to the length of the displacement corresponding to $\mathbf{a}$. Absolute values of vectors satisfy the relations (1.2-5). A vector of

* Some authors refer to the **component vectors** $\alpha_1\mathbf{e}_1$, $\alpha_2\mathbf{e}_2$, $\alpha_3\mathbf{e}_3$ as components.

magnitude 1 is a **unit vector.** The (mutually perpendicular) base vectors **i**, **j**, **k** are defined to be unit vectors, so that $|a_x\mathbf{i}| = |a_x|$, $|a_y\mathbf{j}| = |a_y|$, $|a_z\mathbf{k}| = |a_z|$, and

$$|\mathbf{a}| = \sqrt{a_x{}^2 + a_y{}^2 + a_z{}^2} \qquad (4.2\text{-}4)$$

4.2-5   Scalar Product (Dot Product, Inner Product) of Two Vectors.   The **scalar product (dot product, inner product) a · b** [alternative notation **(ab)**] of two euclidean vectors **a** and **b** is the scalar

$$\mathbf{a} \cdot \mathbf{b} = |\mathbf{a}|\,|\mathbf{b}|\cos\gamma \qquad (4.2\text{-}5)$$

where γ is the angle $\sphericalangle\mathbf{a}, \mathbf{b}$.   Table 4.2-1 summarizes the principal relations involving scalar products.   *Two nonzero vectors* **a** *and* **b** *are perpendicular to each other if and only if* **a · b** = 0.

Table 4.2-1   *Relations involving scalar products*

(a) **Basic Relations**

$\mathbf{a} \cdot \mathbf{b} = \mathbf{b} \cdot \mathbf{a}$ $\mathbf{a} \cdot (\mathbf{b} + \mathbf{c}) = \mathbf{a} \cdot \mathbf{b} + \mathbf{a} \cdot \mathbf{c}$ $(\alpha\mathbf{a}) \cdot \mathbf{b} = \alpha(\mathbf{a} \cdot \mathbf{b})$

$\mathbf{a} \cdot \mathbf{a} = \mathbf{a}^2 = |\mathbf{a}^2| \geq 0$ $|\mathbf{a} \cdot \mathbf{b}| \leq |\mathbf{a}|\,|\mathbf{b}|$ $\cos\gamma = \dfrac{\mathbf{a} \cdot \mathbf{b}}{\sqrt{\mathbf{a}^2\mathbf{b}^2}}$

(b) *In terms of rectangular cartesian components*

$\mathbf{i} \cdot \mathbf{i} = \mathbf{j} \cdot \mathbf{j} = \mathbf{k} \cdot \mathbf{k} = 1$ $\mathbf{i} \cdot \mathbf{j} = \mathbf{j} \cdot \mathbf{k} = \mathbf{k} \cdot \mathbf{i} = 0$

$\mathbf{a} \cdot \mathbf{b} = (a_x\mathbf{i} + a_y\mathbf{j} + a_z\mathbf{k}) \cdot (b_x\mathbf{i} + b_y\mathbf{j} + b_z\mathbf{k}) = a_xb_x + a_yb_y + a_zb_z$

$a_x = \mathbf{a} \cdot \mathbf{i}$ $a_y = \mathbf{a} \cdot \mathbf{j}$ $a_z = \mathbf{a} \cdot \mathbf{k}$

4.2-6   The Vector (Cross) Product (*Fig. 4.2-1*).   The **vector (cross) product a × b** (alternative notation **[ab]**) of two vectors **a** and **b** is the vector of magnitude

$$|\mathbf{a} \times \mathbf{b}| = |\mathbf{a}|\,|\mathbf{b}|\sin\gamma \qquad (4.2\text{-}6)$$

whose direction is perpendicular to both **a** and **b** and such that the axial motion of a right-handed screw turning **a** into **b** is in the direction of **a × b.**   *Two vectors are linearly dependent (Sec. 4.2-2) if and only if their vector product is zero.*   Table 4.2-2 summarizes the principal relations involving vector products.

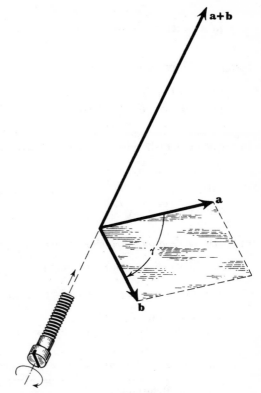

Fig. 4.2-1 The vector product **a** ✕ **b** is a vector perpendicular to the plane determined by **a** and **b** and directed in the direction of travel of a right-handed screw turning **a** into **b**. |**a** ✕ **b**| = |**a**| |**b**| sin γ equals the area of the parallelogram formed by **a** and **b**.

4.2-7   *The Scalar Triple Product (Box Product) (Fig. 4.2-2)*

$$
\begin{aligned}
\mathbf{a} \cdot (\mathbf{b} \times \mathbf{c}) &\equiv [\mathbf{abc}] = [\mathbf{bca}] = [\mathbf{cab}] \\
&= -[\mathbf{bac}] = -[\mathbf{cba}] = -[\mathbf{acb}] \quad\quad (4.2\text{-}7)
\end{aligned}
$$

$$
\begin{aligned}
[\mathbf{abc}]^2 &= [(\mathbf{a} \times \mathbf{b})(\mathbf{b} \times \mathbf{c})(\mathbf{c} \times \mathbf{a})] = a^2b^2c^2 - a^2(\mathbf{b} \cdot \mathbf{c})^2 \\
&\quad - b^2(\mathbf{a} \cdot \mathbf{c})^2 - c^2(\mathbf{a} \cdot \mathbf{b})^2 + 2(\mathbf{a} \cdot \mathbf{b})(\mathbf{b} \cdot \mathbf{c})(\mathbf{a} \cdot \mathbf{c}) \\[4pt]
&= \begin{vmatrix} \mathbf{a} \cdot \mathbf{a} & \mathbf{a} \cdot \mathbf{b} & \mathbf{a} \cdot \mathbf{c} \\ \mathbf{b} \cdot \mathbf{a} & \mathbf{b} \cdot \mathbf{b} & \mathbf{b} \cdot \mathbf{c} \\ \mathbf{c} \cdot \mathbf{a} & \mathbf{c} \cdot \mathbf{b} & \mathbf{c} \cdot \mathbf{c} \end{vmatrix} \quad \text{(GRAM'S DETERMINANT)} \quad (4.2\text{-}8)
\end{aligned}
$$

$$[abc][def] = \begin{vmatrix} a \cdot d & a \cdot e & a \cdot f \\ b \cdot d & b \cdot e & b \cdot f \\ c \cdot d & c \cdot e & c \cdot f \end{vmatrix} \tag{4.2-9}$$

In terms of any basis e_1, e_2, e_3

$$[abc] = \begin{vmatrix} \alpha_1 & \beta_1 & \gamma_1 \\ \alpha_2 & \beta_2 & \gamma_2 \\ \alpha_3 & \beta_3 & \gamma_3 \end{vmatrix} [e_1 e_2 e_3] \tag{4.2-10}$$

In terms of right-handed rectangular cartesian components

$$[abc] = \begin{vmatrix} a_x & b_x & c_x \\ a_y & b_y & c_y \\ a_z & b_z & c_z \end{vmatrix} \quad \begin{array}{l} (>0 \text{ if } \mathbf{a}, \mathbf{b}, \mathbf{c} \text{ are directed like} \\ \text{right-handed cartesian axes}) \end{array} \tag{4.2-11}$$

4.2-8   *Other Products Involving More than Two Vectors*

$$\mathbf{a} \times (\mathbf{b} \times \mathbf{c}) = (\mathbf{a} \cdot \mathbf{c})\mathbf{b} - (\mathbf{a} \cdot \mathbf{b})\mathbf{c} = \begin{vmatrix} \mathbf{b} & \mathbf{c} \\ \mathbf{a} \cdot \mathbf{b} & \mathbf{a} \cdot \mathbf{c} \end{vmatrix} \quad \begin{array}{c} \text{(VECTOR TRIPLE} \\ \text{PRODUCT)} \end{array} \tag{4.2-12}$$

$$(\mathbf{a} \times \mathbf{b}) \cdot (\mathbf{c} \times \mathbf{d}) = (\mathbf{a} \cdot \mathbf{c})(\mathbf{b} \cdot \mathbf{d}) - (\mathbf{a} \cdot \mathbf{d})(\mathbf{b} \cdot \mathbf{c}) = \begin{vmatrix} \mathbf{a} \cdot \mathbf{c} & \mathbf{b} \cdot \mathbf{c} \\ \mathbf{a} \cdot \mathbf{d} & \mathbf{b} \cdot \mathbf{d} \end{vmatrix} \tag{4.2-13}$$

$$(\mathbf{a} \times \mathbf{b})^2 = \mathbf{a}^2 \mathbf{b}^2 - (\mathbf{a} \cdot \mathbf{b})^2 \tag{4.2-14}$$

$$(\mathbf{a} \times \mathbf{b}) \times (\mathbf{c} \times \mathbf{d}) = [acd]\mathbf{b} - [bcd]\mathbf{a} = [abd]\mathbf{c} - [abc]\mathbf{d} \tag{4.2-15}$$

Table 4.2-2   *Relations involving vector (cross) products*

(a) **Basic Relations**

$\mathbf{a} \times \mathbf{b} = -(\mathbf{b} \times \mathbf{a})$

$\mathbf{a} \times \mathbf{a} = 0 \qquad \mathbf{a} \cdot (\mathbf{a} \times \mathbf{b}) = \mathbf{b} \cdot (\mathbf{a} \times \mathbf{b}) = 0$

$(\alpha \mathbf{a}) \times \mathbf{b} = \alpha(\mathbf{a} \times \mathbf{b}) \qquad \mathbf{a} \times (\mathbf{b} + \mathbf{c}) = \mathbf{a} \times \mathbf{b} + \mathbf{a} \times \mathbf{c}$

$[(\alpha + \beta)\mathbf{a}] \times \mathbf{b} = (\alpha + \beta)(\mathbf{a} \times \mathbf{b}) = \alpha(\mathbf{a} \times \mathbf{b}) + \beta(\mathbf{a} \times \mathbf{b})$

(b) *In terms of any basis* e_1, e_2, e_3

$\mathbf{a} = \alpha_1 e_1 + \alpha_2 e_2 + \alpha_3 e_3 \qquad \mathbf{b} = \beta_1 e_1 + \beta_2 e_2 + \beta_3 e_3$

$$\mathbf{a} \times \mathbf{b} = \begin{vmatrix} e_2 \times e_3 & \alpha_1 & \beta_1 \\ e_3 \times e_1 & \alpha_2 & \beta_2 \\ e_1 \times e_2 & \alpha_3 & \beta_3 \end{vmatrix}$$

(c) *In terms of right-handed rectangular cartesian components*

$\mathbf{i} \times \mathbf{i} = \mathbf{j} \times \mathbf{j} = \mathbf{k} \times \mathbf{k} = 0 \qquad \mathbf{i} \times \mathbf{j} = \mathbf{k} \qquad \mathbf{j} \times \mathbf{k} = \mathbf{i} \qquad \mathbf{k} \times \mathbf{i} = \mathbf{j}$

$$\mathbf{a} \times \mathbf{b} = \begin{vmatrix} \mathbf{i} & a_x & b_x \\ \mathbf{j} & a_y & b_y \\ \mathbf{k} & a_z & b_z \end{vmatrix} = \mathbf{i} \begin{vmatrix} a_y & a_z \\ b_y & b_z \end{vmatrix} + \mathbf{j} \begin{vmatrix} a_z & a_x \\ b_z & b_x \end{vmatrix} + \mathbf{k} \begin{vmatrix} a_x & a_y \\ b_x & b_y \end{vmatrix}$$

$$= \mathbf{i}(a_y b_z - a_z b_y) + \mathbf{j}(a_z b_x - a_x b_z) + \mathbf{k}(a_x b_y - a_y b_x)$$

4.3   VECTOR CALCULUS: FUNCTIONS OF A SCALAR PARAMETER

4.3-1   *Vector Functions and Limits.* A vector function $\mathbf{v} = \mathbf{v}(t)$ of a scalar parameter t associates one (single-valued function) or more (multiple-valued function) "values" of the vector $\mathbf{v}$ with every value of the scalar parameter t (independent variable) for which $\mathbf{v}(t)$ is defined (see also Sec. 3.2-1). In terms of rectangular cartesian components

$$\mathbf{v} = \mathbf{v}(t) = v_x(t)\mathbf{i} + v_y(t)\mathbf{j} + v_z(t)\mathbf{k} \tag{4.3-1}$$

A vector function $\mathbf{v}(t)$ is **bounded** if $|\mathbf{v}(t)|$ is bounded. $\mathbf{v}(t)$ has the **limit** (see also Sec. 3.4-1) $\mathbf{v}_1 = \lim_{t \to t_1} \mathbf{v}(t)$ if and only if for every positive number ϵ there exists a number $\delta > 0$ such that $|t - t_1| < \delta$ implies $|\mathbf{v}_1 - \mathbf{v}(t)| < \epsilon$. If $\lim_{t \to t_1} \mathbf{v}(t)$ exists,

$$\lim_{t \to t_1} \mathbf{v}(t) = [\mathbf{i} \lim_{t \to t_1} v_x(t) + \mathbf{j} \lim_{t \to t_1} v_y(t) + \mathbf{k} \lim_{t \to t_1} v_z(t)] \tag{4.3-2}$$

Formulas analogous to those of Sec. 3.4-2 (limits of sums, products, etc.) apply to vector sums, scalar products, and vector products. $\mathbf{v}(t)$ is **continuous** for $t = t_1$ if and only if $\lim_{t \to t_1} \mathbf{v}(t) = \mathbf{v}(t_1)$.

4.3-2   *Differentiation.* A vector function $\mathbf{v}(t)$ is **differentiable** for $t = t_1$ if and only if the **derivative**

$$\frac{d\mathbf{v}(t)}{dt} = \lim_{\Delta t \to 0} \frac{\mathbf{v}(t + \Delta t) - \mathbf{v}(t)}{\Delta t} \tag{4.3-3}$$

exists and is unique for $t = t_1$. If the derivative $d^2\mathbf{v}(t)/dt^2$ of $d\mathbf{v}(t)/dt$ exists, it is called the **second derivative** of $\mathbf{v}(t)$, and so forth. Table 4.3-1 summarizes the principal differentiation rules.

Analogous rules apply to the *partial derivatives* $\partial\mathbf{v}/\partial t_1 \equiv \mathbf{v}_{t_1}$, $\partial\mathbf{v}/\partial t_2 \equiv \mathbf{v}_{t_2}$, . . . of a vector function $\mathbf{v} = \mathbf{v}(t_1, t_2, . . .)$ of two or more scalar parameters $t_1, t_2, ...$

NOTE: If $\mathbf{u}(t)$ is a unit vector (of constant magnitude but variable direction) and $\mathbf{v}(t) = v(t)\mathbf{u}(t)$,

$$\frac{d\mathbf{u}}{dt} = \boldsymbol{\omega} \times \mathbf{u} \quad \text{and} \quad \frac{d\mathbf{v}}{dt} = \frac{dv}{dt}\mathbf{u} + v\frac{d\mathbf{u}}{dt} = \frac{dv}{dt}\mathbf{u} + \boldsymbol{\omega} \times \mathbf{v} \tag{4.3-4}$$

$\boldsymbol{\omega}$ is directed along the axis about which $\mathbf{u}(t)$ [and thus also $\mathbf{v}(t)$] turns as t varies, so that a right-handed screw turning with $\mathbf{u}(t)$ would be propelled in the direction of $\boldsymbol{\omega}$. Its magnitude is equal to the *angular rate of turn* of $\mathbf{u}(t)$ [and thus also of $\mathbf{v}(t)$]

Table 4.3-1   *Differentiation of vector functions with respect to a scalar parameter*

(a) **Basic Rules**

$$\frac{d}{dt}\left[\mathbf{v}(t) \pm \mathbf{w}(t)\right] = \frac{d\mathbf{v}}{dt} \pm \frac{d\mathbf{w}}{dt} \qquad \frac{d}{dt}\left[\alpha\mathbf{v}(t)\right] = \alpha\,\frac{d\mathbf{v}}{dt} \;(\alpha \text{ constant})$$

$$\frac{d}{dt}\left[f(t)\mathbf{v}(t)\right] = \frac{df}{dt}\mathbf{v} + f\frac{d\mathbf{v}}{dt} \qquad \frac{d}{dt}\left[\mathbf{v}(t)\cdot\mathbf{w}(t)\right] = \frac{d\mathbf{v}}{dt}\cdot\mathbf{w} + \frac{d\mathbf{w}}{dt}\cdot\mathbf{v}$$

$$\frac{d}{dt}\left[\mathbf{v}(t)\times\mathbf{w}(t)\right] = \frac{d\mathbf{v}}{dt}\times\mathbf{w} + \mathbf{v}\times\frac{d\mathbf{w}}{dt} \qquad \frac{d}{dt}\mathbf{v}[f(t)] = \frac{d\mathbf{v}}{df}\frac{df}{dt}$$

$$\frac{d}{dt}\left[\mathbf{v}(t)\mathbf{w}(t)\mathbf{u}(t)\right] = \left[\frac{d\mathbf{v}}{dt}\mathbf{w}\mathbf{u}\right] + \left[\mathbf{v}\frac{d\mathbf{w}}{dt}\mathbf{u}\right] + \left[\mathbf{v}\mathbf{w}\frac{d\mathbf{u}}{dt}\right]$$

(b) *In terms of rectangular cartesian components*

$$\frac{d\mathbf{v}(t)}{dt} = \frac{dv_x(t)}{dt}\mathbf{i} + \frac{dv_y(t)}{dt}\mathbf{j} + \frac{dv_z(t)}{dt}\mathbf{k}$$

(c) If the base vectors $\mathbf{e}_1(t)$, $\mathbf{e}_2(t)$, $\mathbf{e}_3(t)$ are functions of t, and $\mathbf{v}(t) = \alpha_1(t)\mathbf{e}_1(t) + \alpha_2(t)\mathbf{e}_2(t) + \alpha_3(t)\mathbf{e}_3(t)$, then

$$\frac{d\mathbf{v}(t)}{dt} = \left[\frac{d\alpha_1}{dt}\mathbf{e}_1 + \frac{d\alpha_2}{dt}\mathbf{e}_2 + \frac{d\alpha_3}{dt}\mathbf{e}_3\right] + \left[\alpha_1\frac{d\mathbf{e}_1}{dt} + \alpha_2\frac{d\mathbf{e}_2}{dt} + \alpha_3\frac{d\mathbf{e}_3}{dt}\right]$$

---

with respect to t (EXAMPLE: *angular-velocity vector* in physics).   *Equation* (4) *describes the separate contributions of changes in the magnitude and direction of* $\mathbf{v}(t)$.

4.4 SCALAR AND VECTOR FIELDS

4.4-1   Introduction.   The remainder of this chapter deals specifically with *scalar and vector functions of position in three-dimensional euclidean space.*   Unless the contrary is stated, the scalar and vector functions of position are assumed to be single-valued, continuous, and suitably differentiable functions of the coordinates, and thus of the position vector $\mathbf{r} \equiv x\mathbf{i} + y\mathbf{j} + k\mathbf{z}$.   In Secs. 4.4-2 to 4.6-2 relations involving scalar and vector functions are stated

1. In coordinate-free (invariant) form, and
2. In terms of vector components along *right-handed rectangular* cartesian coordinate axes (Sec. 4.2-3), so that*

$$\mathbf{F}(\mathbf{r}) \equiv \mathbf{F}(x, y, z) \equiv \mathbf{i}F_x(x, y, z) + \mathbf{j}F_y(x, y, z) + \mathbf{k}F_z(x, y, z)$$
$$(4.4\text{-}1)$$

---

* Throughout Chap. 4, the subscripts in F_x, F_y, F_z, . . . do *not* indicate differentiation with respect to x, y, z, . . . ; in fact, no scalar function $F(x, y, z)$ is introduced.

The relations to be described are independent of the coordinate system used to specify position in space. The representation of vector relations in terms of vector components along, or perpendicular to, suitable *curvilinear* coordinate lines (and thus along different directions at different points) is treated in Refs. 1 to 5.

4.4-2 Scalar Fields. A **scalar field** is a **scalar function of position (scalar point function)** $\Phi(\mathbf{r}) \equiv \Phi(x, y, z)$ together with its region of definition. The surfaces

$$\Phi(\mathbf{r}) \equiv \Phi(x, y, z) = \text{constant} \qquad (4.4\text{-}2)$$

are called **level surfaces** of the field and permit its geometrical representation.

4.4-3 Vector Fields. A **vector field** is a **vector function of position (vector point function)** $\mathbf{F}(\mathbf{r}) \equiv F(x, y, z)$ together with its region of definition. The **field lines (streamlines)** of the vector field defined by $\mathbf{F}(\mathbf{r})$ have the direction of the field vector $\mathbf{F}(\mathbf{r})$ at each point $(\mathbf{r})$ and are specified by the differential equations

$$d\mathbf{r} \times \mathbf{F}(\mathbf{r}) = 0 \qquad \text{or} \qquad dx : dy : dz = F_x : F_y : F_z \qquad (4.4\text{-}3)$$

A vector field may be represented geometrically by its field lines, with the relative density of the field lines at each point $(\mathbf{r})$ proportional to the absolute value $|\mathbf{F}(\mathbf{r})|$ of the field vector.

4.4-4 Vector Path Element and Arc Length (*see also Sec. 3.6-7*). (*a*) The **vector path element (vector element of distance)** $d\mathbf{r}$ along a curve C described by

$$\mathbf{r} = \mathbf{r}(t) \qquad \text{or} \qquad x = x(t) \qquad y = y(t) \qquad z = z(t) \qquad (4.4\text{-}4)$$

is defined at every point $(\mathbf{r}) \equiv [x(t), y(t), z(t)]$ where C has a unique tangent:

$$d\mathbf{r} = \mathbf{i}\, dx + \mathbf{j}\, dy + \mathbf{k}\, dz = \left(\mathbf{i} \frac{dx}{dt} + \mathbf{j} \frac{dy}{dt} + \mathbf{k} \frac{dz}{dt} \right) dt = \frac{d\mathbf{r}(t)}{dt}\, dt$$

$$(4.4\text{-}5)$$

$d\mathbf{r}$ is directed along the tangent to C at $(\mathbf{r})$.

(*b*) The arc length s on a rectifiable curve (4) (Sec. 3.6-7) is given by

$$s = \int_{t_{0_C}}^{t} ds$$

with

$$
\begin{aligned}
ds &= \sqrt{dx^2 + dy^2 + dz^2} \\
&= \sqrt{\left(\frac{dx}{dt}\right)^2 + \left(\frac{dy}{dt}\right)^2 + \left(\frac{dz}{dt}\right)^2}\, dt = \frac{ds}{dt}\, dt \\
&= \sqrt{d\mathbf{r} \cdot d\mathbf{r}} = \sqrt{\frac{d\mathbf{r}}{dt} \cdot \frac{d\mathbf{r}}{dt}}\, dt
\end{aligned}
\tag{4.4-6}
$$

at each regular point $(\mathbf{r}) \equiv [x(t),\, y(t),\, z(t)]$ of the curve

The sign of ds is assigned arbitrarily, e.g., so that $ds/dt > 0$.

4.4-5 Line Integrals *(see also Sec. 3.6-8).* Given a rectifiable arc C represented by Eq. (4), the scalar line integrals

$$\int_C \Phi(\mathbf{r})\, ds = \int_C \Phi(x,\, y,\, z)\, ds = \int_C \Phi[x(t),\, y(t),\, z(t)]\, \frac{ds}{dt}\, dt$$

$$
\begin{aligned}
\int_C d\mathbf{r} \cdot \mathbf{F}(\mathbf{r}) &= \int_C \frac{d\mathbf{r}}{dt} \cdot \mathbf{F}(\mathbf{r})\, dt \\
&= \int_C [F_x(x,\, y,\, z)\, dx + F_y(x,\, y,\, z)\, dy \\
&\qquad\qquad\qquad + F_z(x,\, y,\, z)\, dz] \\
&= \int_C \left(F_x \frac{dx}{dt} + F_y \frac{dy}{dt} + F_z \frac{dz}{dt} \right) dt
\end{aligned}
\tag{4.4-7}
$$

can be defined directly as limits of sums in the manner of Sec. 3.6-8; it is, however, more convenient to substitute the functions $x(t)$, $y(t)$, $z(t)$, dx/dt, dy/dt, and dz/dt obtained from Eq. (4) into Eq. (7) and to integrate over t.

Unless special conditions are satisfied (Sec. 4.6-3), the value of a scalar or vector line integral depends on the path of integration C.

4.4-6 Surface Integrals. (a) At each regular point of a two-sided surface represented by $\mathbf{r} = \mathbf{r}(u, v)$ (Sec. 2.5-7), it is possible to define a **vector element of area**

$$dA = \left(\frac{\partial \mathbf{r}}{\partial u} \times \frac{\partial \mathbf{r}}{\partial v} \right) du \, dv = \left[\mathbf{i} \left(\frac{\partial y}{\partial u} \frac{\partial z}{\partial v} - \frac{\partial z}{\partial u} \frac{\partial y}{\partial v} \right) \right.$$

$$\left. + \mathbf{j} \left(\frac{\partial z}{\partial u} \frac{\partial x}{\partial v} - \frac{\partial x}{\partial u} \frac{\partial z}{\partial v} \right) + \mathbf{k} \left(\frac{\partial x}{\partial u} \frac{\partial y}{\partial v} - \frac{\partial y}{\partial u} \frac{\partial x}{\partial v} \right) \right] du \, dv \qquad (4.4\text{-}8)$$

at each surface point (u, v). In the case of a closed surface, the sense and order of the surface coordinates u, v are customarily chosen so that the direction of $d\mathbf{A}$ (direction of the positive surface normal) is *outward from the bounded volume*.

The **scalar element of area** at the surface point (u, v) is defined as

$$dA = \pm |d\mathbf{A}| = \pm \left| \frac{\partial \mathbf{r}}{\partial u} \times \frac{\partial \mathbf{r}}{\partial v} \right| du \, dv = \sqrt{a(u, v)} \, du \, dv \qquad (4.4\text{-}9)$$

The sign of dA may be arbitrarily assigned.

In particular, for $u = x$, $v = y$, $z = z(x, y)$,

$$dA = \left(-\mathbf{i} \frac{\partial z}{\partial x} - \mathbf{j} \frac{\partial z}{\partial y} + \mathbf{k} \right) dx \, dy$$

$$dA = \pm |d\mathbf{A}| = \sqrt{1 + \left(\frac{\partial z}{\partial x} \right)^2 + \left(\frac{\partial z}{\partial y} \right)^2} \, dx \, dy \qquad (4.4\text{-}10)$$

(b) In the following it will be assumed that the area $\int_S |d\mathbf{A}|$ of each surface region S under consideration exists. The scalar surface integrals

$$\int_S |d\mathbf{A}| \Phi(\mathbf{r}) \qquad \text{and} \qquad \int_S d\mathbf{A} \cdot \mathbf{F}(\mathbf{r}) \qquad (4.4\text{-}11)$$

and the vector surface integrals

$$\int_S d\mathbf{A} \, \Phi(\mathbf{r}) \qquad \text{and} \qquad \int_S d\mathbf{A} \times \mathbf{F}(\mathbf{r}) \qquad (4.4\text{-}12)$$

of suitable field functions $\Phi(\mathbf{r})$ and $\mathbf{F}(\mathbf{r})$ may then be defined directly as limits of sums in the manner of Sec. 3.6-1.

4.4-7 Volume Integrals (*see also Sec. 3.6-6*). Given a simply connected region V of three-dimensional euclidean space, the scalar volume integral

$$\int_V \Phi(\mathbf{r}) \, dV = \iiint_V \Phi(x, y, z) \, dx \, dy \, dz \qquad (4.4\text{-}13)$$

and the vector volume integral

$$\int_V \mathbf{F}(\mathbf{r}) \, dV = \iiint_V [\mathbf{i}F_x(x, y, z) + \mathbf{j}F_y(x, y, z)$$
$$+ \mathbf{k}F_z(x, y, z)] \, dx \, dy \, dz \qquad (4.4\text{-}14)$$

may be defined as limits of sums in the manner of Sec. 3.6-1, or they may be expressed directly in terms of triple integrals over x, y, and z.

4.5 DIFFERENTIAL OPERATORS

4.5-1 Gradient, Divergence, and Curl: Coordinate-free Definitions in Terms of Integrals.

The **gradient** grad $\Phi(\mathbf{r}) \equiv \nabla\Phi$ of a scalar point function $\Phi(\mathbf{r}) \equiv \Phi(x, y, z)$ is a vector point function defined at each point $(\mathbf{r}) \equiv (x, y, z)$ where $\Phi(\mathbf{r})$ is suitably differentiable. In coordinate-free form,

$$\text{grad } \Phi(\mathbf{r}) \equiv \nabla\Phi = \lim_{\delta \to 0} \frac{\int_{S_1} d\mathbf{A} \, \Phi(\varrho)}{\int_{V_1} dV} \qquad (4.5\text{-}1)$$

where V_1 is a region containing the point $(\mathbf{r})$ and bounded by a closed surface S_1 such that the greatest distance between the point $(\mathbf{r})$ and any point of S_1 is less than $\delta > 0$.

Given a suitably differentiable vector point function $\mathbf{F}(\mathbf{r}) \equiv \mathbf{F}(x, y, z)$, it is similarly possible to define a scalar point function, the **divergence** of $\mathbf{F}(\mathbf{r})$ at the point $\mathbf{r}$,

$$\text{div } \mathbf{F}(\mathbf{r}) \equiv \nabla \cdot \mathbf{F} = \lim_{\delta \to 0} \frac{\int_{S_1} d\mathbf{A} \cdot \mathbf{F}(\varrho)}{\int_{V_1} dV} \qquad (4.5\text{-}2)$$

and a vector point function, the **curl** (rotational) of $\mathbf{F}(\mathbf{r})$ at the point $\mathbf{r}$,

$$\text{curl } \mathbf{F}(\mathbf{r}) \equiv \nabla \times \mathbf{F} = \lim_{\delta \to 0} \frac{\int_{S_1} d\mathbf{A} \times \mathbf{F}(\varrho)}{\int_{V_1} dV} \qquad (4.5\text{-}3)$$

NOTE: At each point where the vector grad $\Phi \equiv \nabla\Phi$ exists, it has the magnitude

$$|\nabla\Phi| = \sqrt{\left(\frac{\partial\Phi}{\partial x}\right)^2 + \left(\frac{\partial\Phi}{\partial y}\right)^2 + \left(\frac{\partial\Phi}{\partial z}\right)^2} \qquad (4.5\text{-}4)$$

of, as well as the direction associated with, the greatest directional derivative $d\Phi/ds$ (Sec. 4.5-3c) at that point. $\nabla\Phi$ defines a vector field whose field lines are specified by the differential equations

$$d\mathbf{r} \times (\nabla\Phi) = 0 \quad \text{or} \quad dx:dy:dz = \frac{\partial\Phi}{\partial x}:\frac{\partial\Phi}{\partial y}:\frac{\partial\Phi}{\partial z} \tag{4.5-5}$$

The **gradient lines** defined by Eq. (5) intersect the level surfaces (4.4-2) perpendicularly.

4.5-2 The Operator ∇. In terms of rectangular cartesian coordinates, the linear operator ∇ (**del or nabla**) is defined by

$$\nabla \equiv \mathbf{i}\frac{\partial}{\partial x} + \mathbf{j}\frac{\partial}{\partial y} + \mathbf{k}\frac{\partial}{\partial z} \tag{4.5-6}$$

Its application to a scalar point function $\Phi(\mathbf{r})$ or a vector point function $\mathbf{F}(\mathbf{r})$ corresponds formally to a noncommutative multiplication operation with a vector having the rectangular cartesian "components" $\partial/\partial x$, $\partial/\partial y$, $\partial/\partial z$; thus, in terms of right-handed rectangular cartesian coordinates x, y, z,

$$\nabla\Phi(x, y, z) \equiv \text{grad } \Phi(x, y, z) \equiv \mathbf{i}\frac{\partial\Phi}{\partial x} + \mathbf{j}\frac{\partial\Phi}{\partial y} + \mathbf{k}\frac{\partial\Phi}{\partial z}$$

$$\nabla \cdot \mathbf{F}(x, y, z) \equiv \text{div } \mathbf{F}(x, y, z) \equiv \frac{\partial F_x}{\partial x} + \frac{\partial F_y}{\partial y} + \frac{\partial F_z}{\partial z}$$

$$\nabla \times \mathbf{F}(x, y, z) \equiv \text{curl } \mathbf{F}(x, y, z)$$

$$\equiv \mathbf{i}\left(\frac{\partial F_z}{\partial y} - \frac{\partial F_y}{\partial z}\right) + \mathbf{j}\left(\frac{\partial F_x}{\partial z} - \frac{\partial F_z}{\partial x}\right)$$

$$+ \mathbf{k}\left(\frac{\partial F_y}{\partial x} - \frac{\partial F_x}{\partial y}\right) \tag{4.5-7}$$

$$\equiv \begin{vmatrix} \mathbf{i} & \dfrac{\partial}{\partial x} & F_x \\ \mathbf{j} & \dfrac{\partial}{\partial y} & F_y \\ \mathbf{k} & \dfrac{\partial}{\partial z} & F_z \end{vmatrix}$$

$$(\mathbf{G} \cdot \nabla)\mathbf{F} \equiv G_x\frac{\partial\mathbf{F}}{\partial x} + G_y\frac{\partial\mathbf{F}}{\partial y} + G_z\frac{\partial\mathbf{F}}{\partial z}$$

$$\equiv \mathbf{i}(\mathbf{G} \cdot \nabla F_x) + \mathbf{j}(\mathbf{G} \cdot \nabla F_y) + \mathbf{k}(\mathbf{G} \cdot \nabla F_z)$$

Table 4.5-1 summarizes a number of rules for operations with the operator ∇.

Table 4.5-1   Rules for operations involving the operator ∇

(a) Linearity

$$\nabla(\Phi + \Psi) = \nabla\Phi + \nabla\Psi \qquad\qquad \nabla(\alpha\Phi) = \alpha\nabla\Phi$$
$$\nabla \cdot (\mathbf{F} + \mathbf{G}) = \nabla \cdot \mathbf{F} + \nabla \cdot \mathbf{G} \qquad\qquad \nabla \cdot (\alpha\mathbf{F}) = \alpha\nabla \cdot \mathbf{F}$$
$$\nabla \times (\mathbf{F} + \mathbf{G}) = \nabla \times \mathbf{F} + \nabla \times \mathbf{G} \qquad \nabla \times (\alpha\mathbf{F}) = \alpha\nabla \times \mathbf{F}$$

(b) Operations on Products

$$\nabla(\Phi\Psi) = \Psi\nabla\Phi + \Phi\nabla\Psi$$
$$\nabla(\mathbf{F} \cdot \mathbf{G}) = (\mathbf{F} \cdot \nabla)\mathbf{G} + (\mathbf{G} \cdot \nabla)\mathbf{F} + \mathbf{F} \times (\nabla \times \mathbf{G}) + \mathbf{G} \times (\nabla \times \mathbf{F})$$
$$\nabla \cdot (\Phi\mathbf{F}) = \Phi\nabla \cdot \mathbf{F} + (\nabla\Phi) \cdot \mathbf{F}$$
$$\nabla \cdot (\mathbf{F} \times \mathbf{G}) = \mathbf{G} \cdot \nabla \times \mathbf{F} - \mathbf{F} \cdot \nabla \times \mathbf{G}$$
$$(\mathbf{G} \cdot \nabla)\Phi\mathbf{F} = \mathbf{F}(\mathbf{G} \cdot \nabla\Phi) + \Phi(\mathbf{G} \cdot \nabla)\mathbf{F}$$
$$\nabla \times (\Phi\mathbf{F}) = \Phi\nabla \times \mathbf{F} + (\nabla\Phi) \times \mathbf{F}$$
$$\nabla \times (\mathbf{F} \times \mathbf{G}) = (\mathbf{G} \cdot \nabla)\mathbf{F} - (\mathbf{F} \cdot \nabla)\mathbf{G} + \mathbf{F}(\nabla \cdot \mathbf{G}) - \mathbf{G}(\nabla \cdot \mathbf{F})$$
$$(\mathbf{G} \cdot \nabla)\mathbf{F} = \tfrac{1}{2}[\nabla \times (\mathbf{F} \times \mathbf{G}) + \nabla(\mathbf{F} \cdot \mathbf{G}) - \mathbf{F}(\nabla \cdot \mathbf{G}) + \mathbf{G}(\nabla \cdot \mathbf{F})$$
$$- \mathbf{F} \times (\nabla \times \mathbf{G}) - \mathbf{G} \times (\nabla \times \mathbf{F})]$$

Note that vector equations involving $\nabla\Phi$, $\nabla \cdot \mathbf{F}$, and/or $\nabla \times \mathbf{F}$ have a meaning independent of the coordinate system used.

4.5-3   Absolute Differential, Intrinsic Derivative, and Directional Derivative.

(*a*) The change (**absolute differential**) $d\Phi$ of a scalar point function $\Phi(\mathbf{r})$ associated with a change $d\mathbf{r} \equiv \mathbf{i}\, dx + \mathbf{j}\, dy + \mathbf{k}\, dz$ in position is

$$d\Phi = \frac{\partial\Phi}{\partial x}\, dx + \frac{\partial\Phi}{\partial y}\, dy + \frac{\partial\Phi}{\partial z}\, dz = d\mathbf{r} \cdot \text{grad }\Phi = (d\mathbf{r} \cdot \nabla)\Phi$$

$$(4.5\text{-}8)$$

(*b*) The **intrinsic (absolute) derivative** (see also Table 3.5-2*a*) $d\Phi/dt$ of $\Phi(\mathbf{r})$ along the curve $\mathbf{r} = \mathbf{r}(t)$ is, at each point $(\mathbf{r})$ of the curve, the rate of change of $\Phi(\mathbf{r})$ with respect to the parameter t as $\mathbf{r}$ varies as a function of t:

$$\frac{d\Phi}{dt} = \left(\frac{d\mathbf{r}}{dt} \cdot \nabla\right)\Phi = \frac{dx}{dt}\frac{\partial\Phi}{\partial x} + \frac{dy}{dt}\frac{\partial\Phi}{\partial y} + \frac{dz}{dt}\frac{\partial\Phi}{\partial z}$$

with

$$\mathbf{r} = \mathbf{r}(t) \quad \text{or} \quad x = x(t) \quad y = y(t) \quad z = z(t)$$

$$(4.5\text{-}9)$$

NOTE: If Φ depends explicitly on t [$\Phi = \Phi(\mathbf{r}, t)$], then

$$\frac{d\Phi}{dt} = \left(\frac{d\mathbf{r}}{dt} \cdot \nabla\right)\Phi + \frac{\partial\Phi}{\partial t}$$

$$(4.5\text{-}10)$$

(*c*) The **directional derivative** $d\Phi/ds$ of $\Phi(\mathbf{r})$ at the point $(\mathbf{r})$ is the rate of change of $\Phi(\mathbf{r})$ with the distance s from the point $(\mathbf{r})$ as a function of direction. The directional derivative of $\Phi(\mathbf{r})$ in the direction of the unit vector $\mathbf{u} \equiv \mathbf{i} \cos \alpha_x + \mathbf{j} \cos \alpha_y + \mathbf{k} \cos \alpha_z$ defined by the direction cosines (Sec. 2.5-4) $\cos \alpha_x$, $\cos \alpha_y$, $\cos \alpha_z$ is

$$\frac{d\Phi}{ds} = \cos \alpha_x \frac{\partial \Phi}{\partial x} + \cos \alpha_y \frac{\partial \Phi}{\partial y} + \cos \alpha_z \frac{\partial \Phi}{\partial z} = (\mathbf{u} \cdot \mathbf{\nabla})\Phi$$

$$(4.5\text{-}11)$$

$d\Phi/ds$ is the intrinsic derivative of $\Phi(\mathbf{r})$ with respect to the path length s along a curve directed along $\mathbf{u} = d\mathbf{r}/ds$.

(*d*) The absolute differential, intrinsic derivative, and directional derivative of a vector point function $\mathbf{F}(\mathbf{r})$ are defined in a manner analogous to that for a scalar point function. Thus

$$dF = (d\mathbf{r} \cdot \mathbf{\nabla})F = [\mathbf{i}(d\mathbf{r} \cdot \mathbf{\nabla})F_x + \mathbf{j}(d\mathbf{r} \cdot \mathbf{\nabla})F_y + \mathbf{k}(d\mathbf{r} \cdot \mathbf{\nabla})F_z]$$
$$= [\mathbf{i}\, dF_x + \mathbf{j}\, dF_y + \mathbf{k}\, dF_z] \qquad (4.5\text{-}12)$$

4.5-4   The Laplacian Operator. The **Laplacian operator** $\mathbf{\nabla}^2 \equiv (\mathbf{\nabla} \cdot \mathbf{\nabla})$ (sometimes denoted by Δ), expressed in terms of rectangular cartesian coordinates by

$$\mathbf{\nabla}^2 \equiv (\mathbf{\nabla} \cdot \mathbf{\nabla}) \equiv \left(\frac{\partial^2}{\partial x^2} + \frac{\partial^2}{\partial y^2} + \frac{\partial^2}{\partial z^2}\right) \qquad (4.5\text{-}13)$$

may be applied to both scalar and vector point functions by non-commutative scalar "multiplication," so that

$$\mathbf{\nabla}^2\Phi \equiv \left(\frac{\partial^2}{\partial x^2} + \frac{\partial^2}{\partial y^2} + \frac{\partial^2}{\partial z^2}\right)\Phi$$

$$\mathbf{\nabla}^2\mathbf{F} \equiv (\mathbf{i}\mathbf{\nabla}^2 F_x + \mathbf{j}\mathbf{\nabla}^2 F_y + \mathbf{k}\mathbf{\nabla}^2 F_z)$$

$$(4.5\text{-}14)$$

Note

$$\mathbf{\nabla}^2(\alpha\Phi + \beta\Psi) = \alpha\mathbf{\nabla}^2\Phi + \beta\mathbf{\nabla}^2\Psi \qquad \text{(LINEARITY)} \qquad (4.5\text{-}15)$$
$$\text{and} \quad \mathbf{\nabla}^2(\Phi\Psi) = \Psi\mathbf{\nabla}^2\Phi + 2(\mathbf{\nabla}\Phi) \cdot (\mathbf{\nabla}\Psi) + \Phi\mathbf{\nabla}^2\Psi \qquad (4.5\text{-}16)$$

4.5-5   Repeated Operations. Note the following rules for repeated operations with the operator $\mathbf{\nabla}$:

$$\text{div grad } \Phi = \nabla \cdot (\nabla\Phi) = \nabla^2\Phi$$
$$\text{grad div } \mathbf{F} = \nabla(\nabla \cdot \mathbf{F}) = \nabla^2\mathbf{F} + \nabla \times (\nabla \times \mathbf{F})$$
$$\text{curl curl } \mathbf{F} = \nabla \times (\nabla \times \mathbf{F}) = \nabla(\nabla \cdot \mathbf{F}) - \nabla^2\mathbf{F} \qquad (4.5\text{-}17)$$
$$\text{curl grad } \Phi = \nabla \times (\nabla\Phi) = 0$$
$$\text{div curl } \mathbf{F} = \nabla \cdot (\nabla \times \mathbf{F}) = 0$$

4.5-6 Operations on Special Functions. A number of results of differential operations on scalar and vector functions of the position vector $\mathbf{r} \equiv (x, y, z)$ are tabulated in Tables 4.5-2 and 4.5-3, respectively. Additional formulas may be derived with the aid of Table 4.5-1. Note also

$$[\mathbf{F}(\mathbf{r}) \cdot \nabla]\mathbf{r} = \mathbf{F}(\mathbf{r}) \qquad (4.5\text{-}18)$$

$$\nabla \frac{\mathbf{a} \cdot \mathbf{r}}{r^3} = -\nabla \times \frac{\mathbf{a} \times \mathbf{r}}{r^3} \qquad (4.5\text{-}19)$$

where $\mathbf{a}$ is a constant vector.

Table 4.5-2 Operations on scalar functions $(r \equiv |\mathbf{r}|;\ \mathbf{a}$ *is a constant vector;* $n = 0, \pm 1, \pm 2, \ldots)$

Φ	$\nabla\Phi$	$\nabla^2\Phi$
$\mathbf{a} \cdot \mathbf{r}$	$\mathbf{a}$	0
r^n	$nr^{n-2}\mathbf{r}$	$n(n+1)r^{n-2}$
$\log_e r$	$\mathbf{r}/r^2$	$1/r^2$

Table 4.5-3 Operations on vector point functions $(r \equiv |\mathbf{r}|;\ \mathbf{a}$ *is a constant vector;* $n = 0, \pm 1, \pm 2, \ldots)$

$\mathbf{F}$	$\nabla \cdot \mathbf{F}$	$\nabla \times \mathbf{F}$	$(\mathbf{G} \cdot \nabla)\mathbf{F}$	$\nabla^2\mathbf{F}$	$\nabla\nabla \cdot \mathbf{F}$
$\mathbf{r}$	3	0	$\mathbf{G}$	0	0
$\mathbf{a} \times \mathbf{r}$	0	$2\mathbf{a}$	$\mathbf{a} \times \mathbf{G}$	0	0
$\mathbf{a}r^n$	$nr^{n-2}(\mathbf{r} \cdot \mathbf{a})$	$nr^{n-2}(\mathbf{r} \times \mathbf{a})$	$nr^{n-2}(\mathbf{r} \cdot \mathbf{G})\mathbf{a}$	$n(n+1)r^{n-2}\mathbf{a}$	$nr^{n-2}\mathbf{a} + n(n-2)r^{n-4}(\mathbf{r} \cdot \mathbf{a})\mathbf{r}$
$\mathbf{r}r^n$	$(n+3)r^n$	0	$r^n\mathbf{G} + nr^{n-2}(\mathbf{r} \cdot \mathbf{G})\mathbf{r}$	$n(n+3)r^{n-2}\mathbf{r}$	$n(n+3)r^{n-2}\mathbf{r}$
$\mathbf{a}\log_e r$	$\mathbf{r} \cdot \mathbf{a}/r^2$	$\mathbf{r} \times \mathbf{a}/r^2$	$\dfrac{(\mathbf{G} \cdot \mathbf{r})\mathbf{a}}{r^2}$	$\dfrac{\mathbf{a}}{r^2}$	$\dfrac{\mathbf{a}}{r^2} - \dfrac{2(\mathbf{r} \cdot \mathbf{a})\mathbf{r}}{r^4}$

4.6 INTEGRAL THEOREMS

4.6-1 The Divergence Theorem and Related Theorems. (a)
Table 4.6-1 summarizes a number of important theorems relating volume integrals over a region V to surface integrals over the boundary surface S of the region V. In the formulas of Table 4.6-1, volume integrals are taken over a bounded, simply connected open region V bounded by a (two-sided) regular closed surface S (Sec. 2.5-8). All functions are

Table 4.6-1 Theorems relating volume integrals and surface integrals (see also Sec. 4.6-1)

	Theorem	Vector formulas	Sufficient conditions* (a) Throughout V	(b) On S
1	**Divergence theorem** (Gauss' integral theorem)	$\int_V \nabla \cdot \mathbf{F}(\mathbf{r})\, dV = \int_S d\mathbf{A} \cdot \mathbf{F}(\mathbf{r})$	$\mathbf{F}(\mathbf{r})$, $\Phi(\mathbf{r})$ differentiable with continuous partial derivatives	Existence of integrals is sufficient
2	Theorem of the rotational	$\int_V \nabla \times \mathbf{F}(\mathbf{r})\, dV = \int_S d\mathbf{A} \times \mathbf{F}(\mathbf{r})$		
3	Theorem of the gradient	$\int_V \nabla\Phi(\mathbf{r})\, dV = \int_S d\mathbf{A}\,\Phi(\mathbf{r})$		
4	**Green's theorems**	$\int_V \nabla\Phi \cdot \nabla\Psi\, dV + \int_V \Psi\nabla^2\Phi\, dV$ $= \int_S d\mathbf{A} \cdot (\Psi\nabla\Phi)$ $= \int_S \Psi \frac{\partial\Phi}{\partial n}\, dA$	$\Phi(\mathbf{r})$, $\Psi(\mathbf{r})$ differentiable with continuous partial derivatives; $\Phi(\mathbf{r})$ twice differentiable with continuous second partial derivatives	$\Psi(\mathbf{r})$ continuous; $\Phi(\mathbf{r})$ differentiable with continuous partial derivatives
5		$\int_V (\Psi\nabla^2\Phi - \Phi\nabla^2\Psi)\, dV$ $= \int_S d\mathbf{A} \cdot (\Psi\nabla\Phi - \Phi\nabla\Psi)$ $= \int_S \left(\Psi \frac{\partial\Phi}{\partial n} - \Phi \frac{\partial\Psi}{\partial n} \right) dA$	$\Phi(\mathbf{r})$, $\Psi(\mathbf{r})$ twice differentiable with continuous second partial derivatives	$\Phi(\mathbf{r})$, $\Psi(\mathbf{r})$ differentiable with continuous partial derivatives
6	Special cases	$\int_V \nabla^2\Phi\, dV = \int_S d\mathbf{A} \cdot \nabla\Phi$ $= \int_S \frac{\partial\Phi}{\partial n}\, dA$ **(Gauss' Theorem)**		
7		$\int_V \lvert\nabla\Phi\rvert^2\, dV + \int_V \Phi\nabla^2\Phi\, dV$ $= \int_S d\mathbf{A} \cdot (\Phi\nabla\Phi) = \int_S \Phi \frac{\partial\Phi}{\partial n}\, dA$		

* Less stringent conditions are discussed in Ref. 3.

assumed to be single-valued throughout V and on S. *The existence of the (proper or improper) volume integrals is assumed. All theorems hold for unbounded regions V as well as for bounded regions if the ratio of absolute value of each surface-integral integrand to r^3 is bounded as $r \to \infty$.*

(b) NORMAL-DERIVATIVE NOTATION. The **normal derivative** of a scalar function $\Phi(\mathbf{r})$ at a regular point of the surface S is the directional derivative of $\Phi(\mathbf{r})$ in the direction of the positive normal (usually the outward normal), and thus in the direction of the vector $d\mathbf{A}$. The normal derivative is customarily denoted by $\partial\Phi/\partial n$, so that

$$\frac{\partial \Phi}{\partial n}\, dA \equiv (d\mathbf{A} \cdot \boldsymbol{\nabla})\Phi$$

4.6-2   Stokes' Theorem and Related Theorems. Given a vector function $\mathbf{F}(\mathbf{r})$ single-valued and differentiable with continuous partial derivatives throughout a finite region V containing a simply connected regular (one-sided) surface segment S bounded by a regular closed curve C,

$$\int_S d\mathbf{A} \cdot [\boldsymbol{\nabla} \times \mathbf{F}(\mathbf{r})] = \oint_C d\mathbf{r} \cdot \mathbf{F}(\mathbf{r}) \quad \text{(STOKES' THEOREM)}$$

$$(4.6\text{-}1)$$

i.e., the line integral of $\mathbf{F}(\mathbf{r})$ around C equals the flux of $\boldsymbol{\nabla} \times \mathbf{F}$ through the surface bounded by C.

Equation (1) applies to unbounded regions V if the integrands of the line integrals on the right are $O(1/r^2)$ in absolute value as $r \to \infty$ (Sec. 3.4-3).

4.6-3   Irrotational Vector Fields. A vector point function $\mathbf{F}(r)$ (as well as the field described by it) is called **irrotational** (**lamellar**) throughout a region V if and only if, for every point of V,

$$\begin{aligned} &\boldsymbol{\nabla} \times \mathbf{F}(\mathbf{r}) = 0 \\ \text{or}\quad &\frac{\partial F_y}{\partial z} - \frac{\partial F_z}{\partial y} = \frac{\partial F_z}{\partial x} - \frac{\partial F_x}{\partial z} = \frac{\partial F_x}{\partial y} - \frac{\partial F_y}{\partial x} = 0 \end{aligned}$$

$$(4.6\text{-}2)$$

This is true if and only if $-\mathbf{F}(\mathbf{r})$ is the gradient $\boldsymbol{\nabla}\Phi(\mathbf{r})$ of a scalar point function $\Phi(\mathbf{r})$ at every point of V [see also Eqs. (4.5-17)]; in this case

$$\begin{aligned} d\mathbf{r} \cdot \mathbf{F}(\mathbf{r}) &\equiv F_x(x, y, z)\, dx + F_y(x, y, z)\, dy + F_z(x, y, z)\, dz \\ &\equiv -d\mathbf{r} \cdot \boldsymbol{\nabla}\Phi(\mathbf{r}) \equiv -d\Phi \end{aligned}$$

$$(4.6\text{-}3)$$

is an exact differential (Sec. 3.3-6). $\Phi(\mathbf{r})$ is often called the **scalar potential** of the irrotational vector field.

If V is simply connected (Sec. 3.3-6), $\Phi(\mathbf{r})$ is a single-valued function uniquely determined by $\mathbf{F}(\mathbf{r})$ except for an additive constant, and the line integral

$$\int_{\rho=a}^{\mathbf{r}} d\varrho \cdot \mathbf{F}(\varrho) = -[\Phi(\mathbf{r}) - \Phi(\mathbf{a})] \tag{4.6-4}$$

is independent of the path of integration C if the latter comprises only points of V; the line integral $\oint_C d\varrho \cdot \mathbf{F}(\varrho)$ around any closed path C ["circulation" of $\mathbf{F}(\mathbf{r})$ around C] in V is zero. If V is multiply connected, $\Phi(\mathbf{r})$ may be a multiple-valued function.

As a special case,
$$\frac{\partial F_x}{\partial y} - \frac{\partial F_y}{\partial x} = 0 \tag{4.6-5}$$

is a necessary and sufficient condition that the line integral

$$\int_C [F_x(x, y)\, dx + F_y(x, y)\, dy]$$

is independent of the path of integration, i.e., that the integrand is an exact differential.

4.6-4 Solenoidal Vector Fields. A vector point function $\mathbf{F}(\mathbf{r})$ (as well as the field described by it) is called **solenoidal** throughout a region V if and only if, for every point of V,

$$\boldsymbol{\nabla} \cdot \mathbf{F}(\mathbf{r}) = 0 \qquad \text{or} \qquad \frac{\partial F_x}{\partial x} + \frac{\partial F_y}{\partial y} + \frac{\partial F_z}{\partial z} = 0 \tag{4.6-6}$$

This is true if and only if $\mathbf{F}(\mathbf{r})$ is the curl $\boldsymbol{\nabla} \times \mathbf{A}(\mathbf{r})$ of a vector point function $\mathbf{A}(\mathbf{r})$, the **vector potential** of the vector field described by $\mathbf{F}(\mathbf{r})$.

References and Bibliography

1. Brand, L.: *Vector and Tensor Analysis*, Wiley, New York, 1947.
2. Coffin, J. G.: *Vector Analysis*, Wiley, New York, 1938.
3. Lass, H.: *Vector and Tensor Analysis*, McGraw-Hill, New York, 1950.
4. Sokolnikoff, I. S.: *Tensor Analysis*, Wiley, New York, 1951.
5. Weatherburn, C. E.: *Elementary Vector Analysis*, Open Court, LaSalle, Ill., 1948.

5 FUNCTIONS OF A COMPLEX VARIABLE AND LAPLACE TRANSFORMS

5.1 FUNCTIONS OF A COMPLEX VARIABLE

5.1-1 *Introduction.* The theory of analytic functions of a complex variable furnishes the scientist or engineer with many useful mathematical models. Many mathematical theorems are simplified if the real variables are considered as special values of complex variables. Complex variables are used to describe two-dimensional vectors in physics; analytical functions of a complex variable describe two-dimensional scalar and vector fields. Finally, analytic functions of a complex variable represent conformal mappings of the points of a plane into another plane.

5.1-2 *Functions of a Complex Variable* (*see also Secs. 1.2-7 and 3.2-1 and Table 5.1-1*). A complex function

$$w \equiv f(z) \equiv u(x, y) + iv(x, y) \equiv |w|e^{i\vartheta}$$
$$(z = x + iy = |z|e^{i\varphi}) \qquad (5.1\text{-}1)$$

Table 5.1-1* *Real and imaginary parts, zeros, and singularities for a number of frequently used functions* $f(z) = u(x, y) + iv(x, y)$ *of a complex variable* $z = x + iy$ [*note* $|f(z)| = \sqrt{u^2 + v^2}$, $\arg f(z) = \arctan(v/u)$]

Function $f(z)$	$u(x, y)$	$v(x, y)$	Zeros (order m)	Isolated singularities
z	x	y	$z = 0$ $\quad m = 1$	Pole ($m = 1$) at $z = \infty$
z^2	$x^2 - y^2$	$2xy$	$z = 0$ $\quad m = 2$	Pole ($m = 2$) at $z = \infty$
$\dfrac{1}{z}$	$\dfrac{x}{x^2 + y^2}$	$-\dfrac{y}{x^2 + y^2}$	$z = \infty$ $\quad m = 1$	Pole ($m = 1$) at $z = 0$
$\dfrac{1}{z^2}$	$\dfrac{x^2 - y^2}{(x^2 + y^2)^2}$	$\dfrac{-2xy}{(x^2 + y^2)^2}$	$z = \infty$ $\quad m = 2$	Pole ($m = 2$) at $z = 0$
$\dfrac{1}{z - (a + ib)}$ (a, b real)	$\dfrac{(x - a)}{(x - a)^2 + (y - b)^2}$	$-\dfrac{y - b}{(x - a)^2 + (y - b)^2}$	$z = \infty$ $\quad m = 1$	Pole ($m = 1$) at $z = a + ib$
$\sqrt{z}$	$\pm\left(\dfrac{x + \sqrt{x^2 + y^2}}{2}\right)^{1/2}$	$\pm\left(\dfrac{-x + \sqrt{x^2 + y^2}}{2}\right)^{1/2}$	Zero of order 1 at $z = 0$ (branch point)	Branch point ($m = 1$) at $z = 0$ Branch point ($m = 1$) at $z = \infty$
e^z	$e^x \cos y$	$e^x \sin y$	. . . .	Essential singularity at $z = \infty$
$\sin z$	$\sin x \cosh y$	$\cos x \sinh y$	$z = k\pi$ $\quad m = 1$ ($k = 0, \pm 1,$ $\pm 2, \pm \ldots$)	Essential singularity at $z = \infty$
$\cos z$	$\cos x \cosh y$	$-\sin x \sinh y$	$z = (k + \frac{1}{2})\pi$ $m = 1$ ($k = 0, \pm 1,$ $\pm 2, \pm \ldots$)	Essential singularity at $z = \infty$
$\sinh z$	$\sinh x \cos y$	$\cosh x \sin y$	$z = k\pi i$ $\quad m = 1$ ($k = 0, \pm 1,$ $\pm 2, \pm \ldots$)	Essential singularity at $z = \infty$
$\cosh z$	$\cosh x \cos y$	$\sinh x \sin y$	$z = (k + \frac{1}{2})\pi i$ $m = 1$ ($k = 0, \pm 1,$ $\pm 2, \pm \ldots$)	Essential singularity at $z = \infty$
$\tan z$	$\dfrac{\sin 2x}{\cos 2x + \cosh 2y}$	$\dfrac{\sinh 2y}{\cos 2x + \cosh 2y}$	$z = k\pi$ $\quad m = 1$ ($k = 0, \pm 1,$ $\pm 2, \pm \ldots$)	Essential singularity at $z = \infty$ Poles ($m = 1$) at $z = (k + \frac{1}{2})\pi$ ($k = 0, \pm 1,$ $\pm 2, \pm \ldots$)
$\tanh z$	$\dfrac{\sinh 2x}{\cosh 2x + \cos 2y}$	$\dfrac{\sin 2y}{\cosh 2x + \cos 2y}$	$z = k\pi i$ $\quad m = 1$ ($k = 0, \pm 1,$ $\pm 2, \pm \ldots$)	Essential singularity at $z = \infty$ Poles ($m = 1$) at $z = (k + \frac{1}{2})\pi i$ ($k = 0, \pm 1,$ $\pm 2, \pm \ldots$)
$\log_e z$	$\frac{1}{2}\log_e(x^2 + y^2)$	$\arctan\left(\dfrac{y}{x}\right) + 2k\pi$ ($k = 0, \pm 1, \pm 2, \pm \ldots$)	$z = 1$ $\quad m = 1$ (branch corresponding to $k = 0$ only)	Branch points of infinite order at $z = 0$, $z = \infty$; both are essential singularities

* From G. A. Korn and T. M. Korn, *Mathematical Handbook for Scientists and Engineers*, McGraw-Hill, New York, 1961.

associates one or more values of the complex dependent variable w with each value of the complex independent variable z in a given domain of definition.

Single-valued, multiple-valued, and *bounded* functions of a complex variable are defined as in Secs. 3.2-2 and 3.3-3. *Limits of complex functions and sequences* and *continuity of complex functions* as well as *convergence, absolute convergence,* and *uniform convergence of complex infinite series and improper integrals* are defined as in Chap. 3; THE THEOREMS OF CHAP. 3 APPLY TO COMPLEX FUNCTIONS AND VARIABLES UNLESS A RESTRICTION TO REAL QUANTITIES IS SPECIFICALLY STATED. In particular, *every complex power series* $\sum_{k=0}^{\infty} a_k(z - a)^k$ *has a real radius of convergence* r_c $(0 \leq r_c \leq \infty)$ *such that the series converges uniformly and absolutely for* $|z - a| < r_c$ *and diverges for* $|z - a| > r_c$ (Sec. 3.8-1).

5.1-3 *z Plane and w Plane.*

Values of the independent variable $z = x + iy$ are associated with unique points (x, y) of an Argand plane (Sec. 1.2-7), the *z plane*. Values of $w = u + iv$ are similarly associated with points (u, v) of a *w plane*.

An (open) **δ-neighborhood** of the point $z = a$ in the finite portion of the plane is defined as the set of points z such that $|z - a| < \delta$ for some $\delta > 0$. A **neighborhood** of $z = q$ is any region containing such a δ-neighborhood.

The **point at infinity** $(z = \infty)$ is defined as the point $\bar{z}$ transformed into the origin $(z = 0)$ by the transformation $\bar{z} = 1/z$. A region containing the exterior of any circle is a **neighborhood of the point** $z = \infty$.

5.1-4 *Complex Contour Integrals* (see also Secs. 3.6-8 and 4.4-5).

Given a **contour** (continuous rectifiable curve without multiple points, see also Sec. 3.6-7) C connecting $z = a = z_0$ and $z = b = z_m$, one defines

$$\int_C f(z)\,dz = \lim_{\max|z_i - z_{i-1}| \to 0} \sum_{i=1}^{m} f(\zeta_i)(z_i - z_{i-1}) \tag{5.1-2a}$$

where the points $z_0 < \zeta_1 < z_1 < \zeta_2 < z_2 < \cdots < \zeta_m < z_m$ lie on the contour C. If the limit exists, then

$$\int_C f(z)\, dz = \int_C [u(x, y)\, dx - v(x, y)\, dy]$$

$$+ i \int_C [v(x, y)\, dx + u(x, y)\, dy] \quad (5.1\text{-}2b)$$

where the real line integrals are taken over the same path as the complex integral. *The integration rules of Table 3.6-1 apply;* in particular, reversal of the sense of integration on the contour C reverses the sign of the integral.

5.1-5　Derivative of a Function (*see also Sec. 3.5-1*). A function $w = f(z)$ is **differentiable** at the point $z = a$ if and only if the limit

$$\frac{dw}{dz} = f'(z) = \lim_{\Delta z \to 0} \frac{f(z + \Delta z) - f(z)}{\Delta z} \quad (5.1\text{-}3)$$

[**derivative of** $f(z)$ **with respect to** z] exists for $z = a$ and is independent of the manner in which Δz approaches zero. A function may be differentiable at a point (e.g., $|z|^2$ at $z = 0$), on a curve, or throughout a region.

5.1-6　The Cauchy-Riemann Equations. $f(z) \equiv u(x, y) + iv(x, y)$ *is differentiable at the point* $z = x + iy$ *if and only if* $u(x, y)$ *and* $v(x, y)$ *are continuously differentiable throughout a neighborhood of* z, *and*

$$\frac{\partial u}{\partial x} = \frac{\partial v}{\partial y} \qquad \frac{\partial u}{\partial y} = -\frac{\partial v}{\partial x} \qquad \text{(CAUCHY-RIEMANN EQUATIONS)}$$

$$(5.1\text{-}4)$$

at the point z, *so that*

$$\frac{dw}{dz} = \frac{\partial u}{\partial x} + i\frac{\partial v}{\partial x} = \frac{\partial v}{\partial y} - i\frac{\partial u}{\partial y} \quad (5.1\text{-}5)$$

5.1-7　Analytic Functions. (*a*) A single-valued function $f(z)$ shall be called **analytic** (**regular, holomorphic**) at the point $z = a$ if and only if $f(z)$ is differentiable *throughout a neighborhood of* $z = a$. $f(z)$ *is analytic at* $z = a$ *if and only if* $f(z)$ *can be represented by a power series*

$$f(z) = \sum_{k=0}^{\infty} a_k(z - a)^k \quad \text{convergent throughout a neighborhood of} \quad z = a$$

(*alternative definition*). One extends the theory of analytic functions to suitable multiple-valued functions by considering **branches** $f_1(z)$, $f_2(z)$,

. . . of $f(z)$ each defined as a single-valued continuous function throughout its region of definition.   Each branch assumes one set of the function values of $f(z)$.   Multiple-valued analytic functions are treated in Refs. 1 to 5.

THROUGHOUT THIS HANDBOOK, STATEMENTS ABOUT ANALYTIC FUNCTIONS REFER TO SINGLE-VALUED ANALYTIC FUNCTIONS OR TO SINGLE-VALUED BRANCHES OF ANALYTIC FUNCTIONS UNLESS SPECIFIC REFERENCE TO MULTIPLE-VALUED FUNCTIONS IS MADE.

(b) $f(z)$ is **analytic at infinity** if and only if $F(\bar{z}) \equiv f(1/\bar{z})$ is analytic at $\bar{z} = 0$.   One defines $f'(\infty) = -\bar{z}^2 \dfrac{dF}{d\bar{z}}\bigg]_{\bar{z}=0}$.

5.1-8 Properties of Analytic Functions.   *Let $f(z)$ be analytic throughout an open region D.   Then, throughout D,*

1. *The Cauchy-Riemann equations (4) are satisfied (the converse is true).*
2. *$u(x, y)$ and $v(x, y)$ are conjugate harmonic functions, i.e., they satisfy* Laplace's *partial differential equation (6.3-20).*
3. *All derivatives of $f(z)$ with respect to z exist and are analytic (see also Sec. 5.2-1).*

If the open region D is simply connected (this applies, in particular, to the exterior of a bounded simply connected region),

4. *The integral $\displaystyle\int_{a}^{z} f(\zeta)\, d\zeta$ is independent of the path of integration, pro-*

   vided that C is a contour of finite length situated entirely in D; the integral is a single-valued analytic function of z, and its derivative is $f(z)$ (see also Sec. 5.2-1).
5. *The values of $f(z)$ on a contour arc or a subregion in D define $f(z)$ uniquely throughout D.*

All ordinary differentiation and integration rules apply to analytic functions of a complex variable.   If $f(z)$ is analytic at $z = a$ and $f'(a) \neq 0$, then $f(z)$ has an analytic inverse function at $z = a$.

5.1-9 Conformal Mapping.   (a) A function $w = f(z)$ maps points of the z plane into corresponding points of the w plane.   *At every point z such that $f(z)$ is analytic and $f'(z) \neq 0$, the mapping $w = f(z)$ is* **conformal**; *i.e., the angle between two curves through such a point is reproduced* *in magnitude and sense by the angle between the corresponding curves in the w plane.*

(b) The mapping $w = f(z)$ is **conformal at infinity** if and only if $w = f(1/\bar{z}) = F(\bar{z})$ maps the origin $\bar{z} = 0$ conformally into the w plane. Two curves are said to intersect at an angle γ at $z = \infty$ if and only if the transformation $\bar{z} = 1/z$ results in two corresponding curves intersecting at an angle γ at $\bar{z} = 0$. Similarly, $w = f(z)$ maps the point $z = a$ conformally into $w = \infty$ if and only if $\bar{w} = 1/f(z)$ maps $z = a$ conformally into the origin $\bar{w} = 0$.

5.2 INTEGRAL THEOREMS AND SERIES EXPANSIONS

5.2-1 *Integral Theorems.* *Let z be a point inside the boundary contour C of a region D throughout which $f(z)$ is analytic, and let $f(z)$ be analytic on C. Then*

$$\oint_C f(\zeta)\, d\zeta = 0 \quad \text{(CAUCHY-GOURSAT INTEGRAL THEOREM)}$$

$$(5.2\text{-}1)$$

$$f(z) = \frac{1}{2\pi i} \oint_C \frac{f(\zeta)}{\zeta - z}\, d\zeta \quad \text{(CAUCHY'S INTEGRAL FORMULA)}$$

$$f'(z) = \frac{1}{2\pi i} \oint_C \frac{f(\zeta)}{(\zeta - z)^2}\, d\zeta$$

$$f''(z) = \frac{2!}{2\pi i} \oint_C \frac{f(\zeta)}{(\zeta - z)^3}\, d\zeta$$

$$\cdots \cdots \cdots \cdots \cdots$$

$$f^{(n)}(z) = \frac{n!}{2\pi i} \oint_C \frac{f(\zeta)}{(\zeta - z)^{n+1}}\, d\zeta$$

$$(5.2\text{-}2)$$

Figure 5.2-1 illustrates the application of the Cauchy-Goursat integral theorem (1) to *multiply connected* domains.

Equation (2) yields $f(z)$ and its derivatives in terms of the boundary values of $f(z)$. Specifically,

$$\oint_C \frac{d\zeta}{\zeta - z} = 2\pi i \tag{5.2-3}$$

5.2-2 *Taylor-series Expansion* (*see also Sec. 3.10-3*). (a) *If $f(z)$ is analytic inside and on the circle K of radius r about $z = a$, then there exists a unique and uniformly convergent series expansion in powers of $(z - a)$,*

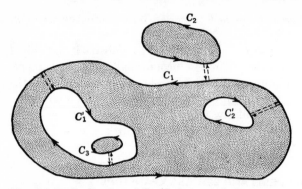

Fig. 5.2-1 Application of Cauchy's integral theorem to a multiply connected region of the z plane. A region D bounded by exterior contours C_1, C_2, . . . and interior contours C'_1, C'_2, . . . is made simply connected by cuts (shown in broken lines). The integrals over each cut cancel, and *Cauchy's integral theorem becomes*

$$\sum_j \oint_{C_i} f(\zeta)\, d\zeta - \sum_k \oint_{C_k'} f(\zeta)\, d\zeta = 0$$

where all integrals are taken in the positive (counterclockwise) direction. The same technique applies if D is not bounded.

$$f(z) = \sum_{k=0}^{\infty} a_k (z - a)^k \qquad (|z - a| \leq r,\ a \neq \infty)$$

with

$$a_k = \frac{1}{k!} f^{(k)}(a) = \frac{1}{2\pi i} \oint_K \frac{f(\zeta)}{(\zeta - a)^{k+1}}\, d\zeta$$

(5.2-4)

The largest circle K_c or $|z - a| = r_c$ all of whose interior points are inside the region where $f(z)$ is analytic is the **convergence circle** of the power series (4); r_c is the **radius of convergence** (Sec. 3.10-2). A number of useful power-series expansions are tabulated in Sec. 11.1-11.

(b) If Taylor's series (4) is terminated with the term $a_{n-1}(z - a)^{n-1}$, the *remainder* $R_n(z)$ is given by

$$R_n(z) = \frac{(z - a)^n}{2\pi i} \oint_K \frac{f(\zeta)\, d\zeta}{(\zeta - a)^n(\zeta - z)}$$

$$|R_n(z)| \leq \left(\frac{|z - a|}{r}\right)^n \frac{M(r) r}{r - |z - a|}$$

(5.2-5)

where $M(r)$ is an upper bound of $|f(z)|$ on K.

5.2-3   Laurent-series Expansion.   *If $f(z)$ is analytic throughout the annular region between and on the concentric circles K_1 and K_2 centered at $z = a$ and of radii r_1 and $r_2 < r_1$, respectively, there exists a unique series expansion in terms of positive and negative powers of $(z - a)$,*

$$f(z) = \sum_{k=0}^{\infty} a_k(z - a)^k + \sum_{k=1}^{\infty} b_k(z - a)^{-k} \quad (r_1 > |r - a| > r_2)$$

with   (5.2-6)

$$a_k = \frac{1}{2\pi i} \oint_{K_1} \frac{f(\zeta)\, d\zeta}{(\zeta - a)^{k+1}} \qquad b_k = \frac{1}{2\pi i} \oint_{K_2} (\zeta - a)^{k-1} f(\zeta)\, d\zeta$$

*The first term of Eq. (6) is analytic and converges uniformly for $|z - a| \leq r_1$; the second term [**principal part** of $f(z)$] is analytic and converges uniformly for $|z - a| \geq r_2$.*

5.3   ZEROS, ISOLATED SINGULARITIES, AND RESIDUES

5.3-1   Zeros.   The points z for which $f(z) = 0$ are called the **zeros of** $f(z)$ [roots of $f(z) = 0$]. A function $f(z)$ analytic at $z = a$ has a **zero of order** m, where m is a positive integer, at $z = a$ if and only if the first m coefficients $a_0, a_1, a_2, \ldots, a_{m-1}$ in the Taylor-series expansion (5.2-4) of $f(z)$ about $z = a$ vanish, so that $f(z)(z - a)^{-m}$ is analytic and different from zero at $z = a$.

5.3-2   Singularities.   A **singular point** or **singularity** of the function $f(z)$ is any point where $f(z)$ is not analytic. The point $z = a$ is an **isolated singularity** of $f(z)$ if and only if there exists a real number $\delta > 0$ such that $f(z)$ is analytic for $0 < |z - a| < \delta$ but not for $z = a$. An isolated singularity of $f(z)$ at $z = a \neq \infty$ is

1. A **removable singularity** if and only if $f(z)$ is finite throughout a neighborhood of $z = a$, except possibly at $z = a$ itself; i.e., if and only if all coefficients b_k in the Laurent expansion (5.2-6) of $f(z)$ about $z = a$ vanish.

2. A **pole of order** m $(m = 1, 2, \ldots)$ if and only if $(z - a)^m f(z)$ but not $(z - a)^{m-1} f(z)$ is analytic at $z = a$; i.e., if and only if

$$b_m \neq 0 \qquad b_{m+1} = b_{m+2} = \cdots = 0$$

in the Laurent expansion (5.2-6) of $f(z)$ about $z = a$; or if and only if $1/f(z)$ is analytic and has a zero of order m at $z = a$.   In this case, $\lim\limits_{z \to a} |f(z)| = \infty$ no matter how z approaches $z = a$.

3. An **isolated essential singularity** if and only if the Laurent expansion (5.2-6) of $f(z)$ about $z = a$ has an infinite number of terms involving negative powers of $(z - a)$; $|f(z)|$ becomes indefinitely large as z approaches the value $z = a$ for some approach paths but not for others.*

The point $z = \infty$ is a zero or a singularity if $f(1/z)$ behaves correspondingly at the origin.   The behavior of $f(z)$ at infinity may be investigated with the aid of the Laurent expansion of $f(1/z)$ about the origin.

See Refs. 1 to 5 for singularities peculiar to multiple-valued functions (*branch points*).

5.3-3   Zeros and Poles of Meromorphic Functions. $f(z)$ is **meromorphic** throughout a region D if and only if its only singularities throughout D are poles.   The number of such poles in any finite region D is necessarily finite.   Many authors alternatively define a function as meromorphic if and only if its only singularities *throughout the finite portion of the plane* are poles.

Let $f(z)$ be meromorphic throughout the bounded region inside and continuous on a closed contour C on which $f(z) \neq 0$.   Let N be the number of zeros and P the number of poles of $f(z)$ inside C, respectively, where a zero or pole of order m is counted m times.   Then

$$\frac{1}{2\pi i} \oint_C \frac{f'(\zeta)}{f(\zeta)} \, d\zeta = N - P \qquad (5.3\text{-}1)$$

For $P = 0$, Eq. (1) reduces to the *principle of the argument*

$$N = \frac{\Delta_C \vartheta}{2\pi} \qquad (5.3\text{-}2)$$

where $\Delta_C \vartheta$ is the variation of the argument ϑ of $f(z)$ around the contour C.

Equation (2) means that $w = f(z)$ maps a moving point z describing the contour C once into a moving point w which encircles the w-plane origin $N = 0, 1, 2, \ldots$

---

* Sometimes the definition of an isolated essential singularity is extended to cover limit points of poles.

times if $f(z)$ has, respectively, 0, 1, 2, ... zeros inside the contour C in the z plane. Equations (1) and (2) yield important criteria for locating zeros and poles of $f(z)$, such as the famous *Nyquist criterion*.

5.3-4   Residues.   Given a point $z = a$ where $f(z)$ is either analytic or has an isolated singularity, the **residue** $\text{Res}_f (a)$ of $f(z)$ at $z = a$ is the coefficient of $(z - a)^{-1}$ in the Laurent expansion (5.2-6), or

$$\text{Res}_f (a) = \frac{1}{2\pi i} \oint_C f(\zeta) \, d\zeta \qquad (5.3\text{-}3a)$$

where C is any contour enclosing $z = a$ but no singularities of $f(z)$ other than $z = a$.

The residue $\text{Res}_f (\infty)$ of $f(z)$ at $z = \infty$ is defined as

$$\text{Res}_f (\infty) = \frac{1}{2\pi i} \oint f(\zeta) \, d\zeta \qquad (5.3\text{-}3b)$$

where the integral is taken in the *negative* sense around any contour enclosing all singularities of $f(z)$ in the finite portion of the plane.   Note that

$$\text{Res}_f (\infty) = \lim_{z \to \infty} \left[-zf(z) \right] \qquad (5.3\text{-}4)$$

if the limit exists.

If $f(z)$ is either analytic or has a removable singularity at $z = a \neq \infty$, then $\text{Res}_f (a) = 0$ [see also Eq. (5.2-1)].   If $z = a \neq \infty$ is a pole of order m, then

$$\text{Res}_f (a) = \frac{1}{(m-1)!} \frac{d^{m-1}}{dz^{m-1}} (z - a)^m f(z) \bigg]_{z=a} \qquad (5.3\text{-}5)$$

In particular, let $z = a \neq \infty$ be a simple pole of $f(z) \equiv p(z)/q(z)$, where $p(z)$ and $q(z)$ are analytic at $z = a$, and $p(a) \neq 0$.   Then

$$\text{Res}_f (a) = \frac{p(a)}{q'(a)} \qquad (5.3\text{-}6)$$

5.3-5   The Residue Theorem.   *For every simple closed contour C enclosing at most a finite number of (necessarily isolated) singularities $z_1, z_2, \ldots, z_n$ of a single-valued function $f(z)$ continuous on C,*

$$\frac{1}{2\pi i} \oint_C f(\zeta) \, d\zeta = \sum_{k=1}^{n} \text{Res}_f (z_k) \qquad (\text{RESIDUE THEOREM}) \qquad (5.3\text{-}7)$$

One of the z_k may be the point at infinity.   See Refs. 1 to 5 for the case of multiple-valued functions.

One can often evaluate a real definite integral $\int_b^a f(x)\,dx$ as a portion of a complex contour integral $\oint_C f(z)\,dz$ such that the contour C includes the interval (a, b) of the real axis.   The residue theorem (7) may aid in such computations and may, in particular, relate the unknown integral to one that is already known (Refs. 1 to 5).

5.4 THE LAPLACE TRANSFORMATION

5.4-1 Introduction.   The Laplace transformation associates a unique function $F(s)$ of a complex variable s with each suitable function $f(t)$ of a real variable t.   This correspondence is essentially reciprocal one-to-one for most practical purposes (Sec. 5.4-5); corresponding pairs of functions $f(t)$ and $F(s)$ can often be found by reference to tables.   The Laplace transformation is defined so that many relations between, and operations on, the functions $f(t)$ correspond to simpler relations between, and operations on, the functions $F(s)$ (Sec. 5.4-6).   This applies particularly to the solution of differential and integral equations.   It is, thus, often useful to transform a given problem involving functions $f(t)$ into an equivalent problem expressed in terms of the associated Laplace transforms $F(s)$ ("operational calculus" based on Laplace transformations or "transformation calculus," Sec. 6.2-6).

5.4-2 Definition.   (a) The **one-sided Laplace transformation**

$$
\begin{aligned}
F(s) \equiv \mathcal{L}[f(t)] &\equiv \int_0^\infty f(t)e^{-st}\,dt \\
&\equiv \lim_{\substack{a \to 0 \\ b \to \infty}} \int_a^b f(t)e^{-st}\,dt \qquad (0 < a < b) \qquad (5.4\text{-}1)
\end{aligned}
$$

associates a unique **result or image function** $F(s)$ of the complex variable $s = \sigma + i\omega$ with every single-valued **object or original function** $f(t)$ (t real) such that the improper integral (1) exists. $F(s)$ is called the **(one-sided) Laplace transform** of $f(t)$.   The more explicit notation $\mathcal{L}[f(t); s]$ is also used.

(*b*) *The Laplace transform* (1) *exists for* $\sigma \geq \sigma_0$, *and the improper integral converges absolutely and uniformly* (*Sec.* 3.6-2*a*) *to a function* $F(s)$ *analytic* (*Sec.* 5.1-7) *for* $\sigma > \sigma_0$ *if*

$$\int_0^\infty |f(t)|e^{-\sigma t}\, dt = \lim_{\substack{a \to 0 \\ b \to \infty}} \int_a^b |f(t)|e^{-\sigma t}\, dt \qquad (0 < a < b) \qquad (5.4\text{-}2)$$

exists for $\sigma = \sigma_0$. The greatest lower bound σ_a of the real numbers σ_0 for which this is true is called the **abscissa of absolute convergence** of the Laplace transform $\mathcal{L}[f(t)]$.

Although certain theorems relating to Laplace transforms require only the existence (simple convergence) of the transforms, THE EXISTENCE OF AN ABSCISSA OF ABSOLUTE CONVERGENCE WILL BE IMPLICITLY ASSUMED THROUGHOUT THE FOLLOWING SECTIONS. Wherever necessary, it is customary to specify the region of absolute convergence associated with a relation involving Laplace transforms by writing $\sigma > \sigma_a$ to the right of the relation in question.

(*c*) The region of definition of the analytic function

$$F(s) = \mathcal{L}[f(t)] \qquad (\sigma > \sigma_a)$$

can usually be extended so as to include the entire s plane with the exception of singular points (Sec. 5.3-2) situated to the left of the abscissa of absolute convergence. Such an extension of the region of definition is implied wherever necessary.

5.4-3 *Inverse Laplace Transformation.* The **inverse Laplace transform** $\mathcal{L}^{-1}[F(s)]$ of a (suitable) function $F(s)$ of the complex variable $s = \sigma + i\omega$ is a function $f(t)$ whose Laplace transform (1) is $F(s)$. *Not every function* $F(s)$ *has an inverse Laplace transform.*

5.4-4 *The Inversion Theorem.* Given $F(s) = \mathcal{L}[f(t)]$, $\sigma > \sigma_a$, then *throughout every open interval where* $f(t)$ *is bounded and has a finite number of maxima, minima, and discontinuities,*

$$\begin{aligned}
f_I(t) &= \frac{1}{2\pi i} \lim_{R \to \infty} \int_{\sigma_1 - iR}^{\sigma_1 + iR} F(s)e^{st}\, ds \\
&= \left. \begin{cases} \tfrac{1}{2}[f(t-0) + f(t+0)] & \text{for } t > 0 \\ \tfrac{1}{2}f(0+0) & \text{for } t = 0 \\ 0 & \text{for } t < 0 \end{cases} \right\} \quad (\sigma_1 > \sigma_a) \quad (5.4\text{-}3a)
\end{aligned}$$

In particular, for every $t > 0$ where $f(t)$ is continuous

$$f_I(t) = \frac{1}{2\pi i} \lim_{R \to \infty} \int_{\sigma_1 - iR}^{\sigma_1 + iR} F(s)e^{st}\, ds = f(t) \qquad (\sigma_1 > \sigma_a)$$

$$(5.4\text{-}3b)$$

The path of integration in Eq. (3) lies to the right of all singularities of $F(s)$. The **inversion integral** $f_I(t)$ reduces to $\dfrac{1}{2\pi i} \int_{\sigma_1 - i\infty}^{\sigma_1 + i\infty} F(s)e^{st}\, ds$ if the integral exists.

5.4-5 Uniqueness of the Laplace Transform and Its Inverse. *The Laplace transform* (1) *is unique for each function $f(t)$ having such a transform. Conversely, two functions $f_1(t)$ and $f_2(t)$ possessing identical Laplace transforms are identical for all $t > 0$ where both functions are continuous (Lerch's Theorem).* A given function $F(s)$ cannot have more than one inverse Laplace transform continuous for all $t > 0$.

Different discontinuous functions may have the same Laplace transform. In particular, the generalized unit step function defined by $f(t) = 0$ for $t < 0$, $f(t) = 1$ for $t > 0$ has the Laplace transform $1/s$ regardless of the value assigned to $f(t)$ for $t = 0$.

5.4-6 Corresponding Operations. Table 5.4-1 lists a number of theorems each establishing a correspondence between an operation on a function $f_1(t)$ and an operation on its Laplace transform $F_1(s)$, and vice versa. These theorems are the basis of Laplace-transform techniques for the simplified representation of operations (operational calculus based on the use of Laplace transforms).

5.4-7 Limit Theorems. *If $F(s)$ is the Laplace transform of $f(t)$ and $\mathcal{L}[f'(t)]$ exists, then*

$$\lim_{s \to \infty} sF(s) = f(0 + 0) \tag{5.4-4}$$

if the limit on the left exists. If, in addition to the first two conditions, $sF(s)$ is analytic for $\sigma \geq 0$, then

$$\lim_{s \to 0} sF(s) = \lim_{t \to \infty} f(t) \tag{5.4-5}$$

5.4-8 Inverse Laplace Transforms of Rational Algebraic Functions. *If $F(s)$ is a rational algebraic function expressible as the ratio of two polynomials in s,*

$$F(s) = \frac{D_1(s)}{D(s)} \tag{5.4-6}$$

such that the degree of the polynomial $D(s)$ is higher than that of the poly-

Table 5.4-1 *Theorems relating corresponding operations on object and result functions* (the following theorems are valid whenever the Laplace transforms $F(s) = \mathcal{L}[f(t)]$ in question exist in the sense of absolute convergence)*

Theorem number	Operation	Object function	Result function
1	**Linearity** $(\alpha, \beta$ constant)	$\alpha f_1(t) + \beta f_2(t)$	$\alpha F_1(s) + \beta F_2(s)$
2a 2b	**Differentiation of object function†** ... if $f'(t)$ exists for all $t > 0$ ... if $f^{(r)}(t)$ exists for all $t > 0$	$f'(t)$ $f^{(r)}(t)$ $(r = 1, 2, \ldots)$	$sF(s) - f(0 + 0)$ $s^r F(s) - s^{r-1}f(0 + 0)$ $\quad - s^{r-2}f'(0 + 0)$ $\quad - \cdots - f^{(r-1)}(0 + 0)$
2c	... if $f(t)$ is bounded for $t > 0$, and $f'(t)$ exists for $t > 0$ except for $t = t_1, t_2, \ldots$ where $f(t)$ has unilateral limits	$f'(t)$	$sF(s) - f(0 + 0)$ $\quad - \sum_k e^{-t_k s}[f(t_k + 0) - f(t_k - 0)]$
3	**Integration of object function** ... if $f'(t)$ exists for $t > 0$	$\int_0^t f(\tau)\, d\tau + C$	$\dfrac{F(s)}{s} + \dfrac{C}{s}$
4	**Change of scale**	$f(at) \quad (a > 0)$	$\dfrac{1}{a} F\left(\dfrac{s}{a}\right)$
5	**Translation (shift) of object function** ... if $f(t) = 0$ for $t \leq 0$	$f(t - b) \quad (b \geq 0)$	$e^{-bs}F(s)$
6	**Convolution of object functions‡**	$f_1 * f_2$ $\equiv \int_0^\infty f_1(\tau)f_2(t - \tau)\,d\tau$ $\equiv f_2 * f_1$	$F_1(s)F_2(s)$
7	**Corresponding limits of object and result function** (continuity theorem; α is independent of t and s)	$\lim_{\alpha \to a} f(t, \alpha)$	$\lim_{\alpha \to a} F(s, \alpha)$
8a 8b	**Differentiation and integration with respect to a parameter** α independent of t and s	$\dfrac{\partial}{\partial \alpha} f(t, \alpha)$ $\int_{a_1}^{a_2} f(t, \alpha)\, d\alpha$	$\dfrac{\partial}{\partial \alpha} F(s, \alpha)$ $\int_{a_1}^{a_2} F(s, \alpha)\, d\alpha$
9a 9b	**Differentiation of result function**	$-tf(t)$ $(-1)^r t^r f(t)$	$F'(s)$ $F^{(r)}(s)$
10	**Integration of result function** (path of integration situated to the right of the abscissa of absolute convergence)	$\dfrac{1}{t} f(t)$	$\int_s^\infty F(s)\, ds$
11	**Translation of result function**	$e^{at}f(t)$	$F(s - a)$

* From G. A. Korn and T. M. Korn, *Mathematical Handbook for Scientists and Engineers*, McGraw-Hill, New York, 1961.
† The abscissa of absolute convergence for $\mathcal{L}[f^{(r)}(t)]$ is 0 or σ_a, whichever is greater.
‡ The existence of $f_1 * f_2$ is assumed; absolute convergence of $\mathcal{L}[f_1(t)]$ and $\mathcal{L}[f_2(t)]$ is a sufficient condition for the absolute convergence of $\mathcal{L}[f_1 * f_2]$.

nomial $D_1(s)$, then $\mathcal{L}^{-1}[F(s)]$ *equals the sum of the residues (Sec. 5.3-4) of* $F(s)e^{st}$ *at all the singular points (poles) of* $F(s)$. To compute the inverse Laplace transform $\mathcal{L}^{-1}[F(s)]$, first find the roots s_k of $D(s) = 0$ [which determine the poles of $F(s)$]. One may then expand $F(s) = D_1(s)/D(s)$ as a sum of partial fractions by one of the methods described in Sec. 1.5-4. If $D(s)$ and $D_1(s)$ have no common zeros, each real root $s_k = a$ of $D(s) = 0$ will give rise to m_k partial fractions of the form

$$\frac{b_1}{s - a} \qquad \frac{b_2}{(s - a)^2} \qquad \ldots \qquad \frac{b_{m_k}}{(s - a)^{m_k}}$$

where m_k is the order of the root $s_k = a$. Each pair of complex-conjugate roots $s_k = a \pm i\omega_1$ will give rise to m_k partial fractions of the form

$$c_1 \frac{s + d_1}{(s - a)^2 + \omega_1{}^2}$$

$$c_2 \frac{s + d_2}{[(s - a)^2 + \omega_1{}^2]^2}$$

$$\cdots\cdots\cdots\cdots\cdots$$

$$c_{m_k} \frac{s + d_{m_k}}{[(s - a)^2 + \omega_1{}^2]^{m_k}}$$

where m_k is the order of the roots $s_k = a \pm i\omega_1$. $\mathcal{L}^{-1}[F(s)]$ is then obtained as the sum of the inverse Laplace transforms of such terms. Table D-3 lists a number of Laplace-transform pairs with rational algebraic result functions (see also Sec. 6.2-6).

References and Bibliography

Functions of a complex variable

1. Knopp, K.: *Theory of Functions* (2 vols.), Dover, New York, 1945, 1947.
2. Ahlfors, L. V.: *Complex Analysis*, McGraw-Hill, New York, 1953.
3. Caratheodory, C.: *Theory of Functions of a Complex Variable* (2 vols.), Chelsea, New York, 1958, 1960.
4. Churchill, R. V.: *Complex Variables and Applications*, 2d ed., McGraw-Hill, New York, 1960.
5. Nehari, Z.: *Introduction to Complex Analysis*, Allyn and Bacon, Boston, 1961.

Laplace transforms

6. Scott, E. J.: *Transform Calculus*, Harper, New York, 1955.
7. Churchill, R. V.: *Operational Mathematics*, 2d ed., McGraw-Hill, New York, 1958.
8. Aseltine, J. A.: *Transform Method in Linear System Analysis*, McGraw-Hill, New York, 1958.

9. Holl, D. L., et al.: *Introduction to the Laplace Transform*, Appleton-Century-Crofts, New York, 1959.

10. Nixon, F. E.: *Handbook of Laplace Transformation*, 2d ed., Prentice-Hall, Englewood Cliffs, N.J., 1965.

6 DIFFERENTIAL EQUATIONS

6.1 ORDINARY DIFFERENTIAL EQUATIONS

6.1-1 Introduction. Differential equations express relations between changes of continuously variable quantities. Models relating small changes in the state of a physical system by suitable differential equations (performance equations, equations of motion, circuit equations) permit us to predict the performance of the system as a result of given inputs and/or initial conditions. Hence, a large portion of applied mathematics deals with methods for solving differential equations, or, at least, with schemes for inferring properties of solutions.

Methods for producing solutions of ordinary differential equations (Sec. 6.2-1) in closed form are largely restricted to *linear* problems (Secs. 6.2-1 to 6.2-7); most nonlinear differential equations can be solved only by numerical approximation (Chap. 10). The differential equations themselves may, however, yield considerable insight into system behavior, input-output and feedback relationships, etc.

The most important methods for the solution of linear differential equations involve *superposition of judiciously chosen particular solutions or trial functions* to construct solutions which match given forcing functions, given boundary conditions, and/or given initial conditions.

6.1-2 Ordinary Differential Equations. (*a*) An **ordinary differential equation of order** r is an equation

$$F[x,\ y(x),\ y'(x),\ y''(x),\ \ldots,\ y^{(r)}(x)] = 0 \qquad (6.1\text{-}1)$$

to be satisfied by the function $y = y(x)$ together with its derivatives $y'(x), y''(x), \ldots, y^{(r)}(x)$ with respect to a single independent variable x. To **solve** (**integrate**) a given differential equation (1) means to find functions (**solutions, integrals**) $y(x)$ which satisfy Eq. (1) for all values of x in a specified bounded or unbounded interval (a, b). *Note that solutions can be checked by resubstitution.*

The **complete primitive** (**complete integral, general solution**) of an ordinary differential equation of order r has the form

$$y = y(x, C_1, C_2, \ldots, C_r) \qquad (6.1\text{-}2)$$

where $C_1, C_2, \ldots, C_r$ are r *arbitrary constants* (**constants of integration**). Each particular choice of these r constants yields a **particular integral** (2) of the given differential equation. Typical problems require one to find the particular integral (2) subject to r **initial conditions**

$$y(x_0) = y_0$$

$$y'(x_0) = y_0'$$

$$y''(x_0) = y_0'' \qquad (6.1\text{-}3)$$

$$\cdots \cdots \cdots$$

$$y^{(r-1)}(x_0) = y_0^{(r-1)}$$

which determine the r constants $C_1, C_2, \ldots, C_r$. Alternatively, one may be given r **boundary conditions** on $y(x)$ and its derivatives for $x = a$ and $x = b$.

Many ordinary differential equations admit additional solutions known as **singular integrals**.

(*b*) A system of ordinary differential equations

$$F_i(x; y_1, y_2, \ldots; y_1', y_2', \ldots) = 0 \quad (i = 1, 2, \ldots)$$

$$(6.1\text{-}4)$$

involves a set of unknown functions $y_1 = y_1(x)$, $y_2 = y_2(x)$, ... and their derivatives with respect to a single independent variable x. The **order** r_i of each differential equation (4) is that of the highest derivative occurring. In general, one will require n differential equations (4) to determine n unknown functions $y_k(x)$; and the general solution $y_1 = y_1(x)$, $y_2 = y_2(x)$ will involve a number of arbitrary constants equal to $r = r_1 + r_2 + \cdots + r_n$.

The solution of a system (4) can be reduced to that of a single ordinary differential equation of order r through elimination of $n - 1$ variables y_k and their derivatives. More importantly, *one can reduce every system* (4) *to an equivalent system of r first-order equations* by introducing higher-order derivatives as new variables. Typical applications describe the "state" of a dynamical (mechanical, electrical, and/or chemical-process system) by the values of r *state variables* $y_1(t)$, $y_2(t)$, ..., $y_r(t)$ at each time t; the $y_i(t)$ are determined by a system of first-order performance equations

$$\frac{dy_i}{dt} = f_i(t; y_1, y_2, \ldots, y_r) \quad (i = 1, 2, \ldots, r) \quad (6.1\text{-}5)$$

together with the "initial state" given by $y_1(t_0)$, $y_2(t_0)$, ..., $y_r(t_0)$. Some of the y_i can be derivatives of others, so that an equation (5) can take the form $dy_i/dt = \dot{y}_i = y_k$.

A properly posed differential-equation problem requires an **existence proof** indicating the construction of a solution subject to the given type of initial or boundary conditions. The existence of physical phenomena described by a given differential equation may suggest but does *not* prove the existence of a solution; an existence proof checks the *self-consistency of the mathematical model*.

6.1-3 *Special Types of First-order Equations.* The following special types of first-order equations are relatively easy to solve.

1. **The variables are separable:** $y' = f_1(x)/f_2(y)$. Obtain the solution from $\int f_2(y)\, dy = \int f_1(x)\, dx + C$.

2. **"Homogeneous" first-order equations:**[*] $y' = f(y/x)$. Introduce $\bar{y} = y/x$ to reduce to type 1.

3. **Exact differential equations** can be written in the form

$$P(x, y)\, dx + Q(x, y)\, dy = 0 \qquad (6.1\text{-}6)$$

where the expression on the left is an exact differential $d\varphi \left(\dfrac{\partial P}{\partial y} = \dfrac{\partial Q}{\partial x} \right)$. Obtain the solution from

$$\varphi(x, y) = \int P(x, y)\, dx + \int \left[Q(x, y) - \frac{\partial}{\partial y} \int P(x, y)\, dx \right] dy = C$$
$$(6.1\text{-}7)$$

If the expression on the left of Eq. (6) is not an exact differential $\left(\dfrac{\partial P}{\partial y} \neq \dfrac{\partial Q}{\partial x} \right)$, one may be able to find an **integrating factor** $\mu = \mu(x, y)$ such that multiplication of Eq. (6) by $\mu(x, y)$ yields an exact differential equation. The integrating factor $\mu(x, y)$ satisfies the partial differential equation

$$\mu \left(\frac{\partial P}{\partial y} - \frac{\partial Q}{\partial x} \right) = Q \frac{\partial \mu}{\partial x} - P \frac{\partial \mu}{\partial y} \qquad (6.1\text{-}8)$$

4. **The linear first-order equation** $y' + a(x)y = f(x)$ admits the integrating factor

$$\mu = \mu(x) = \exp \int a(x)\, dx \qquad (6.1\text{-}9)$$

The complete primitive is then

$$y = \mu(x) \left[\int f(x) \frac{1}{\mu(x)}\, dx + C \right] \qquad (6.1\text{-}10)$$

Many first-order equations can be reduced to one of the above types by transformation of variables,

$$x = X(\bar{x}, \bar{y}) \qquad y = Y(\bar{x}, \bar{y}) \qquad \left[\frac{\partial(x, y)}{\partial(\bar{x}, \bar{y})} \neq 0 \right]$$

$$p \equiv \frac{dy}{dx} = \frac{\dfrac{\partial Y}{\partial \bar{x}} + \dfrac{\partial Y}{\partial \bar{y}} \bar{p}}{\dfrac{\partial X}{\partial \bar{x}} + \dfrac{\partial X}{\partial \bar{y}} \bar{p}} \qquad \left(\bar{p} \equiv \frac{d\bar{y}}{d\bar{x}} \right) \qquad (6.1\text{-}11)$$

---

[*] Note that the expression "homogeneous" differential equation is here *not* used in the sense defined in Sec. 6.2-1.

Example:

$$y' = f_1(x)y + f_2(x)y^n \qquad (n = 2, 3, \ldots) \qquad \text{(BERNOULLI'S DIFFERENTIAL EQUATION)}$$

reduces to a linear equation if one introduces $\bar{y} = y^{1-n}$.

6.1-4 General Methods of Solution. (a) PICARD'S METHOD OF SUCCESSIVE APPROXIMATIONS.

To solve the differential equation $y' = f(x, y)$ for a given initial value $y(x_0) = y_0$, start with a trial solution $y^{[0]}(x)$ and compute successive approximations

$$y^{[j+1]}(x) = y_0 + \int_{x_0}^{x} f[x, y^{[j]}(x)] \, dx \qquad (j = 0, 1, 2, \ldots)$$

$$(6.1\text{-}12)$$

to the desired solution $y(x)$. *The process converges whenever the solution exists.* Picard's method is useful mainly if the integrals in Eq. (12) can be evaluated in closed form.

(b) TAYLOR-SERIES EXPANSION. If the given function $f(x, y)$ is suitably differentiable, obtain the coefficients $y^{(m)}(x_0)/m!$ of the Taylor series

$$y(x) = y(x_0) + y'(x_0)(x - x_0) + \frac{1}{2!} y''(x_0)(x - x_0)^2 + \cdots$$

$$(6.1\text{-}13)$$

by successive differentiations of the given differential equation:

$$y'(x) = f(x, y)$$

$$y''(x) = \frac{\partial f}{\partial x} + \frac{\partial f}{\partial y} y'(x) = \frac{\partial f}{\partial x} + \frac{\partial f}{\partial y} f(x, y)$$

$$\cdots \cdots \cdots \cdots \cdots \cdots \cdots \cdots \cdots \cdots$$

with $x = x_0$, $y = y(x_0) = y_0$.

6.1-5 Geometrical Interpretation.

If x, y are regarded as rectangular cartesian coordinates, a first-order differential equation

$$F(x, y, p) = 0 \qquad \left(p \equiv \frac{dy}{dx} \right) \qquad (6.1\text{-}14)$$

describes a "field" of **line elements** (x, y, p) or elements of straight lines through (x, y) with slope $p = dy/dx = f(x, y)$. Each line element is tangent to a curve of the one-parameter family of solutions

$$y = y(x, \lambda) \qquad \text{or} \qquad \varphi(x, y, \lambda) = 0 \qquad (6.1\text{-}15)$$

where λ is a constant of integration.

A plot of the field of tangent directions permits at least rough *graphical determination of solutions.* It may be helpful to know that the curves $F(x, y, p_1) = 0$ or $f(x, y) = p_1$ are **isoclines** where the solution curves have a specified fixed slope p_1. The curves $\dfrac{\partial f}{\partial x} + \dfrac{\partial f}{\partial y} f = 0$ are *loci of points of inflection* (see also Fig. 6.1-1).

6.2   LINEAR DIFFERENTIAL EQUATIONS

6.2-1   *Linear Differential Equations.*   *Superposition Theorems.*

(*a*) A **linear** ordinary differential equation of order r relating the real or complex variables x and $y = y(x)$ has the form

$$\mathsf{L}y \equiv a_0(x)\frac{d^r y}{dx^r} + a_1(z)\frac{d^{r-1}y}{dx^{r-1}} + \cdots + a_r(x)y = f(x)$$

$$(6.2\text{-}1)$$

where the $a_k(x)$ and $f(x)$ are real or complex functions of x. *The general solution of a linear differential equation* (1) *can be expressed as the sum of any particular integral and the general solution of the homogeneous linear differential equation*

$$\mathsf{L}y \equiv a_0(x)\frac{d^r y}{dx^r} + a_1(x)\frac{d^{r-1}y}{dx^{r-1}} + \cdots + a_r(x)y = 0 \qquad (6.2\text{-}2)$$

For any given nonhomogeneous or "complete" linear differential equation (1), the homogeneous equation (2) is known as the **complementary equation** or **reduced equation,** and its general solution as the **complementary function.**

Let $y_1(x)$ and $y_2(x)$ *be particular integrals of the linear differential equation* (1) *for the respective "forcing functions"* $f(x) \equiv f_1(x)$ *and* $f(x) \equiv f_2(x)$. *Then* $\alpha y_1(x) + \beta y_2(x)$ *is a particular integral for the forcing function* $f(x) \equiv \alpha f_1(x) + \beta f_2(x)$ *(Superposition Principle)*. In particular, *every linear combination of solutions of a homogeneous linear differential equation* (2) *is also a solution.*

The superposition theorems often represent some physical superposition principle. Mathematically, they permit one to construct solutions of Eq. (1) or (2) subject to given initial or boundary conditions by linear superposition.

Analogous theorems apply to systems of linear differential equations.

(*b*) REDUCTION OF TWO-POINT BOUNDARY-VALUE PROBLEMS TO INITIAL-VALUE PROBLEMS. The following method is often useful in connection with numerical solution methods.

Given an rth-order linear differential equation $\mathsf{L}y = f(x)$ with r suitable

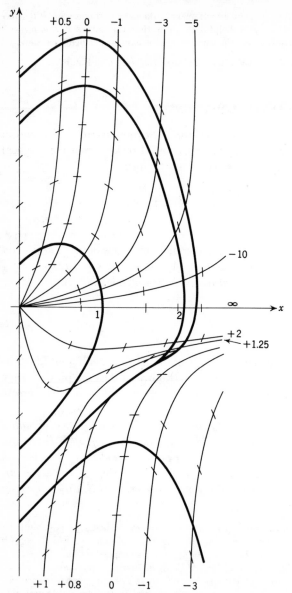

Fig. 6.1-1 Isoclines, tangent directions, and some solutions of the differential equation

$$\frac{dy}{dx} = 1 - x^2 - \frac{x}{y}$$

boundary conditions to be satisfied by $y(x)$ and its derivatives for $x = a$, $x = b$, write the solution as

$$y = y_0(x) + \sum_{k=1}^{r} \alpha_k y_k(x)$$

where the $y_k(x)$ are defined by the $r + 1$ *initial-value problems*

$$\mathbf{L}y_0(x) = f(x) \quad \text{with} \quad y_0^{(j)}(a) = 0 \quad (j = 0, 1, 2, \ldots, r - 1)$$

$$\mathbf{L}y_k(x) = 0 \quad \text{with} \quad y_k^{(j)}(a) = \begin{cases} 0 \text{ for } j \neq k - 1 \\ 1 \text{ for } j = k - 1 \end{cases}$$

$$(j = 0, 1, 2, \ldots, r - 1; k = 1, 2, \ldots, r)$$

Apply the r given boundary conditions to the general solution to obtain r simultaneous equations for the r unknown coefficients α_k.

NOTE: Given a *nonlinear* boundary-value problem like

$$\frac{d^2y}{dx^2} = f(x, y, y') \quad \text{with} \quad y(a) = y_a \quad y(b) = y_b$$

one can often calculate $y(b)$ for two or three trial values of the unknown initial value $y'(a)$; the correct value of $y'(a)$ is then approximated by interpolation.

6.2-2   *Linear Independence and Fundamental Systems of Solutions.*   Let $y_1(x)$, $y_2(x)$, $\ldots$, $y_r(x)$ be $r - 1$ times continuously differentiable solutions of a homogeneous linear differential equation (2) with continuous coefficients in a domain D of values of x. The r solutions $y_k(x)$ are *linearly independent* in D if and only if $\sum_{k=1}^{r} \lambda_k y_k(x) \equiv 0$ in D implies $\lambda_1 = \lambda_2 = \cdots = \lambda_r = 0$. *This is true if and only if the* **Wronskian determinant (Wronskian)**

$$W[y_1, y_2, \ldots, y_r] \equiv \begin{vmatrix} y_1(x) & y_2(x) & \cdots & y_r(x) \\ y_1'(x) & y_2'(x) & \cdots & y_r'(x) \\ \cdot\cdot\cdot\cdot\cdot\cdot\cdot\cdot\cdot\cdot\cdot\cdot\cdot\cdot\cdot\cdot\cdot\cdot\cdot\cdot\cdot\cdot \\ y_1^{(r-1)}(x) & y_2^{(r-1)}(x) & \cdots & y_r^{(r-1)}(x) \end{vmatrix}$$

$$(6.2\text{-}3)$$

differs from zero throughout D. $W = 0$ for any x in D implies $W \equiv 0$ for all x in D.*

A homogeneous linear differential equation (2) of order r has at most r linearly independent solutions. r linearly independent solutions $y_1(x)$, $y_2(x)$, $\ldots$, $y_k(x)$ constitute a **fundamental system** of solutions

---

* Note that the theorem in this simple form does *not* apply to every set of $r - 1$ times continuously differentiable functions $y_k(x)$; they must be solutions of a suitable differential equation (2).

whose linear combinations $\sum_{k=1}^{r} \alpha_k y_k(x)$ include all particular integrals of Eq. (2).

6.2-3 Solution by Variation of Constants (Variation of Parameters).
Given r linearly independent solutions $y_1(x), y_2(x), \ldots, y_r(x)$ of the homogeneous linear differential equation (2), the general solution of the complete nonhomogeneous equation (1) is

$$y = C_1(x)y_1(x) + C_2(z)y_2(x) + \cdots + C_r(z)y_r(x) \qquad (6.2\text{-}4)$$

with

$$\sum_{k=1}^{r} C_k'(x)y_k^{(j)}(x) = 0 \qquad (j = 0, 1, 2, \ldots, r-2)$$

$$\sum_{k=1}^{r} C_k'(x)y_k^{(r-1)}(x) = \frac{f(x)}{a_0(x)} \qquad (6.2\text{-}5)$$

After solving the r simultaneous equations (5) for the r unknown derivatives $C_k'(x)$, one obtains each $C_k(x) = \int C_k'(x)\,dx + K_k$ by a simple integration. In principle, *this procedure reduces the solution of any linear ordinary differential equation to the solution of a homogeneous linear differential equation.*

6.2-4 Homogeneous Linear Equations with Constant Coefficients.
(*a*) The *first-order differential equation*

$$a_0 \frac{dy}{dt} + a_1 y = 0 \qquad (a_0 \neq 0) \qquad (6.2\text{-}6)$$

has the solution

$$y = Ce^{-(a_1/a_0)t} \qquad [C = y(0)] \qquad (6.2\text{-}7)$$

For $a_0/a_1 > 0$

$$y\left(\frac{a_0}{a_1}\right) = \frac{1}{e}\,y(0) \approx 0.37y(0) \qquad y\left(\frac{4a_0}{a_1}\right) \approx 0.02y(0) \qquad (6.2\text{-}8)$$

a_0/a_1 is often referred to as the **time constant**.

(*b*) The *second-order equation*

$$a_0 \frac{d^2y}{dt^2} + a_1 \frac{dy}{dt} + a_2 y = 0 \qquad (a_0 \neq 0) \qquad (6.2\text{-}9)$$

has the solution

$$y = C_1 e^{s_1 t} + C_2 e^{s_2 t}$$
$$\left.\begin{array}{l} \\ s_{1,2} = \dfrac{-a_1 \pm \sqrt{a_1{}^2 - 4a_0 a_2}}{2a_0} \end{array}\right\} \qquad (a_1{}^2 - 4a_0 a_2 \neq 0) \qquad (6.2\text{-}10a)$$

$$y = (C_1 + C_2 t)e^{-(a_1/2a_0)t} \qquad (a_1{}^2 - 4a_0 a_2 = 0) \qquad (6.2\text{-}10b)$$

If a_0, a_1, and a_2 are real, s_1 and s_2 become complex for $a_1{}^2 - 4a_0 a_2 < 0$; in this case, Eq. (10a) can be written as

$$y = e^{\sigma_1 t}(A \cos \omega_N t + B \sin \omega_N t) = R e^{\sigma_1 t} \sin (\omega_N t + \alpha) \qquad (6.2\text{-}10c)$$

where the quantities

$$\sigma_1 = -\frac{a_1}{2a_0} \qquad \omega_N = \frac{\sqrt{4a_0 a_2 - a_1{}^2}}{2a_0} \qquad (6.2\text{-}10d)$$

are respectively known as the **damping constant** and the **natural (characteristic) circular frequency.** The constants C_1, C_2, A, B, R, and α are chosen so as to match given initial or boundary conditions (see also Fig. 6.2-1).

If $a_0 a_2 > 0$, the quantity $\zeta = a_1/2\sqrt{a_0 a_2}$ is called the **damping ratio;** for $\zeta > 1$, $\zeta = 1$, $0 < \zeta < 1$ one obtains, respectively, an *overdamped* solution (10a), a *critically damped* solution (10b), or an *underdamped (oscillatory)* solution (10c). In the latter case, the **logarithmic decrement** $2\pi\sigma_1/\omega_N$ is the natural logarithm of the ratio of successive maxima of $y(t)$.

Equation (9) is often written in the *nondimensional form*

$$\frac{1}{\omega_1{}^2} \frac{d^2 y}{dt^2} + 2\frac{\zeta}{\omega_1} \frac{dy}{dt} + y = 0 \qquad (6.2\text{-}11)$$

with $\quad s_{1,2} = -\omega_1 \zeta \pm \omega_1 \sqrt{\zeta^2 - 1} \qquad (6.2\text{-}12)$

$\omega_1 = \sqrt{a_2/a_0}$ is called the **undamped natural circular frequency;** for weak damping ($\zeta^2 \ll 1$), $\omega_1 \approx \omega_N$.

(c) To solve the rth-*order differential equation*

$$\boxed{\mathbf{L}y \equiv a_0 \frac{d^r y}{dt^r} + a_1 \frac{d^{r-1} y}{dt^{r-1}} + \cdots + a_r y = 0 \qquad (a_0 \neq 0)}$$
$$(6.2\text{-}13)$$

find the roots of the rth-degree algebraic equation

$$a_0 s^r + a_1 s^{r-1} + \cdots + a_0 = 0 \qquad (\text{CHARACTERISTIC EQUATION})$$
$$(6.2\text{-}14)$$

obtained, for example, on substitution of a trial solution $y = e^{st}$. If the

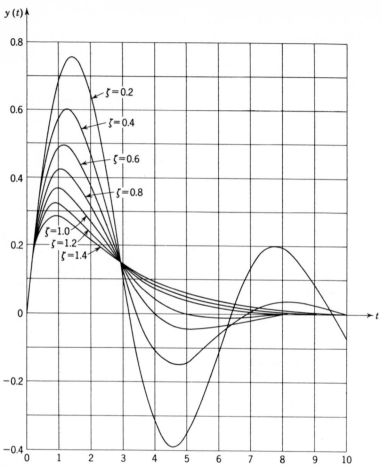

Fig. 6.2-1 Solution of the second-order differential equation

$$\frac{d^2y}{dt^2} + 2\zeta\frac{dy}{dt} + y = 0$$

for $y(0) = 0$, $dy/dt]_0 = 1$.   Response is overdamped for $\zeta > 1$, critically damped for $\zeta = 1$, and underdamped for $\zeta < 1$.

r roots s_1, s_2, . . . of the characteristic equation (14) are distinct, the given differential equation (13) has the general solution

$$y = C_1 e^{s_1 t} + C_2 e^{s_2 t} + \cdots + C_r e^{s_r t} \tag{6.2-15a}$$

If a root s_k is of multiplicity m_k, replace the corresponding term in Eq. (15a) by

$$(C_k + C_{k1}t + C_{k2}t^2 + \cdots + C_{km_k-1}t^{m_k-1})e^{s_kt} \tag{6.2-15b}$$

The various terms of the solution (15) are known as **normal modes** of the given differential equation. The r constants C_k and C_{kj} must be chosen so as to match given initial or boundary conditions.

If the given differential equation (13) is real, complex roots of the characteristic equation appear as pairs of complex conjugates $\sigma \pm i\omega$. The corresponding pairs of solution terms will also be complex conjugates and may be combined to form real terms:

$$
\begin{aligned}
t^m C e^{(\sigma+i\omega)t} + t^m C^* e^{(\sigma-i\omega)t} &= t^m e^{\sigma t}(A \cos \omega t + B \sin \omega t) \\
&= R t^m e^{\sigma t} \sin (\omega t + \alpha)
\end{aligned}
\tag{6.2-15c}
$$

where A and B, or R and α, are new real constants of integration.

(d) Given a *system of n homogeneous linear differential equations with constant coefficients*

$$
\begin{aligned}
\varphi_{j1}\left(\frac{d}{dt}\right) y_1 + \varphi_{j2}\left(\frac{d}{dt}\right) y_2 + \cdots + \varphi_{jn}\left(\frac{d}{dt}\right) y_n &= 0 \\
(j = 1, 2, \ldots, n)
\end{aligned}
\tag{6.2-16}
$$

where the $\varphi_{jk}\left(\dfrac{d}{dt}\right)$ are polynomials in d/dt, each of the n solution functions $y_k = y_k(t)$ $(k = 1, 2, \ldots, n)$ has the form (15); the s_k are now the roots of the algebraic equation

$$D(s) \equiv \det [\varphi_{jk}(s)] = 0 \quad \begin{bmatrix}\text{CHARACTERISTIC EQUATION} \\ \text{OF THE SYSTEM } (16)\end{bmatrix} \tag{6.2-17}$$

The constants of integration must again be matched to the given initial or boundary conditions.

6.2-5 Nonhomogeneous Equations. Normal Response, Steady-state Solution, and Transients.

(a) The superposition theorems and solution methods of Secs. 6.2-1 to 6.2-3 apply to all linear ordinary differential equations. Thus the general solution of the nonhomogeneous differential equation

$$\mathsf{L}y \equiv a_0 \frac{d^r y}{dt^r} + a_1 \frac{d^{r-1}y}{dt^{r-1}} + \cdots + a_r y = f(t) \tag{6.2-18}$$

can be expressed as the sum of the general solution (15) of the reduced equation (13) and any particular integral of Eq. (18).

If, as in many applications, $f(t) = 0$ for $t \leq 0$, the particular integral $y = y_N(t)$ of Eq. (18) with $y_N = y'_N = y''_N = \cdots = y_N{}^{(r-1)} = 0$ for $t \leq 0$ will be called the **normal response** to the given forcing function $f(t)$. *To solve Eq. (18) for $t > 0$ with given initial values for $y, y', y'', \ldots, y^{(r-1)}$, one adds the solution of the corresponding initial-value problem for Eq. (13) to the normal response $y_N(t)$.*

In many applications (stable electric circuits, vibrations), all roots of the characteristic equation (17) have negative real parts, and the complementary function (15) dies out more or less rapidly (stable "transient solution"). In such cases, one is often mainly interested in a suitable nontransient particular integral $y = y_{SS}(t)$, the "steady-state solution" due to the given forcing function $f(t)$. In other cases, $y_{SS}(t)$ is not uniquely defined by the given differential equation but depends on the initial conditions. The normal response $y_N(t)$ may or may not include a transient term.

(b) In the same manner, each solution function $y_k = y_k(t)$ of a system of linear differential equations with constant coefficients,

$$
\varphi_{j1}\left(\frac{d}{dt}\right) y_1 + \varphi_{j2}\left(\frac{d}{dt}\right) y_2 + \cdots + \varphi_{jn}\left(\frac{d}{dt}\right) y_n = f_j(t)
$$

$$
(j = 1, 2, \ldots, n) \quad (6.2\text{-}19)
$$

can be expressed as the sum of the corresponding solution function of the complementary homogeneous system (16) and a particular solution function of the given system (19). The **normal response** of the system (19) to a set of forcing functions $f_j(t)$ equal to zero for $t \leq 0$ is the particular solution such that all y_k vanish for $t \leq 0$ together with all derivatives which can be arbitrarily chosen.

(c) If a forcing function contains a periodic term whose frequency equals that of an undamped sinusoidal term in the complementary function (15), then the differential equation or system may not have a finite solution (*resonance;* see also Sec. 6.2-7).

6.2-6 The Laplace-transform Method of Solution (*see also Secs. 5.4-1 to 5.4-8*).

(a) To solve a linear differential equation (10) with given initial values $y(0 + 0)$, $y'(0 + 0)$, $y''(0 + 0)$, $\ldots$, $y^{(r-1)}(0 + 0)$, apply the Laplace transformation (5.4-1) to both sides, and let $\mathcal{L}[y(t)] \equiv Y(s)$, $\mathcal{L}[f(t)] \equiv F(s)$. The resulting linear *algebraic* equation (*subsidiary equation*)

$$(a_0 s^r + a_1 s^{r-1} + \cdots + a_r) Y(s) = F(s) + G(s)$$

$$\begin{aligned} G(s) \equiv \; & y(0+0)(a_0 s^{r-1} + a_1 s^{r-2} + \cdots + a_{r-1}) \\ & + y'(0+0)(a_0 s^{r-2} + a_1 s^{r-3} + \cdots + a_{r-2}) \\ & + \cdots \\ & + y^{(r-2)}(0+0)(a_0 s + a_1) + a_0 y^{(r-1)}(0+0) \end{aligned}$$

(6.2-20)

is easily solved to yield the Laplace transform of the desired solution $y(t)$ in the form

$$Y(s) = \frac{F(s)}{a_0 s^r + a_1 s^{r-1} + \cdots + a_r} + \frac{G(s)}{a_0 s^r + a_1 s^{r-1} + \cdots + a_r}$$

(6.2-21)

Here the first term is the *Laplace transform $Y_N(s)$ of the normal response* $y_N(t)$ (Sec. 6.2-5a), and the second term represents the effects of nonzero initial values of $y(t)$ and its derivatives. The solutions $y(t)$ and $y_N(t)$ are found as inverse Laplace transforms by reference to tables (Appendix D), or by one of the methods of Sec. 5.4-8. In particular, each of the r terms in the partial-fraction expansion of $G(s)/(a_0 s^r + a_1 s^{r-1} + \cdots + a_r)$ (Sec. 5.4-8) yields a corresponding term of the force-free solution (15).

(b) In the same manner, one applies the Laplace transformation to a system of linear differential equations (11) to obtain

$$\varphi_{j1}(s) Y_1(s) + \varphi_{j2}(s) Y_2(s) + \cdots + \varphi_{jn}(s) Y_n(s) = F_j(s) + G_j(s)$$
$$(j = 1, 2, \ldots, n) \quad (6.2\text{-}22)$$

where the functions $G_j(s)$ depend on the given initial conditions. The linear *algebraic* equations (22) are solved by Cramer's rule (1.6-6) to yield the unknown solution transforms

$$Y_k(s) = \sum_{j=1}^{n} \frac{A_{jk}(s)}{D(s)} F_j(s) + \sum_{j=1}^{n} \frac{A_{jk}(s)}{D(s)} G_j(s)$$
$$(k = 1, 2, \ldots, n) \quad (6.2\text{-}23)$$

where $A_{jk}(s)$ is the cofactor of $\varphi_{jk}(s)$ in the **system determinant** $D(s) \equiv \det [\varphi_{jk}(s)]$ (see also Sec. 1.6-2). The first sum in Eq. (23) is the Laplace transform of the normal-response solution, while the second sum represents the effect of the initial conditions.

The desired solutions $y_k(t)$ are obtained from Eq. (23) by inverse Laplace transformation.

6.2-7 Sinusoidal Forcing Functions and Solutions. The Phasor Method.

Every system of linear differential equations (19) *with sinusoidal forcing functions of equal frequency*,

$$f_j(t) \equiv B_j \sin(\omega t + \beta_j) \qquad (j = 1, 2, \ldots, n) \qquad (6.2\text{-}24a)$$

admits a unique particular solution of the form

$$y_k(t) \equiv A_k \sin(\omega t + \alpha_k) \qquad (k = 1, 2, \ldots, n) \qquad (6.2\text{-}24b)$$

In particular, *if all roots of the characteristic equation* (17) *have negative real parts (stable systems), the sinusoidal solution* (24b) *is the unique steady-state solution obtained after all transients have died out* (Sec. 6.2-5).

Given a system of linear differential equations (19) relating sinusoidal forcing functions and solutions (24), *one introduces a reciprocal one-to-one representation of these sinusoids by corresponding complex numbers (vectors, **phasors**)*

$$F_j = \frac{B_j}{\sqrt{2}} e^{i\beta_i} = \frac{B_j}{\sqrt{2}} \underline{/\beta_j} \qquad (j = 1, 2, \ldots, n)$$

$$\vec{Y}_k = \frac{A_k}{\sqrt{2}} e^{i\alpha_k} = \frac{A_k}{\sqrt{2}} \underline{/\alpha_k} \qquad (k = 1, 2, \ldots, n) \qquad (6.2\text{-}25)$$

The absolute value of each phasor equals the root-mean-square value of the corresponding sinusoid, while the phasor argument defines the phase of the sinusoid. *The phasors* (25) *are related by the (complex) linear algebraic equations (phasor equations)*

$$\varphi_{j1}(i\omega)\vec{Y}_1 + \varphi_{j2}(i\omega)\vec{Y}_2 + \cdots + \varphi_{jn}(i\omega)\vec{Y}_n = \vec{F}_j$$
$$(j = 1, 2, \ldots, n) \qquad (6.2\text{-}26)$$

which correspond to Eq. (19) and may be solved for the unknown phasors

$$\vec{Y}_k = \sum_{j=1}^{n} \frac{A_{jk}(i\omega)}{D(i\omega)} \vec{F}_j \qquad (k = 1, 2, \ldots, n) \qquad (6.2\text{-}27)$$

(see also Sec. 6.2-6b). In the case of *resonance* (Sec. 6.2-5c), the expression (27) may not exist (may become "infinitely large").

6.3 PARTIAL DIFFERENTIAL EQUATIONS

6.3-1 Partial Differential Equations.

A **partial differential equation of order** r is a functional equation of the form

$$F\left(x_1, x_2, \ldots, x_n; \Phi; \frac{\partial \Phi}{\partial x_1}, \frac{\partial \Phi}{\partial x_2}, \ldots, \frac{\partial \Phi}{\partial x_n}; \frac{\partial^2 \Phi}{\partial x_1^2}, \ldots\right) = 0$$

$$(6.3\text{-}1)$$

which involves at least one r^{th}-order partial derivative of the unknown function $\Phi = \Phi(x_1, x_2, \ldots, x_n)$ of two or more independent variables $x_1, x_2, \ldots, x_n$. A function $\Phi(x_1, x_2, \ldots, x_n)$ which satisfies the given partial differential equation on a specified region of "points" $(x_1, x_2, \ldots, x_n)$ is called a **solution** or **integral** of the partial differential equation.

The **general solution** (**general integral**) of a given r^{th}-order equation (1) will, in general, involve *arbitrary functions*. Substitution of specific functions yields **particular integrals** corresponding to given accessory conditions, e.g., given conditions on $\Phi(x_1, x_2, \ldots, x_n)$ and/or its derivatives on a curve, surface, etc., in the space of "points" $(x_1, x_2, \ldots, x_n)$ (*boundary conditions, initial conditions*). Many partial differential equations admit additional solutions (**singular integrals**) which are not obtainable through substitution of specific functions for the arbitrary functions in the general integral.

6.3-2 Separation of Variables (*see also Sec. 6.3-4*). In many important applications, an attempt to write solutions of the form

$$\Phi = \Phi(x_1, x_2, \ldots, x_n) = \varphi_1(x_1)\varphi_0(x_2, x_3, \ldots, x_n) \qquad (6.3\text{-}2)$$

permits one to rewrite a given partial differential equation (1) in the "separated" form

$$F_1\left(x_1, \varphi_1, \frac{d\varphi_1}{dx_1}, \frac{d^2\varphi_1}{dx_1^2}, \ldots\right)$$

$$= F_0\left(x_2, x_3, \ldots, x_n; \varphi_0; \frac{\partial\varphi_0}{\partial x_2}, \frac{\partial\varphi_0}{\partial x_3}, \ldots\right) \qquad (6.3\text{-}3)$$

Then the unknown functions $\varphi_1(x_1)$ and $\varphi_0(x_2, x_3, \ldots, x_n)$ must satisfy the differential equations

$$F_1\left(x_1, \varphi_1, \frac{d\varphi_1}{dx_1}, \frac{d^2\varphi_1}{dx_1^2}, \ldots\right) = C \qquad (6.3\text{-}4a)$$

$$F_2\left(x_2, x_3, \ldots, x_n; \varphi_0; \frac{\partial\varphi_0}{\partial x_2}, \frac{\partial\varphi_0}{\partial x_3}, \ldots\right) = C \qquad (6.3\text{-}4b)$$

where C is a constant of integration (**separation constant**) to be determined in accordance with suitably given boundary conditions or other accessory conditions. Note that Eq. (4a) is an *ordinary* differential equation for the unknown function $\varphi_1(x_1)$; it may be possible to repeat the separation process with Eq. (4b).

Separation of variables applies particularly well to many linear

Table 6.3-1 The most important linear partial differential equations of classical physics*

Type	Physical background	One-dimensional	Multidimensional	Accessory conditions
Parabolic	**Heat conduction, diffusion**	$\dfrac{\partial^2 \Phi}{\partial x^2} - \dfrac{1}{\gamma^2}\dfrac{\partial \Phi}{\partial t}$ $= f(x, t)$	$\nabla^2 \Phi - \dfrac{1}{\gamma^2}\dfrac{\partial \Phi}{\partial t}$ $= f(\mathbf{r}, t)$	Boundary conditions; initial conditions on Φ
Hyperbolic	**Waves** (strings, membranes, fluids, electromagnetic)	$\dfrac{\partial^2 \Phi}{\partial x^2} - \dfrac{1}{c^2}\dfrac{\partial^2 \Phi}{\partial t^2}$ $= f(x, t)$	$\nabla^2 \Phi - \dfrac{1}{c^2}\dfrac{\partial^2 \Phi}{\partial t^2}$ $= f(\mathbf{r}, t)$	Boundary conditions; initial conditions on Φ and $\dfrac{\partial \Phi}{\partial t}$
	Damped waves, transmission lines	$\dfrac{\partial^2 \Phi}{\partial x^2} - a_0 \dfrac{\partial^2 \Phi}{\partial t^2}$ $- a_0 \dfrac{\partial \Phi}{\partial t} - a_2 \Phi$ $= f(x, t)$	$\nabla^2 \Phi - a_0 \dfrac{\partial^2 \Phi}{\partial t}$ $- a_1 \dfrac{\partial \Phi}{\partial t} - a_2 \Phi$ $= f(\mathbf{r}, t)$	
Elliptic	**Static case**	$\dfrac{\partial^2 \Phi}{\partial x^2} = f(x)$	$\nabla^2 \Phi = f(\mathbf{r})$	Boundary conditions only
4th order	**Elastic vibrations**	$\dfrac{\partial^4 \Phi}{\partial x^4} + \dfrac{1}{c^2}\dfrac{\partial^2 \Phi}{\partial t^2}$ $= f(x, t)$	$\nabla^2 \nabla^2 \Phi + \dfrac{1}{c^2}\dfrac{\partial^2 \Phi}{\partial t^2}$ $= f(\mathbf{r}, t)$	Boundary conditions; initial conditions on Φ and $\dfrac{\partial \Phi}{\partial t}$
	Static case	$\dfrac{\partial^4 \Phi}{\partial x^4} = f(x)$	$\nabla^2 \nabla^2 \Phi = f(\mathbf{r})$	Boundary conditions only

*From G. A. Korn and T. M. Korn, *Mathematical Handbook for Scientists and Engineers*, McGraw-Hill, New York, 1961.

homogeneous partial differential equations of physics; sometimes separation becomes possible after an appropriate change of variables.

6.3-3 Linear Partial Differential Equations in Physics. Many problems of classical physics require one to find a solution $\Phi(x, t)$ or $\Phi(\mathbf{r}, t)$ of a linear partial differential equation on a given space interval or region V (Table 6.3-1). The unknown function Φ and/or its derivatives must, in addition, satisfy given *initial conditions* for $t = 0$ and linear *boundary conditions* on the boundary S of V. Related problems arise in quantum mechanics.

Each partial differential equation listed in Table 6.3-1 is **homogeneous** if $f \equiv 0$. A given boundary condition is, again, homogeneous if and only if it holds for every multiple $\alpha\Phi$ of any function which satisfies the condition. Inhomogeneities represent the action of external influences (forces, heat sources, electric charges or currents) on the physical system under consideration. Typically, an elliptic differential equation describes an *equilibrium situation* (steady-state heat flow, elastic deformation, electrostatic field). Parabolic and hyperbolic differential equations describe *transients* (free vibrations, return to equilibrium after a given initial disturbance) or, if there are time-dependent inhomogeneities ("forcing functions" in the differential equation or boundary conditions), such equations describe the *propagation of disturbances* (forced vibrations, radiation).

The system of coordinates x^1, x^2, or x^1, x^2, x^3 used to specify the point ($\mathbf{r}$) is usually chosen so that (1) *separation of variables is possible* (Sec. 6.3-2) and/or (2) *the given boundary S becomes a coordinate line or surface, or a pair of coordinate lines or surfaces.*

6.3-4 Particular Solutions of Laplace's Differential Equation.
(a) RECTANGULAR CARTESIAN COORDINATES x, y, z.

$$\nabla^2\Phi \equiv \frac{\partial^2\Phi}{\partial x^2} + \frac{\partial^2\Phi}{\partial y^2} + \frac{\partial^2\Phi}{\partial z^2} = 0 \tag{6.3-5}$$

admits the particular solutions

$$\begin{aligned}
\Phi_{k_1k_2k_3}(x, y, z) &= e^{k_1 x + k_2 y + k_3 z} \quad (k_1{}^2 + k_2{}^2 + k_3{}^2 = 0) \\
\Phi_{000}(x, y, z) &= (a + bx)(\alpha + \beta y)(A + Bz)
\end{aligned} \tag{6.3-6}$$

which combine into various products of real linear, exponential, trigonometric, and/or hyperbolic functions.

(*b*) CYLINDRICAL COORDINATES r', φ, z. Let $\Phi = u(\varphi)v(z)w(r')$ (Sec. 6.3-2). Then

$$\nabla^2\Phi \equiv \frac{1}{r'}\frac{\partial}{\partial r'}\left(r'\frac{\partial \Phi}{\partial r'}\right) + \frac{1}{r'^2}\frac{\partial^2 \Phi}{\partial \varphi^2} + \frac{\partial^2 \Phi}{\partial z^2} = 0 \qquad (6.3\text{-}7)$$

separates into

$$\frac{d^2}{d\varphi^2}u(\varphi) + m^2 u(\varphi) = 0 \qquad (6.3\text{-}8)$$

$$\frac{d^2}{dz^2}v(z) + K^2 v(z) = 0 \qquad (6.3\text{-}9)$$

$$\frac{d^2}{dr'^2}w(r') + \frac{1}{r'}\frac{d}{dr'}w(r') - \left(K^2 + \frac{m^2}{r'^2}\right)w(r') = 0 \qquad (6.3\text{-}10)$$

where uniqueness requires $u(\varphi + 2\pi) = u(\varphi)$ or $m = 0, \pm 1, \pm 2, \ldots$, and K is an arbitrary constant (separation constant, Sec. 6.3-2) to be determined by the given boundary conditions. Equation (7) admits particular solutions (**cylindrical harmonics**) of the form

$$\Phi_{\pm Km}(r', \varphi, z) = e^{\pm iKz}Z_m(iKr')(\alpha \cos m\varphi + \beta \sin m\varphi)$$
$$\Phi_{\pm K0}(r', \varphi, z) = e^{\pm iKz}Z_0(iKr')(\alpha + \beta\varphi)$$
$$\Phi_{0m}(r', \varphi, z) = (a + bz)\left(Ar' + \frac{B}{r'}\right)(\alpha \cos m\varphi + \beta \sin m\varphi)$$
$$\Phi_{00}(r', \varphi, z) = (a + bz)(A + B \log_e r')(\alpha + \beta\varphi)$$
$$(m = 0, 1, 2, \ldots) \qquad (6.3\text{-}11)$$

where $Z_m(\zeta)$ is a *cylinder function* (Sec. 11.3-3); in particular, if a given problem requires Φ to be analytic for $r = 0$, then $Z_m(\zeta)$ must be a *Bessel function of the first kind* (Sec. 11.3-3). Note that *complex-conjugate solutions* (11) *combine into real particular solutions* like

$$(a \cos Kz + b \sin Kz)[AZ_m(iKr') + A^*Z_m(-iKr')]$$
$$\cdot (\alpha \cos m\varphi + \beta \sin m\varphi) \qquad (6.3\text{-}12)$$

for real K. Such solutions can be superimposed to form real Fourier series. Note that $m = 0$ in cases of *axial symmetry*.

(*c*) SPHERICAL COORDINATES r, ϑ, φ. Let $\Phi = u(\varphi)v(\cos \vartheta)w(r)$. Then

$$r^2\nabla^2\Phi \equiv \frac{\partial}{\partial r}\left(r^2\frac{\partial \Phi}{\partial r}\right) + \frac{1}{\sin \vartheta}\frac{\partial}{\partial \vartheta}\left(\sin \vartheta \frac{\partial \Phi}{\partial \vartheta}\right) + \frac{1}{\sin^2 \vartheta}\frac{\partial^2 \Phi}{\partial \varphi^2} = 0$$
$$(6.3\text{-}13)$$

separates into

$$\frac{d^2}{d\varphi^2} u(\varphi) + m^2 u(\varphi) = 0 \tag{6.3-14}$$

$$(1 - \zeta^2) \frac{d^2}{d\zeta^2} v(\zeta) - 2\zeta \frac{d}{d\zeta} v(\zeta) + \left[j(j+1) - \frac{m^2}{1 - \zeta^2} \right] v(\zeta) = 0$$
$$(\zeta = \cos \vartheta) \tag{6.3-15}$$

$$\frac{d^2}{dr^2} w(r) + \frac{2}{r} \frac{d}{dr} w(r) - \frac{j(j+1)}{r^2} w(r) = 0 \tag{6.3-16}$$

where regularity for $\vartheta = 0$, $\vartheta = \pi$ and uniqueness require that $m = 0$, $\pm 1, \pm 2, \ldots, \pm j$ and $j = 0, 1, 2, \ldots$. Equation (13) admits particular solutions of the form

$$\Phi_{jm}(r, \vartheta, \varphi) = \left(A r^j + \frac{B}{r^{j+1}} \right) P_j{}^m(\cos \vartheta)(\alpha \cos m\varphi + \beta \sin m\varphi)$$
$$(j = 0, 1, 2, \ldots ; m = 0, 1, 2, \ldots, j) \tag{6.3-17}$$

where the $P_j{}^m(\zeta)$ are *associated Legendre functions of the first kind of degree j*. Combination of such solutions yields more general particular solutions

$$\Phi_j(r, \vartheta, \varphi) = \left(A r^j + \frac{B}{r^{j+1}} \right) Y_j(\vartheta, \varphi) \qquad (j = 0, 1, 2, \ldots) \tag{6.3-18}$$

with

$$Y_j(\vartheta, \varphi) = \sum_{m=0}^{j} P_j{}^m(\cos \vartheta)(\alpha_m \cos m\varphi + \beta_m \sin m\varphi)$$
$$= \sum_{m=-j}^{j} \gamma_m P_j{}^{|m|}(\cos \vartheta)e^{im\varphi} \qquad (j = 0, 1, 2, \ldots) \tag{6.3-19}$$

The functions (19) satisfy Eq. (13) for $r = $ constant and are called **spherical surface harmonics** of degree j (see also Refs. 12 to 14).

    (*d*) TWO-DIMENSIONAL CASE. The two-dimensional Laplace equation

$$\nabla^2 \Phi \equiv \frac{\partial^2 \Phi}{\partial x^2} + \frac{\partial^2 \Phi}{\partial y^2} \equiv \frac{1}{r} \frac{\partial}{\partial r} \left(r \frac{\partial \Phi}{\partial r} \right) + \frac{1}{r^2} \frac{\partial^2 \Phi}{\partial \varphi^2} = 0 \tag{6.3-20}$$

admits the particular solutions

$$\Phi_K(x, y) = e^{\pm K(x + iy)} \qquad \Phi_0(x, y) = (a + bx)(\alpha + \beta y) \tag{6.3-21}$$

$$\Phi_m(r, \varphi) = \left(Ar^m + \frac{B}{r^m} \right) (\alpha \cos m\varphi + \beta \sin m\varphi)$$

$$(m = 0, 1, 2, \ldots) \quad (6.3\text{-}22)$$

$$\Phi_0(r, \varphi) = A + B \log_e r$$

where K, like a, b, α, β, A, B, is an arbitrary parameter to be determined by the boundary conditions.

References and Bibliography

1. Coddington, E. A., and N. Levinson: *Theory of Ordinary Differential Equations*, McGraw-Hill, New York, 1955.
2. Ford, L. R.: *Differential Equations*, 2d ed., McGraw-Hill, New York, 1955.
3. Hurewicz, W.: *Lectures on Ordinary Differential Equations*, MIT Press, Cambridge, Mass., 1958.
4. Agnew, R. P.: *Differential Equations*, 2d ed., McGraw-Hill, New York, 1960.
5. Coddington, E. A.: *An Introduction to Ordinary Differential Equations*, Prentice-Hall, Englewood Cliffs, N.J., 1961.
6. Tricomi, F. G.: *Differential Equations*, Hafner, New York, 1961.
7. Pontryagin, L. S.: *Ordinary Differential Equations*, Addison-Wesley, Reading, Mass., 1962.
8. Birkhoff, G., and G. Rota: *Ordinary Differential Equations*, Blaisdell, New York, 1962.
9. Lefschetz, S.: *Differential Equations: Geometric Theory*, 2d ed., Interscience, New York, 1963.
10. Tenenbaum, M., and H. Pollard: *Ordinary Differential Equations*, Harper and Row, New York, 1963.
11. Golomb, M., and M. Shanks: *Elements of Ordinary Differential Equations*, 2d ed., McGraw-Hill, New York, 1965.

Partial differential equations

12. Hopf, L.: *Introduction to the Partial Differential Equations of Physics*, Dover, New York, 1948.
13. Courant, R., and D. Hilbert: *Methods of Mathematical Physics* (2 vols.), Wiley, New York, 1953.
14. Morse, P. M., and H. Feshbach: *Methods of Theoretical Physics*, McGraw-Hill, New York, 1953.
15. Friedman, B.: *Principles and Techniques of Applied Mathematics*, Wiley, New York, 1956.
16. Sneddon, I. N.: *Elements of Partial Differential Equations*, McGraw-Hill, New York, 1957.
17. Epstein, B.: *Partial Differential Equations*, McGraw-Hill, New York, 1962.
18. Bers, L., F. John, and M. Schechter: *Partial Differential Equations*, Wiley, New York, 1963.
19. Churchill, R. V.: *Fourier Series and Boundary-value Problems*, 2d ed., McGraw-Hill, New York, 1963.
20. Garabedian, P. R.: *Partial Differential Equations*, Wiley, New York, 1964.

7 MAXIMA AND MINIMA

7.1 INTRODUCTION

7.1-1 Introductory Remarks. A large class of problems can be stated as *extreme-value problems:* one desires to find parameter values or functions which *maximize* or *minimize* a quantity dependent upon them. In many engineering problems it is, for instance, desirable to maximize a measure of performance or to minimize cost. Again, one can at least approximate the solutions of many problems by choosing unknown parameter values or functions so as to minimize errors in trial solutions; restatement of a problem as an extreme-value problem may then lead to powerful numerical approximation methods.

7.2 MAXIMA AND MINIMA FUNCTIONS

7.2-1 Relative Maxima and Minima. A real function $f(x)$ defined for $x = a$ has a (**relative**) **maximum** or a (**relative**) **minimum** $f(a)$, for $x = a$ if and only if there exists a positive real number δ such that, respectively,

$$\Delta f \equiv f(a + \Delta x) - f(a) < 0 \qquad \text{or} \qquad \Delta f \equiv f(a + \Delta x) - f(a) > 0$$

for all $\Delta x = x - a$ such that $f(a + \Delta x)$ exists and $0 < |\Delta x| < \delta.$* The relative maximum (minimum) is an **interior maximum (interior minimum)** or a **boundary maximum (boundary minimum)** if $x = a$ is, respectively, an interior point or a boundary point of the domain of definition assigned to $f(x).$†

7.2-2 Conditions for the Existence of Interior Maxima and Minima. (a) *If $f'(x)$ exists and is continuous for $x = a$, then $f(a)$ can be a (necessarily interior) maximum or minimum only if $f(x)$ has a* **stationary value** *for $x = a$, i.e.,*

$$f'(a) = 0 \tag{7.2-1}$$

(b) *If $f(x)$ has a continuous second derivative $f''(x)$ for $x = a$, then $f(a)$ is*

A maximum if $f'(a) = 0$ and $f''(a) < 0$
A minimum if $f'(a) = 0$ and $f''(a) > 0$

(c) More generally, *if $f(x)$ has n continuous derivatives $f'(x)$, $f''(x)$, . . . , $f^{(n)}(x)$ for $x = a$, and $f'(a) = f''(a) = \cdots = f^{(n-1)}(a) = 0$, then $f(a)$ is*

A maximum if n is even and $f^{(n)}(a) < 0$
A minimum if n is even and $f^{(n)}(a) > 0$

If n is odd, $f(x)$ has neither a maximum nor a minimum for $x = a$, but a *point of inflection.*

Examples: Each of the functions x^2, x^4, x^6, . . . has a minimum for $x = 0$. Each of the functions x^3, x^5, x^7, . . . has a point of inflection for $x = 0$.

* Δf is defined as the change of a given function $f(x)$ resulting from a change Δx in the independent variable x. Δf is a function of a and Δx. Δf must not be confused with the *variation δf* introduced in Sec. 7.3-1.

† The problem statement must specify the domain of definition of $f(x)$. Note that $f_1(x) = x$ $(-\infty < x < \infty)$ has no maximum, but $f_2(x) = x$ $(x \leq 1)$ has a boundary maximum for $x = 1$.

7.2-3   *Relative Maxima and Minima of Functions of Two or More Variables.** A real function $f(x_1, x_2, \ldots, x_n)$ defined for $x_1 = a_1, x_2 = a_2, \ldots, x_n = a_n$ has a (**relative**) **maximum** or a (**relative**) **minimum** $f(a_1, a_2, \ldots, a_n)$ for $x_1 = a_1, x_2 = a_2, \ldots, x_n = a_n$ if and only if there exists a positive real number δ such that

$$\Delta f \equiv f(a_1 + \Delta x_1, a_2 + \Delta x_2, \ldots, a_n + \Delta x_n) \\ - f(a_1, a_2, \ldots, a_n) \quad (7.2\text{-}2)$$

is, respectively, less than zero or greater than zero for all $\Delta x_1, \Delta x_2, \ldots, \Delta x_n$ such that $f(a_1 + \Delta x_1, a_2 + \Delta x_2, \ldots, a_n + \Delta x_n)$ exists and $0 < \Delta x_1^2 + \Delta x_2^2 + \cdots + \Delta x_n^2 < \delta$. The relative maximum (minimum) is an **interior maximum** (**interior minimum**) or a **boundary maximum** (**boundary minimum**) if the point $(a_1, a_2, \ldots, a_n)$ is, respectively, an interior point or a boundary point of the region of definition assigned to $f(x_1, x_2, \ldots, x_n)$.

The quantity Δf defined by Eq. (2) is a function of $a_1, a_2, \ldots, a_n$ and $\Delta x_1, \Delta x_2, \ldots, \Delta x_n$. If $f(x_1, x_2, \ldots, x_n)$ is suitably differentiable,

$$\Delta f = \sum_{i=1}^{n} \frac{\partial f}{\partial x_i}\bigg]_{a_1, a_2, \ldots, a_n} \Delta x_i + \frac{1}{2} \sum_{i=1}^{n} \sum_{k=1}^{n} \frac{\partial^2 f}{\partial x_i \, \partial x_k}\bigg]_{a_1, a_2, \ldots, a_n} \Delta x_i \, \Delta x_k + \cdots$$

$$(7.2\text{-}3)$$

7.2-4   *Conditions for the Existence of Interior Maxima and Minima.*   (a) *If $f(x_1, x_2, \ldots, x_n)$ is continuously differentiable for $x_1 = a_1, x_2 = a_2, \ldots, x_n = a_n$, $f(a_1, a_2, \ldots, a_n)$ can be a (necessarily interior) maximum or minimum only if*

$$\boxed{\frac{\partial f}{\partial x_1} = 0 \qquad \frac{\partial f}{\partial x_2} = 0 \qquad \cdots \qquad \frac{\partial f}{\partial x_n} = 0 \qquad (7.2\text{-}4)}$$

for $x_1 = a_1, x_2 = a_2, \ldots, x_n = a_n$. $f(x_1, x_2, \ldots, x_n)$ is then said to have a **stationary value** for $x_1 = a_1, x_2 = a_2, \ldots, x_n = a_n$.

(b) *If $f(x_1, x_2, \ldots, x_n)$ is twice continuously differentiable and satisfies the necessary condition (4) for $x_1 = a_1, x_2 = a_2, \ldots, x_n = a_n$, then $f(a_1, a_2, \ldots, a_n)$ is a maximum if the (real symmetric) quadratic form*

$$\Delta^2 f = \frac{1}{2} \sum_{i=1}^{n} \sum_{k=1}^{n} \frac{\partial^2 f}{\partial x_i \, \partial x_k}\bigg]_{a_1, a_2, \ldots, a_n} \Delta x_i \, \Delta x_k \qquad (7.2\text{-}5)$$

*See footnotes to Sec. 7.2-1.

is negative definite, i.e., if it is negative whenever the Δx_i are not all zero; $f(a_1, a_2, \ldots, a_n)$ *is a minimum if the quadratic form* (5) *is positive definite* (i.e., if $-\Delta^2 f$ is negative definite).

Example: Find the maxima and minima of the function

$$z = 3x^3 - x + y^3 - 3y^2 - 1$$

Here the necessary conditions

$$\frac{\partial z}{\partial x} = 9x^2 - 1 = 0 \quad \text{and} \quad \frac{\partial z}{\partial y} = 3y^2 - 6y = 0$$

are satisfied for $x = \frac{1}{3}$, $y = 0$; $x = -\frac{1}{3}$, $y = 0$; $x = \frac{1}{3}$, $y = 2$; $x = -\frac{1}{3}$, $y = 2$. But $\partial^2 z/\partial x^2 = 18x$, $\partial^2 z/\partial y^2 = 6y - 6$, $\partial^2 z/(\partial x\, \partial y) = 0$, and inspection shows that the only extreme values are

a *maximum* $(\mu_1 = -6, \mu_2 = -6)$, $z = -\frac{7}{9}$　　for $x = -\frac{1}{3}$ and $y = 0$
and　a *minimum* $(\mu_1 = 6, \mu_2 = 6)$, $z = -\frac{47}{9}$　　for $x = \frac{1}{3}$ and $y = 2$

7.2-5　Extreme-value Problems with Constraints or Accessory Conditions.　The Method of Lagrange Multipliers. Maxima and minima of a real function $f(x_1, x_2, \ldots, x_n)$ of n variables $x_1, x_2, \ldots, x_n$ subject to suitably differentiable *constraints* or *accessory conditions* in the form of $m < n$ equations

$$\begin{aligned}
&\varphi_1(x_1, x_2, \ldots, x_n) = 0 \\
&\varphi_2(x_1, x_2, \ldots, x_n) = 0 \\
&\cdots\cdots\cdots\cdots\cdots\cdots \\
&\varphi_m(x_1, x_2, \ldots, x_n) = 0
\end{aligned} \qquad (7.2\text{-}6)$$

may, in principle, be found in the manner of Sec. 7.2-3 after m of the n variables $x_1, x_2, \ldots, x_n$ have been eliminated with the aid of the relations (6). If it is impossible or impractical to eliminate m variables directly, one applies the following *necessary condition for a maximum or minimum of* $f(x_1, x_2, \ldots, x_n)$ *subject to the constraints* (6):

$$\frac{\partial \Phi}{\partial x_1} = \frac{\partial \Phi}{\partial x_2} = \cdots = \frac{\partial \Phi}{\partial x_n} = 0$$

with

$$\Phi(x_1, x_2, \ldots, x_n)$$
$$\equiv f(x_1, x_2, \ldots, x_n) + \sum_{j=1}^{m} \lambda_j \varphi_j(x_1, x_2, \ldots, x_n) \quad (7.2\text{-}7)$$

The m parameters λ_j are called **Lagrange multipliers.** The $n + m$

unknowns $x_i = a_i$ and λ_j are obtained from the $n + m$ equations (6) and (7).

Note that Eq. (7) is a necessary condition for a stationary value of the function $\Phi(x_1, x_2, \ldots, x_n)$ if $x_1, x_2, \ldots, x_n$ are *independent* variables.

Example: Find the sides of the rectangle of maximum area inscribed in the circle

$$x^2 + y^2 = r^2$$

The rectangle area A may be expressed in the form

$$A = 4xy$$

Then

$$\Phi(x, y) = 4xy + \lambda(x^2 + y^2 - r^2)$$

The necessary condition for a maximum or minimum yields

$$\frac{\partial \Phi}{\partial x} = 4y + 2\lambda x = 0 \quad \text{and} \quad \frac{\partial \Phi}{\partial y} = 4x + 2\lambda y = 0$$

so that $\lambda = -2$, and $x = y$ yields the desired maximum.

7.2-6 Boundary Maxima and Minima. Linear-programming Problems.
An interesting class of problems deals with maxima and minima situated on the boundary of a specified interval or region. In particular, one may wish to maximize $f(x_1, x_2, \ldots, x_n)$ subject to a set of constraints

$$\varphi_j(x_1, x_2, \ldots, x_n) \geq 0 \qquad (j = 1, 2, \ldots, m) \tag{7.2-8}$$

This problem has been treated in detail for the practically important special case where $f(x_1, x_2, \ldots, x_n)$ and all $\varphi_j(x_1, x_2, \ldots, x_n)$ are *linear* functions of the variables $x_1, x_2, \ldots, x_n$, and $m \geq n$ (*linear-programming problems* in operations analysis, mathematical economics, and game theory). Solutions are usually obtained by numerical methods (Refs. 5, 6, and 8).

7.3 CALCULUS OF VARIATIONS. MAXIMA AND MINIMA OF DEFINITE INTEGRALS

7.3-1 Variations. A **variation** δy of a function $y(x)$ of x is a function of x defined for each value of x as the difference $\delta y \equiv Y(x) - y(x)$ between a new function $Y(x)$ and $y(x)$.

Each variation δy defines *a change in the functional relationship of y and x* and must not be confused with a change Δy in the *value* of a given function $y(x)$ due to a change Δx in the independent variable.

7.3-2 Maxima and Minima of Definite Integrals. While the theory of ordinary maxima and minima (Secs. 7.2-1 to 7.2-6) is concerned with *unknown values of independent variables* x or x_i corresponding to maxima and minima of given functions, it is the objective of the

calculus of variations to find *unknown functions* $y(x)$ *or* $y_i(x)$ *which will maximize or minimize definite integrals* like

$$I = \int_{x_1}^{x_2} F[y(x), y'(x), x] \, dx \tag{7.3-1a}$$

or

$$I = \int_{x_1}^{x_2} F[y_1(x), y_2(x), \ldots, y_n(x);$$
$$y_1'(x), y_2'(x), \ldots, y_n'(x); x] \, dx \tag{7.3-1b}$$

for a specified function F and given finite integration limits x_1, x_2 and boundary values $y(x_1)$, $y(x_2)$ or $y_i(x_1)$, $y_i(x_2)$. In other problems, limits of integration and/or boundary values are also unknowns to be determined.

A definite integral (1) has a (**relative**) **maximum** for a given function $y(x)$ or a given set of functions $y_i(x)$ if and only if there exists a positive real number ϵ such that

$$\delta I = \delta \int_{x_1}^{x_2} F \, dx = \int_{x_1}^{x_2} \delta F \, dx < 0 \tag{7.3-2}$$

for all variations δy, or all sets of variations δy_1, δy_2, $\ldots$, δy_n whose absolute values are less than ϵ and not all identically zero for $x_1 \leq x \leq x_2$. A (**relative**) **minimum** of a definite integral (1) is similarly defined by $\delta I > 0$.

In most applications, the maximizing or minimizing functions $y(x)$ or $y_i(x)$ need not be compared with *all* possible functions of x. IN THE FOLLOWING, THE EXISTENCE OF THE DEFINITE INTEGRALS IN QUESTION IS ASSUMED WHEREVER NECESSARY, AND IT IS UNDERSTOOD THAT (1) MAXIMIZING OR MINIMIZING FUNCTIONS ARE TO BE CHOSEN FROM THE SET OF ALL FUNCTIONS HAVING CONTINUOUS SECOND DERIVATIVES ON THE INTERVAL OR REGION UNDER CONSIDERATION. IN ADDITION, IT WILL BE ASSUMED THAT (2) EACH INTEGRAND F IS TWICE CONTINUOUSLY DIFFERENTIABLE WHEREVER NECESSARY.

Condition (1) is less restrictive than it looks. *Functions $y(x)$ or $y_i(x)$ which actually maximize or minimize a definite integral (1) satisfying condition (2) necessarily have continuous second derivatives for $x_1 < x < x_2$ if one assumes merely that they are piecewise continuously differentiable for $x_1 \leq x \leq x_2$, and $y(x_1) = y(x_2) = 0$, $\partial^2 F / \partial y'^2 \neq 0$ (Theorem of Du Bois-Reymond).*

It is not a trivial observation that *a given problem of the type discussed here may not possess any solution.* Every solution derived with the aid of the necessary (not sufficient) conditions of Secs. 7.3-3 to 7.3-5 *must be tested for actual maximum or minimum properties.*

7.3-3   Necessary Conditions for the Existence of Maxima and Minima.

(a) *A necessary condition for the existence of either a maximum or a minimum of the definite integral*

$$I = \int_{x_1}^{x_2} F[y(x), y'(x), x] \, dx \qquad (7.3\text{-}3)$$

for fixed x_1, x_2 *is*

$$\delta^1 I = \int_{x_1}^{x_2} \delta^1 F \, dx = \frac{\partial F}{\partial y'} \, \delta y \bigg]_{x_1}^{x_2} - \int_{x_1}^{x_2} \left[\frac{d}{dx} \left(\frac{\partial F}{\partial y'} \right) - \frac{\partial F}{\partial y} \right] \delta y \, dx = 0$$

for an arbitrary small variation δy. *Hence every maximizing or minimizing function* $y(x)$ *must satisfy the differential equation*

$$\boxed{\;\frac{d}{dx} \left(\frac{\partial F}{\partial y'} \right) - \frac{\partial F}{\partial y} = 0 \quad \text{(EULER'S DIFFERENTIAL EQUATION)} \\[6pt] \hspace{10cm} (7.3\text{-}4)\;}$$

In addition, $y(x)$ must either assume given boundary values $y(x_1)$ and/or $y(x_2)$, or $y(x)$ must satisfy other conditions determining its boundary values.

(b) Similarly, *every set of* n *functions* $y_1(x)$, $y_2(x)$, . . . , $y_n(x)$ *maximizing or minimizing the definite integral*

$$I = \int_{x_1}^{x_2} F[y_1(x), y_2(x), \ldots, y_n(x); \\ y_1'(x), y_2'(x), \ldots, y_n'(x); x] \, dx \qquad (7.3\text{-}5)$$

must satisfy the set of n *differential equations*

$$\boxed{\;\frac{d}{dx} \left(\frac{\partial F}{\partial y_i'} \right) - \frac{\partial F}{\partial y_i} = 0 \qquad (i = 1, 2, \ldots, n) \\[6pt] \hspace{3cm} \text{(EULER'S DIFFERENTIAL EQUATIONS)} \qquad (7.3\text{-}6)\;}$$

together with suitably given boundary conditions.

(c) Functions $y(x)$ or $y_i(x)$ satisfying the Euler equation or equations associated with a given variation problem are called **extremals** for the problem in question.

NOTE: The derivation of the conditions (4) and (6) from $\delta^1 I = 0$ is based on the *fundamental lemma of the calculus of variations: if* $f(x)$ *is continuous on the bounded interval* $[x_1, x_2]$ *and* $\int_{x_1}^{x_2} f(x)g(x) \, dx = 0$ *for arbitrary* $g(x)$, *then* $f(x) = 0$ *on* $[x_1, x_2]$.

Example: *Brachistochrone in Three Dimensions.* Given a three-dimensional rectangular cartesian coordinate system with the positive x axis vertically downward, this classical problem requires the determination of the space curve $y = y(x)$, $z = z(x)$ which will minimize the time t taken by a particle sliding on the curve without friction under the action of gravity to get from the origin to some specified point $[x_2 > 0,$ $y(x_2), z(x_2)]$. Since by conservation of energy

$$gx = \frac{1}{2} v^2 = \frac{1}{2} \left[\left(\frac{dx}{dt} \right)^2 + \left(\frac{dy}{dt} \right)^2 + \left(\frac{dz}{dt} \right)^2 \right]$$

where g is the acceleration of gravity, the quantity to be minimized is

$$t \sqrt{2g} = \int_0^{x_2} \frac{1}{x^{1/2}} \sqrt{1 + (y')^2 + (z')^2} \, dx$$

The Euler equations (6) become

$$\frac{d}{dx} \left(\frac{y'}{x^{1/2} \sqrt{1 + (y')^2 + (z')^2}} \right) = \frac{d}{dx} \left(\frac{z'}{x^{1/2} \sqrt{1 + (y')^2 + (z')^2}} \right) = 0$$

or

$$\frac{y'}{x^{1/2} \sqrt{1 + (y')^2 + (z')^2}} = c_1 \qquad \frac{z'}{x^{1/2} \sqrt{1 + (y')^2 + (z')^2}} = c_2$$

where c_1 and c_2 are constants. Since $dy/dz = c_1/c_2$, the curve must lie in a vertical plane, which will be the xy plane if the boundary conditions

$$y(x_2) = y_2 \qquad z(x_2) = 0$$

are assumed. In this case, $z' = 0$ and

$$y' = \frac{x}{\sqrt{\dfrac{x}{c_1^2} - x^2}}$$

so that

$$y = a \arccos \left(1 - \frac{x}{a} \right) - \sqrt{2ax - x^2} + k \qquad \left(a = \frac{1}{2c_1^2} \right)$$

7.3-4 Variation Problems with Constraints or Accessory Conditions. Isoperimetric Problems.

It is desired to find sets of functions $y_1(x)$, $y_2(x)$, . . . , $y_n(x)$ which maximize or minimize the definite integral (1b) while also subject to $m < n$ suitably differentiable *constraints* or *accessory conditions*

$$\varphi_j(y_1, y_2, \ldots, y_n; x) = 0 \qquad (j = 1, 2, \ldots ; m < n) \tag{7.3-7}$$

and/or r accessory conditions of the form

$$\int_{x_1}^{x_2} \Psi_k(y_1, y_2, \ldots, y_n; y_1', y_2', \ldots, y_n'; x) \, dx = c_k$$

$$(k = 1, 2, \ldots, r) \tag{7.3-8}$$

with given constants c_k.

Unless it is possible to eliminate m of the n variables y_i directly with the aid of relations (7) and (8), one obtains the deisred sets of functions $y_1(x)$, $y_2(x)$, . . . , $y_n(x)$ as solutions of the set of differential equations (Euler equations)

$$\frac{d}{dx}\left(\frac{\partial \Phi}{\partial y_i'}\right) - \frac{\partial \Phi}{\partial y_i} = 0 \qquad (i = 1, 2, \ldots, n) \qquad (7.3\text{-}9)$$

subject to the constraints (7) and (8), where

$$\Phi \equiv F + \sum_{j=1}^{m} \lambda_j \varphi_j + \sum_{k=1}^{r} \mu_k \Psi_k \qquad (7.3\text{-}10)$$

The m Lagrange multipliers λ_j are unknown *functions* of x, and the r Lagrange multipliers μ_k are unknown *constants;* one determines the functions y_i and λ_j together with the constants μ_k from the $n + m + r$ relations (7), (8), and (9) subject to suitable boundary conditions on the y_i.

Example: Variation problems having only constraints of the form (8) are called **isoperimetric problems.**

Thus, the area of a closed plane curve $x = x(t)$, $y = y(t)$ can be written in the form

$$I = \frac{1}{2} \int_0^{2\pi} \left(x \frac{dy}{dt} - y \frac{dx}{dt} \right) dt$$

if the parameter t is suitably chosen. To maximize I subject to the accessory condition

$$\int_0^{2\pi} \left[\left(\frac{dx}{dt}\right)^2 + \left(\frac{dy}{dt}\right)^2 \right] dt = R^2$$

where R is a constant different from zero, write

$$\Phi \equiv \frac{1}{2}\left(x \frac{dy}{dt} - y \frac{dx}{dt} \right) + \mu \left[\left(\frac{dx}{dt}\right)^2 + \left(\frac{dy}{dt}\right)^2 \right]$$

The resulting Euler equations (9), viz.

$$-\frac{dy}{dt} + 2\mu \frac{d^2 x}{dt^2} = 0 \qquad \frac{dx}{dt} + 2\mu \frac{d^2 y}{dt^2} = 0$$

and the given accessory condition are satisfied by

$$x = R \cos \frac{t}{2\mu} + x_0 \qquad y = -R \sin \frac{t}{2\mu} + y_0 \qquad \text{with } \mu = \sqrt{\frac{\pi}{2}}$$

i.e., the desired curve is a circle of radius R.

7.3-5 *Variation Problems with Unknown Boundary Values.* To maximize or minimize the definite integral (3) when one or more of the boundary values $y_i(x_1)$ and/or $y_i(x_2)$ are not specified, replace each missing boundary condition by a corresponding *natural boundary condition*

$$\frac{\partial F}{\partial y_i'}\bigg]_{x_1} = 0 \qquad \frac{\partial F}{\partial y_i'}\bigg]_{x_2} = 0 \qquad (7.3\text{-}11)$$

References and Bibliography

1. Bellman, R.: *Dynamic Programming*, Princeton University Press, Princeton, N.J., 1957.
2. ——— and S. E. Dreyfus: *Applied Dynamic Programming*, Princeton University Press, Princeton, N.J., 1962.
3. Bliss, G. A.: *Calculus of Variations*, Open Court, Chicago, 1925.
4. Elsgolc, L. E.: *Calculus of Variations*, Pergamon, Addison-Wesley, Reading, Mass., 1962.
5. Gale, D.: *The Theory of Linear Economic Models*, McGraw-Hill, New York, 1960.
6. Gass, S. I.: *Linear Programming*, 2d ed., McGraw-Hill, New York, 1964.
7. Gelfand, I. M., and S. V. Fomin: *Calculus of Variations*, Prentice-Hall, Englewood Cliffs, N.J., 1963.
8. Hadley, G.: *Linear Programming*, Addison-Wesley, Reading, Mass., 1962.
9. Weinstock, R.: *Calculus of Variations*, McGraw-Hill, New York, 1952.
10. Wilde, D. J.: *Optimum-seeking Methods*, Prentice-Hall, Englewood Cliffs, N.J., 1964.

8 MODERN ALGEBRA

8.1 BASIC ABSTRACT MODELS

8.1-1 Introduction (*see also Secs. 1.1-1 to 1.1-4*). Modern (abstract) **algebra** deals with mathematical models defined in terms of binary operations ("algebraic" operations, usually referred to as various types of "addition" and "multiplication") which associate *pairs* of mathematical objects (operands, or operator and operand) with corresponding results. Sections 8.1-3 through 8.1-6 introduce some of the most generally useful models of this kind, notably *groups, rings, fields, vector spaces*, and *linear algebras; Boolean algebras* are treated separately in Secs. 8.3-1 through 8.3-4.

8.1-2 "Equality" (*Equivalence Relations*). THE DESCRIPTIVE DEFINITION OF EACH CLASS OF MATHEMATICAL OBJECTS DISCUSSED IN THIS CHAPTER IS UNDERSTOOD TO IMPLY THE EXISTENCE OF A RULE STATING WHETHER OR NOT TWO GIVEN MATHEMATICAL OBJECTS a, b ARE

"EQUAL" (EQUIVALENT OR INDISTINGUISHABLE IN THE CONTEXT OF THE MODEL, $a = b$); the rule must be such that

1. $a = a$ (REFLEXIVITY OF THE EQUALITY RELATION)
2. $a = b$ implies $b = a$ (SYMMETRY)
3. $a = b$, $b = c$ implies $a = c$ (TRANSITIVITY)

8.1-3 Models with a Single Defining Operation: Groups. (a) A class G of objects (elements) a, b, c, . . . is a **group** if and only if it is possible to define a binary operation (rule of combination) which associates an object (result) $a \odot b$ with every pair of elements a, b of G so that

1. $a \odot b$ is an element of G (CLOSURE under the defining operation)
2. $a \odot (b \odot c) = (a \odot b) \odot c$ (ASSOCIATIVE LAW)
3. G contains a (left) **identity** (**identity element**) E such that, for each element a of G, $E \odot a = a$
4. For each element a of G, G contains a (left) **inverse** a^{-1} such that $a^{-1} \odot a = E$

Two elements a, b of a group **commute** if and only if $a \odot b = b \odot a$. If all elements a, b of a group G commute, the defining operation of G is **commutative,** and G is a **commutative** or **Abelian group.** A group G containing a finite number g of elements is **of finite order** g; otherwise G is an **infinite group (of infinite order).** In the latter case, G may or may not be a countable set.

(b) *Every group G has a unique left identity and a unique right identity, and the two are identical* ($E \odot a = a \odot E = a$). *Each element a has a unique left inverse and a unique right inverse, and the two are identical* ($a^{-1} \odot a = a \odot a^{-1} = E$).

Hence

$$c \odot a = c \odot b \text{ implies } a = b$$
$$a \odot c = b \odot c \text{ implies } a = b$$
       (CANCELLATION LAWS)   (8.1-1)

G contains a unique solution x of every equation $c \odot x = b$ or $x \odot c = b$; i.e., unique right and left "division" is possible.

(c) The operation defining a group is often referred to as (abstract) *multiplication;* its result is then written as a *product ab,* and the inverse of a is written as a^{-1}. Multiple products aa, aaa, . . . are written as *integral powers* a^2, a^3, . . . , with

$(a^{-1})^n = a^{-n}$, $a^0 = E$. Note

$$(a^{-1})^{-1} = a \qquad a^m a^n = a^{m+n} \qquad (a^m)^n = a^{mn} \qquad (ab)^{-1} = b^{-1}a^{-1} \qquad (8.1\text{-}2)$$

(*d*) *The set G of all reciprocal one-to-one (nonsingular) transformations $x' = f(x)$ of any class C onto itself is a group;* the defining operation is the successive application of two transformations (*multiplication of transformations or operators*). **Examples:** permutations, translations, rotations.

8.1-4 Models with Two Defining Operations: Rings, Fields, and Integral Domains. (*a*) A class R of objects (elements) a, b, c, . . . is a **ring** if and only if it is possible to define two binary operations, usually denoted as (abstract) *addition* and *multiplication*, such that

---

1. R is a commutative group with respect to addition; i.e., R is closed under addition, and

   $$a + b = b + a \qquad a + (b + c) = (a + b) + c$$
   $$a + 0 = a \qquad a + (-a) = a - a = 0$$

2. ab is an element of R (CLOSURE UNDER MULTIPLICATION)

3. $a(bc) = (ab)c$ (ASSOCIATIVE LAW FOR MULTIPLICATION)

4. $a(b + c) = ab + ac \qquad (b + c)a = ba + ca$

   (DISTRIBUTIVE LAWS)

Note that $a0 = 0a = 0$ for every element a of R. Two elements p and q of R such that $pq = 0$ are called **left and right divisors of zero.** *For a* **ring without divisors of zero** *(other than zero itself), $ab = 0$ implies $a = 0$, or $b = 0$, or $a = b = 0$, and the cancellation laws* (1) *hold.*

(*b*) A **ring with identity (unity)** is a ring containing a multiplicative (left) identity E such that $Ea = a$ for all a. *E is necessarily a unique right identity as well as a unique left identity.* A given element a of a ring with identity may or may not have a multiplicative (left) inverse a^{-1}; *if a^{-1} does exist, it is necessarily a unique right inverse as well as a unique left inverse.*

(*c*) A **field*** is a ring with identity which contains (1) at least one element different from zero and (2) a multiplicative inverse a^{-1} for each element $a \neq 0$. *The nonzero elements of a field F constitute a group with respect to multiplication.*

Given any pair of elements b, $c \neq 0$ of F, the equations $cx = b$ and $xc = b$ have solutions in F. These solutions are unique whenever $b \neq 0$

---

* Some writers require every field to be an integral domain.

(unique left and right division); they are unique even for $b = 0$ *if F is a field without divisors of zero.*

(*d*) A ring or field is **commutative** if and only if $ab = ba$ for all a, b. A commutative field is sometimes simply called a field, as opposed to a **skew** or **noncommutative field**. A **Galois field** is a finite commutative field. An **integral domain** is a commutative ring with identity and without divisors of zero. *Every finite integral domain is a Galois field.*

Examples of fields: rational numbers, real numbers, complex numbers; continuous functions defined on a finite interval (has zero divisors); polynomials. *Examples of integral domains:* real integers, complex numbers with integral coefficients. *Example of a commutative ring without identity:* even integers.

8.1-5 Models Involving Two Classes of Objects: Linear Vector Spaces.

(*a*) DEFINITION. Let R be a ring with (multiplicative) identity 1; the elements α, β, . . . of R shall be referred to as **scalars.** A class $\mathcal{V}$ of objects (elements) **a, b, c,** . . . is a **(linear) vector space over the ring** R, and the elements of $\mathcal{V}$ are called **vectors** if and only if it is possible to define two binary operations called **vector addition** and **multiplication of vectors by scalars** such that

---

1. $\mathcal{V}$ is a commutative group with respect to vector addition; for every pair of elements **a, b** of $\mathcal{V}$, $\mathcal{V}$ contains a **vector sum a + b**, and

   $$\mathbf{a + b = b + a} \qquad \mathbf{a + (b + c) = (a + b) + c}$$
   $$\mathbf{a + 0 = a} \qquad \mathbf{a + (-a) = a - a = 0}$$

   where **0** is the additive identity element (**null vector**) of $\mathcal{V}$, and $-\mathbf{a}$ is the additive inverse of **a**
2. Given any vector **a** of $\mathcal{V}$ and any scalar α of R, $\mathcal{V}$ contains a vector $\alpha\mathbf{a}$, the **product of the vector a by the scalar** α (CLOSURE UNDER MULTIPLICATION BY SCALARS)
3. $(\alpha\beta)\mathbf{a} = \alpha(\beta\mathbf{a})$
   (ASSOCIATIVE LAW FOR MULTIPLICATION BY SCALARS)
4. $\alpha(\mathbf{a + b}) = \alpha\mathbf{a} + \alpha\mathbf{b} \qquad (\alpha + \beta)\mathbf{a} = \alpha\mathbf{a} + \beta\mathbf{a}$
   (DISTRIBUTIVE LAWS)
5. $1\mathbf{a} = \mathbf{a}$

Note that

$$0\mathbf{a} = \mathbf{0} \qquad (-1)\mathbf{a} = -\mathbf{a} \qquad (-\alpha)\mathbf{a} = -(\alpha\mathbf{a}) \qquad (8.1\text{-}3)$$

Unless the contrary is specifically stated, all linear vector spaces considered in this handbook are understood to be **real vector spaces** or **complex vector spaces** respectively defined as linear vector spaces over the field of real numbers and over the field of complex numbers.

In the case of vector spaces admitting a definition of infinite sums, many authors refer to a set of vectors with the above properties as a **linear manifold** and reserve the term **vector space** for a linear manifold which is *closed*, i.e., which contains all its limit points; the two terms are equivalent in the case of finite-dimensional manifolds, Sec. 8.1-4c.

(*b*) LINEAR INDEPENDENCE. A finite set of vectors $\mathbf{a}_1$, $\mathbf{a}_2$, . . . is **linearly independent** if and only if

$$\lambda_1\mathbf{a}_1 + \lambda_2\mathbf{a}_2 + \cdots = 0 \qquad \text{implies} \qquad \lambda_1 = \lambda_2 = \cdots = 0$$

Otherwise, the vectors $\mathbf{a}_1$, $\mathbf{a}_2$, . . . are **linearly dependent,** and at least one vector of the set, say $\mathbf{a}_k$, can be expressed as a linear combination $\mathbf{a}_k = \sum_i \mu_i \mathbf{a}_i$ of the other vectors $\mathbf{a}_i$ of the set. As a trivial special case, this is true whenever $\mathbf{a}_k$ is a null vector.

(*c*) DIMENSION AND REFERENCE SYSTEMS. A **(linear) basis** in the linear manifold $\mho$ is a set of linearly independent vectors $\mathbf{e}_1$, $\mathbf{e}_2$, . . . of $\mho$ such that every vector $\mathbf{a}$ of $\mho$ can be expressed as a linear form

$$\mathbf{a} = \alpha_1\mathbf{e}_1 + \alpha_2\mathbf{e}_2 + \cdots \qquad\qquad (8.1\text{-}4)$$

in the base vectors $\mathbf{e}_i$. Every set of linearly independent vectors forms a basis for the linear manifold comprising all linear combinations of the given vectors.

In a **finite-dimensional** *linear manifold or vector space spanned by n base vectors*

1. *Every set of n linearly independent vectors is a basis.*
2. *No set of m < n vectors is a basis.*
3. *Every set of m > n vectors is necessarily linearly dependent.*

The number n is called the **(linear) dimension** of the vector space. An **infinite-dimensional** vector space does not admit a finite basis.

In every finite-dimensional real or complex vector space, the numbers α_1, α_2, . . . , α_n are unique **components** or **coordinates** of the vector $\mathbf{a} = \alpha_1\mathbf{e}_1 + \alpha_2\mathbf{e}_2 + \cdots + \alpha_n\mathbf{e}_n$ in a **reference system (coordinate system)** defined by the base vectors $\mathbf{e}_1$, $\mathbf{e}_2$, . . . , $\mathbf{e}_n$. Note that $\mathbf{a} + \mathbf{b}$ has the components $\alpha_i + \beta_i$, and $\alpha\mathbf{a}$ has the components $\alpha\alpha_i$ ($i = 1, 2, \ldots, n$; see also Sec. 4.2-2).

8.1-6　Linear Algebras.　Given a ring R of scalars with identity 1, a class L is a **linear algebra (linear associative algebra, system of hypercomplex numbers) over the ring** R if and only if it is possible to define three binary operations (**addition and multiplication in** L and **multiplication of elements of** L **by scalars**) such that

> 1. L is a ring.
> 2. L is a linear vector space over the ring R of scalars.

The **order** of a linear algebra is its dimension as a vector space. A linear algebra is a **division algebra** if and only if it is a field.

Example: The *field of complex numbers* is a commutative division algebra of order 2 over the field of real numbers.

8.2 MATRICES AND LINEAR TRANSFORMATIONS

8.2-1　Introduction.　*Matrices* (Sec. 8.2-2) are the building blocks of an important class of mathematical models.　Matrix techniques permit *a simplified representation of various mathematical and physical operations in terms of numerical operations on matrix elements.*

8.2-2　Rectangular Matrices.　(*a*) An array

$$A \equiv \begin{bmatrix} a_{11} & a_{12} & \cdots & a_{1n} \\ a_{21} & a_{22} & \cdots & a_{2n} \\ \cdot & \cdot & \cdots & \cdot \\ a_{m1} & a_{m2} & \cdots & a_{mn} \end{bmatrix} \equiv [a_{ik}] \tag{8.2-1}$$

of "scalars" a_{ik} taken from a commutative field (Sec. 8.1-4) F is called a (**rectangular**) $m \times n$ **matrix** over the field F whenever one of the "matrix operations" defined in Sec. 8.2-3 is to be used.　The elements a_{ik} are called **matrix elements;** the matrix element a_{ik} is situated in the ith **row** and in the kth **column** of the matrix (1).　m is the number of rows, and n is the number of columns.　A matrix is **finite** if and only if it has a finite number of rows and a finite number of columns; otherwise the matrix is **infinite.**

THROUGHOUT THIS HANDBOOK ALL MATRICES WILL BE UNDERSTOOD TO BE MATRICES OVER THE FIELD OF COMPLEX NUMBERS, UNLESS THE CONTRARY IS SPECIFICALLY STATED.　A matrix $A \equiv [a_{ik}]$ is **real** if and only if all matrix elements a_{ik} are real numbers.

(*b*) $n \times 1$ matrices are **column matrices,** and $1 \times n$ matrices are **row matrices.**　The following notation will be used:

$$\begin{bmatrix} \xi_1 \\ \xi_2 \\ \cdot \\ \cdot \\ \cdot \\ \xi_n \end{bmatrix} \equiv \{\xi_i\} \equiv x \qquad [\xi_1 \xi_2 \cdots \xi_n] \equiv [\xi_k] \equiv \tilde{x} \qquad (8.2\text{-}2)$$

(*c*) An $n \times n$ matrix is called a **square matrix** of **order** n. A square matrix $A \equiv [a_{ik}]$ is

Triangular (superdiagonal) if and only if $i > k$ implies $a_{ik} = 0$
Strictly triangular if and only if $i \geq k$ implies $a_{ik} = 0$
Diagonal if and only if $i \neq k$ implies $a_{ik} = 0$
Monomial if and only if each row and column has one and only one element different from zero

8.2-3 Basic Operations. Operations on matrices are defined in terms of operations on the matrix elements.

---

1. Two $m \times n$ matrices $A \equiv [a_{ik}]$ and $B \equiv [b_{ik}]$ are **equal** ($A = B$) if and only if $a_{ik} = b_{ik}$ for all i, k (see also Sec. 8.1-2).

2. The **sum of two** $m \times n$ **matrices** $A \equiv [a_{ik}]$ and $B \equiv [b_{ik}]$ is the $m \times n$ matrix
$$A + B \equiv [a_{ik}] + [b_{ik}] \equiv [a_{ik} + b_{ik}]$$

3. The **product of the** $m \times n$ **matrix** $A \equiv [a_{ik}]$ **by the scalar** α is the $m \times n$ matrix
$$\alpha A \equiv \alpha[a_{ik}] \equiv [\alpha a_{ik}]$$

4. The **product of the** $m \times n$ **matrix** $A \equiv [a_{ij}]$ **and the** $n \times r$ **matrix** $B \equiv [b_{jk}]$ is the $m \times r$ matrix
$$AB \equiv [a_{ij}][b_{jk}] \equiv \Big[\sum_{j=1}^{n} a_{ij} b_{jk} \Big]$$

In every matrix product AB the number n of columns of A must match the number of rows of B (A and B must be **conformable**). The existence of AB implies that of BA if and only if A and B are square matrices; in general $BA \neq AB$. Note

$A + B = B + A$	$A + (B + C) = (A + B) + C$
$\alpha(\beta A) = (\alpha\beta)A$	$\alpha(AB) = (\alpha A)B = A(\alpha B)$
$A(BC) = (AB)C$	$(8.2\text{-}3)$
$\alpha(A + B) = \alpha A + \alpha B$	$(\alpha + \beta)A = \alpha A + \beta A$
$A(B + C) = AB + AC$	$(B + C)A = BA + CA$

8.2-4 *Identities and Inverses.* Note the following definitions:

1. The $m \times n$ **null matrix (additive identity)** $[0]$ is the $m \times n$ matrix all of whose elements are equal to zero. Then

   $$A + [0] = A \qquad 0A = [0]$$
   $$[0]B = C[0] = [0]$$

   where A is any $m \times n$ matrix, B is any matrix having n rows, and C is any matrix having m columns.

2. The **additive inverse (negative)** $-A$ of the $m \times n$ matrix $A \equiv [a_{ik}]$ is the $m \times n$ matrix

   $$-A \equiv (-1)A \equiv [-a_{ik}]$$

   with $A + (-A) = A - A = [0]$.

3. The **identity matrix (unit matrix, multiplicative identity)** I **of order** n is the $n \times n$ diagonal matrix with unit diagonal elements:

   $$I \equiv [\delta_k^i] \qquad \text{where}^* \qquad \delta_k^i = \begin{cases} 0 \text{ if } i \neq k \\ 1 \text{ if } i = k \end{cases}$$

   Then

   $$IB = B \qquad CI = C$$

   where B is any matrix having n rows, and C is any matrix having n columns; and for any $n \times n$ matrix A

   $$IA = AI = A$$

4. A (necessarily square) matrix A is **nonsingular (regular)** if and only if it has a (necessarily unique) **multiplicative inverse** or **reciprocal** A^{-1} defined by

   $$AA^{-1} = A^{-1}A = I$$

   Otherwise A is a **singular** matrix.

   A finite $n \times n$ matrix $A \equiv [a_{ik}]$ is nonsingular if and only if $\det (A) \equiv \det [a_{ik}] \neq 0$; *in this case A^{-1} is the $n \times n$ matrix*

   $$A^{-1} \equiv [a_{ik}]^{-1} \equiv \left[\frac{\mathrm{A}_{ki}}{\det [a]_{ik}} \right]$$

   where A_{ik} is the cofactor of the element a_{ik} in the determinant $\det [a_{ik}]$ (see also Sec. 1.6-2).

---

* The symbol δ_k^i (or δ_i^k) is known as the **Kronecker delta.**

Products and reciprocals of nonsingular matrices are nonsingular; if
A and B are nonsingular, and $\alpha \neq 0$,

$$(AB)^{-1} = B^{-1}A^{-1} \qquad (\alpha A)^{-1} = \alpha^{-1}A^{-1}$$
$$(A^{-1})^{-1} = A \tag{8.2-4}$$

One defines $A^0 = I$, $A^1 = A$, $A^2 = AA$, $A^3 = AAA$, . . . and, if A is non-singular,

$$A^{-p} = (A^{-1})^p = (A^p)^{-1} \qquad (p = 1, 2, . . .)$$

The ordinary rules for operations with exponents apply.

8.2-5 Matrices as Building Blocks of Mathematical Models.
The definitions of Secs. 8.2-3 and 8.2-4 (*constructive* definitions, Sec. 1.1-3) imply the following results:

1. Given any pair of (finite) positive integers m, n, *the class of all $m \times n$ matrices over a field F is an mn-dimensional vector space over F.* In particular, n-element column or row matrices form n-dimensional vector spaces.
2. *The class of all square matrices of a given (finite) order n over a field F is a linear algebra of order n^2 over F; singular matrices are zero divisors* (Sec. 8.1-4).
3. *The class of all nonsingular square matrices of a given (finite) order n over a field F constitutes a multiplicative group* (Sec. 8.1-3) *and, together with the $n \times n$ null matrix, a division algebra of order n^2 over the field F* (Sec. 8.1-6).

8.2-6 Rank, Trace, and Determinant of a Matrix.
The **rank** of a given matrix is the largest number r such that at least one r^{th}-order determinant (Sec. 1.3-1) formed from the matrix by deleting rows and/or columns is different from zero. *An $m \times n$ matrix A is nonsingular if and only if $m = n = r$, i.e., if and only if A is square and* $\det (A) \neq 0$.

The **trace** (**spur**) of an $n \times n$ matrix $A \equiv [a_{ik}]$ is the sum

$$\text{Tr} (A) = \sum_{i=1}^{n} a_{ii}$$

of the diagonal terms.

For finite matrices A, B

$$\text{Tr} (A + B) = \text{Tr} (A) + \text{Tr} (B) \qquad \text{Tr} (\alpha A) = \alpha \, \text{Tr} (A)$$
$$\text{Tr} (BA) = \text{Tr} (AB) \qquad \text{Tr} (AB - BA) = 0 \tag{8.2-5}$$

$$\det (AB) = \det (BA) = \det (A) \det (B) \tag{8.2-6}$$

8.2-7 Transformation of Vectors and Components: "Alibi" Point of View.
(*a*) Given two linear vector spaces $\mathcal{V}$ and $\mathcal{V}'$ over the same field of scalars α, β, . . . , a (**homogeneous**) **linear transformation of $\mathcal{V}$ into $\mathcal{V}'$** is a correspondence

$$\mathbf{x}' = \mathbf{f}(\mathbf{x}) \equiv \mathbf{A}\mathbf{x}$$

which relates vectors $\mathbf{x}'$ of $\mathcal{V}'$ to vectors $\mathbf{x}$ of $\mathcal{V}$ so as to preserve the "linear" operations of vector addition and multiplication of vectors by scalars:

$$\mathbf{f}(\mathbf{x} + \mathbf{y}) \equiv \mathbf{f}(\mathbf{x}) + \mathbf{f}(\mathbf{y}) \qquad \mathbf{f}(\alpha\mathbf{x}) \equiv \alpha\mathbf{f}(\mathbf{x})$$

Each linear transformation can be written as a multiplication by a **linear operator A (linear operation)**, with

$$\mathbf{A}(\mathbf{x} + \mathbf{y}) \equiv \mathbf{A}\mathbf{x} + \mathbf{A}\mathbf{y} \qquad \mathbf{A}(\alpha\mathbf{x}) \equiv \alpha(\mathbf{A}\mathbf{x}) \tag{8.2-7}$$

(b) Consider a finite-dimensional real or complex vector space $\mathcal{V}_n$ with a reference system defined by n base vectors $\mathbf{e}_1, \mathbf{e}_2, \ldots, \mathbf{e}_n$ (Sec. 8.1-5). Each vector

$$\mathbf{x} = \xi_1\mathbf{e}_1 + \xi_2\mathbf{e}_2 + \cdots + \xi_n\mathbf{e}_n = \sum_{k=1}^{n} \xi_k\mathbf{e}_k \tag{8.2-8}$$

is described by its components $\xi_1, \xi_2, \ldots, \xi_n$. A linear transformation (operator) $\mathbf{A}$ mapping $\mathcal{V}_n$ into itself transforms each base vector $\mathbf{e}_k$ into a corresponding vector

$$\mathbf{e}'_k = \mathbf{A}\mathbf{e}_k = a_{1k}\mathbf{e}_1 + a_{2k}\mathbf{e}_2 + \cdots + a_{nk}\mathbf{e}_n = \sum_{i=1}^{n} a_{ik}\mathbf{e}_i$$
$$(k = 1, 2, \ldots, n) \tag{8.2-9}$$

and each vector $\mathbf{x}$ of $\mathcal{V}_n$ into a corresponding vector $\mathbf{x}'$ of $\mathcal{V}_n$:

$$\mathbf{x}' = \mathbf{A}\mathbf{x} = \mathbf{A} \sum_{k=1}^{n} \xi_k\mathbf{e}_k = \sum_{k=1}^{n} \xi_k\mathbf{e}'_k = \sum_{i=1}^{n} \xi'_i\mathbf{e}_i \tag{8.2-10}$$

The components ξ'_i of the vector $\mathbf{x}'$ and the components ξ_k of the vector $\mathbf{x}$, **both referred to the $\mathbf{e}_1, \mathbf{e}_2, \ldots, \mathbf{e}_n$ reference system,** are related by the n linear homogeneous transformation equations

$$
\begin{aligned}
\xi'_1 &= a_{11}\xi_1 + a_{12}\xi_2 + \cdots + a_{1n}\xi_n && \text{(TRANSFORMATION} \\
\xi'_2 &= a_{21}\xi_1 + a_{22}\xi_2 + \cdots + a_{2n}\xi_n && \text{OF VECTOR COM-} \\
&\cdots\cdots\cdots\cdots\cdots\cdots\cdots && \text{PONENTS, ``ALIBI''} \\
\xi'_n &= a_{n1}\xi_1 + a_{n2}\xi_2 + \cdots + a_{nn}\xi_n && \text{POINT OF VIEW)}
\end{aligned}
\tag{8.2-11}
$$

8.2-8 Matrix Representation of Vectors and Linear Transformations (Operators). For each given reference basis $\mathbf{e}_1, \mathbf{e}_2, \ldots, \mathbf{e}_n$ in $\mathcal{V}_n$

1. The vectors $\mathbf{x} \equiv \xi_1 \mathbf{e}_1 + \xi_2 \mathbf{e}_2 + \cdots + \xi_n \mathbf{e}_n$ of $\mathcal{V}_n$ are represented on a reciprocal one-to-one basis by the column matrices $\{\xi_k\}$.

2. The linear transformations (operators) mapping $\mathcal{V}_n$ into itself are represented on a reciprocal one-to-one basis by the $n \times n$ matrices $A \equiv [a_{ik}]$ defined by Eq. (9) or (11).

In particular, the coordinate-free vector equation

$$\mathbf{x}' = \mathbf{A}\mathbf{x} \tag{8.2-12}$$

is represented in the $\mathbf{e}_1, \mathbf{e}_2, \ldots, \mathbf{e}_n$ reference system by the matrix equation

$$x' = \begin{bmatrix} \xi_1' \\ \xi_2' \\ \cdots \\ \xi_n' \end{bmatrix} = \begin{bmatrix} a_{11} & a_{12} & \cdots & a_{1n} \\ a_{21} & a_{22} & \cdots & a_{2n} \\ \cdots & \cdots & \cdots & \cdots \\ a_{n1} & a_{n2} & \cdots & a_{nn} \end{bmatrix} \begin{bmatrix} \xi_1 \\ \xi_2 \\ \cdots \\ \xi_n \end{bmatrix} = Ax \tag{8.2-13}$$

which is equivalent to the n transformation equations (11); and the product of two linear transformations $\mathbf{A}$ and $\mathbf{B}$ is represented by the product of the corresponding matrices A and B.

The **product BA** of two linear transformations **A**, **B** and the **inverse A**$^{-1}$ of a **nonsingular** transformation **A** are defined by

$$(\mathbf{BA})\mathbf{x} \equiv \mathbf{B}(\mathbf{A}\mathbf{x}) \qquad \mathbf{A}^{-1}\mathbf{A}\mathbf{x} \equiv \mathbf{A}\mathbf{A}^{-1}\mathbf{x} \equiv \mathbf{x} \tag{8.2-14}$$

If **A** and **B** are represented by matrices A, B, then **BA** is represented by the matrix product BA, and **A**$^{-1}$ is represented by the matrix A^{-1}. The identity matrix represents the **identity transformation I** defined by $\mathbf{I}\mathbf{x} \equiv \mathbf{x}$.

8.2-9 Matrix Notation for Simultaneous Linear Equations (see also Secs. 1.6-2 and 8.2-4). A set of simultaneous linear equations

$$\sum_{k=1}^{n} a_{ik}x_k = b_i \qquad (i = 1, 2, \ldots, m) \tag{8.2-15}$$

is equivalent to the matrix equation

$$Ax = b \qquad \text{or} \qquad \begin{bmatrix} a_{11} & a_{12} & \cdots & a_{1n} \\ a_{21} & a_{22} & \cdots & a_{2n} \\ \cdots & \cdots & \cdots & \cdots \\ a_{m1} & a_{m2} & \cdots & a_{mn} \end{bmatrix} \begin{bmatrix} x_1 \\ x_2 \\ \cdots \\ x_n \end{bmatrix} = \begin{bmatrix} b_1 \\ b_2 \\ \cdots \\ b_m \end{bmatrix} \tag{8.2-16}$$

The unknowns x_k may be regarded as components of an unknown vector such that the transformation (16) yields the vector represented by the b_i. If, in particular, the matrix $[a_{ik}]$ is nonsingular (Sec. 8.2-4), then the matrix equation (16) can be solved to yield the unique result

$$x = A^{-1}b \tag{8.2-17}$$

which is equivalent to Cramer's rule (1.6-4).

8.2-10   Change of Reference System.   (*a*) For every reference basis $\bar{\mathbf{e}}_1, \bar{\mathbf{e}}_2, \ldots, \bar{\mathbf{e}}_n$ in $\mathcal{V}_n$

$$\bar{\mathbf{e}}_k = t_{1k}\mathbf{e}_1 + t_{2k}\mathbf{e}_2 + \cdots + t_{nk}\mathbf{e}_n$$

$$= \sum_{i=1}^{n} t_{ik}\mathbf{e}_i \quad (k = 1, 2, \ldots, n) \quad \begin{matrix} \text{(TRANSFORMATION} \\ \text{OF BASE VECTORS)} \end{matrix} \tag{8.2-18}$$

with

$$\det [t_{ik}] \neq 0$$

The matrix $T \equiv [t_{ik}]$ represents a (necessarily nonsingular) transformation **T** relating the old base vectors $\mathbf{e}_i$ and the new base vectors $\bar{\mathbf{e}}_k = \mathbf{T}\mathbf{e}_k$.

(*b*) Now each vector **x** of $\mathcal{V}_n$ can be expressed in terms of vector components ξ_i referred to the $\mathbf{e}_i$ system or in terms of vector components $\bar{\xi}_k$ referred to the $\bar{\mathbf{e}}_k$ system:

$$\mathbf{x} = \sum_{i=1}^{n} \xi_i \mathbf{e}_i = \sum_{k=1}^{n} \bar{\xi}_k \bar{\mathbf{e}}_k$$

The vector components ξ_i and $\bar{\xi}_k$ of the same vector **x** are related by the n linear homogeneous transformation equations

$$\begin{aligned} \xi_1 &= t_{11}\bar{\xi}_1 + t_{12}\bar{\xi}_2 + \cdots + t_{1n}\bar{\xi}_n \\ \xi_2 &= t_{21}\bar{\xi}_1 + t_{22}\bar{\xi}_2 + \cdots + t_{2n}\bar{\xi}_n \\ &\;\cdots\cdots\cdots\cdots\cdots\cdots\cdots\cdots \\ \xi_n &= t_{n1}\bar{\xi}_1 + t_{n2}\bar{\xi}_2 + \cdots + t_{nn}\bar{\xi}_n \end{aligned} \qquad \begin{matrix} \text{(TRANS-} \\ \text{FORMA-} \\ \text{TION OF} \\ \text{VECTOR} \\ \text{COMPO-} \end{matrix}$$

or in matrix form

$$x = \begin{bmatrix} \xi_1 \\ \xi_2 \\ \cdots \\ \xi_n \end{bmatrix} = \begin{bmatrix} t_{11} & t_{12} & \cdots & t_{1n} \\ t_{21} & t_{22} & \cdots & t_{2n} \\ \cdots & \cdots & \cdots & \cdots \\ t_{n1} & t_{n2} & \cdots & t_{nn} \end{bmatrix} \begin{bmatrix} \bar{\xi}_1 \\ \bar{\xi}_2 \\ \cdots \\ \bar{\xi}_n \end{bmatrix} = T\bar{x} \quad \begin{matrix} \text{NENTS,} \\ \text{``ALIAS''} \\ \text{POINT OF} \\ \text{VIEW)} \end{matrix}$$

$$\tag{8.2-19}$$

The meaning of the transformation equations (19) must be carefully distinguished from that of the formally analogous relations (11) and (13).

Note also the inverse relations, viz.,

$$\mathbf{e}_i = \mathbf{T}^{-1}\bar{\mathbf{e}}_i = \sum_{k=1}^{n} \frac{\mathbf{T}_{ik}}{\det[t_{ik}]}\,\bar{\mathbf{e}}_k \qquad (i = 1, 2, \ldots, n) \tag{8.2-20}$$

$$\bar{\xi}_k = \sum_{i=1}^{n} \frac{\mathbf{T}_{ki}}{\det[t_{ik}]}\,\xi_i \qquad (k = 1, 2, \ldots, n) \tag{8.2-21}$$

or $\quad \bar{x} = T^{-1}x$

where $\mathbf{T}_{ik}$ is the cofactor of t_{ik} in the determinant $\det[t_{ik}]$.

8.3 BOOLEAN ALGEBRAS

8.3-1 Boolean Algebras. A **Boolean algebra** is a class S of objects $A, B, C, \ldots$ admitting two binary operations, denoted as *(logical) addition and multiplication*, with the following properties:

(a) For all A, B, C in S

1. S contains $A + B$ and AB (CLOSURE)

2. $\left.\begin{array}{l} A + B = B + A \\ AB = BA \end{array}\right\}$ (COMMUTATIVE LAWS)

3. $A + (B + C) = (A + B) + C$
   $A(BC) = (AB)C$ (ASSOCIATIVE LAWS)

4. $A(B + C) = AB + AC$
   $A + BC = (A + B)(A + C)$ (DISTRIBUTIVE LAWS)

5. $A + A = AA = A$ (IDEMPOTENCY)

6. $A + B = B$ if and only if $AB = A$ (CONSISTENCY)

(b) In addition,

7. S contains elements I and 0 such that, for every A in S,
   $\quad A + 0 = A \qquad AI = A$
   $\quad A0 = 0 \qquad A + I = I$

8. For every element A, S contains an element $\tilde{A}$ (**complement** of A, also written $\overline{A}$ or $I - A$) such that
   $\quad A + \tilde{A} = I \qquad A\tilde{A} = 0$

In every Boolean algebra

$$A(A + B) \equiv A + AB \equiv A \quad \text{(LAWS OF ABSORPTION)} \tag{8.3-1}$$

$$(\overline{A + B}) \equiv \tilde{A}\tilde{B} \Bigg\}$$
$$(\widetilde{AB}) \equiv \tilde{A} + \tilde{B} \Bigg\}$$
(DUALIZATION, OR
DE MORGAN'S LAWS)   (8.3-2)

$$\tilde{\tilde{A}} \equiv A \qquad \tilde{I} = 0 \qquad \tilde{0} = I \tag{8.3-3}$$

$$A + \tilde{A}B \equiv A + B \qquad AB + AC + B\tilde{C} \equiv AC + B\tilde{C} \tag{8.3-4}$$

If $A + B = B$, one may write AB as $B - A$ (*complement of A with respect to B*). Two or more objects $A, B, C, \ldots$ of a Boolean algebra are **disjoint** if and only if every product involving distinct elements of the set equals 0.

The symbols $\cup$ (cup) and $\cap$ (cap) used in Secs. 3.3-2, 8.3-4, and 9.1-2 to denote union and intersection of sets and events are frequently employed to denote logical addition and multiplication in any Boolean algebra, so that $A \cup B$ stands for $A + B$, and $A \cap B$ stands for AB.

8.3-2 Boolean Functions.

Given n **Boolean variables** X_1, $X_2, \ldots, X_n$, each of which can equal any element of a given Boolean algebra, a **Boolean function**

$$Y = F(X_1, X_2, \ldots, X_n)$$

is an expression built up from $X_1, X_2, \ldots, X_n$ through addition, multiplication, and complementation.

In every Boolean algebra there exist exactly $2^{(2^n)}$ different Boolean functions of n variables. Every Boolean function either is identically equal to 0 or can be expressed uniquely as a sum of **minimal polynomials** $Z_1Z_2 \cdots Z_n$, *where Z_i is either X_i or $\tilde{X}_i$ (canonical form of a Boolean function;* see Fig. 8.3-1 for a geometrical illustration). A given Boolean function $Y = F(X_1, X_2, \ldots, X_n)$ may be reduced to canonical form as follows:

1. Use Eq. (2) to expand complements of sums and products.
2. Reduce $F(X_1, X_2, \ldots, X_n)$ to a sum of products with the aid of the first distributive law.
3. Simplify the resulting expression with the aid of the identities $X_iX_i \equiv X_i$, $X_i\tilde{X}_i \equiv 0$, and Eq. (4).
4. If a term f does not contain one of the variables, say X_i, rewrite f as $fX_i + f\tilde{X}_i$.

In many applications (e.g., design of switching circuits, Sec. 8.3-4c), it may be advantageous to omit step 4 and to continue step 3 so as to simplify each term of the expansion as much as possible.

8.3-3 The Inclusion Relation.   (a) *Either $A + B = B$ or $AB = A$ is equivalent to a reflexive partial ordering relation $A \leq B$ [or $B \geq A$;* (**logical**) **inclusion relation**].

(b) *In every Boolean algebra $A \leq B$, $B \leq A$ implies $A = B$, and*

$$A + B \equiv \sup (A, B) \qquad AB \equiv \inf (A, B) \tag{8.3-5}$$

where the bounds are defined by the inclusion relation.

(c) *Given any element A of a Boolean algebra $\mathcal{S}$, the elements $XA \leq A$ of $\mathcal{S}$ constitute a Boolean algebra in which A takes the place of I.*

8.3-4 Examples and Applications.   (a) ALGEBRA OF CLASSES. The subsets (subclasses) $A, B, \ldots$ of any set (class) I constitute a Boolean algebra (**algebra of classes**) under the operations of logical addition (union), logical multiplication (intersection), and complementation defined in Sec. 3.3-2a. The empty set (or any set which contains no element of I) is denoted by 0. The relation $\leq$ becomes the logical inclusion relation $\subset$.

Every Boolean algebra is isomorphic to an algebra of classes; Venn diagrams (Euler diagrams) like that shown in Fig. 8.3-1 conveniently illustrate the properties of Boolean algebras in terms of an algebra of classes.

(b) EVENT ALGEBRAS AND SYMBOLIC LOGIC. **Event algebras** (Sec. 9.1-2) serve as models for the compounding of events. In **two-valued** (**Aristotelian**) **logic,** an algebra of hypothetical events (**logical propositions,**

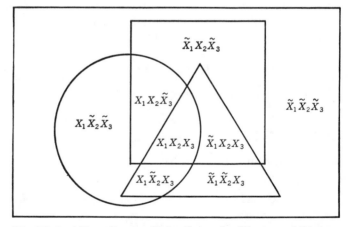

Fig. 8.3-1   A Venn diagram (Euler diagram).   Diagrams of this type illustrate relations in an algebra of classes. If the rectangle, circle, square, and triangle are respectively labeled by I, X_1, X_2, X_3, the diagram shows how a Boolean function of X_1, X_2, X_3 can be represented as a union of minimal polynomials in X_1, X_2, X_3. Note that there are $2^3 = 8$ different minimal polynomials.

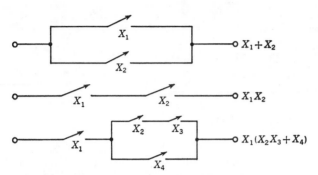

Fig. 8.3-2 Electrical switching circuits representing Boolean functions in a Boolean algebra comprising only the elements 0 and I. Each switch or combination of switches represents 0 if the circuit is open and I if the circuit is closed.

assertions) E is related to a simpler Boolean algebra of **truth values** $T[E]$ equal to either I' (E is **true**) or 0 (E is **false**) by

$$T[I] = I' \qquad\qquad T[0] = 0$$
$$T[E_1 \cup E_2] = T[E_1] + T[E_2] \qquad T[E_1 \cap E_2] = T[E_1]T[E_2]$$

On the basis of these assumptions, a proposition E is either true or false (*law of the excluded middle*), and the truth value of any proposition E expressible as a Boolean function of ("logically related to") a set of events $E_1, E_2, \ldots$ is given by

$$T[E] = T[F(E_1, E_2, \ldots)] = T[F\{T[E_1], T[E_2], \ldots\}] \tag{8.3-6}$$

with
$$\begin{array}{llll} 0 + 0 = 0 & 0 + I' = I' & I' + I' = I' \\ 00 = 0 & 0I' = 0 & I'I' = I' \end{array} \tag{8.3-7}$$

(c) SWITCHING CIRCUITS. Figure 8.3-2 shows electric switching circuits representing Boolean functions in a Boolean algebra comprising only the elements 0 and I, such as the truth-value algebra of Sec. 8.3-4b. Diagrams and actual circuits of this type aid in the solution of problems in the algebra of propositions and relate the design of electric switching circuits and digital computers to the formulas of Boolean algebra.

References and Bibliography

Algebra: general

1. Birkhoff, G., and S. MacLane: *A Survey of Modern Algebra*, rev. ed., Macmillan, New York, 1965.
2. Hall, M.: *The Theory of Groups*, Macmillan, New York, 1961.
3. Johnson, R. E.: *First Course in Abstract Algebra*, Prentice-Hall, Englewood Cliffs, N.J., 1953.
4. McCoy, N. H.: *Introduction to Modern Algebra*, Allyn and Bacon, Boston, 1960.
5. Mostow, G. D., et al.: *Fundamental Structures of Algebra*, McGraw-Hill, New York, 1963.

6. Vander Waerden, B. L.: *Modern Algebra*, rev. ed. (2 vols.), Ungar, New York, 1950, 1953.

Matrices and vector spaces

7. Halmos, P. R.: *Finite-dimensional Vector Spaces*, 2d ed., Princeton University Press, Princeton, N.J., 1958.
8. Hohn, F. E.: *Elementary Matrix Algebra*, 2d ed., Macmillan, New York, 1964.
9. Nering, E. D.: *Linear Algebra and Matrix Theory*, Interscience, New York, 1963.
10. Shields, P. C.: *Linear Algebra*, Addison-Wesley, Reading, Mass., 1964.
11. Thrall, R. M., and L. Tornheim: *Vector Spaces and Matrices*, Wiley, New York, 1957.

Boolean algebras and logic

12. Church, A.: *Introduction to Mathematical Logic*, Princeton University Press, Princeton, N.J., 1956.
13. Copi, I. M.: *Symbolic Logic*, Macmillan, New York, 1954.
14. Flegg, H. G.: *Boolean Algebra and Its Applications*, Wiley, New York, 1964.
15. Hohn, F. E.: *Applied Boolean Algebra*, Macmillan, New York, 1960.
16. Suppes, P. C.: *Introduction to Logic*, Van Nostrand, Princeton, N.J., 1958.
17. Whitesitt, J. E.: *Boolean Algebra and Its Applications*, Addison-Wesley, Reading, Mass., 1961.

Switching logic

18. Caldwell, S. H.: *Switching Circuits and Logical Design*, Wiley, New York, 1958.
19. Marcus, M. P.: *Switching Circuits for Engineers*, Prentice-Hall, Englewood Cliffs, N.J., 1962.
20. Miller, R. E.: *Switching Theory*, vol. 1, *Combinational Circuits*, Wiley, New York, 1965.

9 PROBABILITY AND STATISTICS

9.1 ELEMENTS OF PROBABILITY THEORY

9.1-1 Introduction. Mathematical probabilities are values of a real numerical function defined on a class of idealized events, which represent results of an experiment or observation. Mathematical probabilities are *not* defined directly in terms of "likelihood" or relative frequency of occurrence; they are introduced by a set of defining postulates (Sec. 9.1-2; see also Sec. 1.1-2) which abstract essential properties of statistical relative frequencies (Sec. 9.2-4). The concept of probability can, then, often be related to reality by the assumption that, in practically every sequence of independently repeated experiments, the relative frequency of each event tends to a limit represented by the corresponding probability.

9.1-2 Events and Probabilities. Given a specific idealized experiment or observation having a class of theoretically possible results (events, states) E permitting the following definitions.

1. The **union (logical sum)** $E_1 \cup E_2 \cup \cdots$ (or $E_1 + E_2 + \cdots$) of a countable (finite or infinite) set of events $E_1, E_2, \ldots$ is the event of realizing *at least one* of the events $E_1, E_2, \ldots$.
2. The **intersection (logical product)** $E_1 \cap E_2$ (or $E_1 E_2$) of two events E_1 and E_2 is the *joint event* of realizing *both E_1 and E_2*.
3. The **(logical) complement** $\tilde{E}$ of an event E is the event of *not* realizing E ("opposite" or complementary event of E).

Mathematical **probabilities** $P[E]$ are real numbers assigned to each event E in accordance with the following defining postulates:

---

1. $P[E] \geq 0$ for every event E of $\mathcal{S}$
2. $P[E] = 1$ if the event E is *certain*
3. $P[E_1 \cup E_2 \cup \cdots] = P[E_1] + P[E_2] + \cdots$ for every countable (finite or infinite) set of *mutually exclusive* events $E_1, E_2, \ldots$

Postulates 1 to 3 imply $0 \leq P[E] \leq 1$; in particular, $P[E] = 0$ if E is an impossible event. Note carefully that $P[E] = 1$ or $P[E] = 0$ do *not* necessarily imply that E is, respectively, certain or impossible.

A fourth defining postulate relates the "absolute" probability $P[E]$ associated with the given experiment to the "conditional" probabilities $P[E|E_1]$ referring to a "simpler" experiment restricted by the hypothesis that E_1 occurs. The **conditional probability $P[E|E_1]$ of E on (relative to) the hypothesis that the event E_1 occurs** is defined by the postulate

---

4. The probability of the joint event $E \cap E_1$ is $P[E \cap E_1] = P[E_1]P[E|E_1]$ (MULTIPLICATION LAW, LAW OF COMPOUND PROBABILITIES)

$P[E|E_1]$ *is not defined if $P[E_1] = 0$.*

9.1-3 Statistical Independence.
Two events E_1 and E_2 are **statistically independent (stochastically independent)** if and only if

$$P[E_1 \cap E_2] = P[E_1]P[E_2]$$

so that $P[E_1|E_2] = P[E_1]$ if $P[E_2] \neq 0$, and $P[E_2|E_1] = P[E_2]$ if $P[E_1] \neq 0$.

N events $E_1, E_2, \ldots, E_N$ are statistically independent if and only if not only each pair of events E_i, E_k but also each pair of possible joint events like $E_1 \cap E_2 \cap E_{17}$, $E_9 \cap E_{10}$, . . . is statistically independent.

9.1-4   Combination Rules.   (a) Probability of NOT realizing the event E

$$P[\tilde{E}] = 1 - P[E]$$

Probability of realizing AT LEAST ONE OF TWO EVENTS E_1 and E_2 (E_1 or E_2 or both)

$$P[E_1 \cup E_2] = P[E_1] + P[E_2] - P[E_1 \cap E_2]$$

Probability of realizing ALL OF N EVENTS E_1, E_2, . . . , E_N

$$P[E_1 \cap E_2 \cap \cdots \cap E_N] = P[E_1]P[E_2|E_1]P[E_3|E_1 \cap E_2] \cdots$$
$$P[E_N|E_1 \cap E_2 \cap \cdots \cap E_{N-1}]$$

(b) Probability of realizing AT LEAST ONE OF N STATISTICALLY INDEPENDENT EVENTS E_1, E_2, . . . , E_N

$$P[E_1 \cup E_2 \cup \cdots \cup E_N] = 1 - \{1 - P[E_1]\} \{1 - P[E_2]\} \cdots \{1 - P[E_N]\}$$

Probability of realizing ALL OF N STATISTICALLY INDEPENDENT EVENTS E_1, E_2, . . . , E_N

$$P[E_1 \cap E_2 \cap \cdots \cap E_N] = P[E_1]P[E_2] \cdots P[E_N]$$

Examples: If the probability of each throw with a die is $\frac{1}{6}$, then

The probability of throwing *either* 1 *or* 6 is $\frac{1}{6} + \frac{1}{6} = \frac{1}{3}$.
The probability of *not* throwing 6 is $1 - \frac{1}{6} = \frac{5}{6}$.
The probability of throwing 6 *at least once* in two throws is $\frac{1}{6} + \frac{1}{6} - \frac{1}{36} = \frac{11}{36}$.
The probability of throwing 6 *exactly once* in two throws is $\frac{1}{3} - \frac{2}{36} = \frac{5}{18}$.
The probability of throwing 6 twice in two throws is $\frac{1}{36}$, etc.

9.1-5   Random Variables and Distribution Functions.   (a) The outcomes of physical experiments are usually labeled with values of numerical **random variables** x, y, . . . so that each event E corresponds to a set of random-variable values, e.g., $x = a$, $x > a$, $a < x \leq b$, etc.   The probabilities of such events are uniquely defined by the (cumulative) distribution function of the random variable x,

$$\Phi_x(X) \equiv \Phi(X) \equiv P[x \leq X] \tag{9.1-1}$$

(b) If $\Phi_x(X)$ is continuously differentiable, then x is a **continuous random variable** permitting definition of the **probability density**

$$\varphi_x(X) \equiv \varphi(X) \equiv \lim_{\Delta x \to 0} \frac{P[X < x \leq X + \Delta x]}{\Delta x} \equiv \frac{d\Phi}{dX} \tag{9.1-2}$$

and

$$P[x \leq X] \equiv \Phi(X) \equiv \int_{-\infty}^{X} \varphi(x) \, dx$$
$$P[a < x \leq b] = \Phi(b) - \Phi(a) = \int_{a}^{b} \varphi(x) \, dx \qquad (9.1\text{-}3)$$

$$\int_{-\infty}^{\infty} \varphi(x) \, dx = \Phi(\infty) = 1 \qquad (9.1\text{-}4)$$

(c) x is a **discrete random variable** (has a **discrete probability distribution**) if and only if the probability

$$p_x(X) \equiv p(X) \equiv P[x = X] \qquad (9.1\text{-}5)$$

differs from zero only on a countable set of values $X = X_{(1)}, X_{(2)}, \ldots$ of x.

9.1-6 *Expected Value and Variance.* The **expected value (mean, mean value, mathematical expectation)** $E\{x\} = \xi$ and the **variance** Var $\{x\} = \sigma^2$ of a discrete or continuous one-dimensional random variable x, defined by

$$E\{x\} = \xi = \begin{cases} \sum_x xp(x) & (x \text{ discrete}) \\ \int_{-\infty}^{\infty} x\varphi(x) \, dx & (x \text{ continuous}) \end{cases}$$

$$\text{Var } \{x\} = \sigma^2 = E\{(x - \xi)^2\} \qquad (9.1\text{-}6)$$

$$= \begin{cases} \sum_x (x - \xi)^2 p(x) & (x \text{ discrete}) \\ \int_{-\infty}^{\infty} (x - \xi)^2 \varphi(x) \, dx & (x \text{ continuous}) \end{cases}$$

are, respectively, a measure of the *location* and a measure of the *dispersion* of the probability distribution of x.

For computation purposes note

$$\text{Var } \{x\} = \sigma^2 = E\{x^2\} - \xi^2 \qquad (9.1\text{-}7)$$

9.1-7 *Two-dimensional Probability Distributions.* (a) The joint distribution of two random variables x_1, x_2 is defined by its (cumulative) distribution function

$$\Phi_x(X_1, X_2) \equiv \Phi(X_1, X_2) \equiv P[x_1 \leq X_1, x_2 \leq X_2] \tag{9.1-8}$$

The distributions of x_1 and x_2 (**marginal distributions** derived from the joint distribution of x_1 and x_2) are described by the corresponding **marginal distribution functions**

$$\Phi_1(X_1) \equiv P[x_1 \leq X_1] \equiv P[x_1 \leq X_1, x_2 \leq \infty] \equiv \Phi(X_1, \infty)$$
$$\Phi_2(X_2) \equiv P[x_2 \leq X_2] \equiv P[x_1 \leq \infty, x_2 \leq X_2] \equiv \Phi(\infty, X_2)$$
$$\tag{9.1-9}$$

(*b*) A two-dimensional random variable $\mathbf{x} \equiv (x_1, x_2)$ is a **discrete random variable** (has a **discrete probability distribution**) if and only if the **joint probability**

$$p_x(X_1, X_2) \equiv p(X_1, X_2) \equiv P[x_1 = X_1, x_2 = X_2] \tag{9.1-10}$$

is different from zero only for a countable set (**spectrum**) of "points" (X_1, X_2), i.e., if and only if both x_1 and x_2 are discrete random variables (Sec. 9.1-5). The **marginal probabilities** respectively associated with the marginal distributions of x_1 and x_2 are

$$p_1(X_1) \equiv P[x_1 = X_1] \equiv \sum_{x_2} p(X_1, X_2)$$
$$p_2(X_2) \equiv P[x_2 = X_2] \equiv \sum_{x_1} p(X_1, X_2)$$
$$\tag{9.1-11}$$

(*c*) A two-dimensional random variable $\mathbf{x} \equiv (x_1, x_2)$ is a **continuous random variable** (has a **continuous probability distribution**) if and only if (1) $\Phi(X_1, X_2)$ is continuous for all X_1, X_2, and (2) the **joint frequency function** (**probability density**)

$$\varphi_x(X_1, X_2) \equiv \varphi(X_1, X_2) \equiv \frac{\partial^2 \Phi(X_1, X_2)}{\partial X_1 \, \partial X_2} \tag{9.1-12}$$

exists and is piecewise continuous everywhere. The **marginal frequency functions** respectively associated with the (necessarily continuous) marginal distributions of x_1 and x_2 are

$$\varphi_1(X_1) \equiv \frac{\partial \Phi_1(X_1)}{\partial X_1} \equiv \int_{-\infty}^{\infty} \varphi(x_1, x_2) \, dx_2$$

$$\varphi_2(X_2) \equiv \frac{\partial \Phi_2(X_2)}{\partial X_2} \equiv \int_{-\infty}^{\infty} \varphi(x_1, x_2) \, dx_1$$

(9.1-13)

(d) The joint distribution of two random variables x_1, x_2 defines a **conditional distribution of x_1 relative to the hypothesis that** $x_2 = X_2$ for each value X_2 of x_2 and a conditional distribution of x_2 relative to each hypothesis $x_1 = X_1$. The conditional distributions of x_1 and x_2 derived from a *discrete* joint distribution are discrete and may be described by the respective *conditional probabilities* (Sec. 9.1-2)

$$p_{1|2}(X_1|X_2) \equiv P[x_1 = X_1|x_2 = X_2] \equiv \frac{p(X_1, X_2)}{p_2(X_2)}$$

$$p_{2|1}(X_2|X_1) \equiv P[x_2 = X_2|x_1 = X_1] \equiv \frac{p(X_1, X_2)}{p_1(X_1)}$$

(9.1-14)

The conditional distributions of x_1 and x_2 derived from a *continuous* joint distribution are continuous and may be described by the respective **conditional frequency functions**

$$\varphi_{1|2}(X_1|X_2) \equiv \frac{\varphi(X_1, X_2)}{\varphi_2(X_2)} \qquad \varphi_{2|1}(X_2|X_1) \equiv \frac{\varphi(X_1, X_2)}{\varphi_1(X_1)}$$

(9.1-15)

9.1-8 Expected Values, Moments, Covariance, and Correlation Coefficient.

(a) The **expected value (mean value, mathematical expectation)** of a function $y = y(x_1, x_2)$ of two random variables x_1, x_2 with respect to their joint distribution is

$$E\{y(x_1, x_2)\} = \int_{-\infty}^{\infty} \int_{-\infty}^{\infty} y(x_1, x_2) \, d\Phi(x_1, x_2)$$

$$= \begin{cases} \displaystyle\sum_{x_1} \sum_{x_2} y(x_1, x_2) p(x_1, x_2) & \text{for discrete distributions} \\[2ex] \displaystyle\int_{-\infty}^{\infty} \int_{-\infty}^{\infty} y(x_1, x_2) \varphi(x_1, x_2) \, dx_1 \, dx_2 & \text{for continuous distributions} \end{cases}$$

(9.1-16)

(*b*) Note the following definitions:

$$\lambda_{11} = E\{(x_1 - \xi_1)^2\} = \text{Var } \{x_1\} = \sigma_1{}^2$$
$$\lambda_{22} = E\{(x_2 - \xi_2)^2\} = \text{Var } \{x_2\} = \sigma_2{}^2$$

(VARIANCES OF x_1 AND x_2)

$$\lambda_{12} = \lambda_{21} = E\{(x_1 - \xi_1)(x_2 - \xi_2)\} = \text{Cov } \{x_1, x_2\}$$

(COVARIANCE OF x_1 AND x_2)

$$\rho_{12} = \rho_{21} = \rho\{x_1, x_2\} = \frac{\lambda_{12}}{+\sqrt{\lambda_{11}\lambda_{22}}}$$

$$= \frac{\text{Cov } \{x_1, x_2\}}{+\sqrt{\text{Var } \{x_1\} \text{ Var } \{x_2\}}} = E\left\{\frac{x_1 - \xi_1}{\sigma_1} \frac{x_2 - \xi_2}{\sigma_2}\right\}$$

(CORRELATION COEFFICIENT OF x_1 AND x_2)

(9.1-17)

Note $-1 \le \rho_{12} \le 1$, and

$$\text{Cov } \{x_1, x_2\} = E\{x_1 x_2\} - \xi_1 \xi_2 = \rho_{12}\sigma_1\sigma_2 \tag{9.1-18}$$

9.1-9   *Examples of Discrete Probability Distributions.* (*a*) THE BINOMIAL DISTRIBUTION (Fig. 9.1-1). The probability of realizing an event ("success") exactly x times in n independent repeated trials (Bernoulli trials) such that the probability of success in each trial is ϑ is given by

$$p(x) = \binom{n}{x} \vartheta^x (1 - \vartheta)^{n-x} \qquad (x = 0, 1, 2, \ldots ; 0 \le \vartheta \le 1)$$

$$E\{x\} = n\vartheta \qquad \text{Var } \{x\} = n\vartheta(1 - \vartheta)$$

(9.1-19)

(*b*) THE POISSON DISTRIBUTION (Fig. 9.1-2). The Poisson distribution approximates a binomial distribution as $n \to \infty$, $\vartheta/n \to 0$ in such a manner that ϑn has a finite limit ξ (*Law of Small Numbers*). The approximation is often useful for $\vartheta \le 0.1$, $n\vartheta \ge 1$.

$$p(x) = e^{-\xi} \frac{\xi^x}{x!} \qquad (x = 0, 1, 2, \ldots ; \xi > 0)$$

$$E\{x\} = \text{Var } \{x\} = \xi$$

(9.1-20)

9.1-10   *The Normal (Gaussian) Distribution.* A continuous random variable x is **normally distributed (normal) with mean ξ and variance σ^2** [or **normal with parameters ξ, σ^2; normal with parameters ξ, σ; normal (ξ, σ^2); normal (ξ, σ)**] if

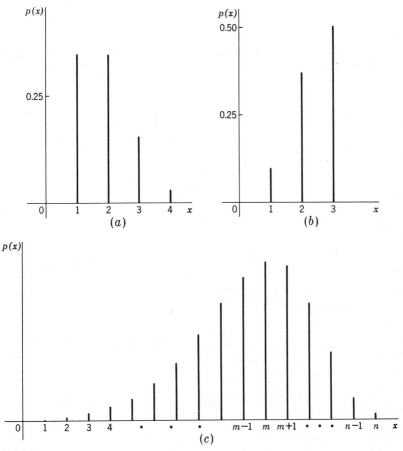

Fig. 9.1-1 The binomial distribution: (a) $n = 4$, $\vartheta = 0.4$; (b) $n = 3$, $\vartheta = 0.8$; (c) $n = 16$, $\vartheta = 0.7$. m is the mode. (*From A. M. Mood, Introduction to the Theory of Statistics, McGraw-Hill, New York, 1950.*)

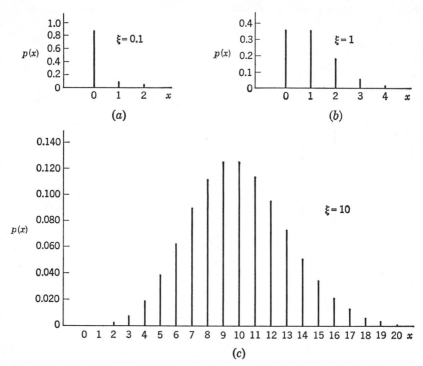

Fig. 9.1-2 The Poisson distribution. (*From H. H. Goode and R. E. Machol, System Engineering, McGraw-Hill, New York, 1957.*)

$$\varphi(X) \equiv \frac{1}{\sqrt{2\pi}\,\sigma}\, e^{-\frac{1}{2}\left(\frac{X-\xi}{\sigma}\right)^2} \equiv \frac{1}{\sigma}\,\varphi_u\left(\frac{X-\xi}{\sigma}\right)$$

$$\Phi(X) \equiv \frac{1}{\sqrt{2\pi}\,\sigma} \int_{-\infty}^{X} e^{-\frac{1}{2}\left(\frac{x-\xi}{\sigma}\right)^2}\, dx \equiv \Phi_u\left(\frac{X-\xi}{\sigma}\right) \qquad (9.1\text{-}21)$$

$$\equiv \frac{1}{2}\left[1 + \mathrm{erf}\left(\frac{1}{\sqrt{2}}\frac{X-\xi}{\sigma}\right)\right]$$

The distribution of the **standardized normal variable (normal deviate)** $u = (x - \xi)/\sigma$ is given by

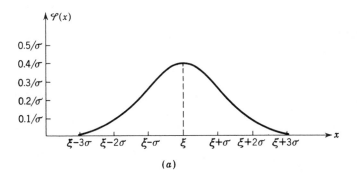

(a)

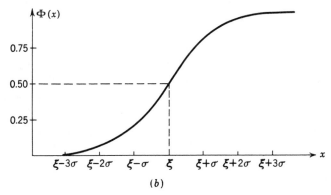

(b)

Fig. 9.1-3 (a) The normal frequency function

$$\varphi(X) = \frac{1}{\sqrt{2\pi}\,\sigma}\, e^{-\frac{1}{2}\left(\frac{x-\xi}{\sigma}\right)^2} = \frac{1}{\sigma}\,\varphi_u(U) \qquad \left(U = \frac{X-\xi}{\sigma}\right)$$

and (b) the normal distribution function

$$\Phi(X) = \frac{1}{\sqrt{2\pi}\,\sigma}\int_{-\infty}^{X} e^{-\frac{1}{2}\left(\frac{x-\xi}{\sigma}\right)^2}\,dx = \Phi_u(U) \qquad \left(U = \frac{X-\xi}{\sigma}\right)$$

$$\varphi_u(U) \equiv \frac{1}{\sqrt{2\pi}} e^{-\frac{U^2}{2}} \quad \text{(NORMAL FREQUENCY FUNCTION)}$$

$$\Phi_u(U) \equiv \frac{1}{\sqrt{2\pi}} \int_{-\infty}^{U} e^{-\frac{U^2}{2}} du \equiv \frac{1}{2}\left[1 + \operatorname{erf}\left(\frac{U}{\sqrt{2}}\right)\right] \quad (9.1\text{-}22)$$

(NORMAL DISTRIBUTION FUNCTION)

$$E\{u\} = 0 \qquad \text{Var }\{u\} = 1$$

(see also Fig. 9.1-3). erf z is the frequently tabulated **error function** (**normal error integral, probability integral**)

$$\operatorname{erf} z \equiv -\operatorname{erf}(-z) \equiv \frac{2}{\sqrt{\pi}} \int_{0}^{z} e^{-\zeta^2} d\zeta \equiv 2\Phi_u(z\sqrt{2}) - 1 \quad (9.1\text{-}23)$$

Note the following measures of dispersion for normal distributions:

The *mean deviation* (m.a.e.) $E\{|x - \xi|\} = \sigma E\{|u|\} = \sqrt{2/\pi}\,\sigma \approx 0.798\sigma$

The *probable deviation* (p.e., median of $|x - \xi|$) $|u|_{\frac{1}{2}}\sigma = -u_{\frac{1}{4}}\sigma = u_{\frac{3}{4}}\sigma \approx 0.674\sigma$

One-half the half width $\sqrt{2 \log_e 2}\,\sigma \approx 1.177\sigma$

The lower and upper *quartiles* $x_{\frac{1}{4}} = \xi - u_{\frac{1}{4}}\sigma = \xi - |u|_{\frac{1}{2}}\sigma$

$$x_{\frac{3}{4}} = \xi + u_{\frac{3}{4}}\sigma = \xi + |u|_{\frac{1}{2}}\sigma$$

The *precision measure* $h = 1/(\sqrt{2}\sigma)$

9.1-11 Convergence in Probability. Limit Theorems.

(a) A sequence of random variables $y_1, y_2, \ldots$ **converges in probability** to the random variable y (y_n converges in probability to y as $n \to \infty$) if and only if the probability that y_n differs from y by any finite amount converges to zero as $n \to \infty$, or

$$y_n \xrightarrow[\text{in } p]{} y \text{ as } n \to \infty \text{ if and only if}$$

$$\lim_{n \to \infty} P[|y - y_n| > \epsilon] = 0 \qquad \text{for all } \epsilon > 0 \quad (9.1\text{-}24)$$

This is, in particular, true if y_n **converges in mean** to y as $n \to \infty$,

$$\lim_{n \to \infty} E\{y - y_n\} = \lim_{n \to \infty} \text{Var }\{y - y_n\} = 0 \quad (9.1\text{-}25)$$

The (probability distribution of a) random variable y_n with the distribution function $\Phi_{y_n}(Y, n)$ is **asymptotically normal with mean η_n and variance σ_n^2** if and only if there exists a sequence of pairs of real numbers η_n, σ_n^2 such that the random variable $(y_n - \eta_n)/\sigma_n$ converges in probability to a standardized normal variable.

(b) *For every class of events E permitting the definition of probabilities* $P[E]$

1. *The relative frequency* $h[E] = n_E/n$ *(Sec. 9.2-4) of realizing the event E in n independent repeated trials is a random variable which converges to $P[E]$ in mean, and thus also in probability, as $n \to \infty$ (Bernoulli's Theorem).*
2. *$h[E]$ is asymptotically normal with mean $P[E]$ and variance $(1/n)P[E]\{1 - P[E]\}$.*

Let $x_1, x_2, \ldots$ be a sequence of statistically independent random variables all having the same probability distribution with (finite) mean value ξ. Then, as $n \to \infty$,

1. *The random variable $\bar{x} = (1/n)(x_1 + x_2 + \cdots + x_n)$ converges in probability to ξ (Khinchine's Theorem, Law of Large Numbers).*
2. *x is asymptotically normal with mean ξ and variance σ^2/n, provided that the common variance σ^2 of $x_1, x_2, \ldots$ exists (Lindeberg-Lévy Theorem, Central Limit Theorem).*

9.2 INTRODUCTION TO STATISTICAL METHODS

9.2-1 Statistics. In the most general sense of the word, **statistics** is the art of using quantitative empirical data to describe experience and to infer and test propositions (numerical estimates, hypothetical correspondences, predicted results, decisions). More specifically, statistics deals (1) with the *statistical description* of processes or experiments, and (2) with the induction and testing of corresponding mathematical models involving the *probability concept*. The relevant portions of probability theory constitute the field of *mathematical statistics*. These techniques extend the possibility of scientific prediction and rational decisions to many situations where deterministic prediction fails because essential parameters cannot be known or controlled with sufficient accuracy.

Statistical description and probability models apply to physical processes exhibiting the *empirical* phenomenon of *statistical regularity: even though individual measurements of a physical quantity x cannot be predicted with sufficient accuracy, a suitably determined function $y = y(x_1, x_2, \ldots)$ of a set* (**sample**) *of repeated measurements $x_1, x_2, \ldots$ of x can often be predicted with substantially better accuracy,* and the prediction of y may still yield useful decisions.   Such a function y of a set of sample values is called a **statistic.**

Frequently a statistic can be predicted with increasing accuracy as the **size** n of the sample $(x_1, x_2, \ldots, x_n)$ increases (*physical laws of large numbers*).   The best-known statistics are *statistical relative frequencies* and *sample averages* (Sec. 9.2-4).

9.2-2 Random-sample Statistics. Concept of a Population.

In an important class of applications, a continuously variable physical quantity (observable) x is regarded as a one-dimensional random variable with the inferred or estimated probability density $\varphi(x)$.   Each sample $(x_1, x_2, \ldots, x_n)$ of measurements of x is postulated to be the result of n *repeated independent measurements*.   Hence $x_1, x_2, \ldots, x_n$ are *statistically independent random variables with identical probability density.*   A sample $(x_1, x_2, \ldots, x_n)$ defined in this manner is called **a random sample of size** n and constitutes an n-dimensional random variable.   The probability density in the n-dimensional sample space of "sample points" $(x_1, x_2, \ldots, x_n)$ is the **likelihood function**

$$L(x_1, x_2, \ldots, x_n) = \varphi(x_1)\varphi(x_2) \cdots \varphi(x_n) \tag{9.2-1}$$

Every random-sample statistic $y = y(x_1, x_2, \ldots, x_n)$ is a random variable whose probability distribution (**sampling distribution** of y) is uniquely determined by the likelihood function, and hence by the distribution of x.   Each sampling distribution will, in general, depend on the sample size n.

As the size n of random sample increases, many sample statistics converge in probability to corresponding parameters of the theoretical distribution of x; in particular, statistical relative frequencies converge in mean to the corresponding probabilities (Sec. 9.1-11).   Thus one considers each sample drawn from an infinite (theoretical) **population** (**universe, ensemble**) whose sample distribution (Sec. 9.2-5) is identical with the theoretical probability distribution of x.   The probability distribution is then referred to as the **population distribution,** and its parameters are **population parameters.**   In many applications, the theoretical population is an idealization of an actual population from which samples are drawn.

9.2-3 Relation between Probability Model and Reality: Estimation and Testing. (a) ESTIMATION OF PARAMETERS. Statis-

tical methods use empirical data (sample values) to infer specifications of a *probability model*, e.g., to estimate the probability density $\varphi(x)$ of a random variable x. An important application of such inferred models is to make *decisions* based on inferred probabilities of future events. In most applications, statistical relative frequencies (Sec. 9.2-4) are used directly only for rough *qualitative* (graphical) estimates of the population distribution. Instead, one infers (postulates) the general form of the theoretical distribution, say

$$\varphi = \varphi(x; \eta_1, \eta_2, \ldots) \tag{9.2-2}$$

where $\eta_1, \eta_2, \ldots$ are unknown *population parameters* to be estimated on the basis of the given random sample $(x_1, x_2, \ldots, x_n)$.

The parameters $\eta_1, \eta_2, \ldots$ usually measure specific properties of the theoretical distribution of x (e.g., population mean, population variance). In general, one attempts to estimate values of the parameters $\eta_1, \eta_2, \ldots$ "fitting" a given sample $(x_1, x_2, \ldots, x_n)$ by the empirical values of corresponding sample statistics $y_1(x_1, x_2, \ldots, x_n)$, $y_2(x_1, x_2, \ldots, x_n)$, $\ldots$ which measure analogous properties of the sample (e.g., sample average, sample variance, Sec. 9.2-4). "Fitting" is interpreted subjectively and not necessarily uniquely; in particular, one prefers estimates $y(x_1, x_2, \ldots, x_n)$ which converge in probability to η as $n \to \infty$ (**consistent estimates**), whose expected value equals η (**unbiased estimates**), whose sampling distribution has a small variance, and/or which are easy to compute.

(*b*) TESTING STATISTICAL HYPOTHESES. Tests of a *statistical hypothesis* specifying some property of a theoretical distribution (say, an inferred set of parameter values $\eta_1, \eta_2, \ldots$) are based on the likelihood (1) of a *test sample* $(x_1, x_2, \ldots, x_n)$ when the hypothetical probability density (2) is used to compute $L(x_1, x_2, \ldots, x_n)$. Generally speaking, the test will *reject* the hypothesis if the test sample $(x_1, x_2, \ldots, x_n)$ falls into a region of small likelihood; or equivalently, if the corresponding value of a *test statistic* $y(x_1, x_2, \ldots, x_n)$ is improbable on the basis of the hypothetical likelihood function. The choice of specific conditions of rejection is again subjective and is ultimately based on the penalties of false rejection and/or acceptance and, to some extent, on the cost of obtaining test samples of various sizes.

NOTE: Incorrect use of statistical methods can lead to grave errors and seriously wrong conclusions. All (possibly tacit) assumptions regarding a theoretical distribution must be checked. *Never use the same sample for estimation and testing.*

Finally, remember that statistical tests cannot *prove* any hypothesis; they can only demonstrate a "lack of disproof."

9.2-4 Statistical Relative Frequencies.

Consider an event E which occurs if and only if a measurement of the random variable x yields a value in some set S_E (usually a *class interval*). Given a random sample $(x_1, x_2, \ldots, x_n)$ of x, let n_E denote the number of times a sample value x_k implies the occurrence of the event E. The **statistical relative frequency** of the event E obtained from the given random sample is

$$h[E] = \frac{n_E}{n} \tag{9.2-3}$$

where n is the size of the sample. Note

$$E\{h[E]\} = P[E] \qquad \text{Var}\,\{h[E]\} = \frac{P[E]\{1 - P[E]\}}{n} \tag{9.2-4}$$

The statistical relative frequency $h[E]$ is an unbiased, consistent estimate of the corresponding probability $P[E]$; as $n \to \infty$, $h[E]$ is asymptotically normal with the parameters (4) (Sec. 9.1-11).

9.2-5 The Distribution of the Sample. Grouped Data.

For a given random sample $(x_1, x_2, \ldots, x_n)$, the **empirical cumulative distribution function**

$$F(X) = h[x \leq X] \tag{9.2-5}$$

is a nondecreasing step function, with $F(-\infty) = 0$, $F(\infty) = 1$. *$F(X)$ is an unbiased, consistent estimate of the cumulative distribution function* $\Phi(X) = P[x \leq X]$ and defines the **distribution (frequency distribution) of the sample (empirical distribution** based on the given sample).

Let the range of the random variable x be partitioned into a finite or infinite number of conveniently chosen **class intervals (cells)** $X_j - (\Delta X_j)/2 < x \leq X_j + (\Delta X_j)/2$ $(j = 1, 2, \ldots)$ respectively of length $\Delta X_1, \Delta X_2, \ldots$ and centered at $x = X_1 < X_2 < \cdots$. For a given random sample, the **class frequency (occupation number)** n_j is the number of times an x_k falls into the jth class interval (description of the sample in terms of **grouped data**). The statistical relative frequencies $h_j = n_j/n$ (**relative frequencies of observations in the j class interval**) must add up to unity and are consistent, unbiased estimates of the corresponding probabilities.

For sufficiently large samples and sufficiently small class intervals, all sample statistics can be calculated from the statistical relative frequencies $h_j = n_j/n$ just as corresponding population parameters are calculated from the corresponding probabilities. The use of grouped data often becomes an economic necessity for computations involving sample sizes n larger than 25. The statistics $F(X)$, n_j, h_j yield various graphical representations of sample distributions and hence of estimated population distributions (bar charts, histograms, frequency polygons, probability graph paper, etc.).

SAMPLE FRACTILES. The **sample P-fractiles** (**sample quantiles**) X_P are defined by

$$h[x \leq X_P] = F(X_P) = P \qquad (0 < P < 1) \qquad (9.2\text{-}6)$$

Equation (6) does not define X_P uniquely but brackets it by two adjacent sample values x_k. $X_{1/2}$ is the **sample median**, and $X_{1/4}$, $X_{1/2}$, $X_{3/4}$ are **sample quartiles,** with analogous definitions for **sample deciles** and **sample percentiles**.

9.2-6 Sample Averages and Sample Variances. (*a*) Given a random sample $(x_1, x_2, \ldots, x_n)$, the **sample average** of x is

$$\bar{x} = \frac{1}{n}(x_1 + x_2 + \cdots + x_n) = \frac{1}{n}\sum_{k=1}^{n} x_k \qquad (9.2\text{-}7)$$

In terms of the sample distribution over a set of class intervals centered at $x = X_1, X_2, \ldots, X_m$, $\bar{x}$ is approximated by

$$\bar{x}_G = \frac{1}{n}(n_1 X_1 + n_2 X_2 + \cdots + n_m X_m) = \frac{1}{n}\sum_{j=1}^{m} n_j X_j$$

$$\text{(SAMPLE AVERAGE FROM GROUPED DATA)} \qquad (9.2\text{-}8)$$

$\bar{x}$ is a *measure of location* of the sample distribution. Note

$$E\{\bar{x}\} = \xi \qquad \text{Var}\,\{\bar{x}\} = \frac{\sigma^2}{n} \qquad (9.2\text{-}9)$$

whenever the quantity on the right exists. *$\bar{x}$ is an unbiased, consistent estimate of the population mean $\xi = E\{x\}$; if σ^2 exists, $\bar{x}$ is asymptotically normal with the parameters* (9) *as $n \to \infty$.*

(*b*) The **sample variances**

$$s^2 = \overline{(x - \bar{x})^2} = \frac{1}{n}\sum_{k=1}^{n}(x_k - \bar{x})^2$$

$$S^2 = \frac{n}{n-1}s^2 = \frac{1}{n-1}\sum_{k=1}^{n}(x_k - \bar{x})^2 \qquad (9.2\text{-}10)$$

are *measures of dispersion* of the sample distribution; s is called **sample standard deviation** or **sample dispersion.** Note

$$E\{s^2\} = \frac{n-1}{n}\sigma^2 \qquad E\{S^2\} = \sigma^2 \tag{9.2-11}$$

whenever the quantity on the right exists. S^2 *is an unbiased, consistent estimate of the population variance* $\sigma^2 = \mathrm{Var}\ \{x\}$ and is thus often more useful than s^2.

9.2-7 *Some Sampling Distributions.* For samples with a normal population distribution (samples drawn from a *normal population,* normal samples), all sample values are normal variables, and many sampling distributions can be calculated explicitly. The assumption of a normal population can often be justified by the central-limit theorem. For any sample of size n drawn from a normal population with mean ξ and variance σ^2

1. $\dfrac{\bar{x} - \xi}{\sigma/\sqrt{n}}$ has a **standardized normal distribution** (u **distribution,** Sec. 9.1-10).

2. $\dfrac{\bar{x} - \xi}{S/\sqrt{n}} = \dfrac{\bar{x} - \xi}{s/\sqrt{n-1}}$ (**Student's ratio**) has a t **distribution with** $n - 1$ **degrees of freedom.**

3. $\dfrac{(n-1)S^2}{\sigma^2} = \dfrac{ns^2}{\sigma^2} = \dfrac{1}{\sigma^2}\displaystyle\sum_{k=1}^{n}(x_k - \bar{x})^2$ has a χ^2 **distribution with** $n - 1$ **degrees of freedom.**

4. $\dfrac{x_i - \xi}{\sigma}$ has a **standardized normal distribution.**

5. $\dfrac{x_i - \xi}{S} = \dfrac{x_i - \xi}{s}\sqrt{\dfrac{n-1}{n}}$ has a t **distribution with** $n - 1$ **degrees of freedom.**

The χ^2 **distribution with** m **degrees of freedom** is defined by

$$\varphi_y(Y) \equiv \varphi_{\chi^2(m)}(Y) = \begin{cases} 0 & \text{for } Y < 0 \\[2mm] \dfrac{1}{\Gamma\left(\dfrac{m}{2}\right)\sqrt{2^m}}\, Y^{(m-2)/2}e^{-Y/2} & \text{for } Y > 0 \end{cases} \tag{9.2-12}$$

with $E\{y\} = m \qquad \mathrm{Var}\ \{y\} = 2m$

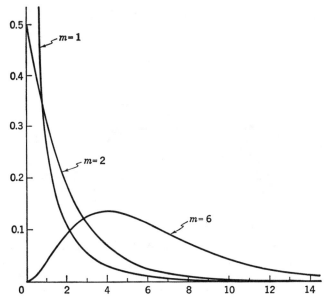

Fig. 9.2-1   The χ^2 distribution for various values of m.

(see also Fig. 9.2-1). Given any m statistically independent standardized normal variables $u_k = (x_k - \xi_k)/\sigma_k$, the sum $\chi^2 = \sum_{k=1}^{m} u_k^2$ has a χ^2 distribution with m degrees of freedom.

Student's t distribution with m degrees of freedom is defined by

$$\varphi_y(Y) \equiv \varphi_{t(m)}(Y) \equiv \frac{\Gamma\left(\dfrac{m+1}{2}\right)}{\Gamma\left(\dfrac{m}{2}\right)\sqrt{m\pi}}\left(1 + \frac{Y^2}{m}\right)^{-(m+1)/2} \tag{9.2-13}$$

with $E\{y\} = 0$ $(m > 1)$ $\mathrm{Var}\{y\} = \dfrac{m}{m-2}$ $(m > 2)$

(see also Fig. 9.2-2). y is distributed like the ratio

$$y = t = \frac{x_0}{\sqrt{\dfrac{1}{m}(x_1^2 + x_2^2 + \cdots + x_m^2)}}$$

where $x_0, x_1, x_2, \ldots, x_m$ are $m + 1$ statistically independent normal variables, each having the mean 0 and the variance σ^2. Note that t is independent of σ^2. Both χ^2 and t are asymptotically normal as $m \to \infty$.

9.2-8   *Statistics Derived from Multivariate Samples.*

Given a multidimensional random variable $\mathbf{x} \equiv (x_1, x_2, \ldots, x_\nu)$, one pro-

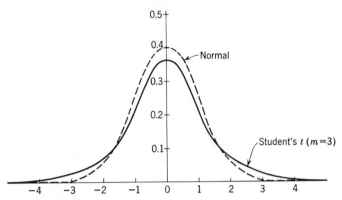

Fig. 9.2-2 Student's t distribution compared with the standardized normal distribution.

ceeds by analogy with Sec. 9.2-2 to introduce a **random sample of size** n $(\mathbf{x}_1, \mathbf{x}_2, \ldots, \mathbf{x}_n) \equiv (x_{11}, x_{21}, \ldots, x_{\nu1}; x_{12}, x_{22}, \ldots, x_{\nu2};$ $\ldots; x_{1n}, x_{2n}, \ldots, x_{\nu n})$ and the statistics

$$\bar{x}_i = \frac{1}{n} \sum_{k=1}^{n} x_{ik} \qquad (i = 1, 2, \ldots, \nu)$$

(SAMPLE AVERAGE OF x_i)   (9.2-14)

$$\overline{f(x_1, x_2, \ldots, x_\nu)} = \frac{1}{n} \sum_{k=1}^{n} f(x_{1k}, x_{2k}, \ldots, x_{\nu k})$$

[SAMPLE AVERAGE OF $f(x_1, x_2, \ldots, x_\nu)$]   (9.2-15)

$$l_{ij} = \overline{(x_i - \bar{x}_i)(x_j - \bar{x}_j)} = l_{ji} \qquad (i, j = 1, 2, \ldots, \nu)$$

(SAMPLE VARIANCES s_i^2 for $i = j$, SAMPLE COVARIANCES for $i \neq j$)

(9.2-16)

$$r_{ij} = \frac{l_{ij}}{\sqrt{l_{ii}l_{jj}}} = r_{ji} \qquad (i, j = 1, 2, \ldots, \nu)$$

(SAMPLE CORRELATION COEFFICIENTS)   (9.2-17)

The "point" corresponding to $\bar{\mathbf{x}} \equiv (\bar{x}_1, \bar{x}_2, \ldots, \bar{x}_\nu)$ is the **sample center of gravity,** and the matrix $L \equiv [l_{ij}]$ is the **sample moment matrix;** det $[l_{ij}]$ is the **generalized variance** of the sample. *The statistics (14) to (17) are consistent estimates of the corresponding population parameters.*

References and Bibliography

Probability theory

1. Cramér, H.: *The Elements of Probability Theory and Some of Its Applications,* Wiley, New York, 1955.
2. Feller, W.: *An Introduction to Probability Theory and Its Applications,* 2d ed., Wiley, New York, 1958.
3. Gnedenko, B. V., and A. I. Khinchine: *An Elementary Introduction to the Theory of Probability,* Dover, New York, 1961.
4. Neyman, J.: *First Course in Probability and Statistics,* Holt, Rinehart, and Winston, New York, 1950.
5. Parzen, E.: *Modern Probability Theory and Its Applications,* Wiley, New York, 1960.
6. Papoulis, A.: *Probability, Random Variables, and Stochastic Processes,* McGraw-Hill, New York, 1965.

Statistics

7. Arley, N., and K. R. Buch: *Introduction to the Theory of Probability and Statistics,* Wiley, New York, 1950.
8. Burlington, R. S., and D. C. May: *Handbook of Probability and Statistics with Tables,* Handbook Publishers, Sandusky, Ohio, 1953.
9. Cramér, H.: *Mathematical Methods of Statistics,* Princeton University Press, Princeton, N.J., 1951.
10. Dixon, W. J., and F. J. Massey, Jr.: *An Introduction to Statistical Analysis,* 2d ed., McGraw-Hill, New York, 1957.
11. Hald, A.: *Statistical Theory with Engineering Applications,* Wiley, New York, 1952.
12. Hoel, P. G.: *Introduction to Mathematical Statistics,* Wiley, New York, 1947.
13. Korn, G. A., and T. M. Korn: *Mathematical Handbook for Scientists and Engineers,* McGraw-Hill, New York, 1961.
14. Mood, A. M.: *Introduction to the Theory of Statistics,* McGraw-Hill, New York, 1950.

10 SOME NUMERICAL METHODS

10.1 NUMERICAL SOLUTION OF EQUATIONS

10.1-1 Introduction. The numerical solution of any equation

$$f(z) = 0 \qquad\qquad (10.1\text{-}1)$$

should be preceded by a rough (often graphical) survey yielding information regarding the existence and position of real roots, estimates for trial solutions, etc. (see also Secs. 1.4-4 and 5.3-5). Solutions may be checked by resubstitution.

10.1-2 Iteration Methods. The following procedures apply, in particular, to the solution of transcendental equations.

(a) Rewrite the given equation (1) in the form

$$z = \varphi(z) \qquad\qquad (10.1\text{-}2)$$

(see also Sec. 10.1-2b). Starting with a *trial solution* $z^{[0]}$, compute *successive approximations*

$$z^{[j+1]} = \varphi(z^{[j]}) \qquad (j = 0,\ 1,\ 2,\ \ldots) \tag{10.1-3}$$

The convergence of such approximations to a desired solution z requires a separate investigation.

(*b*) In general, *there are many possible ways of rewriting the given equation* (1) *in the form* (2). Particular choices of $\varphi(z)$ yield the following special forms of the iteration formula (3):

$$z^{[j+1]} = z^{[j]} - kf(z^{[j]}) \tag{10.1-4}$$

$$z^{[j+1]} = z^{[j]} - \frac{f(z^{[j]})}{f'(z^{[j]})} \qquad \text{(NEWTON-RAPHSON METHOD)} \tag{10.1-5}$$

These iteration schemes are especially useful for the computation of real roots. To find complex roots of real equations, one must start with a complex trial solution $z^{[0]}$.

Useful examples: Application of Eq. (5) to $1/z - a = 0$, $z^2 - a = 0$, and $1/z^2 - 1/a = 0$ yields iteration routines for $1/a$ and $\sqrt{a}$:

$$z^{[j+1]} = z^{[j]}(2 - az^{[j]}) \to 1/a \qquad \text{as } j \to \infty \tag{10.1-6}$$

$$z^{[j+1]} = \tfrac{1}{2}(z^{[j]} + a/z^{[j]}) \to \sqrt{a} \qquad \text{as } j \to \infty \tag{10.1-7}$$

$$z^{[j+1]} = z^{[j]}[1 + (a - z^{[j]2})/2a] \to \sqrt{a} \qquad \text{as } j \to \infty \tag{10.1-8}$$

(*c*) THE REGULA FALSI. The following iteration scheme applies particularly well to real equations and real roots and is used when $f'(z)$ is not easily computed. Given Eq. (1), start with two trial values $z = z^{[0]}$, $z = z^{[1]}$ and obtain successive approximations

$$z^{[j+1]} = z^{[j]} - \frac{z^{[j]} - z^{[k]}}{f(z^{[j]}) - f(z^{[k]})} f(z^{[j]})$$
$$(j = 0,\ 1,\ 2,\ \ldots\ ;\ k < j) \tag{10.1-9}$$

For continuous real functions $f(z)$, one attempts to bracket each real root between approximations $z^{[j]}$ and $z^{[k]}$ such that $f(z^{[j]})$ and $f(z^{[k]})$ have opposite signs. Each $z^{[j]}$ can then be obtained by graphical straight-line interpolation; the scale of the graph should be appropriately increased at each step.

(*d*) MULTIPLE ROOTS. Iteration schemes based on Eq. (5) (Newton-Raphson method) will not converge in the neighborhood of a multiple root of the given equation. Note that multiple zeros of $f(z)$ are zeros of $f'(z)$.

10.1-3 *Special Methods for Algebraic Equations.* (*a*) COMPUTATION OF POLYNOMIAL VALUES. To compute values of a polynomial

$$f(z) \equiv a_0 z^n + a_1 z^{n-1} + \cdots + a_{n-1} z + a_n \qquad (10.1\text{-}10)$$

for use in the iteration methods of Sec. 10.1-3b, compute successively $a_0 z + a_1$, $z(a_0 z + a_1) + a_2$, . . . ; or obtain the desired quantities $f(c)$, $f'(c), f''(c)/2!$, . . . by *Horner's scheme.*

Horner's scheme: Long division of $f(z)$ by $(z - c)$ yields a new polynomial $f_1(z)$ and the remainder $f(c)$ (Sec. 1.5-2); long division of $f_1(z)$ by $(z - c)$ in turn yields a new polynomial $f_2(z)$ and the remainder $f'(c)$. Continuing in this manner, one obtains successive remainders $f''(c)/2!$, $f'''(c)/3!$, ... Note that these remainders are the coefficients of the polynomial

$$F(u) \equiv f(u + c) \equiv f(c) + f'(c)u + \frac{1}{2!} f''(c)u^2 + \cdots \equiv f(z) \qquad (10.1\text{-}11)$$

(*b*) ITERATION METHODS FOR REAL ROOTS. To compute single simple roots of an algebraic equation

$$f(z) \equiv a_0 z^n + a_1 z^{n-1} + \cdots + a_{n-1} z + a_n = 0 \qquad (10.1\text{-}12)$$

one may

1. Use the *Newton-Raphson method* of Eq. (5)
2. Employ Eq. (4) with $k = 1/a_{n-1}$, calculating successive values of the polynomial

$$z^{[j+1]} = z^{[j]} - f(z^{[j]})/a_{n-1} \qquad (10.1\text{-}13)$$

by Horner's scheme. If $a_{n-1} = 0$, introduce $u = z - c$ and use Eq. (11) to rewrite Eq. (12) as $F(u) = 0$.
3. Attempt to bracket the root between argument values yielding function values of opposite signs, or use the *regula falsi* (Sec. 10.1-2c).

Horner's method (for real roots) evaluates the coefficients of successive polynomials $F_1(u) \equiv f(u + c_1)$, $F_2(u) \equiv F_1(u + c_2)$, . . . by Horner's scheme, where $c_1, c_2,$ . . . are chosen so as to reduce the absolute values of the remainders. If one succeeds in obtaining $F_j(c_j) \approx 0$, then the desired root is approximated by $c_1 + c_2 + \cdots + c_j$.

(*c*) COMPLEX ROOTS. The iteration schemes of Eqs. (4) and (5) apply to the case of complex roots; start with a complex trial value near the suspected root.

(*d*) GRAEFFE'S ROOT-SQUARING PROCESS. Given the real algebraic equation

$$f(z) \equiv \prod_{k=1}^{n} (z - z_k) \equiv z^n + a_1 z^{n-1} + \cdots + a_n = 0 \qquad (10.1\text{-}14)$$

obtain the coefficients $a_i^{(1)}$ of

$$f(z)f(-z) \equiv (-1)^n \prod_{k=1}^{n} (z^2 - z_k^2)$$

$$\equiv (-1)^n (z^2)^n + a_1^{(1)}(z^2)^{n-1} + \cdots + a_n^{(1)}$$

by writing the array

$k = n$	$k = n - 1$	$k = n - 2$	$k = n - 3$	(Column number)
a_n	a_{n-1}	a_{n-2}	a_{n-3}	$\cdots$
a_n	$-a_{n-1}$	a_{n-2}	$-a_{n-3}$	
a_n^2	$-a_{n-1}^2$	a_{n-2}^2	$-a_{n-3}^2$	
	$+2a_n a_{n-2}$	$+2a_n a_{n-4}$	$+2a_n a_{n-6}$	$\cdots$
		$-2a_{n-1}a_{n-3}$	$-2a_{n-1}a_{n-5}$	
			$+2a_{n-2}a_{n-4}$	
$a_n^{(1)}$	$a_{n-1}^{(1)}$	$a_{n-2}^{(1)}$	$a_{n-3}^{(1)}$	$\cdots$

Repeat this process, obtaining successively the coefficients $a_i^{(j)}$ of

$$(-1)^n \prod_{k=1}^{n} (z^{2j} - z_k^{2j}) \equiv (-1)^n (z^{2j})^n + a_1^{(j)}(z^{2j})^{n-1} + \cdots + a_n^{(j)}$$

As j increases, the array usually assumes a definite pattern: (1) the double products in a column may become negligible, so that successive column entries become squares with equal signs (*regular column*[*]); all entries of a column may have equal signs and absolute values equal to a definite fraction of the squared entry above (*fractionally regular column*); (2) column entries may have regularly alternating signs (*fluctuating column*); and (3) a column may be entirely *irregular*.

Each pair of regular columns (say, k and $k - r$) separated by $r - 1$ nonregular columns corresponds to a set of r roots z of equal magnitude such that

$$\left| \frac{a_k^{(j)}}{a_{k-r}^{(j)}} \right| \rightarrow |z|^{2^{i+r}} \qquad as \; j \rightarrow \infty \tag{10.1-15}$$

These r roots are all either real or pure imaginary if the $r - 1$ separating columns are fractionally regular. Specifically,

---

[*] M. B. Reed and G. B. Reed, *Mathematical Methods in Electrical Engineering*, Harper, New York, 1951.

1. Two adjacent regular columns (say k and $k - 1$) yield a *simple real root* z such that

$$\left|\frac{a_k^{(j)}}{a_{k-1}^{(j)}}\right| \to |z|^{2^j} \qquad \text{as } j \to \infty$$

2. Two regular columns (k and $k - 2$) separated by a fluctuating column indicate a *pair of simple complex-conjugate roots* z such that

$$\left|\frac{a_k^{(j)}}{a_{k-2}^{(j)}}\right| \to |z|^{2^{j+1}} \qquad \text{as } j \to \infty$$

In practice, one first finds the real and purely imaginary roots; determine signs by substitution or with the aid of Sec. 1.4-4. One may then use long division to simplify the given equation, or supplement Eq. (15) by Newton's formulas (1.4-4) to find the complex roots; see also Sec. 10.1-2d for the treatment of multiple roots.

10.1-4 Systems of Equations and the Problem of Finding Maxima and Minima: Iteration Methods (*see also Secs. 7.1-1, 10.1-2, and 10.1-3*).

(*a*) The problem of solving n simultaneous equations

$$f_i(x_1, x_2, \ldots, x_n) = 0 \qquad (i = 1, 2, \ldots, n) \qquad (10.1\text{-}16)$$

for n unknowns $x_1, x_2, \ldots, x_n$ is equivalent to the problem of *minimizing the function*

$$F(x_1, x_2, \ldots, x_n) \equiv \sum_{i=1}^{n} |f_i(x_1, x_2, \ldots, x_n)|^2 \qquad (10.1\text{-}17)$$

or some other increasing real function of the absolute values $|f_i|$ of the n **residuals** (**errors**) $f_i = f_i(x_1, x_2, \ldots, x_n)$. The problem of minimizing (or maximizing) a given function of n variables is of great practical importance in its own right.

A useful class of *iteration methods* starts with a trial solution $x_i^{[0]}$ ($i = 1, 2, \ldots, n$) and attempts to construct successive approximations

$$x_i^{[j+1]} = x_i^{[j]} + \lambda^{[j]} v_i^{[j]}$$
$$(i = 1, 2, \ldots, n; j = 0, 1, 2, \ldots) \qquad (10.1\text{-}18)$$

which converge to a solution x_i as $j \to \infty$.

Once the ratios $v_1^{[j]} : v_2^{[j]} : \cdots : v_n^{[j]}$ ("direction" of the jth step) are chosen, one may minimize $F(x_1^{[j+1]}, x_2^{[j+1]}, \ldots, x_n^{[j+1]})$ as a function $F(\lambda^{[j]})$ of the parameter $\lambda^{[j]}$ which determines the *step size*. For this purpose, $F(\lambda^{[j]})$ may be approximated by a Taylor series or by an interpolation polynomial (Sec. 10.2-2) based on three to five trial values of $\lambda^{[j]}$. *The latter method also applies to the computation of maxima and minima of a tabulated function* $F(x_1, x_2, \ldots, x_n)$.

(*b*) VARYING ONE UNKNOWN AT A TIME. Attempt to minimize F by varying only one of the x_i at each step, either cyclically or so as to reduce the largest absolute residual (see also Sec. 10.1-6*c*, relaxation).

(*c*) THE NEWTON-RAPHSON METHOD. Start with a trial solution $x_i^{[0]}$, and obtain successive approximations $x_i^{[j+1]}$ by solving the simultaneous linear equations

$$f_i + \sum_{k=1}^{n} \frac{\partial f_i}{\partial x_k} (x_k^{[j+1]} - x_k) = 0 \qquad (i = 1, 2, \ldots, n)$$

$$(10.1\text{-}19)$$

with $x_k = x_k^{[j]}$ $(j = 0, 1, 2, \ldots)$.

(*d*) METHOD OF STEEPEST DESCENT (GRADIENT METHOD). Choose $v_i^{[j]} = -\partial F/\partial x_i$, where all derivatives are computed for $x_i = x_i^{[j]}$, and reduce the step size $\lambda^{[j]}$ as the minimum of F is approached.

10.1-5   *Systems of Linear Equations: Elimination Method.* The solution of a suitable system of linear equations

$$\begin{aligned}
a_{11}x_1 + a_{12}x_2 + \cdots + a_{1n}x_n &= b_1 \\
a_{21}x_1 + a_{22}x_2 + \cdots + a_{2n}x_n &= b_2 \\
\cdots \cdots \cdots \cdots \cdots \cdots \cdots \cdots \\
a_{n1}x_1 + a_{n2}x_2 + \cdots + a_{nn}x_n &= b_n
\end{aligned}$$

$$(10.1\text{-}20)$$

by Cramer's rule (Sec. 1.6-2) requires too many multiplications for practical use if $n > 4$. The following procedure solves a given system (20) by successive elimination of unknowns.

Let a_{IJ} be the coefficient having the largest absolute value. To eliminate x_J from the ith equation ($i \neq I$), multiply the Ith equation by a_{iJ}/a_{IJ} and subtract from the ith equation. Repeat the process to eliminate a second unknown from the remaining $n - 1$ equations, etc.

10.1-6 Systems of Linear Equations: Iteration Methods (*see also Sec. 10.1-4*). (*a*) Given a system of linear equations (20) with real coefficients, each of the following iteration methods approximates the solution x_i ($i = 1, 2, \ldots, n$) by successive approximations of the form (18). The residuals obtained at each step of the iteration will be denoted by

$$f_i{}^{[j]} \equiv \sum_{k=1}^{n} a_{ik} x_k{}^{[j]} - b_i \qquad (i = 1, 2, \ldots, n; j = 0, 1, 2, \ldots)$$

$$(10.1\text{-}21)$$

(*b*) GAUSS-SEIDEL-TYPE ITERATION. Rearrange the given system (20) (possibly by recombining equations and/or multiplication by constants) to obtain as large positive diagonal coefficients a_{ii} as practicable. Starting with a trial solution $x_i{}^{[0]}$ ($i = 1, 2, \ldots, n$), compute successive approximations

$$x_i{}^{[j+1]} = x_i{}^{[j]} - \frac{1}{a_{ii}} f_i{}^{[j]} = x_i{}^{[j]} - \frac{1}{a_{ii}} \left(\sum_{k=1}^{n} a_{ik} x_k{}^{[j]} - b_i \right)$$

$$(i = 1, 2, \ldots, n; j = 0, 1, 2, \ldots) \qquad (10.1\text{-}22)$$

or use

$$x_i{}^{[j+1]} = x_i{}^{[j]} - \frac{1}{a_{ii}} \left(\sum_{k=1}^{i-1} a_{ik} x_k{}^{[j+1]} + \sum_{k=i}^{n} a_{ik} x_k{}^{[j]} - b_i \right)$$

$$(i = 1, 2, \ldots, n; j = 0, 1, 2, \ldots) \qquad (10.1\text{-}23)$$

Both schemes are simple but may converge slowly or not at all.

(*c*) **Relaxation methods** depend on the (manual) computer's judgment to obtain rapid convergence of an iteration process. Starting with a trial solution $x_i{}^{[0]}$ (frequently simply $x_1{}^{[0]} = 1$, $x_2{}^{[0]} = x_3{}^{[0]} = \cdots = x_n{}^{[0]} = 0$), one attempts to introduce successive approximations $x_i{}^{[j]}$ in a loosely systematic fashion so as to reduce the n residuals (21) to zero. One tabulates the residuals $f_i{}^{[j]}$ at each step and combines the following procedures:

1. *Basic Relaxation Procedure.* At each step, "liquidate" the residual $f_I{}^{[j]}$ having the greatest absolute value by adjusting x_I alone:

$$x_I{}^{[j+1]} \approx x_I{}^{[j]} - \frac{f_I{}^{[j]}}{a_{II}} \qquad x_i{}^{[j+1]} = x_i{}^{[j]} \qquad (i \neq I) \qquad (10.1\text{-}24)$$

Only rough values of $x_I{}^{[j+1]}$ are required for the initial steps.

2. *Block Relaxation and Group Relaxation.* Apply equal increments $x_i{}^{[j+1]} - x_i{}^{[j]}$ to a set ("block") of $x_i{}^{[j]}$'s so as to liquidate one of the residuals $f_i{}^{[j+1]}$, or so as to reduce the sum of all residuals to zero. The latter procedure is useful particularly if all the initial residuals $f_i{}^{[0]}$ are of equal sign.

Group relaxation applies *different* increments to a chosen set of $x_i{}^{[j]}$'s for similar purposes.

3. *Overrelaxation.* One can often improve the convergence of a relaxation process by *changing the sign* of the residual operated on while reducing its absolute value, without liquidating it entirely at this stage.

(*d*) **Steepest-descent methods (gradient methods)** minimize a positive function like $F \equiv \sum_{i=1}^{n} |f_i|$, $F \equiv \sum_{i=1}^{n} |f_i|^2$, . . . in the manner of Sec. 10.1-4*d*. If the given coefficient matrix $[a_{ik}]$ is symmetric and positive definite, one may use

$$x_i{}^{[j+1]} = x_i{}^{[j]} - \frac{\sum\limits_{k=1}^{n} f_k{}^{[j]2}}{\sum\limits_{k=1}^{n} \sum\limits_{h=1}^{n} a_{kh} f_k{}^{[j]} f_h{}^{[j]}} f_i{}^{[j]}$$

$$(i = 1, 2, \ldots , n; j = 0, 1, 2, \ldots) \qquad (10.1\text{-}25)$$

If the convergence is of an oscillatory nature, it may be possible to accelerate the convergence by multiplying the last term in Eq. (25) by 0.9 for some values of *j*.

10.2 FINITE DIFFERENCES AND INTERPOLATION

10.2-1 Finite Differences. (*a*) Let $y = y(x)$ be a function of the real variable x. Given a set of equally spaced argument values $x_k = x_0 + k \, \Delta x$ ($k = 0, \pm 1, \pm 2, \ldots$; $\Delta x = h > 0$) and a corresponding set or table of function values $y_k = y(x_k) = y(x_0 + k \, \Delta x)$, one defines the **forward differences**

$$\Delta y_k = y_{k+1} - y_k \qquad \text{(FIRST-ORDER}$$
$$\text{FORWARD DIFFERENCES)}$$
$$\Delta^2 y_k = \Delta y_{k+1} - \Delta y_k = y_{k+2} - 2y_{k+1} + y_k$$
$$\text{(SECOND-ORDER}$$
$$\text{FORWARD DIFFERENCES)}$$
$$\cdots\cdots\cdots\cdots\cdots\cdots\cdots\cdots\cdots\cdots\cdots \qquad (10.2\text{-}1)$$
$$\Delta^r y_k = \Delta^{r-1} y_{k+1} - \Delta^{r-1} y_k = \sum_{j=0}^{r} (-1)^j \binom{r}{j} y_{k+r-j}$$
$$(r = 2, 3, \ldots)(r^{\text{th}}\text{-ORDER}$$
$$\text{FORWARD DIFFERENCES)}$$
$$(k = 0, \pm 1, \pm 2, \ldots)$$

and the **backward differences**

$$\nabla y_k = y_k - y_{k-1} = \Delta y_{k-1}$$
$$\nabla^r y_k = \nabla^{r-1} y_k - \nabla^{r-1} y_{k-1} = \Delta^r y_{k-1} \quad (r = 2, 3, \ldots) \qquad (10.2\text{-}2)$$
$$(k = 0, \pm 1, \pm 2, \ldots)$$

(*b*) Even though the function values $y_k = y(x_0 + k\,\Delta x)$ may not be known for half-integral values of k, one can calculate the **central differences**

$$\delta y_k = y_{k+\frac{1}{2}} - y_{k-\frac{1}{2}} = \Delta y_{k-\frac{1}{2}}$$
$$\delta^r y_k = \delta^{r-1} y_{k-\frac{1}{2}} - \delta^{r-1} u_{k-\frac{1}{2}} = \Delta^r y^{k-\frac{1}{2}} \quad (r = 2, 3, \ldots)$$

$$(10.2\text{-}3)$$

for $k = \pm\frac{1}{2}, \pm\frac{3}{2}, \ldots$ if r is odd, and for $k = 0, \pm 1, \pm 2, \ldots$ if r is even.

(*c*) Finite differences are conveniently tabulated in arrays like

$$
\begin{array}{lllllll}
x_{-1} & y_{-1} & & & & & \\
 & & \Delta y_{-1} & & & & \\
x_0 & y_0 & & \Delta^2 y_{-1} & & & \\
 & & \Delta y_0 & & \Delta^3 y_{-1} & & \\
x_1 & y_1 & & \Delta^2 y_0 & & \Delta^4 y_{-1} & \\
 & & \Delta y_1 & & \Delta^3 y_0 & & \\
x_2 & y_2 & & \Delta^2 y_1 & & & \\
 & & \Delta y_2 & & & & \\
x_3 & y_3 & & & & &
\end{array}
$$

10.2-2   ***Lagrange's and Newton's Interpolation Formulas (Argument Values Not Necessarily Equally Spaced).*** An nth-**order polynomial interpolation formula** approximates the function $y(x)$ by an nth-degree polynomial $Y(x)$ such that $Y(x_k) = y(x_k) = y_k$ for a given set of $n + 1$ argument values x_k.

    (*a*) LAGRANGE'S INTERPOLATION FORMULA. Given $y_0 = y(x_0)$, $y_1 = y(x_1)$, $y_2 = y(x_2)$, . . . , $y_n = y(x_n)$,

$$Y(x) = \frac{(x - x_1)(x - x_2) \cdots (x - x_n)}{(x_0 - x_1)(x_0 - x_2) \cdots (x_0 - x_n)} y_0$$
$$+ \frac{(x - x_0)(x - x_2) \cdots (x - x_n)}{(x_1 - x_0)(x_1 - x_2) \cdots (x_1 - x_n)} y_1 + \cdots$$
$$+ \frac{(x - x_0)(x - x_1) \cdots (x - x_{n-1})}{(x_n - x_0)(x_n - x_1) \cdots (x_n - x_{n-1})} y_n$$

(LAGRANGE'S INTERPOLATION FORMULA)   (10.2-4)

    (*b*) DIVIDED DIFFERENCES AND NEWTON'S INTERPOLATION FORMULA. One defines the **divided differences**

$$\Delta_1(x_0, x_1) \equiv \frac{y_1 - y_0}{x_1 - x_0}$$

$$\Delta_r(x_0, x_1, x_2, \ldots, x_r)$$
$$\equiv \frac{\Delta_{r-1}(x_1, x_2, \ldots, x_r) - \Delta_{r-1}(x_0, x_1, \ldots, x_{r-1})}{x_r - x_0}$$

(10.2-5)

$$(r = 2, 3, \ldots)$$

Then

$$Y(x) = y_0 + (x - x_0)\Delta_1(x_0, x_1)$$
$$+ (x - x_0)(x - x_1)\Delta_2(x_0, x_1, x_2) + \cdots$$
$$+ \left[\prod_{k=0}^{n-1} (x - x_k) \right] \Delta_n(x_0, x_1, x_2, \ldots, x_n)$$

(NEWTON'S INTERPOLATION FORMULA)   (10.2-6)

Unlike in Eq. (4), the addition of a new pair of values x_{n+1}, y_{n+1} requires merely the addition of an extra term.

    (*c*) THE REMAINDER. If $y(x)$ is suitably differentiable, the **remainder** (error) $R_{n+1}(x)$ involved in the use of any polynomial-interpolation formula based on the $n + 1$ function values y_0, y_1, y_2, . . . , y_n may be estimated from

$$R_{n+1}(x) \equiv y(x) - Y(x) = \frac{1}{(n+1)!} f^{(n+1)}(\xi) \prod_{k=0}^{n} (x - x_k)$$

$$(10.2\text{-}7)$$

Table 10.2-1 *Symmetric interpolation formulas [one is given an odd number $n + 1 = 2m + 1$ of function values $y_k = y(x_0 + k \Delta x)$ ($k = 0$, ± 1, ± 2, . . . , $\pm m$), where Δx is a fixed increment; $u = (x - x_0)/\Delta x$]*

No.		Interpolation polynomial $Y(x)$	Remainder $R_{n+1}(x) \equiv R_{2m+1}(x)$ (ξ lies in the smallest interval containing x and every $x_0 + k \Delta x$ used)
1	Stirling's interpolation formula*	$y_0 + \displaystyle\sum_{k=0}^{m-1} \binom{u+k}{2k+1} \frac{\delta^{2k+1}y_{-\frac{1}{2}} + \delta^{2k+1}y_{\frac{1}{2}}}{2}$ $\quad + \displaystyle\sum_{k=1}^{m} \frac{u}{2k} \binom{u+k-1}{2k-1} \delta^{2k}y_0$	$\dbinom{u+m}{2m+1} y^{(2m+1)}(\xi) \, \Delta x^{2m+1}$
2	Bessel's interpolation formula†	$\dfrac{y_0 + y_1}{2} + \displaystyle\sum_{k=0}^{m-1} \frac{u - \frac{1}{2}}{2k+1} \binom{u+k-1}{2k} \delta^{2k+1}y_{\frac{1}{2}}$ $\quad + \displaystyle\sum_{k=1}^{m-1} \binom{u+k-1}{2k} \frac{\delta^{2k}y_0 + \delta^{2k}y_1}{2}$	$\dbinom{u+m-1}{2m} y^{(2m)}(\xi) \, \Delta x^{2m}$
3	Everett's interpolation formula*	$(1-u)y_0 + uy_1$ $\quad + \displaystyle\sum_{k=1}^{m-1} \left\{ \binom{u+k}{2k+1} \delta^{2k}y_1 \right.$ $\qquad\qquad \left. - \binom{u+k-1}{2k+1} \delta^{2k}y_0 \right\}$	$\dbinom{u+m-1}{2m} y^{(2m)}(\xi) \, \Delta x^{2m}$
4	Steffensen's interpolation formula	$y_0 + \displaystyle\sum_{k=1}^{m} \left\{ \binom{u+k}{2k} \delta^{2k-1}y_{\frac{1}{2}} \right.$ $\qquad\qquad \left. - \binom{k-u}{2k} \delta^{2k-1}y_{-\frac{1}{2}} \right\}$	$\dbinom{u+m}{2m+1} y^{(2m+1)}(\xi) \, \Delta x^{2m+1}$

* Note that $\dbinom{u+k}{2k+1} = \dfrac{u(u^2 - 1^2)(u^2 - 2^2) \cdots (u^2 - k^2)}{(2k+1)!}$

† *Bessel's modified formula*

$$Y(x) = y_0 + u\, \delta y_{\frac{1}{2}} + \frac{u(u-1)}{2} \frac{\delta^2 y_0 + \delta^2 y_1}{2} + \frac{u(u-\frac{1}{2})(u-1)}{6} \left(\delta^3 y_{\frac{1}{2}} - \frac{13}{120} \delta^5 y_{\frac{1}{2}} \right)$$
$$+ \frac{(u+2)(u+1)u(u-1)}{24} \left(\frac{\delta^4 y_0 + \delta^4 y_1}{2} - \frac{191}{924} \frac{\delta^6 y_0 + \delta^6 y_1}{2} \right)$$

gives a simplified polynomial including the effect of sixth-order differences.

where ξ lies in the smallest interval I containing x_0, x_1, x_2, . . . , x_n, and x (see also Sec. 3.10-3; ξ will, in general, depend on x).

10.2-3 Interpolation Formulas for Equally Spaced Argument Values. Let $y_k = y(x_k)$, $x_k = x_0 + k\,\Delta x$ ($k = 0, \pm 1, \pm 2, \ldots$), where Δx is a fixed increment as in Sec. 10.2-1, and introduce the abbreviation $(x - x_0)/\Delta x = u$.

(a) NEWTON-GREGORY INTERPOLATION FORMULAS. Given y_0, y_1, y_2, . . . or y_0, y_{-1}, y_{-2}, . . . , Eq. (3) becomes, respectively,

$$Y(x) = y_0 + \binom{u}{1}\Delta y_0 + \binom{u}{2}\Delta^2 y_0 + \cdots$$

$$Y(x) = y_0 + \frac{u}{1!}\nabla y_0 + \frac{u(u+1)}{2!}\nabla^2 y_0 + \cdots$$

(NEWTON-GREGORY INTERPOLATION FORMULAS) (10.2-8)

(b) SYMMETRIC INTERPOLATION FORMULAS. More frequently, one is given y_0, y_1, y_2, . . . and y_{-1}, y_{-2}, . . . ; Table 10.2-1 lists the most useful interpolation formulas for this case. Note that Everett's and Steffensen's formulas are of particular interest for use with printed tables, since only even-order or only odd-order differences need be tabulated.

10.3 NUMERICAL INTEGRATION

10.3-1 Numerical Integration Using Equally Spaced Argument Values. Newton-Cotes Quadrature Formulas. *Quadrature formulas of the closed Newton-Cotes type* (Table 10.3-1) use the approximation

$$\int_{x_0}^{x_0+n\,\Delta x} y(x)\,dx \approx a_0 y_0 + a_1 y_1 + a_2 y_2 + \cdots + a_n y_n$$

with (10.3-1)

$$a_k = \frac{(-1)^{n-k}\,\Delta x}{k!(n-k)!}\int_0^n \frac{\lambda(\lambda-1)(\lambda-2)\cdots(\lambda-n)}{(\lambda-k)}\,d\lambda$$

where the $y_k = y(x_k)$ are given function values for $n + 1$ equally spaced argument values $x_k = x_0 + k\,\Delta x$ ($k = 0, 1, 2, \ldots, n$); the resulting error vanishes if $y(x)$ is a polynomial of degree not greater than n. Instead of using values of $n > 6$, one adds m sums (1) of $n \leq 6$ terms for successive subintervals:

$$\int_{x_0}^{x_0+mn\,\Delta x} y(x)\,dx = \int_{x_0}^{x_0+n\,\Delta x} y(x)\,dx + \int_{x_0+n\,\Delta x}^{x_0+2n\,\Delta x} y(x)\,dx + \cdots$$

(10.3-2)

Table 10.3-1 *Quadrature formulas of the closed Newton-Cotes type,*
$[y_k = y(x_k) = y(x + k\,\Delta x), k = 0, 1, 2, \ldots, n]$

No.		$I' \approx \displaystyle\int_{x_0}^{x_0+n\,\Delta x} y(x)\,dx = I$ (add analogous expressions for m successive subintervals)	Error, $I - I'$ $(x_0 < \xi < x_0 + n\,\Delta x)$
1	**Trapezoidal rule** $(n = 1)$	$\dfrac{\Delta x}{2}\,(y_0 + y_1)$	$-\frac{1}{12}(n\,\Delta x)^3 y^{(2)}(\xi)$
2	**Simpson's rule** $(n = 2)$	$\dfrac{\Delta x}{3}\,(y_0 + 4y_1 + y_2)$	$-\dfrac{1}{90}\left(\dfrac{n\,\Delta x}{2}\right)^5 y^{(4)}(\xi)$
3	**Weddle's rule** $(n = 6)$*	$\frac{3}{10}\Delta x(y_0 + 5y_1 + y_2 + 6y_3 + y_4 + 5y_5 + y_6)$	$\dfrac{\vartheta}{212310}\left(\dfrac{n\,\Delta x}{2}\right)^7 y^{(6)}(\xi)$ $(0 < \vartheta < 1)$

* In Weddle's rule, the correct Newton-Cotes coefficient $^{41}\!/_{140}$ of $\Delta^6 y_0$ has been replaced by $\frac{3}{10}$.

10.3-2 Gauss and Chebyshev Quadrature Formulas.

(a) Rewrite the given definite integral $\displaystyle\int_a^b y(x)\,dx$ as $\displaystyle\int_{-1}^{1} \eta(\xi)\,d\xi$ with the aid of the transformation

$$x = \frac{b-a}{2}\,\xi + \frac{a+b}{2} \qquad \eta(\xi) \equiv \frac{b-a}{2}\,y(x) \qquad (10.3\text{-}3)$$

and approximate the latter integral by

$$\int_{-1}^{1} \eta(\xi)\,d\xi \approx \sum_{k=1}^{n} a_k \eta(\xi_k)$$

with

$$a_k = \frac{2}{(1 - \xi_k^2)[P_n'(\xi_k)]^2} \qquad (n = 1, 2, \ldots)$$

(GAUSS QUADRATURE FORMULA) (10.3-4)

where the n argument values ξ_k are the n zeros of the nth-degree Legendre polynomial $P_n(\xi)$ (Sec. 11.3-4). Table 10.3-2 lists the ξ_k and a_k for a number of values of n.

The error due to the use of the Gauss quadrature formula is

$$E = \frac{(n!)^4(b-a)^{2n+1}}{(2n+1)[(2n)!]^3}\,y^{(2n)}(X) \qquad (a < X < b) \qquad (10.3\text{-}5)$$

(b) A simpler class of quadrature formulas is obtained with the aid of the transformation (3) and an approximation of the form

$$\int_{-1}^{1} \eta(\xi)\, d\xi \approx \frac{2}{n}\left[\eta(\xi_1') + \eta(\xi_2') + \cdots + \eta(\xi_n')\right]$$

(CHEBYSHEV QUADRATURE FORMULA) $(n = 2, 3, 4, 5, 6, 7, 9)$ (10.3-6)

Table 10.3-2 lists the ξ_k' for a number of values of n. The use of equal weights minimizes the probable error if $y(x)$ is affected by normally distributed random errors.

For $n = 3$, the error due to the use of the Chebyshev quadrature formula is

$$\frac{1}{360}\left(\frac{b-a}{2}\right)^5 y^{(4)}(X) \qquad (a < X < b)$$

Table 10.3-2   Abscissas and weights for Gauss and Chebyshev quadrature formulas (adapted from Ref. 3)

(a) **Abscissas ξ_k and Weights a_k for the Gauss Quadrature Formula**

n	Abscissas	Weights
2	± 0.577350	1
3	0	$\frac{8}{9}$
	± 0.774597	$\frac{5}{9}$
4	± 0.339981	0.652145
	± 0.861136	0.347855
5	0	0.568889
	± 0.538469	0.478629
	± 0.906180	0.236927

(b) **Abscissas ξ_k' for the Chebychev Quadrature Formula**

n	Abscissas	n	Abscissas
2	± 0.577350	7	0
3	0		± 0.323912
	± 0.707107		± 0.529657
4	± 0.187592		± 0.883862
	± 0.794654	9	0
5	0		± 0.167906
	± 0.374541		± 0.528762
	± 0.832497		± 0.601019
6	± 0.266635		± 0.911589
	± 0.422519		
	± 0.866247		

10.4 NUMERICAL SOLUTION OF ORDINARY DIFFERENTIAL EQUATIONS*

10.4-1 *The Runge-Kutta Method.*

To solve the first-order differential equation

$$y' = f(x, y) \tag{10.4-1}$$

for a given initial value $y(x_0) = y_0$, consider fixed increments $\Delta x = h$ of the independent variable x and use the notation of Sec. 10.2-1, with $x_0 + k\,\Delta x = x_k$, $y(x_k) = y(x_0 + k\,\Delta x) = y_k$, $f(x_k, y_k) = f_k$ ($k = 0, \pm 1, \pm 2, \ldots$). For sufficiently small increments $\Delta x = h$, the following recursion formulas yield stepwise approximations to the solution $y = y(x)$:

$$y_{k+1} = y_k + \tfrac{1}{6}(k_1 + 2k_2 + 2k_3 + k_4)$$

with

$$k_1 = f_k\,\Delta x = f(x_k, y_k)\,\Delta x$$

$$k_2 = f\left(x_k + \frac{\Delta x}{2}, y_k + \frac{k_1}{2}\right)\Delta x$$

$$k_3 = f\left(x_k + \frac{\Delta x}{2}, y_k + \frac{k_2}{2}\right)\Delta x \tag{10.4-2}$$

$$k_4 = f(x_{k+1}, y_k + k_3)\,\Delta x$$

10.4-2 *Milne's Prediction-Correction Scheme.*

Use the simple approximation

$$y_{k+1} = y_{k-3} + \tfrac{4}{3}(2f_k - f_{k-1} + 2f_{k-2})\,\Delta x$$
$$(\text{``predictor''}) \tag{10.4-3}$$

to obtain a trial value of f_{k+1}, and calculate

$$y_{k+1} = y_{k-1} + \tfrac{1}{3}(f_{k+1} + 4f_k + f_{k-1})\,\Delta x$$
$$(\text{``corrector''}) \tag{10.4-4}$$

The step size Δx should be chosen so that the expressions (3) and (4) do not differ by more than 14 digits of the last decimal place required.

To obtain y_{-1}, y_1, and y_2 for the starting solution, Milne recommends the use of successive approximations with the aid of the "starter formulas"

* The formulas (2) to (9) are given for reference. Note, however, that the accuracy of numerical solutions obtained for a given step size Δx depends critically on the nature of the specific differential equations solved (Refs. 1, 2, and 8). Reference 1 derives improved methods and error estimates.

$$y_1 = y_0 + \tfrac{1}{24}(7f_1 + 16f_0 + f_{-1})\,\Delta x + \tfrac{1}{4}y''(x_0)\,\Delta x^2$$
$$y_{-1} = y_0 - \tfrac{1}{24}(f_1 + 16f_0 + 7f_{-1})\,\Delta x + \tfrac{1}{4}y''(x_0)\,\Delta x^2 \tag{10.4-5}$$
$$y_2 = y_0 + \tfrac{2}{3}(5f_1 - f_0 - f_{-1})\,\Delta x - 2y''(x_0)\,\Delta x^2$$

together with Eq. (4) (Ref. 8).

Change of Step Size. To halve the step size, use the following simple inter-polation formulas:

$$f_{k-\frac{1}{2}} = f_k - \tfrac{1}{2}\nabla f_k - \tfrac{1}{8}\nabla^2 f_k - \tfrac{1}{16}\nabla^3 f_k$$
$$f_{k+\frac{1}{2}} = f_k + \tfrac{1}{2}\nabla f_k + \tfrac{3}{8}\nabla^2 f_k + \tfrac{5}{16}\nabla^3 f_k \tag{10.4-6}$$

10.4-3 Differential Equations of Order Higher than the First and Systems of Ordinary Differential Equations.

Each ordinary differential equation of the second or higher order is equivalent to a system of first-order equations (Sec. 6.1-2). In the following, let a first-order system of ordinary differential equations involving two or more unknown functions $y = y(x)$, $z = z(x)$, . . . be given in the form

$$y' = f(x, y, z, \ldots)$$
$$z' = g(x, y, z, \ldots) \tag{10.4-7}$$
$$\cdots \cdots \cdots \cdots \cdots$$

(a) The *Runge-Kutta method* is analogous to the scheme of Sec. 10.4-1:

$$y_{k+1} = y_k + \tfrac{1}{6}(k_1 + 2k_2 + 2k_3 + k_4)$$
$$z_{k+1} = z_k + \tfrac{1}{6}(m_1 + 2m_2 + 2m_3 + m_4)$$
$$\cdots \cdots \cdots \cdots \cdots \cdots \cdots \cdots$$

with

$$k_1 = f(x_k,\ y_k,\ z_k,\ \ldots)\,\Delta x$$
$$m_1 = g(x_k,\ y_k,\ z_k,\ \ldots)\,\Delta x \quad \cdots$$

$$k_2 = f\left(x_k + \frac{\Delta x}{2},\ y_k + \frac{k_1}{2},\ z_k + \frac{m_1}{2},\ \ldots\right)\Delta x$$
$$m_2 = g\left(x_k + \frac{\Delta x}{2},\ y_k + \frac{k_1}{2},\ z_k + \frac{m_1}{2},\ \ldots\right)\Delta x \quad \cdots$$

$$k_3 = f\left(x_k + \frac{\Delta x}{2},\ y_k + \frac{k_2}{2},\ z_k + \frac{m_2}{2},\ \ldots\right)\Delta x$$
$$m_3 = g\left(x_k + \frac{\Delta x}{2},\ y_k + \frac{k_2}{2},\ z_k + \frac{m_2}{2},\ \ldots\right)\Delta x \quad \cdots$$

$$k_4 = f(x_k + \Delta x,\ y_k + k_3,\ z_k + m_3,\ \ldots)\,\Delta x$$
$$m_4 = g(x_k + \Delta x,\ y_k + k_3,\ z_k + m_3,\ \ldots)\,\Delta x \quad \cdots \tag{10.4-8}$$

(b) The *finite-difference schemes* of Sec. 10.4-2 may be applied to each equation (7); one writes

$$y(x_k) = y_k \qquad z(x_k) = z_k \qquad \cdots$$
$$f(x_k, y_k, z_k, \ldots) = f_k \qquad g(x_k, y_k, z_k, \ldots) = g_k \qquad \cdots \qquad (10.4\text{-}9)$$

References and Bibliography

1. Hamming, R. W.: *Numerical Methods for Engineers and Scientists*, McGraw-Hill, New York, 1962.
2. Henrici, P.: *Elements of Numerical Analysis*, Wiley, New York, 1964.
3. Hildebrand, F. B.: *Introduction to Numerical Analysis*, McGraw-Hill, New York, 1956.
4. Householder, A. S.: *Principles of Numerical Analysis*, McGraw-Hill, New York, 1953.
5. Jennings, W.: *First Course in Numerical Methods*, Macmillan, New York, 1964.
6. Kunz, K. S.: *Numerical Analysis*, McGraw-Hill, New York, 1957.
7. Lanczos, C.: *Applied Analysis*, Prentice-Hall, Englewood Cliffs, N.J., 1956.
8. Milne, W. E.: *Numerical Solution of Differential Equations*, Wiley, New York, 1953.
9. Ralston, A.: *A First Course in Numerical Analysis*, McGraw-Hill, New York, 1964.
10. Ralston, A., and H. S. Wilf: *Mathematical Methods for Digital Computers*, Wiley, New York, 1960.
11. Salvadori, M. G., and M. L. Baron: *Numerical Methods in Engineering*, 2d ed., Prentice-Hall, Englewood Cliffs, N.J., 1961.
12. Scarborough, J. B.: *Numerical Mathematical Analysis*, 5th ed., Johns Hopkins Press, Baltimore, Md., 1962.
13. Stiefel, E. L.: *An Introduction to Numerical Mathematics*, Academic Press, New York, 1963.
14. Todd, J.: *Survey of Numerical Analysis*, McGraw-Hill, New York, 1962.

11 FORMULAS RELATING TO SPECIAL FUNCTIONS

11.1 THE ELEMENTARY TRANSCENDENTAL FUNCTIONS

11.1-1 The Trigonometric Functions (*see also Appendix B and Table 5.1-1*). (*a*) The trigonometric functions $w = \sin z$, $w = \cos z$ are defined by their power series (Sec. 11.1-11), as solutions of the differential equation $\dfrac{d^2w}{dz^2} + w = 0$, by $z = \arcsin w$, $z = \arccos w$ (integral representation, Sec. 11.1-4), or, for real z, in terms of right-triangle geometry (goniometry, Fig. 11.1-1). The remaining trigonometric functions are defined by

$$\tan z = \frac{\sin z}{\cos z} \qquad \cot z = \frac{1}{\tan z} = \frac{\cos z}{\sin z} \qquad (11.1\text{-}1)$$

$$\sec z = \frac{1}{\cos z} \qquad \operatorname{cosec} z = \frac{1}{\sin z} \qquad (11.1\text{-}2)$$

(b) sin z and cos z are periodic with period 2π; tan z and cot z are periodic with period π. sin z, tan z, and cot z are odd functions, whereas cos z is an even function. Figure 11.1-2 shows graphs of sin z, cos z, tan z, and cot z for real arguments. Figure 11.1-3 shows triangles which serve as memory aids for the derivation of function values for $z = \pi/6 = 30$ deg, $\pi/4 = 45$ deg, and $\pi/3 = 60$ deg (see also Table 11.1-1).

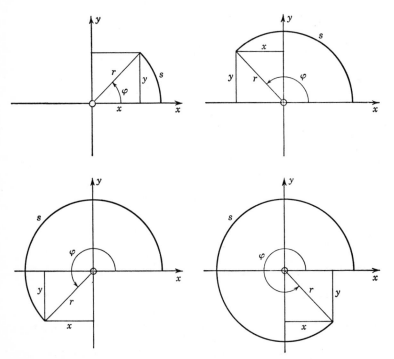

Fig. 11.1-1 Definitions of circular measure and trigonometric functions for a given angle φ:

$$\varphi = \frac{s}{r} \quad \text{(in radians)}$$

$$\sin \varphi = \frac{y}{r} \qquad\qquad \cos \varphi = \frac{x}{r}$$

$$\tan \varphi = \frac{y}{x} = \frac{\sin \varphi}{\cos \varphi} \qquad \cot \varphi = \frac{x}{y} = \frac{\cos \varphi}{\sin \varphi}$$

$$\sec \varphi = \frac{r}{x} = \frac{1}{\cos \varphi} \qquad \operatorname{cosec} \varphi = \frac{r}{y} = \frac{1}{\sin \varphi}$$

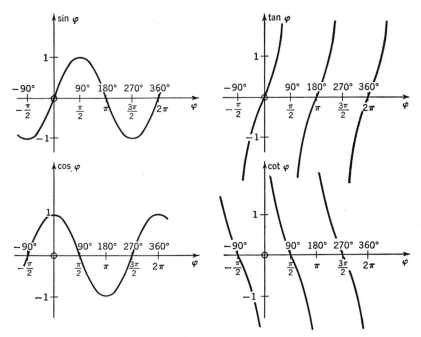

Fig. 11.1-2   Plots of the trigonometric functions for real arguments $z = \varphi$.

(*c*) The relations

$$
\begin{array}{ll}
\sin z = \cos\left(\dfrac{\pi}{2} - z\right) & \cos z = \sin\left(\dfrac{\pi}{2} - z\right) \\[2ex]
\tan z = \cot\left(\dfrac{\pi}{2} - z\right) & \cot z = \tan\left(\dfrac{\pi}{2} - z\right)
\end{array}
\qquad (11.1\text{-}3)
$$

permit one to express trigonometric functions of any real argument in terms of function values for arguments between 0 and $\pi/2 = 90$ deg (Table 11.1-2 and Fig. 11.1-1).

11.1-2 Relations between the Trigonometric Functions.   The basic relations

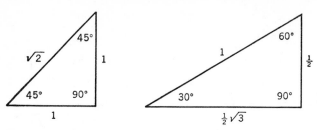

Fig. 11.1-3 Special triangles for deriving the trigonometric functions of 30 deg, 45 deg, and 60 deg.

Table 11.1-1   *Special values of trigonometric functions*

A (degrees)	$0°$ $360°$	$30°$	$45°$	$60°$	$90°$	$180°$	$270°$
A (radians)	0	$\dfrac{\pi}{6}$	$\dfrac{\pi}{4}$	$\dfrac{\pi}{3}$	$\dfrac{\pi}{2}$	π	$\dfrac{3\pi}{2}$
$\sin A$	0	$\frac{1}{2}$	$\dfrac{1}{\sqrt{2}}$	$\frac{1}{2}\sqrt{3}$	1	0	-1
$\cos A$	1	$\frac{1}{2}\sqrt{3}$	$\dfrac{1}{\sqrt{2}}$	$\frac{1}{2}$	0	-1	0
$\tan A$	0	$\dfrac{1}{\sqrt{3}}$	1	$\sqrt{3}$	$\pm\infty$	0	$\pm\infty$
$\cot A$	$\pm\infty$	$\sqrt{3}$	1	$\dfrac{1}{\sqrt{3}}$	0	$\pm\infty$	0

Table 11.1-2   *Relations between trigonometric functions of different arguments*

	$-A$	$90° \pm A$	$180° \pm A$	$270° \pm A$	$n360° \pm A$
$\sin$	$-\sin A$	$\cos A$	$\mp \sin A$	$-\cos A$	$\pm \sin A$
$\cos$	$\cos A$	$\mp \sin A$	$-\cos A$	$\pm \sin A$	$\cos A$
$\tan$	$-\tan A$	$\mp \cot A$	$\pm \tan A$	$\mp \cot A$	$\pm \tan A$
$\cot$	$-\cot A$	$\mp \tan A$	$\pm \cot A$	$\mp \tan A$	$\pm \cot A$

$$\sin^2 z + \cos^2 z = 1$$
$$\frac{\sin z}{\cos z} = \tan z = \frac{1}{\cot z} \tag{11.1-4}$$

yield

$$\sin z = \pm\sqrt{1 - \cos^2 z}$$
$$= \frac{\tan z}{\pm\sqrt{1 + \tan^2 z}} = \frac{1}{\pm\sqrt{1 + \cot^2 z}}$$
$$\cos z = \pm\sqrt{1 - \sin^2 z}$$
$$= \frac{1}{\pm\sqrt{1 + \tan^2 z}} = \frac{\cot z}{\pm\sqrt{1 + \cot^2 z}} \tag{11.1-5}$$
$$\tan z = \frac{\sin z}{\pm\sqrt{1 - \sin^2 z}} = \frac{\pm\sqrt{1 - \cos^2 z}}{\cos z} = \frac{1}{\cot z}$$
$$\cot z = \frac{\pm\sqrt{1 - \sin^2 z}}{\sin z} = \frac{\cos z}{\pm\sqrt{1 - \cos^2 z}} = \frac{1}{\tan z}$$

11.1-3 Addition Formulas and Multiple-angle Formulas. The basic relation

$$\sin (A + B) = \sin A \cos B + \sin B \cos A \tag{11.1-6}$$

yields

$$\left.\begin{array}{l} \sin (A \pm B) = \sin A \cos B \pm \cos A \sin B \\ \cos (A \pm B) = \cos A \cos B \mp \sin A \sin B \\ \tan (A \pm B) = \dfrac{\tan A \pm \tan B}{1 \mp \tan A \tan B} \\ \cot (A \pm B) = \dfrac{\cot A \cot B \mp 1}{\cot A \pm \cot B} \end{array}\right\} \tag{11.1-7}$$

$$\left.\begin{array}{l} \sin 2A = 2 \sin A \cos A \\ \cos 2A = \cos^2 A - \sin^2 A \\ \qquad = 2 \cos^2 A - 1 = 1 - 2 \sin^2 A \\ \tan 2A = \dfrac{2 \tan A}{1 - \tan^2 A} \\ \cot 2A = \dfrac{\cot^2 A - 1}{2 \cot A} = \dfrac{1}{2}(\cot A - \tan A) \end{array}\right\} \tag{11.1-8}$$

$$\sin \frac{A}{2} = \pm \sqrt{\frac{1 - \cos A}{2}}$$

$$\cos \frac{A}{2} = \pm \sqrt{\frac{1 + \cos A}{2}}$$

$$\tan \frac{A}{2} = \frac{\sin A}{1 + \cos A} = \frac{1 - \cos A}{\sin A}$$

$$\cot \frac{A}{2} = \frac{\sin A}{1 - \cos A} = \frac{1 + \cos A}{\sin A}$$

(11.1-9)

$$a \sin A + b \cos A = r \sin (A + B)$$
$$= r \cos (90° - A - B)$$
$$r = +\sqrt{a^2 + b^2} \qquad \tan B = \frac{b}{a}$$

(11.1-10)

$$\sin A \pm \sin B = 2 \sin \frac{A \pm B}{2} \cos \frac{A \mp B}{2}$$

$$\cos A + \cos B = 2 \cos \frac{A + B}{2} \cos \frac{A - B}{2}$$

$$\cos A - \cos B = -2 \sin \frac{A + B}{2} \sin \frac{A - B}{2}$$

$$\tan A \pm \tan B = \frac{\sin (A \pm B)}{\cos A \cos B}$$

$$\cot A \pm \cot B = \frac{\sin (B \pm A)}{\sin A \sin B}$$

(11.1-11)

$$2 \cos A \cos B = \cos (A - B) + \cos (A + B)$$
$$2 \sin A \sin B = \cos (A - B) - \cos (A + B)$$
$$2 \sin A \cos B = \sin (A - B) + \sin (A + B)$$
$$2 \cos^2 A = 1 + \cos 2A$$
$$2 \sin^2 A = 1 - \cos 2A$$

(11.1-12)

11.1-4 The Inverse Trigonometric Functions (*see also Table 5.1-1*).* The **inverse trigonometric functions** $w = \arcsin z$, $w =$

---

* The functions arcsin z, arccos z, arctan z, and arccot z are often denoted by $\sin^{-1} z$, $\cos^{-1} z$, $\tan^{-1} z$, and $\cot^{-1} z$, respectively. This notation tends to be misleading and is not recommended.

arccos z, $w = $ arctan z, $w = $ arccot z are respectively defined by

$$z = \sin w \qquad z = \cos w \qquad z = \tan w \qquad z = \cot w \qquad (11.1\text{-}13)$$

or by

$$\operatorname{arcsin} z = \int_0^z \frac{dz}{\sqrt{1-z^2}}$$

$$\operatorname{arccos} z = -\int_1^z \frac{dz}{\sqrt{1-z^2}}$$

$$(11.1\text{-}14)$$

$$\operatorname{arctan} z = \int_0^z \frac{dz}{1+z^2}$$

$$\operatorname{arccot} z = -\int_{-\infty}^z \frac{dz}{1+z^2}$$

Figure 11.1-4 shows plots of the inverse trigonometric functions for real arguments; note that arcsin z and arccos z are real if and only if z is real and $|z| \leq 1$. All four functions are infinitely-many-valued because of the periodicity of the trigonometric functions. For real arguments, the **principal value** of arcsin z and arctan z is that between $-\pi/2$ and $\pi/2$ (see also Fig. 11.1-4); the principal value of arccos z and arccot z is that between 0 and π.

11.1-5 Hyperbolic Functions *(see also Table 5.1-1).* The **hyperbolic functions*** $w = \sinh z$, $w = \cosh z$ are defined by the power series (11.1-1) as solutions of the differential equation

$$\frac{d^2w}{dz^2} - w = 0$$

or simply by

$$\boxed{\sinh z = \frac{e^z - e^{-z}}{2} \qquad \cosh z = \frac{e^z + e^{-z}}{2} \qquad (11.1\text{-}15)}$$

Four additional hyperbolic functions are defined as

$$\tanh z = \frac{\sinh z}{\cosh z} \qquad \coth z = \frac{\cosh z}{\sinh z}$$

$$(11.1\text{-}16)$$

$$\operatorname{sech} z = \frac{1}{\cosh z} \qquad \operatorname{cosech} z = \frac{1}{\sinh z}$$

---

* The symbols Sin z, Cos z, Tan z, Cot z are also used.

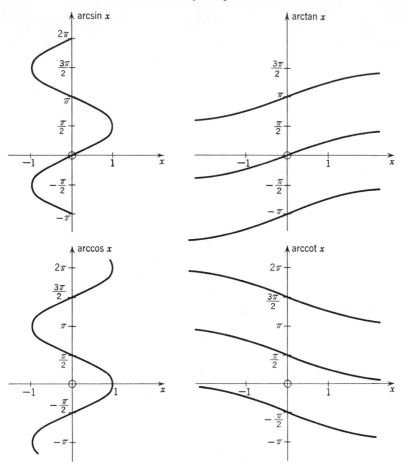

Fig. 11.1-4 Plots of the inverse trigonometric functions.

Geometrical interpretation of sinh t and cosh t for real t: If $t/2$ is the area bounded by the hyperbola $x^2 - y^2 = 1$, the x axis, and the radius vector of the point (x, y) on the hyperbola, then $y = \sinh t$, $x = \cosh t$. Note that, if the hyperbola is replaced by the circle $x^2 + y^2 = 1$, then $y = \sin t$, $x = \cos t$.

11.1-6 Relations between the Hyperbolic Functions. The basic relations

$$\cosh^2 z - \sinh^2 z = 1$$

$$\frac{\sinh z}{\cosh z} = \tanh z = \frac{1}{\coth z} \qquad (11.1\text{-}17)$$

yield

$$\sinh z = \pm\sqrt{\cosh^2 z - 1} = \frac{\tanh z}{\pm\sqrt{1 - \tanh^2 z}} = \frac{1}{\pm\sqrt{\coth^2 z - 1}}$$

$$\cosh z = \pm\sqrt{1 + \sinh^2 z} = \frac{1}{\pm\sqrt{1 - \tanh^2 z}}$$

$$= \frac{\coth z}{\pm\sqrt{\coth^2 z - 1}} \qquad (11.1\text{-}18)$$

$$\tanh z = \frac{\sinh z}{\pm\sqrt{1 + \sinh^2 z}} = \frac{\pm\sqrt{\cosh^2 z - 1}}{\cosh z} = \frac{1}{\coth z}$$

$$\coth z = \frac{\pm\sqrt{1 + \sinh^2 z}}{\sinh z} = \frac{\cosh z}{\pm\sqrt{\cosh^2 z - 1}} = \frac{1}{\tanh z}$$

11.1-7 Formulas Relating Hyperbolic Functions of Compound Arguments

$$\left.\begin{array}{l}
\sinh (A \pm B) = \sinh A \cosh B \pm \cosh A \sinh B \\
\cosh (A \pm B) = \cosh A \cosh B \pm \sinh A \sinh B \\
\tanh (A \pm B) = \dfrac{\tanh A \pm \tanh B}{1 \pm \tanh A \tanh B} \\
\coth (A \pm B) = \dfrac{\coth A \coth B \pm 1}{\coth B \pm \coth A}
\end{array}\right\} \qquad (11.1\text{-}19)$$

$$\left.\begin{array}{l}
\sinh 2A = 2 \cosh A \sinh A \\
\cosh 2A = \cosh^2 A + \sinh^2 A \\
\tanh 2A = \dfrac{2 \tanh A}{1 + \tanh^2 A} \\
\coth 2A = \dfrac{\coth^2 A + 1}{2 \coth A}
\end{array}\right\} \qquad (11.1\text{-}20)$$

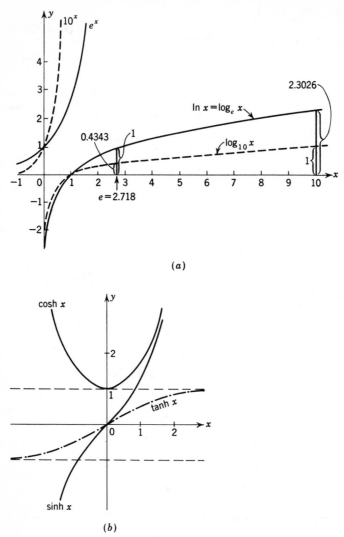

Fig. 11.1-5 Exponential and logarithmic functions (a), and hyperbolic functions (b). (*From L. S. Marks, Mechanical Engineer's Handbook, McGraw-Hill, New York, 1958.*)

$$\sinh \frac{A}{2} = \pm \sqrt{\frac{\cosh A - 1}{2}}$$

$$\cosh \frac{A}{2} = \pm \sqrt{\frac{\cosh A + 1}{2}}$$

$$\tanh \frac{A}{2} = \frac{\sinh A}{\cosh A + 1} = \frac{\cosh A - 1}{\sinh A}$$

$$\coth \frac{A}{2} = \frac{\sinh A}{\cosh A - 1} = \frac{\cosh A + 1}{\sinh A}$$

(11.1-21)

$$\sinh A \pm \sinh B = 2 \sinh \frac{A \pm B}{2} \cosh \frac{A \mp B}{2}$$

$$\cosh A + \cosh B = 2 \cosh \frac{A + B}{2} \cosh \frac{A - B}{2}$$

$$\cosh A - \cosh B = 2 \sinh \frac{A + B}{2} \sinh \frac{A - B}{2}$$

$$\tanh A \pm \tanh B = \frac{\sinh (A \pm B)}{\cosh A \cosh B}$$

$$\coth A \pm \coth B = \frac{\sinh (B \pm A)}{\sinh A \sinh B}$$

(11.1-22)

$$2 \cosh A \cosh B = \cosh (A + B) + \cosh (A - B)$$
$$2 \sinh A \sinh B = \cosh (A + B) - \cosh (A - B)$$
$$2 \sinh A \cosh B = \sinh (A + B) + \sinh (A - B)$$
$$2 \cosh^2 A = 1 + \cosh 2A$$
$$2 \sinh^2 A = \cosh 2A - 1$$

(11.1-23)

11.1-8 Relations between Exponential, Trigonometric, and Hyperbolic Functions

$$e^{iz} = \cos z + i \sin z$$

$$\cos z = \frac{e^{iz} + e^{-iz}}{2} \qquad \sin z = \frac{e^{iz} - e^{-iz}}{2i}$$

(11.1-24)

$$e^{-iz} = \cos z - i \sin z$$
$$e^{z} = \cosh z + \sinh z \qquad e^{-z} = \cosh z - \sinh z$$
$$\cosh z = \frac{e^{z} + e^{-z}}{2} \qquad \sinh z = \frac{e^{z} - e^{-z}}{2}$$

(11.1-25)

$$\left.\begin{aligned}
\cos z &= \cosh iz & \cosh z &= \cos iz \\
\sin z &= -i \sinh iz & \sinh z &= -i \sin iz \\
\tan z &= -i \tanh iz & \tanh z &= -i \tan iz \\
\cot z &= i \coth iz & \coth z &= i \cot iz
\end{aligned}\right\} \qquad (11.1\text{-}26)$$

11.1-9 Inverse Hyperbolic Functions. The inverse hyperbolic functions $w = \sinh^{-1} z$, $w = \cosh^{-1} z$, $w = \tanh^{-1} z$ are respectively defined by $z = \sinh w$, $z = \cosh w$, $z = \tanh w$,* or by integrals in the manner of Sec. 11.1-4.

11.1-10 Decomposition of the Logarithm. Relations between Inverse Trigonometric, Inverse Hyperbolic, and Logarithmic Functions

$$\log_e z = \log_e |z| + i \arg(z) \qquad (11.1\text{-}27)$$

$$\left.\begin{aligned}
\log_e (ix) &= \log_e x + (2n + \tfrac{1}{2})\pi i \\
\log_e (-x) &= \log_e x + (2n + 1)\pi i
\end{aligned}\right\}$$

$$(n = 0, \pm 1, \pm 2, \ldots) \qquad (11.1\text{-}28)$$

$$\left.\begin{aligned}
\arccos z &= i \cosh^{-1} z & \cosh^{-1} z &= i \arccos z \\
\arcsin z &= -i \sinh^{-1} iz & \sinh^{-1} z &= -i \arcsin iz \\
\arctan z &= -i \tanh^{-1} iz & \tanh^{-1} z &= -i \arctan iz \\
\text{arccot } z &= i \coth^{-1} iz & \coth^{-1} z &= i \text{ arccot } iz
\end{aligned}\right\} \qquad (11.1\text{-}29)$$

$$\left.\begin{aligned}
\arccos z &= -i \log_e (z + i \sqrt{1 - z^2}) \\
& \qquad\qquad \cosh^{-1} z = \log_e (z + \sqrt{z^2 - 1}) \\
\arcsin z &= -i \log_e (iz + \sqrt{1 - z^2}) \\
& \qquad\qquad \sinh^{-1} z = \log_e (z + \sqrt{z^2 + 1}) \\
\arctan z &= -\frac{i}{2} \log_e \frac{1 + iz}{1 - iz} & \tanh^{-1} z &= \frac{1}{2} \log_e \frac{1 + z}{1 - z} \\
\text{arccot } z &= -\frac{i}{2} \log_e \frac{iz - 1}{iz + 1} & \coth^{-1} z &= \frac{1}{2} \log_e \frac{z + 1}{z - 1}
\end{aligned}\right\} \qquad (11.1\text{-}30)$$

---

* This notation is the usual one in English-speaking countries, although it tends to be misleading. An alternative notation is ar sinh z, ar cosh z, ar tanh z, or Ar Sin z, Ar Cos z, Ar Tan z.

11.1-11 *Power-series Expansions*

$$\frac{1}{1-z} = 1 + z + z^2 + \cdots$$

$$(|z| < 1; \text{ GEOMETRIC SERIES}) \qquad (11.1\text{-}31)$$

$$(1 + z)^p = 1 + \binom{p}{1} z + \binom{p}{2} z^2 + \cdots$$

$$(|z| < 1; \text{ BINOMIAL SERIES}) \qquad (11.1\text{-}32)$$

$$e^z = 1 + z + \frac{z^2}{2!} + \frac{z^3}{3!} + \cdots \qquad (z \neq \infty) \qquad (11.1\text{-}33)$$

$$\sin z = z - \frac{z^3}{3!} + \frac{z^5}{5!} \mp \cdots \qquad \cos z = 1 - \frac{z^2}{2!} + \frac{z^4}{4!} \mp \cdots$$

$$(z \neq \infty) \qquad (11.1\text{-}34)$$

$$\sinh z = z + \frac{z^3}{3!} + \frac{z^5}{5!} + \cdots \qquad \cosh z = 1 + \frac{z^2}{2!} + \frac{z^4}{4!} + \cdots$$

$$(z \neq \infty) \qquad (11.1\text{-}35)$$

$$\log_e (1 + z) = z - \frac{z^2}{2} + \frac{z^3}{3} - \frac{z^4}{4} \pm \cdots \qquad (|z| < 1) \qquad (11.1\text{-}36)$$

$$\left.\begin{aligned}
\arcsin z &= z + \frac{1}{2} \cdot \frac{z^3}{3} + \frac{1}{2} \cdot \frac{3}{4} \cdot \frac{z^5}{5} + \frac{1}{2} \cdot \frac{3}{4} \cdot \frac{5}{6} \cdot \frac{z^7}{7} + \cdots \\
\sinh^{-1} z &= z - \frac{1}{2} \cdot \frac{z^3}{3} + \frac{1}{2} \cdot \frac{3}{4} \cdot \frac{z^5}{5} - \frac{1}{2} \cdot \frac{3}{4} \cdot \frac{5}{6} \cdot \frac{z^7}{7} \pm \cdots
\end{aligned}\right\}$$

$$(|z| < 1) \qquad (11.1\text{-}37)$$

$$\left.\begin{aligned}
\arctan z &= z - \frac{z^3}{3} + \frac{z^5}{5} \mp \cdots \\
\tanh^{-1} z &= \frac{1}{2} \log_e \frac{1+z}{1-z} = z + \frac{z^3}{3} + \frac{z^5}{5} + \cdots
\end{aligned}\right\}$$

$$(|z| < 1) \qquad (11.1\text{-}38)$$

11.2 THE GAMMA FUNCTION AND RELATED TOPICS

11.2-1 *The Gamma Function.* INTEGRAL REPRESENTATIONS.
The **gamma function** $\Gamma(z)$ is most frequently defined by

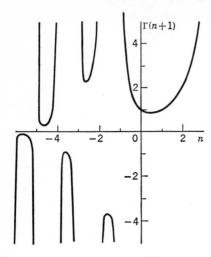

Fig. 11.2-1 $\Gamma(n + 1)$ vs. n for real n. Note $\Gamma(n + 1) = n!$ for $n = 0, 1, 2, \ldots$, and the alternating maxima and minima given approximately by $\Gamma(1.462) = 0.886$, $\Gamma(-0.5040) = -3.545$, $\Gamma(-1.573) = 2.302$, $\Gamma(-2.611) = -0.888, \ldots$.

$$\Gamma(z) = \int_0^\infty e^{-t}t^{z-1}\,dt \qquad [\mathrm{Re}\,(z) > 0]$$

(EULER'S INTEGRAL OF THE SECOND KIND)   (11.2-1)

Figure 11.2-1 shows a graph of $\Gamma(x)$ vs. x for real x.   Note

$$\begin{aligned} \Gamma(\tfrac{1}{2}) &= \sqrt{\pi}_+ \qquad \Gamma(1) = 1 \\ \Gamma(n+1) &= n! \qquad (n = 0, 1, 2, \ldots) \end{aligned}$$

(11.2-2)

$$\Gamma(z) = \lim_{n \to \infty} \frac{n!}{z(z+1)(z+2)\cdots(z+n-1)}\,n^{z-1}$$

(EULER'S DEFINITION)   (11.2-3)

and

$$\Gamma(z+1) = z\Gamma(z)$$

(11.2-4)

11.2-2   Stirling's Expansions for $\Gamma(z)$ and $n!$

$$\Gamma(z) = e^{-z}z^{z-1/2}\sqrt{2\pi}\left[1 + \frac{1}{12z} + \frac{1}{288z^2} - \frac{139}{51,840z^3} - \frac{571}{2,488,320z^4} + O(z^{-5})\right]$$

$(|\arg z| < \pi)$ (STIRLING'S SERIES)   (11.2-5)

Stirling's series is especially useful for large $|z|$; *for real positive z, the absolute value of the error is less than that of the last term used.*   Note, in particular,

$$\lim_{n \to \infty} \frac{n!}{n^n e^{-n} \sqrt{2\pi n}} = 1 \quad \text{or} \quad n! \simeq n^n e^{-n} \sqrt{2\pi n} \quad \text{as } n \to \infty$$

$$\text{(STIRLING'S FORMULA)} \quad (11.2\text{-}6)$$

The fractional error in Stirling's formula is less than 10 per cent for $n = 1$ and decreases as n increases; this asymptotic formula applies particularly to computations of the *ratio* of two factorials or gamma functions, since in such cases the *fractional* error is of paramount interest.

11.3 MISCELLANEOUS FUNCTIONS*

11.3-1 Legendre's Normal Elliptic Integrals (*see also Fig. 11.3-1*).
(*a*) DEFINITIONS. **Legendre's (incomplete) normal elliptic integrals** are defined as

$$F(k, \varphi) \equiv \int_0^\varphi \frac{d\varphi}{\sqrt{1 - k^2 \sin^2 \varphi}}$$

$$\equiv \int_0^z \frac{dz}{\sqrt{(1 - z^2)(1 - k^2 z^2)}} \equiv \overline{F}(k, z)$$

(LEGENDRE'S NORMAL ELLIPTIC INTEGRAL OF THE FIRST KIND)

$$E(k, \varphi) \equiv \int_0^\varphi \sqrt{1 - k^2 \sin^2 \varphi} \, d\varphi \equiv \int_0^z \sqrt{\frac{1 - k^2 z^2}{1 - z^2}} \, dz$$

$$\equiv \overline{E}(k, z)$$

(LEGENDRE'S NORMAL ELLIPTIC INTEGRAL

OF THE SECOND KIND)   (11.3-1)

where $z = \sin \varphi$. k is a complex number called the **modulus (module)** of the elliptic integral. The elliptic integrals (1) are real for real φ between $-\pi/2$ and $\pi/2$ if k^2 is a real number between 0 and 1; $F(k, \varphi)$ and $E(k, \varphi)$ have been tabulated for $0 \leq \varphi \leq \pi/2$ and real values of k^2 between 0 and 1.

(*b*) LEGENDRE'S COMPLETE NORMAL ELLIPTIC INTEGRALS.   The functions

---

* See G. A. Korn and T. M. Korn, *Mathematical Handbook for Scientists and Engineers*, for a more comprehensive treatment, including complex-variable theory.

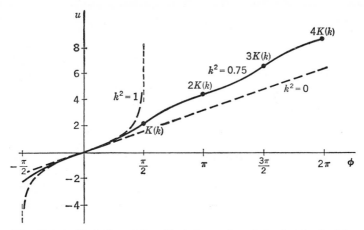

Fig. 11.3-1 Variation of the elliptic integral u of the first kind with ϕ, the amplitude of u for three values of the modulus k. (*From J. Cunningham, Introduction to Nonlinear Analysis, McGraw-Hill, New York, 1958.*)

$$
\begin{aligned}
\mathbf{K} = \mathbf{K}(k) &\equiv \int_0^{\pi/2} \frac{d\varphi}{\sqrt{1 - k^2 \sin^2 \varphi}} \equiv F(k, \pi/2) \\
\mathbf{E} = \mathbf{E}(k) &\equiv \int_0^{\pi/2} \sqrt{1 - k^2 \sin^2 \varphi} \, d\varphi \equiv E(k, \pi/2)
\end{aligned}
\tag{11.3-2}
$$

are respectively known as **Legendre's complete elliptic integrals of the first and second kind.** k and $k' = \sqrt{1 - k^2}$ are called **complementary moduli.** $\mathbf{K}(k)$ and $\mathbf{K}'(k) \equiv \mathbf{K}(k')$ are **associated elliptic integrals of the first kind**; $\mathbf{E}(k)$ and $\mathbf{E}'(k) \equiv \mathbf{E}(k')$ are **associated elliptic integrals of the second kind.** Note

$$
\mathbf{EK}' + \mathbf{E}'\mathbf{K} - \mathbf{KK}' = \frac{\pi}{2} \quad \text{(\footnotesize LEGENDRE'S RELATION)} \tag{11.3-3}
$$

and $\mathbf{K}(0) = \mathbf{K}'(1) = \pi/2$, $\mathbf{K}(1) = \mathbf{K}'(0) = \infty$.

Different values of the multiple-valued elliptic integral $F(k, \varphi)$ differ by $4m\mathbf{K} + 2ni\mathbf{K}'$; different values of $E(k, \varphi)$ differ by $4m\mathbf{E} + 2ni(\mathbf{K}' - \mathbf{E}')$ ($m, n = 0, \pm1, \pm2, \ldots$).

11.3-2 Jacobi's Elliptic Functions. (*a*) DEFINITIONS. Inversion of the elliptic integrals $z = F(k, \varphi)$ and $z = \overline{F}(k, w)$ yields the functions am z (**amplitude** of z) and sn z (**sinus amplitudinis** of z), i.e.,

$$\varphi = \text{am } z \qquad z = \int_0^\varphi \frac{d\varphi}{\sqrt{1 - k^2 \sin^2 \varphi}} = F(k, \varphi)$$

$$w = \text{sn } z = \sin (\text{am } z) \tag{11.3-4}$$

$$z = \int_0^w \frac{dw}{\sqrt{(1 - w^2)(1 - k^2 w^2)}} = \overline{F}(k, w)$$

In addition, one defines the functions cn z (**cosinus amplitudinis of** z) and dn z (**delta amplitudinis** of z) by

$$\begin{aligned}
\text{cn } z &= \cos (\text{am } z) = \sqrt{1 - \text{sn}^2 z} \\
\text{dn } z &= \Delta(\text{am } z, k) = \sqrt{1 - k^2 \text{sn}^2 z}
\end{aligned} \tag{11.3-5}$$

sn z, cn z, and dn z are **Jacobi's elliptic functions.** A given value of the parameter k is implied in each definition; if required, one writes sn (z, k), cn (z, k), dn (z, k) (see also Fig. 11.3-2).

Jacobi's elliptic functions are real for real z and real k^2 between 0 and 1 and reduce to elementary functions for $k^2 = 0$ and $k^2 = 1$; in particular,

$$\text{sn } (z, 0) = \sin z \qquad \text{cn } (z, 0) = \cos z \tag{11.3-6}$$

(*b*) MISCELLANEOUS PROPERTIES. Note also

$$\begin{aligned}
\text{sn}^2 z + \text{cn}^2 z &= k^2 \text{sn}^2 z + \text{dn}^2 z = 1 & \text{dn}^2 z - k^2 \text{cn}^2 z &= k'^2 & (11.3\text{-}7) \\
\text{sn } (-z) &= -\text{sn } z \qquad \text{cn } (-z) = \text{cn } z & \text{dn } (-z) &= \text{dn } (z) & (11.3\text{-}8)
\end{aligned}$$

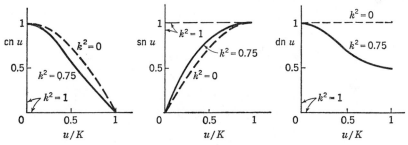

Fig. 11.3-2 One-quarter of a complete cycle of the elliptic functions cn u, sn u, and dn u, plotted against the normalized abscissa $u/\mathbf{K}$, for three values of the modulus k. (*From J. Cunningham, Introduction to Nonlinear Analysis, McGraw-Hill, New York, 1958.*)

$$\text{sn } (2\mathbf{K} - z) = \text{sn } z \qquad \text{sn } (2i\mathbf{K}' - z) = -\text{sn } (z)$$
$$\text{cn } (2\mathbf{K} - z) = -\text{cn } z \qquad \text{cn } (2i\mathbf{K}' - z) = -\text{cn } (z) \qquad (11.3\text{-}9)$$
$$\text{dn } (2\mathbf{K} - z) = \text{dn } z \qquad \text{dn } (2i\mathbf{K}' - z) = -\text{dn } (z)$$

$$\overline{E}(k, \text{sn } z) = \int_0^z \text{dn}^2 z \, dz \qquad (11.3\text{-}10)$$

(*c*) ADDITION FORMULAS

$$\text{sn } (A + B) = \frac{\text{sn } A \text{ cn } B \text{ dn } B + \text{sn } B \text{ cn } A \text{ dn } A}{1 - k^2 \text{ sn}^2 A \text{ sn}^2 B}$$

$$\text{cn } (A + B) = \frac{\text{cn } A \text{ cn } B - \text{sn } A \text{ dn } A \text{ sn } B \text{ dn } B}{1 - k^2 \text{ sn}^2 A \text{ sn}^2 B} \qquad (11.3\text{-}11)$$

$$\text{dn } (A + B) = \frac{\text{dn } A \text{ dn } B - k^2 \text{ sn } A \text{ cn } A \text{ sn } B \text{ cn } B}{1 - k^2 \text{ sn}^2 A \text{ sn}^2 B}$$

(*d*) DIFFERENTIATION

$$\frac{d(\text{sn } z)}{dz} = \text{cn } z \text{ dn } z = \sqrt{(1 - \text{sn}^2 z)(1 - k^2 \text{ sn}^2 z)}$$

$$\frac{d(\text{cn } z)}{dz} = -\text{sn } z \text{ dn } z = \sqrt{(1 - \text{cn}^2 z)(k'^2 + k^2 \text{ cn}^2 z)} \qquad (11.3\text{-}12)$$

$$\frac{d(\text{dn } z)}{dz} = -k^2 \text{ sn } z \text{ cn } z = \sqrt{(\text{dn}^2 z - 1)(k'^2 - \text{dn}^2 z)}$$

11.3-3 Bessel Functions and Other Cylinder Functions. (*a*)
DEFINITIONS (see also Fig. 11.3-3). A **cylinder function (circular-cylinder function) of order** m is a solution $w = Z_m(z)$ of the linear
differential equation

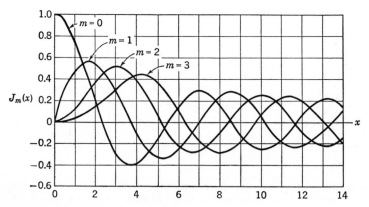

Fig. 11.3-3 The Bessel functions $J_0(x)$, $J_1(x)$, $J_2(x)$, . . . for real arguments. Note that $J_m(-x) = (-1)^m J_m(x)$.

$$\frac{d^2w}{dz^2} + \frac{1}{z}\frac{dw}{dz} + \left(1 - \frac{m^2}{z^2}\right)w = 0$$

(BESSEL'S DIFFERENTIAL EQUATION)   (11.3-13)

where m is any real number; one usually imposes the recurrence relations

$$Z_{m+1}(z) = \frac{2m}{z}Z_m(z) - Z_{m-1}(z) = \frac{m}{z}Z_m(z) - \frac{d}{dz}Z_m(z)$$

$$= -z^m \frac{d}{dz}[z^{-m}Z_m(z)] \tag{11.3-14}$$

as additional defining conditions. The functions $e^{\pm i(Kz \pm m\varphi)}Z_m(iKr')$ are solutions of Laplace's partial differential equation in cylindrical coordinates r', φ, z (*cylindrical harmonics*, Sec. 6.3-4b). Cylinder functions of nonintegral order are multiple-valued; one defines the principal branch by $|\arg z| < \pi$.

(*b*) The most generally useful cylinder functions of order m satisfying the recurrence relations (2) are

$$J_m(z) = \left(\frac{z}{2}\right)^m \sum_{k=0}^{\infty} \frac{(-1)^k}{k!\,\Gamma(m+k+1)} \left(\frac{z}{2}\right)^{2k} \quad (|\arg z| < \pi)$$

(BESSEL FUNCTIONS OF THE FIRST KIND)   (11.3-15)

$$N_m(z) \equiv \frac{1}{\sin m\pi}[J_m(z)\cos m\pi - J_{-m}(z)]$$

$$(m \neq 0,\ \pm 1,\ \pm 2,\ \ldots)$$

$$N_m(z) = (-1)^{-m}N_{-m}(z)$$

$$= \frac{2}{\pi}J_m(z)\left(\log_e\frac{z}{2} + C\right)$$

$$- \frac{1}{\pi}\left(\frac{z}{2}\right)^m \sum_{k=0}^{\infty} \frac{(-1)^k}{k!(m+k)!}\left(\frac{z}{2}\right)^{2k}\left(\sum_{j=1}^{k}\frac{1}{j} + \sum_{j=1}^{m+k}\frac{1}{j}\right)$$

$$- \frac{1}{\pi}\left(\frac{z}{2}\right)^{-m} \sum_{k=0}^{m-1} \frac{(m-k-1)!}{k!}\left(\frac{z}{2}\right)^{2k}$$

$$(m = 0,\ 1,\ 2,\ \ldots ;\ |\arg z| < \pi)$$

(NEUMANN'S BESSEL FUNCTIONS OF THE SECOND KIND)   (11.3-16)

$$H_m^{(1)}(z) \equiv J_m(z) + iN_m(z)$$
$$H_m^{(2)}(z) \equiv J_m(z) - iN_m(z)$$

(HANKEL FUNCTIONS OF THE FIRST AND SECOND KIND)   (11.3-17)

Every cylinder function of order m can be expressed as a linear combination of $J_m(z)$ and $N_m(z)$ and as a linear combination of $H_m^{(1)}(z)$ and $H_m^{(2)}(z)$:

$$Z_m(z) = aJ_m(z) + bN_m(z) = \alpha H_m^{(1)}(z) + \beta H_m^{(2)}(z) \qquad (11.3\text{-}18)$$

(fundamental systems, Sec. 6.2-2).   Note

$$\cos(z \sin t) = J_0(z) + 2 \sum_{k=1}^{\infty} J_{2k}(z) \cos 2kt$$

$$\sin(z \sin t) = 2 \sum_{k=1}^{\infty} J_{2k-1}(z) \sin(2k-1)t \qquad (11.3\text{-}19)$$

$$e^{\pm iz \sin t} = \sum_{m=-\infty}^{\infty} J_m(z) e^{\pm imt}$$

$$= J_0(z) + 2 \sum_{k=1}^{\infty} [J_{2k}(z) \cos 2kt \pm iJ_{2k-1}(z) \sin(2k-1)t]$$

(JACOBI-ANGER FORMULA)   (11.3-20)

11.3-4 Legendre Polynomials and Associated Legendre Polynomials. Spherical Harmonics.

(a) The **Legendre polynomials of degree** n,

$$P_n(x) = \frac{1}{2^n n!} \frac{d^n}{dx^n} (x^2 - 1)^n \qquad (n = 0, 1, 2, \ldots)$$

(RODRIGUES'S FORMULA)   (11.3-21)

satisfy the differential equation

$$(1 - x^2) \frac{d^2 y}{dx^2} - 2x \frac{dy}{dx} + n(n+1)y = 0$$

(LEGENDRE'S DIFFERENTIAL EQUATION)   (11.3-22)

and the recursion relations

$$P_{n+1}(x) = \frac{2n+1}{n+1} x P_n(x) - \frac{n}{n+1} P_{n-1}(x)$$

$$= x P_n(x) + \frac{x^2 - 1}{n+1} \frac{dP_n}{dx} \qquad (n = 1, 2, \ldots) \qquad (11.3\text{-}23)$$

The first five polynomials are

$$P_0(x) \equiv 1$$
$$P_1(x) \equiv x = \cos \vartheta$$
$$P_2(x) \equiv \tfrac{1}{2}(3x^2 - 1) = \tfrac{1}{4}(3 \cos 2\vartheta + 1)$$
$$P_3(x) \equiv \tfrac{1}{2}(5x^3 - 3x) = \tfrac{1}{8}(5 \cos 3\vartheta + 3 \cos \vartheta) \tag{11.3-24}$$
$$P_4(x) \equiv \tfrac{1}{8}(35x^4 - 30x^2 + 3) = \tfrac{1}{64}(35 \cos 4\vartheta + 20 \cos 2\vartheta + 9)$$
$$P_5(x) \equiv \tfrac{1}{8}(63x^5 - 70x^3 + 15x)$$

Note also

$$\int_{-1}^{1} P_n(x)P_{n'}(x)\, dx = \begin{cases} 0 & (n' \neq n) \\ \dfrac{2}{2n+1} & (n' = n) \end{cases} \tag{11.3-25}$$

(b) The **associated Legendre "polynomials" of the first kind of degree** j **and order** m,

$$P_j{}^m(x) = (1 - x^2)^{m/2} \frac{d^m}{dx^m} P_j(x) = \frac{(1 - x^2)^{m/2}}{2^j j!} \frac{d^{j+m}}{dx^{j+m}} (x^2 - 1)^j$$

(real x between -1 and 1; $j = 0, 1, 2, \ldots$; $m = 0, 1, 2, \ldots, j$)

$$\tag{11.3-26}$$

satisfy the differential equation

$$(1 - z^2) \frac{d^2 w}{dz^2} - 2z \frac{dw}{dz} + \left[j(j + 1) - \frac{m^2}{1 - z^2} \right] w = 0 \tag{11.3-27}$$

Functions of the form

$$\Phi(\vartheta, \varphi) = \sum_{j=0}^{\infty} \left[\tfrac{1}{2}\alpha_{j0}P_j(\cos \vartheta) \right.$$

$$\left. + \sum_{m=1}^{j} P_j{}^m(\cos \vartheta)(\alpha_{jm} \cos m\varphi + \beta_{jm} \sin m\varphi) \right] \tag{11.3-28}$$

are known as **spherical surface harmonics** and are important for the solution of Laplace's differential equation in spherical coordinates (Sec. 6.3-4c).

References and Bibliography

1. Abramowitz, M., and I. A. Stegun (eds.): *Handbook of Mathematical Functions*, National Bureau of Standards Appl. Math. Series No. 55, Washington, D.C., 1964.

2. Byrd, P. F., and M. D. Friedman: *Handbook of Elliptic Integrals*, Springer, Berlin, 1954.

3. Erdelyi, A.: *Higher Transcendental Functions*, vols. 1 and 2 (Bateman Project), McGraw-Hill, New York, 1953.

4. Jahnke, E., and F. Emde: *Tables of Functions with Formulae and Curves*, Dover, New York, 1945.

5. Korn, G. A., and T. M. Korn: *Mathematical Handbook for Scientists and Engineers*, McGraw-Hill, New York, 1961.

6. McLachlan, N. W.: *Bessel Functions for Engineers*, Oxford University Press, 1946.

7. Sneddon, I. N.: *The Special Functions of Physics and Chemistry*, Oliver and Boyd, Edinburgh, 1956.

8. Whittaker, E. T., and G. N. Watson: *Modern Analysis*, Macmillan, New York, 1943.

9. Whittaker, E. T., and G. N. Watson: *A Course in Modern Analysis*, Cambridge, 1946.

10. Oberhettinger, F., and W. Magnus: *Formulas and Theorems for the Functions of Mathematical Physics*, Chelsea, New York, 1954.

A-1. The Trapezoid (sides a, b, c, d; a and b are parallel; the **altitude** h is the distance between a and b).   The area S is given by

$$S = \frac{1}{2}(a + b)h \qquad h = \frac{2}{a - b}\sqrt{s(s - a + b)(s - c)(s - d)}$$

$$s = \frac{a - b + c + d}{2} \qquad \text{(A-1)}$$

The trapezoid is a **parallelogram** if $a = b$ and a **rhombus** if $a = b = c = d$.

A-2. Regular Polygons (length of side equal to a)

Number of sides n	Regular polygon	Radius of circumscribed circle, $r = a \big/ 2 \sin \dfrac{\pi}{n}$	Radius of inscribed circle, $\rho = a \big/ 2 \tan \dfrac{\pi}{n}$	Area, $S = \frac{1}{2} n a \rho$
3	Equilateral triangle	$\dfrac{a}{3} \sqrt{3}$	$\dfrac{a}{6} \sqrt{3}$	$\dfrac{a^2}{4} \sqrt{3}$
4	Square	$\dfrac{a}{2} \sqrt{2}$	$\dfrac{a}{2}$	a^2
5	Regular pentagon	$a \sqrt{\frac{1}{2} + \frac{1}{10} \sqrt{5}}$	$a \sqrt{\frac{1}{4} + \frac{1}{10} \sqrt{5}}$	$\dfrac{a^2}{4} \sqrt{25 + 10 \sqrt{5}}$
6	Regular hexagon	a	$\dfrac{a}{2} \sqrt{3}$	$\frac{3}{2} a^2 \sqrt{3}$
8	Regular octagon	$a \sqrt{1 + \frac{1}{2} \sqrt{2}}$	$\dfrac{a}{2} \left(1 + \sqrt{2}\right)$	$2a^2 \left(1 + \sqrt{2}\right)$
10	Regular decagon	$\dfrac{a}{2} \left(1 + \sqrt{5}\right)$	$\dfrac{a}{2} \sqrt{5 + 2 \sqrt{5}}$	$\frac{5}{2} a^2 \sqrt{5 + 2 \sqrt{5}}$

A-3. The Circle (radius r; see also Sec. 2.3-4).

(a)   Circumference $= 2\pi r$ area $= \pi r^2$

(b) A central angle of φ radians subtends

an *arc* of length $r\varphi$ a *sector* of area $\frac{1}{2} r^2 \varphi$

a *chord* of length $2r \sin \dfrac{\varphi}{2}$ a *segment* of area $\frac{1}{2} r^2 (\varphi - \sin \varphi)$

(c) The area between a circle of radius r_1 and an enclosed (not necessarily concentric) circle of radius r_2 is $\pi(r_1 + r_2)(r_1 - r_2)$.

A-4. Prisms, Pyramids, Cylinders, and Cones.
(a) *Volume of a prism or cylinder* (bounded by a plane parallel to the base of area S_1, altitude h) hS_1

(b) *Volume of a pyramid or cone* (base area S_1, altitude h) $\frac{1}{3} h S_1$

(c) *Volume of the frustum of a pyramid or cone* (bounded by parallel planes; base areas S_1, S_2, altitude h) $\frac{1}{3} h (S_1 + \sqrt{S_1 S_2} + S_2)$

(d) *Curved surface area of a right circular cone* (base radius r, altitude h) $\pi r \sqrt{r^2 + h^2}$

A-5. Solids of Revolution

No.	Solid	Surface area	Volume
1	**Sphere of radius** r	$4\pi r^2$	$\dfrac{4}{3}\pi r^3$
2	**Oblate spheroid** $\left(\text{axes } 2a \geq 2b,\ \epsilon = \sqrt{1 - \dfrac{b^2}{a^2}}\right)$	$2\pi a^2 + \pi \dfrac{b^2}{\epsilon}\log_e \dfrac{1+\epsilon}{1-\epsilon}$	$\dfrac{4}{3}\pi a^2 b$
3	**Prolate spheroid** $\left(\text{axes } 2a \geq 2b,\ \epsilon = \sqrt{1 - \dfrac{b^2}{a^2}}\right)$	$2\pi b^2 + 2\pi \dfrac{ab}{\epsilon}\arcsin \epsilon$	$\dfrac{4}{3}\pi a b^2$
4	**Torus (anchor ring)** circle of radius r rotated about an axis at a distance R from the center	$4\pi^2 Rr$	$2\pi^2 Rr^2$
5	**Zone or segment of a sphere of radius** r between parallel planes at a distance h; base radii r_1, r_2	$2\pi rh + \pi(r_1^2 + r_2^2)$	$\dfrac{\pi}{6}h(3r_1^2 + 3r_2^2 + h^2)$

A-6. The Five Regular Polyhedra (length of side equal to a; the respective numbers F of surfaces, E of vertices, and K of edges are related by $E + F - K = 2$).

Regular polyhedron	Number and type of surfaces	Radius of circumscribed sphere	Radius of inscribed sphere	Surface area	Volume
Tetrahedron	4 equilateral triangles	$\dfrac{a}{4}\sqrt{6}$	$\dfrac{a}{12}\sqrt{6}$	$a^2\sqrt{3}$	$\dfrac{a^3}{12}\sqrt{2}$
Cube	6 squares	$\dfrac{a}{2}\sqrt{3}$	$\dfrac{a}{2}$	$6a^2$	a^3
Octahedron	8 equilateral triangles	$\dfrac{a}{2}\sqrt{2}$	$\dfrac{a}{6}\sqrt{6}$	$2a^2\sqrt{3}$	$\dfrac{a^3}{3}\sqrt{2}$
Dodecahedron	12 regular pentagons	$\dfrac{a}{4}(1+\sqrt{5})\sqrt{3}$	$\dfrac{a}{4}\sqrt{10+\dfrac{22}{\sqrt{5}}}$	$3a^2\sqrt{5(5+2\sqrt{5})}$	$\dfrac{a^3}{4}(15+7\sqrt{5})$
Icosahedron	20 equilateral triangles	$\dfrac{a}{4}\sqrt{2(5+\sqrt{5})}$	$\dfrac{a}{4}\sqrt{3}(3+\sqrt{5})$	$5a^2\sqrt{3}$	$\dfrac{5}{12}a^3(3+\sqrt{5})$

B PLANE AND SPHERICAL TRIGONOMETRY

PLANE TRIGONOMETRY

B-1. Introduction. Plane trigonometry describes relations between the sides and angles of plane triangles in terms of trigonometric functions (Secs. 11.1-1 to 11.1-4); note that all plane figures bounded by straight lines may be regarded as combinations of triangles. Since all plane triangles may be resolved into right triangles, *the most important trigonometric relations are those relating the sides and angles of right triangles.*

B-2. Right Triangles. In every right triangle (Fig. B-1) with sides a, b and hypotenuse c,

$$A + B = 90° \quad a^2 + b^2 = c^2 \quad \text{(THEOREM OF PYTHAGORAS)}$$

$$\sin A = \cos B = \frac{a}{c} \qquad \sin B = \cos A = \frac{b}{c}$$

$$\tan A = \cot B = \frac{a}{b} \qquad \tan B = \cot A = \frac{b}{a}$$

(B-1)

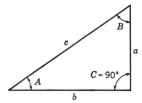

Fɪɢ. B-1. Right triangle.

B-3. Properties of Plane Triangles. In every plane triangle (Fig. B-2), the sum of the angles equals 180 deg. The sum of any two sides is greater than the third, and the greater of two sides opposes the greater

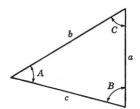

Fɪɢ. B-2. General plane triangle.

of two angles. A plane triangle is *uniquely determined* (except for symmetric images) by

1. Three sides
2. Two sides and the included angle
3. One side and two angles
4. Two sides and the angle opposite the greater side

In every plane triangle, the three bisectors of angles intersect in the center M of the inscribed circle. The three perpendicular bisectors of the sides intersect in the center F of the circumscribed circle. The three medians intersect in the center of gravity G of the triangle. The three altitudes intersect in a point H collinear with the last two points, so that $\overrightarrow{HG} : \overrightarrow{GF} = 2$. The mid-points of the sides, the footpoints of the perpendiculars from the vertices to the sides, and the mid-points of the straight-line segments joining H to each vertex lie on a circle whose radius is half that of the circumscribed circle (**nine-point circle,** or **Feuerbach circle**). The center of the nine-point circle is the mid-point of the straight-line segment HF.

B-4. Formulas for Triangle Computations. In the following relations, A, B, C are the angles opposite the respective sides a, b, c of a plane triangle (Fig. B-2). The triangle area is denoted by S; r and ρ are the respective radii of the circumscribed and inscribed circles, and $s = \frac{1}{2}(a + b + c)$. *Additional formulas are obtained by simultaneous cyclic permutation of A, B, C and a, b, c.* Table B-1 permits the computation of the sides and angles of any plane triangle from three suitable sides and/or angles.

$$a^2 = b^2 + c^2 - 2bc \cos A = (b + c)^2 - 4bc \cos^2 \frac{A}{2} \quad \text{(LAW OF COSINES)}$$
$$\text{(B-2)}$$

$$\frac{a}{\sin A} = \frac{b}{\sin B} = \frac{c}{\sin C} = 2r \qquad \text{(LAW OF SINES)} \quad \text{(B-3)}$$

$$c = a \cos B + b \cos A \quad \text{(PROJECTION THEOREM)} \quad \text{(B-4)}$$

$$\left.\begin{array}{c}
\sin \dfrac{A}{2} = + \sqrt{\dfrac{(s - b)(s - c)}{bc}} \qquad \cos \dfrac{A}{2} = + \sqrt{\dfrac{s(s - a)}{bc}} \\[3mm]
\tan \dfrac{A}{2} = + \sqrt{\dfrac{(s - b)(s - c)}{s(s - a)}} \\[3mm]
\sin A = + \dfrac{2}{bc} \sqrt{s(s - a)(s - b)(s - c)}
\end{array}\right\} \quad \text{(B-5)}$$

$$\frac{b + c}{b - c} = \frac{\tan \dfrac{B + C}{2}}{\tan \dfrac{B - C}{2}} \quad \text{(B-6)}$$

$$(b + c) \sin \frac{A}{2} = a \cos \frac{B - C}{2} \qquad (b - c) \cos \frac{A}{2} = a \sin \frac{B - C}{2} \quad \text{(B-7)}$$

$$\rho = (s - a) \tan \frac{A}{2} = (s - b) \tan \frac{B}{2} = (s - c) \tan \frac{C}{2}$$
$$= 4r \sin \frac{A}{2} \sin \frac{B}{2} \sin \frac{C}{2} = s \tan \frac{A}{2} \tan \frac{B}{2} \tan \frac{C}{2} \quad \text{(B-8)}$$

$$s = \frac{a + b + c}{2} = 4r \cos \frac{A}{2} \cos \frac{B}{2} \cos \frac{C}{2} \quad \text{(B-9)}$$

$$S = \frac{1}{2}ab \sin C = \frac{1}{2}bc \sin A = \frac{1}{2}ac \sin B$$
$$= [s(s - a)(s - b)(s - c)]^{\frac{1}{2}}$$
$$= 2r^2 \sin A \sin B \sin C = \frac{abc}{4r} = \rho s \quad \text{(B-10)}$$

$$\text{Length of } \textit{altitude } h_a = \frac{bc}{2r} \quad \left(S = \frac{1}{2} a h_a\right)$$

$$\text{Length of } \textit{angular bisector } w_a = \frac{1}{b + c} \sqrt{bc(a + b + c)(b + c - a)}$$

$$\text{Length of } \textit{median } m_a = \frac{1}{2} \sqrt{2b^2 + 2c^2 - a^2}$$

Table B-1 *Solution of plane triangles. Obtain all other cases by cyclic permutation* (refer to formulas of Sec. B-4 and to Fig. B-2)

Case	Given	Example	Formulas used Note $A + B + C = 180°$	Conditions for the existence of a solution (see also Sec. B-3)
1	Three sides	a, b, c	A, B, C from (2) or (3)	Sum of two sides must be greater than the third
2	Two sides and the included angle	b, c, A	$\dfrac{B + C}{2} = 90° - \dfrac{A}{2}; \dfrac{B - C}{2}$ from (6) or (7), hence B and C; or B, C from (3) and (4): $$\tan B = \frac{b \sin A}{c - b \cos A}$$ a from (3) or (4)	
3	One side and two angles	a, B, C	b, c from (3); $A = 180° - B - C$	
4	Two sides and an opposite angle	b, c, B	From (3), $a = \dfrac{b \sin A}{\sin B}$, $\sin C = \dfrac{c \sin B}{b}$; $A = 180° - B - C$	Problem has one solution if $b \geq c$; two solutions if $b < c$, $c \sin B < b$

SPHERICAL TRIGONOMETRY

B-5. Spherical Triangles: Introduction. On the surface of a sphere, the shortest distance between two points is measured along a **great circle,** i.e., a circle whose plane passes through the center of the sphere (geodesic, Sec. 7.3-3). The vertices of a **spherical triangle** are the intersections of three directed straight lines passing through the center of the sphere and the spherical surface. The **sides** a, b, c of the spherical triangle are those three angles between the three directed straight lines which are less than 180 deg. Corresponding to each triangle side, there is a great-circle segment on the surface of the sphere (Fig. B-3). The **angles** A, B, C of the spherical triangle opposite the sides a, b, c, respectively, are the angles less than 180 deg between the great-circle segments corresponding to the triangle sides, or the corresponding angles between the three planes defined by the three given straight lines.

Spherical trigonometry is the study of relations between the sides and angles of spherical triangles (e.g., on the surface of the earth and on the celestial sphere).

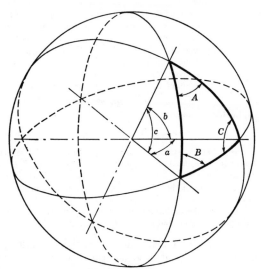

FIG. B-3. Spherical triangle.

B-6. Properties of Spherical Triangles. Each side or angle of a spherical triangle is, by definition, smaller than 180 deg. The geometry on the surface of a sphere is noneuclidean; in every spherical triangle, the sum of the sides will be between 0 and 360 deg, and the sum of the angles will be between 180 and 540 deg. In every spherical triangle, the greater of two sides opposes the greater of two angles. The sum of any two sides is greater than the third, and the sum of any two angles is less than 180 deg plus the third angle. A spherical triangle is *uniquely determined* (except for symmetric images) by

1. Three sides
2. Three angles
3. Two sides and the included angle
4. Two angles and the included side
5. Two sides and an opposite angle, given that the other opposite angle is less than, equal to, or greater than 90 deg
6. Two angles and an opposite side, given that the other opposite side is less than, equal to, or greater than 90 deg

NOTE: In every spherical triangle, it is possible to define great circles as perpendicular isectors of sides, bisectors of angles, medians, and altitudes. The planes of the three reat circles of each type intersect in a straight line.

In analogy to the circumscribed circle of a plane triangle, there exists a *circumscribed right circular cone* containing the three straight lines defining the triangle; the axis of this cone is the straight line formed by the intersection of the planes of the perpendicular bisectors. There is also an *inscribed right circular cone* touching the three planes corresponding to the spherical triangle; the axis of this cone is the straight line formed by the intersection of the planes of the bisectors of the angles. The "radius" r of the circumscribed circle and the "radius" ρ of the inscribed circle are *angles* defined as half the vertex angles of the respective cones.

Given the radius R of the sphere, the *area* S_R of a spherical triangle is given by

$$S_R = R^2 \epsilon \tag{B-11}$$

where ϵ is the **spherical excess**

$$\epsilon = A + B + C - \pi \tag{B-12}$$

measured in *radians*. The quantity $d = 2\pi - (a + b + c)$ is called **spherical defect.**

The **polar triangle** corresponding to a given spherical triangle is defined by three directed straight lines perpendicular to the planes associated with the sides of the original triangle. The sides of the polar triangle are equal to the supplements of the corresponding angles of the original triangle, and conversely. Thus every theorem or formula dealing with the sides and angles of the original triangle may be transformed into one dealing with the angles and sides of the polar triangle.

B-7. The Right Spherical Triangle.

In a right spherical triangle, at least one angle, C, say, is equal to 90 deg; the opposite side, c, is called the **hypotenuse.** All important relations between the sides and angles of the right spherical triangle may be derived from *Napier's rules*, two convenient aids to memory:

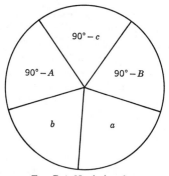

ᵢFɪɢ. B-4. Napier's rules.

Napier's Rules: In the diagram of Fig. B-4, the sine of any of the angles shown is equal

1. *To the product of the tangents of the two angles adjoining it in the diagram*
2. *To the product of the cosines of the two angles opposing it in the diagram*

EXAMPLE: To compute the sides and angles of a right spherical triangle with the hypotenuse c, given c and a.

This problem has a solution only if $\sin a \leq \sin c$; then

$$\cos b = \frac{\cos c}{\cos a} \qquad \cos B = \frac{\tan a}{\tan c} \qquad \sin A = \frac{\sin a}{\sin c}$$

NOTE: If a is less than, equal to, or greater than 90 deg, so is A, and conversely. If b is less than, equal to, or greater than 90 deg, so is B.

If a and A are given, the problem has a solution only if the above condition is satisfied and $\sin a \leq \sin A$; unless $a = A$, there are two solutions. The situation is analogous if b and B are given.

If A and B are given, the problem has a solution only if $90 < A + B < 270$ deg and -90 deg $< A - B < 90$ deg (Sec. B-6).

A spherical triangle having a side equal to 90 deg is called a **quadrantal triangle** and may be treated as the polar triangle (Sec. B-6) of a right spherical triangle.

For all problems involving the spherical-triangle computations (right or oblique triangles), it is strongly recommended that a sketch be drawn which roughly indicates whether the various angles and sides will be less than, equal to, or greater than 90 deg.

B-8. Formulas for Triangle Computations (see also Fig. B-3).

In the following relations, A, B, C are the angles opposite the respective sides a, b, c of a spherical triangle. The respective "radii" of the circumscribed and inscribed cones are denoted by r and ρ. *Additional formulas are obtained by simultaneous cyclic permutation of A, B, C and a, b, c.* Table B-2 permits the computation of the sides or angles of any spherical triangle from three suitable sides and/or angles. The inequalities noted in Sec. B-6 must be observed in order to avoid ambiguous results in triangle computations.

$$\frac{\sin a}{\sin A} = \frac{\sin b}{\sin B} = \frac{\sin c}{\sin C} \qquad \text{(LAW OF SINES)} \qquad \text{(B-13)}$$

$$\cos a = \cos b \cos c + \sin b \sin c \cos A \qquad \begin{array}{l} \text{(LAW OF COSINES} \\ \text{FOR THE SIDES)} \end{array} \qquad \text{(B-14)}$$

$$\cos A = -\cos B \cos C + \sin B \sin C \cos a \qquad \begin{array}{l} \text{(LAW OF COSINES} \\ \text{FOR THE ANGLES)} \end{array} \qquad \text{(B-15)}$$

$$\left. \begin{array}{l} \tan \dfrac{b+c}{2} \cos \dfrac{B+C}{2} = \tan \dfrac{a}{2} \cos \dfrac{B-C}{2} \\[2mm] \tan \dfrac{b-c}{2} \sin \dfrac{B+C}{2} = \tan \dfrac{a}{2} \sin \dfrac{B-C}{2} \\[2mm] \tan \dfrac{B+C}{2} \cos \dfrac{b+c}{2} = \cot \dfrac{A}{2} \cos \dfrac{b-c}{2} \\[2mm] \tan \dfrac{B-C}{2} \sin \dfrac{b+c}{2} = \cot \dfrac{A}{2} \sin \dfrac{b-c}{2} \end{array} \right\} \qquad \begin{array}{l} \text{(NAPIER'S} \\ \text{ANALOGIES)} \end{array} \qquad \text{(B-16)}$$

$$\sin \frac{A}{2} \sin \frac{b+c}{2} = \sin \frac{a}{2} \cos \frac{B-C}{2}$$

$$\sin \frac{A}{2} \cos \frac{b+c}{2} = \cos \frac{a}{2} \cos \frac{B+C}{2}$$

$$\cos \frac{A}{2} \sin \frac{b-c}{2} = \sin \frac{a}{2} \sin \frac{B-C}{2}$$

$$\cos \frac{A}{2} \cos \frac{b-c}{2} = \cos \frac{a}{2} \sin \frac{B+C}{2}$$

(DELAMBRE'S OR GAUSS'S ANALOGIES) (B-17)

$$s = \frac{a+b+c}{2} \qquad S = \frac{A+B+C}{2}$$

$$\sin \frac{A}{2} = \sqrt{\frac{\sin (s-b) \sin (s-c)}{\sin b \sin c}}$$

$$\cos \frac{A}{2} = \sqrt{\frac{\sin s \sin (s-a)}{\sin b \sin c}}$$

$$\sin \frac{a}{2} = \sqrt{\frac{-\cos S \cos (S-A)}{\sin B \sin C}}$$

$$\cos \frac{a}{2} = \sqrt{\frac{\cos (S-B) \cos (S-C)}{\sin B \sin C}}$$

(HALF-ANGLE FORMULAS) (B-18)

$$\sin A = \frac{+2 \sqrt{\sin s \sin (s-a) \sin (s-b) \sin (s-c)}}{\sin b \sin c}$$

$$\sin a = \frac{+2 \sqrt{-\cos S \cos (S-A) \cos (S-B) \cos (S-C)}}{\sin B \sin C}$$

(B-19)

$$\cot r = \sqrt{\frac{\cos (S-A) \cos (S-B) \cos (S-C)}{-\cos S}}$$

$$\tan \rho = \sqrt{\frac{\sin (s-a) \sin (s-b) \sin (s-c)}{\sin s}}$$

$$\cot \frac{A}{2} = \frac{\sin (s-a)}{\tan \rho} \qquad \tan \frac{a}{2} = \frac{\cos (S-A)}{\cot r}$$

(B-20)

$$\tan \frac{\epsilon}{4} = \sqrt{\tan \frac{s}{2} \tan \frac{s-a}{2} \tan \frac{s-b}{2} \tan \frac{s-c}{2}}$$

(B-21)

$$\tan \left(\frac{A}{2} - \frac{\epsilon}{4} \right) = + \sqrt{\frac{\tan \dfrac{s-b}{2} \tan \dfrac{s-c}{2}}{\tan \dfrac{s}{2} \tan \dfrac{s-a}{2}}}$$

(L'HUILIER'S EQUATION) (B-22)

B-9. Formulas Expressed in Terms of the Haversine Function. Certain trigonometrical relations become particularly suitable for logarithmic computations if they are expressed in terms of the new trigonometric functions **versed sine, versed cosine,** and **haversine,** defined by

$$\text{vers } A = 1 - \cos A \qquad \text{covers } A = 1 - \sin A \qquad \text{hav } A = \frac{1}{2}(1 - \cos A) \quad \text{(B-23)}$$

Thus, if tables of the haversine function are available, one may use the following formulas for spherical-triangle computations:

$$\text{hav } A = \frac{\sin (s - b) \sin (s - c)}{\sin b \sin c} \qquad \text{hav } a = \text{hav } (b - c) + \sin b \sin c \text{ hav } A$$

(B-24)

Other similar relations may be obtained by cyclic permutation.

Table B-2 Solution of spherical triangles (refer to formulas of Sec. B-8 and to Fig. B-3)

Case	Given	Example (obtain other cases by cyclic permutation)	Formulas used	Conditions for the existence of a solution (see also Sec. B-6)
1	Three sides	a, b, c	A, B, C from (18) and cyclic permutation	Sum of two sides must be greater than the third
2	Three angles	A, B, C	a, b, c from (18) and cyclic permutation	$540° > A + B + C > 180°$; sum of two angles must be less than $180°$ plus the third angle
3	Two sides and the included angle	b, c, A	$\dfrac{B + C}{2}$ and $\dfrac{B - C}{2}$ from (16), hence B and C: a from (17), (18), or (14)	
4	Two angles and the included side	B, C, a	$\dfrac{b + c}{2}$ and $\dfrac{b - c}{2}$ from (16), hence b and c; A from (17), (18), or (15)	
5	Two sides and an opposite angle	b, c, B	C from (13); A and a from (16)	Problem has either one or two solutions if $\sin c \sin B \leq \sin b$. Retain the values of C which make $A - B$ and $a - b$ of like sign; and $A + B - 180°$ and $a + b - 180°$ of like sign
6	Two angles and an opposite side	B, C, b	c from (13); A and a from (16)	Problem has either one or two solutions if $\sin b \sin C \leq \sin B$. Retain the values of c which make $A - B$ and $a - b$ of like sign, and $A + B - 180°$ and $a + b - 180°$ of like sign

C PERMUTATIONS, COMBINATIONS, AND RELATED TOPICS

Refer to Sec. 1.2-8 for definitions and properties of factorials and binomial coefficients. Stirling's formula (Sec. 11.2-2) is useful in numerical computations. For additional material, see J. Riordan, *An Introduction to Combinatorial Analysis*, Wiley, New York, 1958.

Table C-1 Permutations and partitions

1	Number of different orderings (**permutations**) of a set of n distinct objects	$n!$
2	i. Number of distinguishable sequences of N objects comprising $n \leq N$ indistinguishable objects of type 1 and $N - n$ indistinguishable objects of type 2, **or** ii. Number of distinguishable *partitions* of a set of N distinct objects into 2 classes of $n \leq N$ and $N - n$ objects, respectively	$\binom{N}{n} = \dfrac{N!}{(N - n)!n!}$ (**binomial coefficient**)
3	i. Number of distinguishable sequences of $N = N_1 + N_2 + \cdots + N_r$ objects comprising N_1 indistinguishable objects of type 1, N_2 indistinguishable objects of type 2, . . . , and N_r indistinguishable objects of type r, **or** ii. Number of distinguishable partitions of a set of $N = N_1 + N_2 + \cdots + N_r$ distinct objects into r classes of $N_1, N_2, \ldots, N_r$ objects, respectively	$\dfrac{N!}{N_1!N_2! \cdots N_r!}$ (**multinomial coefficient**)

Table C-2 Combinations and samples. *Each formula holds for* $N < n, N = n$, and $N > n$

1	Number of distinguishable unordered **combinations** of N distinct types of objects taken n at a time: i. Each type of object may occur *at most once* in any combination (*combinations without repetition;* see also Table C-1, 2) ii. Each type of object may occur 0, 1, 2, . . . , or n times in any combination (*combinations with repetition*) iii. Each type of object must occur *at least once* in each combination	$\binom{N}{n}$ $\binom{N + n - 1}{n} = \binom{N + n - 1}{N - 1}$ $\binom{n - 1}{N - 1}$
2	Number of distinguishable **samples** (sequences, ordered sets, variations) of size n taken from a population of N distinct types of objects: i. Each type of object may occur *at most once* in any sample (*samples without replacement,* sequences without repetition) ii. Each type of object may occur 0, 1, 2, . . . , or n times in any sample (*samples with replacement,* sequences with repetition)	$N(N - 1) \cdots (N - n + 1)$ $= \binom{N}{n} n!$ N^n

EXAMPLES: Given a set of $N = 3$ distinct types of elements a, b, c. For $n = 2$, there exist 3 *combinations without repetition* (ab, ac, bc); 6 *combinations with repetition* (aa, ab, ac, bb, bc, cc); 6 distinguishable *samples without replacement* (ab, ac, ba, bc, ca, cb); and 9 distinguishable *samples with replacement* ($aa, ab, ac, ba, bb, bc, ca, cb, cc$).

D TABLES OF FOURIER EXPANSIONS AND LAPLACE-TRANSFORM PAIRS

Table D-1 Fourier coefficients and mean-square values of periodic functions $\left[\text{Sec. 3.11-1; sinc }(x) \equiv \dfrac{\sin \pi x}{\pi x}\right]$

	Periodic function, $f(t) = f(t + T)$	Fourier coefficients (for phasing as shown in diagram)	Average value $\langle f \rangle = \dfrac{a_0}{2}$	Mean-square value $\langle f^2 \rangle$
1	Rectangular pulses	$a_n = 2A \dfrac{T_0}{T}\, \text{sinc}\left(\dfrac{nT_0}{T}\right)$ $b_n = 0$	$A \dfrac{T_0}{T}$	$A^2 \dfrac{T_0}{T}$
2	Symmetrical triangular pulses	$a_n = A \dfrac{T_0}{T}\, \text{sinc}^2\left(\dfrac{nT_0}{2T}\right)$ $b_n = 0$	$A \dfrac{T_0}{2T}$	$A^2 \dfrac{T_0}{3T}$
3	Symmetrical trapezoidal pulses	$a_n = 2A \dfrac{T_0 + T_1}{T}\, \text{sinc}\left(\dfrac{nT_1}{T}\right)\, \text{sinc}\left(\dfrac{n(T_0 + T_1)}{T}\right)$ $b_n = 0$	$A \dfrac{T_0 + T_1}{T}$	$A^2 \dfrac{3T_0 + 2T_1}{3T}$
4	Half-sine pulses*†	$a_n = A \dfrac{T_0}{T}\left\{\text{sinc}\left[\dfrac{1}{2}\left(\dfrac{2nT_0}{T} - 1\right)\right] + \text{sinc}\left[\dfrac{1}{2}\left(\dfrac{2nT_0}{T} + 1\right)\right]\right\}$ $b_n = 0$	$\dfrac{2}{\pi} A \dfrac{T_0}{T}$	$A^2 \dfrac{T_0}{2T}$
5	Clipped sinusoid $A = A_0\left(1 - \cos \dfrac{\pi T_0}{T}\right)$	$a_n = \dfrac{A_0 T_0}{T}\left\{\text{sinc}\left[(n-1)\dfrac{T_0}{T}\right] + \text{sinc}\left[(n+1)\dfrac{T_0}{T}\right] - 2\cos \dfrac{\pi T_0}{T}\, \text{sinc}\left(\dfrac{nT_0}{T}\right)\right\}$	$\dfrac{1}{\pi} A_0\left(\sin \dfrac{\pi T_0}{T} - \dfrac{\pi T_0}{T}\cos \dfrac{\pi T_0}{T}\right)$	$\dfrac{1}{2\pi} A_0^2\left(\dfrac{\pi T_0}{T} - \dfrac{3}{2}\sin \dfrac{2\pi T_0}{T} + \dfrac{2\pi T_0}{T}\cos^2 \dfrac{\pi T_0}{T}\right)$
6	Triangular waveform	$a_n = 0$ $b_n = -\dfrac{A}{n\pi}$ $\Bigg\}$ $n = 1, 2, \ldots$	$\dfrac{A}{2}$	$\dfrac{A^2}{3}$

* For $T_0 = \dfrac{T}{2}$, $f(t) = \dfrac{2}{\pi} A = \dfrac{2}{\pi} A\left(\dfrac{1}{2} + \dfrac{\pi}{4}\cos \omega t + \dfrac{1}{3}\cos 2\omega t - \dfrac{1}{15}\cos 4\omega t + \dfrac{1}{35}\cos 6\omega t \pm \cdots\right)$ (HALF-WAVE RECTIFIED SINUSOID).

† For $T_0 = T = \dfrac{2\pi}{\omega}$, $f(t) = \dfrac{4}{\pi} A = \dfrac{4}{\pi} A\left(\dfrac{1}{2} + \dfrac{1}{3}\cos 2\omega t - \dfrac{1}{15}\cos 4\omega t + \dfrac{1}{35}\cos 6\omega t \pm \cdots\right)$ (FULL-WAVE RECTIFIED SINUSOID).

Appendix D

Table D-2 Fourier-transform pairs*

	$f(t) = \int_{-\infty}^{\infty} F(j\omega)e^{j\omega t}\dfrac{d\omega}{2\pi}$	$F(j\omega) = \int_{-\infty}^{\infty} f(t)e^{-j\omega t}\,dt$	
	$\operatorname{rect}\dfrac{t}{T} = \begin{cases} 1 & (|t| < T/2) \\ 0 & (|t| > T/2) \end{cases}$	$T\operatorname{sinc}\dfrac{\omega T}{2\pi} \equiv T\dfrac{\sin\frac{\omega T}{2}}{\frac{\omega T}{2}}$	
	$\operatorname{sinc}\dfrac{t}{T} \equiv \dfrac{\sin\frac{\pi t}{T}}{\frac{\pi t}{T}}$	$T\operatorname{rect}\dfrac{\omega T}{2\pi} = \begin{cases} 0 & \left(|\omega| < \frac{\pi}{T}\right) \\ T & \left(|\omega| > \frac{\pi}{T}\right) \end{cases}$	
	$\begin{cases} 1 - \dfrac{|t|}{T} & (|t| < T) \\ 0 & (|t| \geq T) \end{cases}$	$T\operatorname{sinc}^2\dfrac{\omega T}{2\pi} \equiv T\left(\dfrac{\sin\frac{\omega T}{2}}{\frac{\omega T}{2}}\right)^2$	
	$e^{-\frac{|t|}{T}}$	$\dfrac{2T}{(\omega T)^2 + 1}$	
	$e^{-\frac{1}{2}\left(\frac{t}{T}\right)^2}$	$\sqrt{2\pi}\,Te^{-\frac{1}{2}(\omega T)^2}$	
	$\delta(t - T)$	$e^{-j\omega T}$	(Complex)
	$\cos\omega_0 t$	$\pi[\delta(\omega - \omega_0) + \delta(\omega + \omega_0)]$	
	$\sin\omega_0 t$	$\dfrac{\pi}{j}[\delta(\omega - \omega_0) - \delta(\omega + \omega_0)]$	(Imaginary)
	$\displaystyle\sum_{k=-\infty}^{\infty}\delta(t - kT)$ $\equiv \dfrac{1}{T}\displaystyle\sum_{i=-\infty}^{\infty} e^{2\pi i j\frac{t}{T}}$	$\dfrac{2\pi}{T}\displaystyle\sum_{i=-\infty}^{\infty}\delta\left(\omega - \dfrac{2\pi i}{T}\right)$ $\equiv \displaystyle\sum_{k=-\infty}^{\infty} e^{jk\omega T}$	

* Reprinted from G. A. Korn, *Basic Tables in Electrical Engineering*, McGraw-Hill, New York, 1965.

Table D-3 Laplace-transform pairs involving rational algebraic functions $F(s) = D_1(s)/D(s)$

Each formula holds for complex as well as for real polynomials $D_1(s)$ and $D(s)$ (Sec. 5.4-8); but the latter case is of greater practical interest. In this case the roots of $D(s) = 0$ are either real or they occur as pairs of complex conjugates, and the functions $f(t)$ are real.

Note $(s - a)^2 + \omega_1{}^2 = [s - (a + i\omega_1)][s - (a - i\omega_1)]$
and $K_1 \sin \omega t + K_2 \cos \omega t = \sqrt{K_1{}^2 + K_2{}^2} \sin (\omega t + \alpha)$, with $\alpha = \arctan K_2/K_1$

No.	$F(s)$	$f(t) \ (t > 0)$			
1.1	$\dfrac{1}{s}$	1			
1.2	$\dfrac{1}{s - a}$	e^{at}			
1.3	$\dfrac{1}{s(s - a)}$	$Ae^{at} + K$	$A = \dfrac{1}{a}$	$K = -\dfrac{1}{a}$	
1.4	$\dfrac{s + d}{s(s - a)}$		$A = \left(1 + \dfrac{d}{a}\right)$	$K = -\dfrac{d}{a}$	
1.5	$\dfrac{1}{(s - a)(s - b)}$	$Ae^{at} + Be^{bt}$	$A = \dfrac{1}{a - b}$	$B = \dfrac{1}{b - a}$	
1.6	$\dfrac{s + d}{(s - a)(s - b)}$		$A = \dfrac{a + d}{a - b}$	$B = \dfrac{b + d}{b - a}$	
1.7	$\dfrac{1}{s(s - a)(s - b)}$	$Ae^{at} + Be^{bt} + K$	$A = \dfrac{1}{a(a - b)}$	$B = \dfrac{1}{b(b - a)}$	$K = \dfrac{1}{ab}$
1.8	$\dfrac{s + d}{s(s - a)(s - b)}$		$A = \dfrac{a + d}{a(a - b)}$	$B = \dfrac{b + d}{b(b - a)}$	$K = \dfrac{d}{ab}$
1.9	$\dfrac{s^2 + gs + d}{s(s - a)(s - b)}$		$A = \dfrac{a^2 + ga + d}{a(a - b)}$	$B = \dfrac{b^2 + gb + d}{b(b - a)}$	$K = \dfrac{d}{ab}$

Table D-3   Laplace-transform pairs involving rational algebraic functions $F(s) = D_1(s)/D(s)$ (Continued)

No.	$F(s)$	$f(t)$ $(t > 0)$			
1.10	$\dfrac{1}{(s-a)(s-b)(s-c)}$	$Ae^{at} + Be^{bt} + Ce^{ct}$	$A = \dfrac{1}{(a-b)(a-c)}$	$B = \dfrac{1}{(b-a)(b-c)}$	$C = \dfrac{1}{(c-a)(c-b)}$
1.11	$\dfrac{s+d}{(s-a)(s-b)(s-c)}$		$A = \dfrac{a+d}{(a-b)(a-c)}$	$B = \dfrac{b+d}{(b-a)(b-c)}$	$C = \dfrac{c+d}{(c-a)(c-b)}$
1.12	$\dfrac{s^2+gs+d}{(s-a)(s-b)(s-c)}$		$A = \dfrac{a^2+ag+d}{(a-b)(a-c)}$	$B = \dfrac{b^2+bg+d}{(b-a)(b-c)}$	$C = \dfrac{c^2+cg+d}{(c-a)(c-b)}$
2.1	$\dfrac{1}{(s-a)^2+\omega_1^2}$	$Ae^{at}\sin(\omega_1 t + \alpha)$	$A = \dfrac{1}{\omega_1}$	$\alpha = 0$	
2.2	$\dfrac{s+d}{(s-a)^2+\omega_1^2}$		$A = \dfrac{1}{\omega_1}[(a+d)^2+\omega_1^2]^{1/2}$	$\alpha = \arctan\dfrac{\omega_1}{a+d}$	
2.3	$\dfrac{1}{s[(s-a)^2+\omega_1^2]}$		$A = \dfrac{1}{\omega_1}\dfrac{1}{(a^2+\omega_1^2)^{1/2}}$ $K = \dfrac{1}{a^2+\omega_1^2}$	$\alpha = -\arctan\dfrac{\omega_1}{a}$	
2.4	$\dfrac{s+d}{s[(s-a)^2+\omega_1^2]}$	$Ae^{at}\sin(\omega_1 t + \alpha) + K$	$A = \dfrac{1}{\omega_1}\left[\dfrac{(a+d)^2+\omega_1^2}{a^2+\omega_1^2}\right]^{1/2}$ $K = \dfrac{d}{a^2+\omega_1^2}$	$\alpha = \arctan\dfrac{\omega_1}{a+d} - \arctan\dfrac{\omega_1}{a}$	
2.5	$\dfrac{s^2+gs+d}{s[(s-a)^2+\omega_1^2]}$		$A = \dfrac{1}{\omega_1}\left[\dfrac{(a^2-\omega_1^2+ag+d)^2+\omega_1^2(2a+g)^2}{(a^2+\omega_1^2)^2}\right]^{1/2}$ $K = \dfrac{d}{a^2+\omega_1^2}$	$\alpha = \arctan\dfrac{\omega_1(2a+g)}{a^2-\omega_1^2+ag+d} - \arctan\dfrac{\omega_1}{a}$	

2.6	$\dfrac{1}{(s-b)[(s-a)^2 + \omega_1^2]}$	$A = \dfrac{1}{\omega_1[(a-b)^2 + \omega_1^2]^{1/2}} \qquad B = \dfrac{1}{(a-b)^2 + \omega_1^2}$ $\alpha = -\arctan \dfrac{\omega_1}{a-b}$
2.7	$\dfrac{s+d}{(s-b)[(s-a)^2 + \omega_1^2]}$	$A = \dfrac{1}{\omega_1}\left[\dfrac{(a+d)^2 + \omega_1^2}{(a-b)^2 + \omega_1^2}\right]^{1/2} \qquad B = \dfrac{b+d}{(a-b)^2 + \omega_1^2}$ $\alpha = \arctan \dfrac{\omega_1}{a+d} - \arctan \dfrac{\omega_1}{a-b}$
2.8	$\dfrac{s^2 + gs + d}{(s-b)[(s-a)^2 + \omega_1^2]}$	$A = \dfrac{1}{\omega_1}\left[\dfrac{(a^2 - \omega_1^2 + ag + d)^2 + \omega_1^2(2a+g)^2}{(a-b)^2 + \omega_1^2}\right]^{1/2} \qquad B = \dfrac{b^2 + bg + d}{(a-b)^2 + \omega_1^2}$ $\alpha = \arctan \dfrac{\omega_1(2a+g)}{a^2 - \omega_1^2 + ag + d} - \arctan \dfrac{\omega_1}{a-b}$
2.9	$\dfrac{1}{s(s-b)[(s-a)^2 + \omega_1^2]}$	$A = \dfrac{1}{\omega_1(a^2 + \omega_1^2)^{1/2}[(a-b)^2 + \omega_1^2]^{1/2}} \qquad K = -\dfrac{1}{b(a^2 + \omega_1^2)}$ $B = \dfrac{1}{b[(b-a)^2 + \omega_1^2]}$ $\alpha = -\arctan \dfrac{\omega_1}{a-b} - \arctan \dfrac{\omega_1}{a}$
2.10	$\dfrac{s+d}{s(s-b)[(s-a)^2 + \omega_1^2]}$	$A = \dfrac{1}{\omega_1(a^2 + \omega_1^2)^{1/2}}\left[\dfrac{(d+a)^2 + \omega_1^2}{(a-b)^2 + \omega_1^2}\right]^{1/2} \qquad K = -\dfrac{d}{b(a^2 + \omega_1^2)}$ $B = \dfrac{b+d}{b[(b-a)^2 + \omega_1^2]}$ $\alpha = \arctan \dfrac{\omega_1}{a+d} - \arctan \dfrac{\omega_1}{a-b} - \arctan \dfrac{\omega_1}{a}$

Middle column (spanning rows 2.6–2.8): $A e^{at} \sin(\omega_1 t + \alpha) + B e^{bt}$

Middle column (spanning rows 2.9–2.10): $A e^{at} \sin(\omega_1 t + \alpha) + B e^{bt} + K$

Table D-3 *Laplace-transform pairs involving rational algebraic functions* $F(s) = D_1(s)/D(s)$ *(Continued)*

No.	F(s)	f(t) (t > 0)	
2.11	$\dfrac{s^2 + gs + d}{s(s-b)[(s-a)^2 + \omega_1^2]}$		$A = \dfrac{1}{\omega_1}\left\{\dfrac{(a^2 - \omega_1^2 + ag + d)^2 + \omega_1^2(2a + g)^2}{(a^2 + \omega_1^2)[(a-b)^2 + \omega_1^2]}\right\}^{1/2}$ $B = \dfrac{b^2 + bg + d}{b[(b-a)^2 + \omega_1^2]} \qquad K = -\dfrac{d}{b(a^2 + \omega_1^2)}$ $\alpha = \arctan\dfrac{\omega_1(2a + g)}{a^2 - \omega_1^2 + ag + d} - \arctan\dfrac{\omega_1}{a - b} - \arctan\dfrac{\omega_1}{a}$
2.12	$\dfrac{1}{[(s-a)^2 + \omega_1^2](s^2 + \omega_2^2)}$		$A = \dfrac{1}{\omega_1}\dfrac{1}{[(a^2 + \omega_1^2 - \omega_2^2)^2 + 4a^2\omega_2^2]^{1/2}}$ $B = \dfrac{1}{\omega_2}\dfrac{1}{[(a^2 + \omega_1^2 - \omega_2^2)^2 + 4a^2\omega_2^2]^{1/2}}$ $\alpha = -\arctan\dfrac{2a\omega_1}{a^2 - \omega_1^2 + \omega_2^2}$ $\beta = \arctan\dfrac{2a\omega_2}{a^2 + \omega_1^2 - \omega_2^2}$
2.13	$\dfrac{s + d}{[(s-a)^2 + \omega_1^2](s^2 + \omega_2^2)}$	$Ae^{at}\sin(\omega_1 t + \alpha) + B\sin(\omega_2 t + \beta)$	$A = \dfrac{1}{\omega_1}\left[\dfrac{(a+d)^2 + \omega_1^2}{(a^2 + \omega_1^2 - \omega_2^2)^2 + 4a^2\omega_2^2}\right]^{1/2}$ $B = \dfrac{1}{\omega_2}\left[\dfrac{d^2 + \omega_2^2}{(a^2 + \omega_1^2 - \omega_2^2)^2 + 4a^2\omega_2^2}\right]^{1/2}$ $\alpha = \arctan\dfrac{\omega_1}{a + d}$ $\qquad - \arctan\dfrac{2a\omega_1}{a^2 - \omega_1^2 + \omega_2^2}$ $\beta = \arctan\dfrac{\omega_2}{d}$ $\qquad + \arctan\dfrac{2a\omega_2}{a^2 + \omega_1^2 - \omega_2^2}$
2.14	$\dfrac{s^2 + gs + d}{[(s-a)^2 + \omega_1^2](s^2 + \omega_2^2)}$		$A = \dfrac{1}{\omega_1}\left[\dfrac{(a^2 - \omega_1^2 + ag + d)^2 + \omega_1^2(2a + g)^2}{(a^2 + \omega_1^2 - \omega_2^2)^2 + 4a^2\omega_2^2}\right]^{1/2}$ $B = \dfrac{1}{\omega_2}\left[\dfrac{(d - \omega_2^2)^2 + g^2\omega_2^2}{(a^2 + \omega_1^2 - \omega_2^2)^2 + 4a^2\omega_2^2}\right]^{1/2}$ $\alpha = \arctan\dfrac{\omega_1(2a + g)}{a^2 - \omega_1^2 + ag + d}$ $\qquad - \arctan\dfrac{2a\omega_1}{a^2 - \omega_1^2 + \omega_2^2}$ $\beta = \arctan\dfrac{g\omega_2}{d - \omega_2^2}$ $\qquad + \arctan\dfrac{2a\omega_2}{a^2 + \omega_1^2 - \omega_2^2}$
3.1	$\dfrac{1}{s^2}$	t	

	$F(s)$				
3.2	$\dfrac{1}{(s-a)^2}$	$(A + A_1 t)e^{at}$	$A = 0$	$A_1 = 1$	
3.3	$\dfrac{s+d}{(s-a)^2}$		$A = 1$	$A_1 = a + d$	
3.4	$\dfrac{1}{s^2(s-a)}$	$Ae^{at} + K + K_1 t$	$A = \dfrac{1}{a^2}$	$K = -A$	$K_1 = -\dfrac{1}{a}$
3.5	$\dfrac{s+d}{s^2(s-a)}$		$A = \dfrac{a+d}{a^2}$	$K = -A$	$K_1 = -\dfrac{d}{a}$
3.6	$\dfrac{s^2+gs+d}{s^2(s-a)}$		$A = \dfrac{a^2+ag+d}{a^2}$	$K = 1 - A$	$K_1 = -\dfrac{d}{a}$
3.7	$\dfrac{1}{s(s-a)^2}$	$(A + A_1 t)e^{at} + K$	$A = -\dfrac{1}{a^2}$	$A_1 = \dfrac{1}{a}$	$K = -A$
3.8	$\dfrac{s+d}{s(s-a)^2}$		$A = -\dfrac{d}{a^2}$	$A_1 = \dfrac{a+d}{a}$	$K = -A$
3.9	$\dfrac{s^2+gs+d}{s(s-a)^2}$		$A = \dfrac{a^2-d}{a^2}$	$A_1 = \dfrac{a^2+ag+d}{a}$	$K = 1 - A$
3.10	$\dfrac{1}{(s-a)^2(s-b)}$	$(A + A_1 t)e^{at} + Be^{bt}$	$A = -\dfrac{1}{(a-b)^2}$	$A_1 = \dfrac{1}{a-b}$	$B = -A$
3.11	$\dfrac{s+d}{(s-a)^2(s-b)}$		$A = -\dfrac{b+d}{(a-b)^2}$	$A_1 = \dfrac{a+d}{a-b}$	$B = -A$

Table D-3 Laplace-transform pairs involving rational algebraic functions $F(s) = D_1(s)/D(s)$ (Continued)

No.	$F(s)$	$f(t)$ $(t > 0)$			
3.12	$\dfrac{s^2 + gs + d}{(s-a)^2(s-b)}$		$A = \dfrac{a^2 - 2ab - bg - d}{(a-b)^2}$	$A_1 = \dfrac{a^2 + ag + d}{a-b}$	$B = \dfrac{b^2 + bg + d}{(a-b)^2}$
3.13	$\dfrac{1}{s^2(s-a)(s-b)}$	$Ae^{at} + Be^{bt} + K + K_1 t$	$A = \dfrac{1}{a^2(a-b)}$ $K = \dfrac{a+b}{a^2b^2}$	$B = \dfrac{1}{b^2(b-a)}$ $K_1 = \dfrac{1}{ab}$	
3.14	$\dfrac{s+d}{s^2(s-a)(s-b)}$		$A = \dfrac{a+d}{a^2(a-b)}$ $K = \dfrac{ab + d(a+b)}{a^2b^2}$	$B = \dfrac{b+d}{b^2(b-a)}$ $K_1 = \dfrac{d}{ab}$	
3.15	$\dfrac{s^2 + gs + d}{s^2(s-a)(s-b)}$		$A = \dfrac{a^2 + ag + d}{a^2(a-b)}$ $K = \dfrac{abg + d(a+b)}{a^2b^2}$	$B = \dfrac{b^2 + bg + d}{b^2(b-a)}$ $K_1 = \dfrac{d}{ab}$	
3.16	$\dfrac{1}{s(s-a)^2(s-b)}$	$(A + A_1 t)e^{at} + Be^{bt} + K$	$A = \dfrac{b - 2a}{a^2(a-b)^2}$ $B = \dfrac{1}{b(a-b)^2}$	$A_1 = \dfrac{1}{a(a-b)}$ $K = -\dfrac{1}{a^2b}$	
3.17	$\dfrac{s+d}{s(s-a)^2(s-b)}$		$A = -\dfrac{a^2 + 2ad - bd}{a^2(a-b)^2}$ $B = \dfrac{b+d}{b(a-b)^2}$	$A_1 = \dfrac{a+d}{a(a-b)}$ $K = -\dfrac{d}{a^2b}$	
3.18	$\dfrac{s^2 + gs + d}{s(s-a)^2(s-b)}$		$A = -\dfrac{a^2(b+g) + d(2a-b)}{a^2(a-b)^2}$ $B = \dfrac{b^2 + bg + d}{b(a-b)^2}$	$A_1 = \dfrac{a^2 + ag + d}{a(a-b)}$ $K = -\dfrac{d}{a^2b}$	

3.19	$\dfrac{1}{(s-a)^2(s-b)(s-c)}$	$(A + A_1 t)e^{at} + Be^{bt} + Ce^{ct}$	$A = \dfrac{(b+c)-2a}{(a-b)^2(a-c)^2}$ $\quad A_1 = \dfrac{1}{(a-b)(a-c)}$ $B = \dfrac{1}{(b-a)^2(b-c)}$ $\quad C = \dfrac{1}{(c-a)^2(c-b)}$
3.20	$\dfrac{s+d}{(s-a)^2(s-b)(s-c)}$		$A = -\dfrac{a^2+2ad-d(b+c)-bc}{(a-b)^2(a-c)^2}$ $\quad A_1 = \dfrac{a+d}{(a-b)(a-c)}$ $B = \dfrac{b+d}{(b-a)^2(b-c)}$ $\quad C = \dfrac{c+d}{(c-a)^2(c-b)}$
3.21	$\dfrac{1}{s^2(s-a)^2}$	$(A + A_1 t)e^{at} + K + K_1 t$	$A = -\dfrac{2}{a^3}$ $\quad A_1 = \dfrac{1}{a^2}$ $K = -A$ $\quad K_1 = \dfrac{1}{a^2}$
3.22	$\dfrac{s+d}{s^2(s-a)^2}$		$A = -\dfrac{a+2d}{a^3}$ $\quad A_1 = \dfrac{a+d}{a^2}$ $K = -A$ $\quad K_1 = \dfrac{d}{a^2}$
3.23	$\dfrac{s^2+gs+d}{s^2(s-a)^2}$		$A = -\dfrac{ag+2d}{a^3}$ $\quad A_1 = \dfrac{a^2+ag+d}{a^2}$ $K = -A$ $\quad K_1 = \dfrac{d}{a^2}$
3.24	$\dfrac{1}{(s-a)^2(s-b)^2}$		$A = -\dfrac{2}{(a-b)^3}$ $\quad A_1 = \dfrac{1}{(a-b)^2}$ $B = -A$ $\quad B_1 = \dfrac{1}{(a-b)^2}$

Table D-3 *Laplace-transform pairs involving rational algebraic functions* $F(s) = D_1(s)/D(s)$ *(Continued)*

No.	$F(s)$	$f(t)\ (t>0)$	Constants
3.25	$\dfrac{s+d}{(s-a)^2(s-b)^2}$	$(A + A_1 t)e^{at} + (B + B_1 t)e^{bt}$	$A = -\dfrac{a+b+2d}{(a-b)^3}$ $\qquad A_1 = \dfrac{a+d}{(a-b)^2}$ $B = -A$ $\qquad B_1 = \dfrac{b+d}{(a-b)^2}$
3.26	$\dfrac{s^2+gs+d}{(s-a)^2(s-b)^2}$	$(A + A_1 t)e^{at} + (B + B_1 t)e^{bt}$	$A = -\dfrac{(a+b)g+2(ab+d)}{(a-b)^3}$ $\qquad A_1 = \dfrac{a^2+ag+d}{(a-b)^2}$ $B = -A$ $\qquad B_1 = \dfrac{b^2+bg+d}{(a-b)^2}$
3.27	$\dfrac{1}{(s-a)^3(s-b)}$	$(A + A_1 t + A_2 t^2)e^{at} + Be^{bt}$	$A = \dfrac{1}{(a-b)^3}$ $\quad A_1 = -\dfrac{1}{(a-b)^2}$ $\quad A_2 = \dfrac{1}{2(a-b)}$ $\quad B = -A$
3.28	$\dfrac{s+d}{(s-a)^3(s-b)}$	$(A + A_1 t + A_2 t^2)e^{at} + Be^{bt}$	$A = \dfrac{b+d}{(a-b)^3}$ $\quad A_1 = -\dfrac{b+d}{(a-b)^2}$ $\quad A_2 = \dfrac{a+d}{2(a-b)}$ $\quad B = -A$
3.29	$\dfrac{s^2+gs+d}{s^2(s-a)^2}$	$(A + A_1 t + A_2 t^2)e^{at} + K + K_1 t$	$A = \dfrac{ag+3d}{a^4}$ $\quad A_1 = -\dfrac{ag+2d}{a^3}$ $\quad A_2 = \dfrac{a^2+ag+d}{2a^2}$ $K = -A$ $\qquad K_1 = -\dfrac{d}{a^3}$
4.1	$\dfrac{1}{s^2[(s-a)^2+\omega_1^2]}$	$Ae^{at}\sin(\omega_1 t + \alpha) + K + K_1 t$	$A = \dfrac{1}{\omega_1(a^2+\omega_1^2)^{1/2}}$ $\qquad \alpha = -2\arctan\dfrac{\omega_1}{a}$ $K = \dfrac{2a}{(a^2+\omega_1^2)^2}$ $\qquad K_1 = \dfrac{1}{a^2+\omega_1^2}$
4.2	$\dfrac{s+d}{s^2[(s-a)^2+\omega_1^2]}$	$Ae^{at}\sin(\omega_1 t + \alpha) + K + K_1 t$	$A = \dfrac{[(a+d)^2+\omega_1^2]^{1/2}}{\omega_1(a^2+\omega_1^2)}$ $\qquad \alpha = \arctan\dfrac{\omega_1}{a+d} - 2\arctan\dfrac{\omega_1}{a}$ $K = \dfrac{a^2+\omega_1^2+2ad}{(a^2+\omega_1^2)^2}$ $\qquad K_1 = \dfrac{d}{a^2+\omega_1^2}$
4.3	$\dfrac{s^2+gs+d}{s^2[(s-a)^2+\omega_1^2]}$	$Ae^{at}\sin(\omega_1 t + \alpha) + K + K_1 t$	$A = \dfrac{[(a^2-\omega_1^2+ag+d)^2+\omega_1^2(2a+g)^2]^{1/2}}{\omega_1(a^2+\omega_1^2)}$ $\alpha = \arctan\dfrac{\omega_1(2a+g)}{a^2-\omega_1^2+ag+d} - 2\arctan\dfrac{\omega_1}{a}$ $K = \dfrac{(a^2+\omega_1^2)g+2ad}{(a^2+\omega_1^2)^2}$ $\qquad K_1 = \dfrac{d}{a^2+\omega_1^2}$

4.4	$\dfrac{1}{(s-b)^2[(s-a)^2+\omega_1^2]}$	$Ae^{at}\sin(\omega_1 t+\alpha)+(B+B_1 t)e^{bt}$	$A=\dfrac{1}{\omega_1[(a-b)^2+\omega_1^2]}$ $\quad \alpha=-2\arctan\dfrac{\omega_1}{a-b}$ $B=\dfrac{2(a-b)}{[(a-b)^2+\omega_1^2]^2}$ $\quad B_1=\dfrac{1}{(a-b)^2+\omega_1^2}$
4.5	$\dfrac{s+d}{(s-b)^2[(s-a)^2+\omega_1^2]}$		$A=\dfrac{[(a+d)^2+\omega_1^2]^{1/2}}{\omega_1[(a-b)^2+\omega_1^2]}$ $\quad \alpha=\arctan\dfrac{\omega_1}{a+d}-2\arctan\dfrac{\omega_1}{a-b}$ $B=\dfrac{(a-b)^2+\omega_1^2+2(a-b)(b+d)}{[(a-b)^2+\omega_1^2]^2}$ $\quad B_1=\dfrac{b+d}{(a-b)^2+\omega_1^2}$
4.6	$\dfrac{s^2+gs+d}{(s-b)^2[(s-a)^2+\omega_1^2]}$		$A=\dfrac{[(a^2-\omega_1^2+ag+d)^2+\omega_1^2(2a+g)^2]^{1/2}}{\omega_1[(a-b)^2+\omega_1^2]}$ $\quad \alpha=\arctan\dfrac{\omega_1(2a+g)}{a^2-\omega_1^2+ag+d}$ $-2\arctan\dfrac{\omega_1}{a-b}$ $B=\dfrac{[(a-b)^2+\omega_1^2](2b+g)+2(a-b)(b^2+bg+d)}{[(a-b)^2+\omega_1^2]^2}$ $\quad B_1=\dfrac{b^2+bg+d}{(a-b)^2+\omega_1^2}$
4.7	$\dfrac{1}{[(s-a)^2+\omega_1^2]^2}$	$\dfrac{1}{2\omega_1^3}e^{at}(\sin\omega_1 t-\omega_1 t\cos\omega_1 t)$	
4.8	$\dfrac{s-a}{[(s-a)^2+\omega_1^2]^2}$	$\dfrac{1}{2\omega_1}te^{at}\sin\omega_1 t$	
4.9	$\dfrac{(s-a)^2-\omega_1^2}{[(s-a)^2+\omega_1^2]^2}$	$te^{at}\cos\omega_1 t$	

Table D-4 Table of Laplace transforms†

	$f(s)$	$F(t)$
1	$\dfrac{1}{s}$	1
2	$\dfrac{1}{s^2}$	t
3	$\dfrac{1}{s^n}$ $(n = 1, 2, \ldots)$	$\dfrac{t^{n-1}}{(n-1)!}$
4	$\dfrac{1}{\sqrt{s}}$	$\dfrac{1}{\sqrt{\pi t}}$
5	$s^{-\frac{3}{2}}$	$2\sqrt{\dfrac{t}{\pi}}$
6	$s^{-(n+\frac{1}{2})}$ $(n = 1, 2, \ldots)$	$\dfrac{2^n t^{n-\frac{1}{2}}}{1 \times 3 \times 5 \cdots (2n-1)\sqrt{\pi}}$
7	$\dfrac{\Gamma(k)}{s^k}$ $(k > 0)$	t^{k-1}
8	$\dfrac{1}{s-a}$	e^{at}
9	$\dfrac{1}{(s-a)^2}$	te^{at}
10	$\dfrac{1}{(s-a)^n}$ $(n = 1, 2, \ldots)$	$\dfrac{1}{(n-1)!}t^{n-1}e^{at}$
11	$\dfrac{\Gamma(k)}{(s-a)^k}$ $(k > 0)$	$t^{k-1}e^{at}$
12*	$\dfrac{1}{(s-a)(s-b)}$	$\dfrac{1}{a-b}(e^{at} - e^{bt})$
13*	$\dfrac{s}{(s-a)(s-b)}$	$\dfrac{1}{a-b}(ae^{at} - be^{bt})$
14*	$\dfrac{1}{(s-a)(s-b)(s-c)}$	$-\dfrac{(b-c)e^{at} + (c-a)e^{bt} + (a-b)e^{ct}}{(a-b)(b-c)(c-a)}$
15	$\dfrac{1}{s^2 + a^2}$	$\dfrac{1}{a}\sin at$
16	$\dfrac{s}{s^2 + a^2}$	$\cos at$

* Here a, b, and (in 14) c represent distinct constants.

† From Ruel V. Churchill, *Operational Mathematics*, 2d ed., McGraw-Hill, New York, 1958.

Table D-4   Table of Laplace transforms (*Continued*)

	$f(s)$	$F(t)$
17	$\dfrac{1}{s^2 - a^2}$	$\dfrac{1}{a} \sinh at$
18	$\dfrac{s}{s^2 - a^2}$	$\cosh at$
19	$\dfrac{1}{s(s^2 + a^2)}$	$\dfrac{1}{a^2}(1 - \cos at)$
20	$\dfrac{1}{s^2(s^2 + a^2)}$	$\dfrac{1}{a^3}(at - \sin at)$
21	$\dfrac{1}{(s^2 + a^2)^2}$	$\dfrac{1}{2a^3}(\sin at - at \cos at)$
22	$\dfrac{s}{(s^2 + a^2)^2}$	$\dfrac{t}{2a} \sin at$
23	$\dfrac{s^2}{(s^2 + a^2)^2}$	$\dfrac{1}{2a}(\sin at + at \cos at)$
24	$\dfrac{s^2 - a^2}{(s^2 + a^2)^2}$	$t \cos at$
25	$\dfrac{s}{(s^2 + a^2)(s^2 + b^2)}\ (a^2 \neq b^2)$	$\dfrac{\cos at - \cos bt}{b^2 - a^2}$
26	$\dfrac{1}{(s - a)^2 + b^2}$	$\dfrac{1}{b} e^{at} \sin bt$
27	$\dfrac{s - a}{(s - a)^2 + b^2}$	$e^{at} \cos bt$
28	$\dfrac{3a^2}{s^3 + a^3}$	$e^{-at} - e^{at/2}\left(\cos \dfrac{at \sqrt{3}}{2} - \sqrt{3} \sin \dfrac{at \sqrt{3}}{2}\right)$
29	$\dfrac{4a^3}{s^4 + 4a^4}$	$\sin at \cosh at - \cos at \sinh at$
30	$\dfrac{s}{s^4 + 4a^4}$	$\dfrac{1}{2a^2} \sin at \sinh at$
31	$\dfrac{1}{s^4 - a^4}$	$\dfrac{1}{2a^3}(\sinh at - \sin at)$
32	$\dfrac{s}{s^4 - a^4}$	$\dfrac{1}{2a^2}(\cosh at - \cos at)$
33	$\dfrac{8a^3 s^2}{(s^2 + a^2)^3}$	$(1 + a^2 t^2) \sin at - at \cos at$
34	$\dfrac{1}{s}\left(\dfrac{s - 1}{s}\right)^n$	$\dfrac{e^t}{n!}\dfrac{d^n}{dt^n}(t^n e^{-t})$
35	$\dfrac{s}{(s - a)^{\frac{3}{2}}}$	$\dfrac{1}{\sqrt{\pi !}} e^{at}(1 + 2at)$
36	$\sqrt{s - a} - \sqrt{s - b}$	$\dfrac{1}{2\sqrt{\pi t^3}}(e^{bt} - e^{at})$

Table D-4   Table of Laplace transforms (*Continued*)

	$f(s)$	$F(t)$
37	$\dfrac{1}{\sqrt{s} + a}$	$\dfrac{1}{\sqrt{\pi t}} - ae^{a^2t}\,\text{erfc}\,(a\,\sqrt{t})$
38	$\dfrac{\sqrt{s}}{s - a^2}$	$\dfrac{1}{\sqrt{\pi t}} + ae^{a^2t}\,\text{erf}\,(a\,\sqrt{t})$
39	$\dfrac{\sqrt{s}}{s + a^2}$	$\dfrac{1}{\sqrt{\pi t}} - \dfrac{2a}{\sqrt{\pi}}\,e^{-a^2t}\displaystyle\int_0^{a\sqrt{t}} e^{\lambda^2}\,d\lambda$
40	$\dfrac{1}{\sqrt{s}\,(s - a^2)}$	$\dfrac{1}{a}\,e^{a^2t}\,\text{erf}\,(a\,\sqrt{t})$
41	$\dfrac{1}{\sqrt{s}\,(s + a^2)}$	$\dfrac{2}{a\,\sqrt{\pi}}\,e^{-a^2t}\displaystyle\int_0^{a\sqrt{t}} e^{\lambda^2}\,d\lambda$
42	$\dfrac{b^2 - a^2}{(s - a^2)(b + \sqrt{s})}$	$e^{a^2t}[b - a\,\text{erf}\,(a\,\sqrt{t})]$ $\qquad - be^{b^2t}\,\text{erfc}\,(b\,\sqrt{t})$
43	$\dfrac{1}{\sqrt{s}\,(\sqrt{s} + a)}$	$e^{a^2t}\,\text{erfc}\,(a\,\sqrt{t})$
44	$\dfrac{1}{(s + a)\,\sqrt{s + b}}$	$\dfrac{1}{\sqrt{b - a}}\,e^{-at}\,\text{erf}\,(\sqrt{b - a}\,\sqrt{t})$
45	$\dfrac{b^2 - a^2}{\sqrt{s}\,(s - a^2)(\sqrt{s} + b)}$	$e^{a^2t}\left[\dfrac{b}{a}\,\text{erf}\,(a\,\sqrt{t}) - 1\right]$ $\qquad + e^{b^2t}\,\text{erfc}\,(b\,\sqrt{t})$
46*	$\dfrac{(1 - s)^n}{s^{n+\frac{1}{2}}}$	$\dfrac{n!}{(2n)!\,\sqrt{\pi t}}\,H_{2n}\,(\sqrt{t})$
47	$\dfrac{(1 - s)^n}{s^{n+\frac{3}{2}}}$	$-\dfrac{n!}{\sqrt{\pi}\,(2n + 1)!}\,H_{2n+1}(\sqrt{t})$
48†	$\dfrac{\sqrt{s + 2a}}{\sqrt{s}} - 1$	$ae^{-at}[I_1(at) + I_0(at)]$
49	$\dfrac{1}{\sqrt{s + a}\,\sqrt{s + b}}$	$e^{-\frac{1}{2}(a+b)t}I_0\left(\dfrac{a - b}{2}\,t\right)$
50	$\dfrac{\Gamma(k)}{(s + a)^k(s + b)^k}\;(k > 0)$	$\sqrt{\pi}\left(\dfrac{t}{a - b}\right)^{k-\frac{1}{2}} e^{-\frac{1}{2}(a+b)t}$ $\qquad\qquad \times\,I_{k-\frac{1}{2}}\left(\dfrac{a - b}{2}\,t\right)$
51	$\dfrac{1}{(s + a)^{\frac{1}{2}}(s + b)^{\frac{3}{2}}}$	$te^{-\frac{1}{2}(a+b)t}\left[I_0\left(\dfrac{a - b}{2}\,t\right)\right.$ $\qquad\qquad \left. + I_1\left(\dfrac{a - b}{2}\,t\right)\right]$
52	$\dfrac{\sqrt{s + 2a} - \sqrt{s}}{\sqrt{s + 2a} + \sqrt{s}}$	$\dfrac{1}{t}\,e^{-at}I_1(at)$

* $H_n(x)$ is the Hermite polynomial.

† $I_n(x) = i^{-n}J_n(ix)$, where J_n is Bessel's function of the first kind.

Table D-4   Table of Laplace transforms (*Continued*)

	$f(s)$	$F(t)$
53	$\dfrac{(a-b)^k}{(\sqrt{s+a}+\sqrt{s+b})^{2k}}$ $(k>0)$	$\dfrac{k}{t}\,e^{-\frac{1}{2}(a+b)t}I_k\left(\dfrac{a-b}{2}\,t\right)$
54	$\dfrac{(\sqrt{s+a}+\sqrt{s})^{-2\nu}}{\sqrt{s}\,\sqrt{s+a}}$ $(\nu>-1)$	$\dfrac{1}{a^\nu}\,e^{-\frac{1}{2}at}I_\nu\left(\dfrac{1}{2}\,at\right)$
55	$\dfrac{1}{\sqrt{s^2+a^2}}$	$J_0(at)$
56	$\dfrac{(\sqrt{s^2+a^2}-s)^\nu}{\sqrt{s^2+a^2}}$ $(\nu>-1)$	$a^\nu J_\nu(at)$
57	$\dfrac{1}{(s^2+a^2)^k}$ $(k>0)$	$\dfrac{\sqrt{\pi}}{\Gamma(k)}\left(\dfrac{t}{2a}\right)^{k-\frac{1}{2}}J_{k-\frac{1}{2}}(at)$
58	$(\sqrt{s^2+a^2}-s)^k$ $(k>0)$	$\dfrac{ka^k}{t}\,J_k(at)$
59	$\dfrac{(s-\sqrt{s^2-a^2})^\nu}{\sqrt{s^2-a^2}}$ $(\nu>-1)$	$a^\nu I_\nu(at)$
60	$\dfrac{1}{(s^2-a^2)^k}$ $(k>0)$	$\dfrac{\sqrt{\pi}}{\Gamma(k)}\left(\dfrac{t}{2a}\right)^{k-\frac{1}{2}}I_{k-\frac{1}{2}}(at)$
61	$\dfrac{e^{-ks}}{s}$	$\begin{cases}0 \text{ when } 0<t<k\\ 1 \text{ when } t>k\end{cases}$
62	$\dfrac{e^{-ks}}{s^2}$	$\begin{cases}0 \quad\text{ when } 0<t<k\\ t-k \text{ when } t>k\end{cases}$
63	$\dfrac{e^{-ks}}{s^\mu}$ $(\mu>0)$	$\begin{cases}0 \qquad\quad\text{ when } 0<t<k\\ \dfrac{(t-k)^{\mu-1}}{\Gamma(\mu)} \text{ when } t>k\end{cases}$
64	$\dfrac{1-e^{-ks}}{s}$	$\begin{cases}1 \text{ when } 0<t<k\\ 0 \text{ when } t>k\end{cases}$
65	$\dfrac{1}{s(1-e^{-ks})}=\dfrac{1+\coth\frac{1}{2}ks}{2s}$	$1+[t/k]=n$ $\quad$ when $(n-1)k<t<nk$ $\quad\quad$ $(n=1,2,\ldots)$ **(Fig. D-1)**
66	$\dfrac{1}{s(e^{ks}-a)}$	$\begin{cases}0 \quad\text{ when } 0<t<k\\ 1+a+a^2+\cdots+a^{n-1}\\ \quad\text{ when } nk<t<(n+1)k\\ \qquad\qquad (n=1,2,\ldots)\end{cases}$
67	$\dfrac{1}{s}\tanh ks$	$M(2k,t)=(-1)^{n-1}$ $\quad$ when $2k(n-1)<t<2kn$ $\quad\quad$ $(n=1,2,\ldots)$ **(Fig. D-2)**
68	$\dfrac{1}{s(1+e^{-ks})}$	$\dfrac{1}{2}M(k,t)+\dfrac{1}{2}=\dfrac{1-(-1)^n}{2}$ $\quad$ when $(n-1)k<t<nk$
69	$\dfrac{1}{s^2}\tanh ks$	$H(2k,t)$ **(Fig. D-3)**

Table D-4 **Table of Laplace transforms** (*Continued*)

	$f(s)$	$F(t)$
70	$\dfrac{1}{s \sinh ks}$	$F(t) = 2(n - 1)$ when $(2n - 3)k < t < (2n - 1)k$ $(t > 0)$
71	$\dfrac{1}{s \cosh ks}$	$M(2k, t + 3k) + 1 = 1 + (-1)^n$ when $(2n - 3)k < t < (2n - 1)k$ $(t > 0)$
72	$\dfrac{1}{s} \coth ks$	$F(t) = 2n - 1$ when $2k(n - 1) < t < 2kn$
73	$\dfrac{k}{s^2 + k^2} \coth \dfrac{\pi s}{2k}$	$\lvert \sin kt \rvert$
74	$\dfrac{1}{(s^2 + 1)(1 - e^{-\pi s})}$	$\begin{cases} \sin t \text{ when} \\ \quad (2n - 2)\pi < t < (2n - 1)\pi \\ 0 \quad \text{when} \\ \quad (2n - 1)\pi < t < 2n\pi \end{cases}$
75	$\dfrac{1}{s} e^{-(k/s)}$	$J_0(2 \sqrt{kt})$
76	$\dfrac{1}{\sqrt{s}} e^{-(k/s)}$	$\dfrac{1}{\sqrt{\pi t}} \cos 2 \sqrt{kt}$
77	$\dfrac{1}{\sqrt{s}} e^{k/s}$	$\dfrac{1}{\sqrt{\pi t}} \cosh 2 \sqrt{kt}$
78	$\dfrac{1}{s^{\frac{3}{2}}} e^{-(k/s)}$	$\dfrac{1}{\sqrt{\pi k}} \sin 2 \sqrt{kt}$
79	$\dfrac{1}{s^{\frac{3}{2}}} e^{k/s}$	$\dfrac{1}{\sqrt{\pi k}} \sinh 2 \sqrt{kt}$
80	$\dfrac{1}{s^\mu} e^{-(k/s)} \; (\mu > 0)$	$\left(\dfrac{t}{k}\right)^{(\mu-1)/2} J_{\mu-1}(2 \sqrt{kt})$
81	$\dfrac{1}{s^\mu} e^{k/s} \; (\mu > 0)$	$\left(\dfrac{t}{k}\right)^{(\mu-1)/2} I_{\mu-1}(2 \sqrt{kt})$
82	$e^{-k\sqrt{s}} \; (k > 0)$	$\dfrac{k}{2 \sqrt{\pi t^3}} \exp\left(-\dfrac{k^2}{4t}\right)$
83	$\dfrac{1}{s} e^{-k\sqrt{s}} \; (k \geqq 0)$	$\operatorname{erfc}\left(\dfrac{k}{2 \sqrt{t}}\right)$
84	$\dfrac{1}{\sqrt{s}} e^{-k\sqrt{s}} \; (k \geqq 0)$	$\dfrac{1}{\sqrt{\pi t}} \exp\left(-\dfrac{k^2}{4t}\right)$
85	$s^{-\frac{3}{2}} e^{-k\sqrt{s}} \; (k \geqq 0)$	$2 \sqrt{\dfrac{t}{\pi}} \exp\left(-\dfrac{k^2}{4t}\right)$ $\qquad\qquad - k \operatorname{erfc}\left(\dfrac{k}{2 \sqrt{t}}\right)$
86	$\dfrac{ae^{-k\sqrt{s}}}{s(a + \sqrt{s})} \; (k \geqq 0)$	$-e^{ak}e^{a^2 t} \operatorname{erfc}\left(a \sqrt{t} + \dfrac{k}{2 \sqrt{t}}\right)$ $\qquad\qquad + \operatorname{erfc}\left(\dfrac{k}{2 \sqrt{t}}\right)$

Table D-4   Table of Laplace transforms (*Continued*)

	$f(s)$	$F(t)$
87	$\dfrac{e^{-k\sqrt{s}}}{\sqrt{s}\,(a + \sqrt{s})}$ $(k \geqq 0)$	$e^{ak}e^{a^2 t}\,\text{erfc}\left(a\,\sqrt{t} + \dfrac{k}{2\,\sqrt{t}}\right)$
88	$\dfrac{e^{-k\sqrt{s(s+a)}}}{\sqrt{s(s+a)}}$	$\begin{cases} 0 & \text{when } 0 < t < k \\ e^{-\frac{1}{2}at}I_0(\frac{1}{2}a\,\sqrt{t^2 - k^2}) & \\ & \text{when } t > k \end{cases}$
89	$\dfrac{e^{-k\sqrt{s^2+a^2}}}{\sqrt{s^2 + a^2}}$	$\begin{cases} 0 & \text{when } 0 < t < k \\ J_0(a\,\sqrt{t^2 - k^2}) & \text{when } t > k \end{cases}$
90	$\dfrac{e^{-k\sqrt{s^2-a^2}}}{\sqrt{s^2 - a^2}}$	$\begin{cases} 0 & \text{when } 0 < t < k \\ I_0(a\,\sqrt{t^2 - k^2}) & \text{when } t > k \end{cases}$
91	$\dfrac{e^{-k(\sqrt{s^2+a^2}-s)}}{\sqrt{s^2 + a^2}}$ $(k \geqq 0)$	$J_0(a\,\sqrt{t^2 + 2kt})$
92	$e^{-ks} - e^{-k\sqrt{s^2+a^2}}$	$\begin{cases} 0 & \text{when } 0 < t < k \\ \dfrac{ak}{\sqrt{t^2 - k^2}}\,J_1(a\,\sqrt{t^2 - k^2}) & \\ & \text{when } t > k \end{cases}$
93	$e^{-k\sqrt{s^2-a^2}} - e^{-ks}$	$\begin{cases} 0 & \text{when } 0 < t < k \\ \dfrac{ak}{\sqrt{t^2 - k^2}}\,I_1(a\,\sqrt{t^2 - k^2}) & \\ & \text{when } t > k \end{cases}$
94	$\dfrac{a^\nu e^{-k\sqrt{s^2+a^2}}}{\sqrt{s^2 + a^2}\,(\sqrt{s^2 + a^2} + s)^\nu}$ $(\nu > -1)$	$\begin{cases} 0 & \text{when } 0 < t < k \\ \left(\dfrac{t-k}{t+k}\right)^{\frac{1}{2}\nu} J_\nu(a\,\sqrt{t^2 - k^2}) & \\ & \text{when } t > k \end{cases}$
95	$\dfrac{1}{s}\log s$	$\Gamma'(1) - \log t$ $[\Gamma'(1) = -0.5772]$
96	$\dfrac{1}{s^k}\log s$ $(k > 0)$	$t^{k-1}\left\{\dfrac{\Gamma'(k)}{[\Gamma(k)]^2} - \dfrac{\log t}{\Gamma(k)}\right\}$
97	$\dfrac{\log s}{s - a}$ $(a > 0)$	$e^{at}[\log a - \text{Ei}\,(-at)]$
98	$\dfrac{\log s}{s^2 + 1}$	$\cos t\,\text{Si}\,t - \sin t\,\text{Ci}\,t$
99	$\dfrac{s\log s}{s^2 + 1}$	$-\sin t\,\text{Si}\,t - \cos t\,\text{Ci}\,t$
100	$\dfrac{1}{s}\log(1 + ks)$ $(k > 0)$	$-\,\text{Ei}\left(-\dfrac{t}{k}\right)$

Table D-4   Table of Laplace transforms (*Continued*)

	$f(s)$	$F(t)$
101	$\log \dfrac{s-a}{s-b}$	$\dfrac{1}{t}\,(e^{bt}-e^{at})$
102	$\dfrac{1}{s}\log\,(1+k^2s^2)$	$-2\,\mathrm{Ci}\left(\dfrac{t}{k}\right)$
103	$\dfrac{1}{s}\log\,(s^2+a^2)\ (a>0)$	$2\log a - 2\,\mathrm{Ci}\,(at)$
104	$\dfrac{1}{s^2}\log\,(s^2+a^2)\ (a>0)$	$\dfrac{2}{a}\,[at\log a + \sin at - at\,\mathrm{Ci}\,(at)]$
105	$\log\dfrac{s^2+a^2}{s^2}$	$\dfrac{2}{t}\,(1-\cos at)$
106	$\log\dfrac{s^2-a^2}{s^2}$	$\dfrac{2}{t}\,(1-\cosh at)$
107	$\arctan\dfrac{k}{s}$	$\dfrac{1}{t}\sin kt$
108	$\dfrac{1}{s}\arctan\dfrac{k}{s}$	$\mathrm{Si}\,(kt)$
109	$e^{k^2s^2}\,\mathrm{erfc}\,(ks)\ (k>0)$	$\dfrac{1}{k\sqrt{\pi}}\exp\left(-\dfrac{t^2}{4k^2}\right)$
110	$\dfrac{1}{s}e^{k^2s^2}\,\mathrm{erfc}\,(ks)\ (k>0)$	$\mathrm{erf}\left(\dfrac{t}{2k}\right)$
111	$e^{ks}\,\mathrm{erfc}\,\sqrt{ks}\ \ (k>0)$	$\dfrac{\sqrt{k}}{\pi\sqrt{t}\,(t+k)}$
112	$\dfrac{1}{\sqrt{s}}\,\mathrm{erfc}\,(\sqrt{ks})$	$\begin{cases} 0 & \text{when }\ 0<t<k \\ (\pi t)^{-\frac{1}{2}} & \text{when } t>k \end{cases}$
113	$\dfrac{1}{\sqrt{s}}\,e^{ks}\,\mathrm{erfc}\,(\sqrt{ks})\ (k>0)$	$\dfrac{1}{\sqrt{\pi(t+k)}}$
114	$\mathrm{erf}\left(\dfrac{k}{\sqrt{s}}\right)$	$\dfrac{1}{\pi t}\sin\,(2k\sqrt{t})$
115	$\dfrac{1}{\sqrt{s}}\,e^{k^2/s}\,\mathrm{erfc}\left(\dfrac{k}{\sqrt{s}}\right)$	$\dfrac{1}{\sqrt{\pi t}}\,e^{-2k\sqrt{t}}$
116	$K_0(ks)$	$\begin{cases} 0 & \text{when } 0<t<k \\ (t^2-k^2)^{-\frac{1}{2}} & \text{when } t>k \end{cases}$
117	$K_0(k\sqrt{s})$	$\dfrac{1}{2t}\exp\left(-\dfrac{k^2}{4t}\right)$
118	$\dfrac{1}{s}e^{ks}K_1(ks)$	$\dfrac{1}{k}\sqrt{t(t+2k)}$
119	$\dfrac{1}{\sqrt{s}}\,K_1(k\sqrt{s})$	$\dfrac{1}{k}\exp\left(-\dfrac{k^2}{4t}\right)$
120	$\dfrac{1}{\sqrt{s}}\,e^{k/s}K_0\left(\dfrac{k}{s}\right)$	$\dfrac{2}{\sqrt{\pi t}}\,K_0(2\sqrt{2kt})$

Table D-4 Table of Laplace transforms (*Continued*)

	$f(s)$	$F(t)$
121	$\pi e^{-ks}I_0(ks)$	$\begin{cases} [t(2k - t)]^{-\frac{1}{2}} & \text{when } 0 < t < 2k \\ 0 & \text{when } t > 2k \end{cases}$
122	$e^{-ks}I_1(ks)$	$\begin{cases} \dfrac{k - t}{\pi k \sqrt{t(2k - t)}} & \text{when } 0 < t < 2k \\ 0 & \text{when } t > 2k \end{cases}$
123	$-e^{as}\,\text{Ei}\,(-as)$	$\dfrac{1}{t + a}\,(a > 0)$
124	$\dfrac{1}{a} + se^{as}\,\text{Ei}\,(-as)$	$\dfrac{1}{(t + a)^2}\,(a > 0)$
125	$\left(\dfrac{\pi}{2} - \text{Si } s\right)\cos s + \text{Ci } s \sin s$	$\dfrac{1}{t^2 + 1}$

Fig. D-1

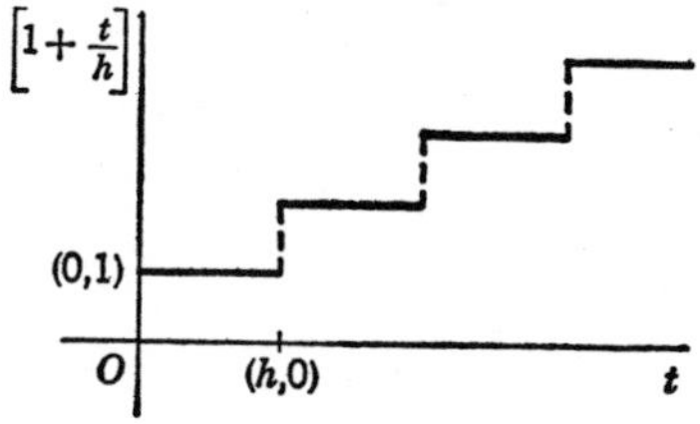

Fig. D-2

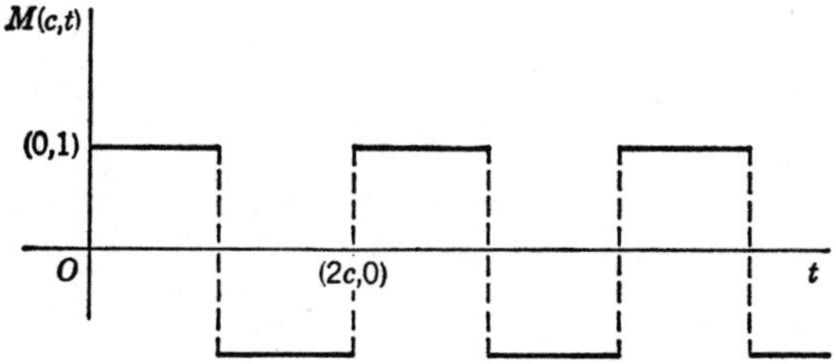

Fig. D-3

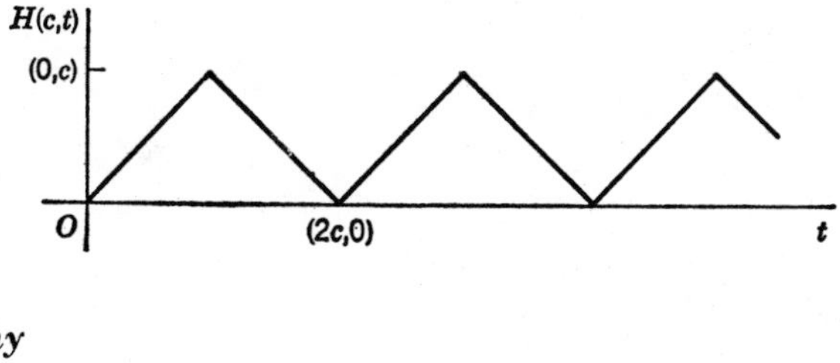

Bibliography

Campbell, C. A., and Foster: *Fourier Integrals for Practical Applications*, Van Nostrand, Princeton, N.J., 1948.

Erdélyi, A.: *Integral Transforms*, vols. 1 and 2 (Bateman Project), McGraw-Hill, New York, 1954.

Oberhettinger, F.: *Tabellen zur Fourier Transformation*, Springer, Berlin, 1957.

Smith, J. J.: Tables of Green's Functions, Fourier Series, and Impulse Functions for Rectangular Coordinates, *Trans. AIEE*, **70**, 22, 1951.

(See also Refs. 8.13 and 10.12.)

E TABLES OF INDEFINITE AND DEFINITE INTEGRALS

Section E-1 lists elementary indefinite integrals.
Section E-2 lists indefinite integrals. To find

Section E-3 lists definite integrals. To find

E-1. Elementary Indefinite Integrals. Add constant of integration in each case.

1. $\displaystyle\int x^n \, dx = \frac{x^{n+1}}{n + 1} \qquad (n \neq -1)$

2. $\displaystyle\int \frac{dx}{x} = \log_e |x| \qquad (x \neq 0)$

3. $\displaystyle\int \sin x \, dx = -\cos x$

4. $\displaystyle\int \cos x \, dx = \sin x$

5. $\displaystyle\int \tan x \, dx = -\log_e |\cos x|$

6. $\displaystyle\int \cot x \, dx = \log_e |\sin x|$

7. $\int \dfrac{dx}{\cos^2 x} = \tan x$

8. $\int \dfrac{dx}{\sin^2 x} = -\cot x$

9. $\int \dfrac{dx}{a^2 + x^2} = \dfrac{1}{a} \arctan \dfrac{x}{a} \qquad (a \neq 0)$

10. $\int \dfrac{dx}{a^2 - x^2} = \dfrac{1}{a} \tanh^{-1} \dfrac{x}{a} = \dfrac{1}{2a} \log_e \dfrac{a + x}{a - x} \qquad (|x| < a)$

11. $\int \dfrac{dx}{x^2 - a^2} = -\dfrac{1}{a} \coth^{-1} \dfrac{x}{a} = \dfrac{1}{2a} \log_e \dfrac{x - a}{x + a} \qquad (|x| > a)$

12. $\int e^x \, dx = e^x$

13. $\int a^x \, dx = \dfrac{a^x}{\log_e a} \qquad (a > 0,\ a \neq 1)$

14. $\int \sinh x \, dx = \cosh x$

15. $\int \cosh x \, dx = \sinh x$

16. $\int \tanh x \, dx = \log_e \cosh x$

17. $\int \coth x \, dx = \log_e |\sinh x|$

18. $\int \dfrac{dx}{\cosh^2 x} = \tanh x$

19. $\int \dfrac{dx}{\sinh^2 x} = -\coth x$

20. $\int \dfrac{dx}{\sqrt{a^2 - x^2}} = \arcsin \dfrac{x}{a} \qquad (a \neq 0)$

21. $\int \dfrac{dx}{\sqrt{a^2 + x^2}} = \sinh^{-1} \dfrac{x}{a} = \log_e |x + \sqrt{a^2 + x^2}| + C_1$

22. $\int \dfrac{dx}{\sqrt{x^2 - a^2}} = \cosh^{-1} \dfrac{x}{a} = \log_e |x + \sqrt{x^2 - a^2}| + C_1$

E-2. Indefinite Integrals.* Add constants of integration as needed. Note: As customary in integral tables, interpret $\log_e f(x)$ as $\log_e |f(x)|$ whenever it occurs on the right-hand side of an integral formula and $f(x)$ is negative. m, n are integers.

(a) Integrals containing $ax + b$ $(a \neq 0)$

1. $\displaystyle\int (ax + b)^n \, dx = \frac{1}{a(n + 1)} (ax + b)^{n+1}$ $(n \neq -1)$

2. $\displaystyle\int \frac{dx}{ax + b} = \frac{1}{a} \log_e (ax + b)$

3. $\displaystyle\int x(ax + b)^n \, dx = \frac{1}{a^2(n + 2)} (ax + b)^{n+2}$

$$- \frac{b}{a^2(n + 1)} (ax + b)^{n+1} \qquad (n \neq -1, -2)$$

4. $\displaystyle\int x^m(ax + b)^n \, dx$

$$= \frac{1}{a(m + n + 1)} \left[x^m(ax + b)^{n+1} - mb \int x^{m-1}(ax + b)^n \, dx \right]$$

$$= \frac{1}{m + n + 1} \left[x^{m+1}(ax + b)^n + nb \int x^m(ax + b)^{n-1} \, dx \right]$$

$$(m > 0, \; m + n + 1 \neq 0)$$

5. $\displaystyle\int \frac{x \, dx}{ax + b} = \frac{x}{a} - \frac{b}{a^2} \log_e (ax + b)$

6. $\displaystyle\int \frac{x \, dx}{(ax + b)^2} = \frac{b}{a^2(ax + b)} + \frac{1}{a^2} \log_e (ax + b)$

7. $\displaystyle\int \frac{x \, dx}{(ax + b)^3} = \frac{b}{2a^2(ax + b)^2} - \frac{1}{a^2(ax + b)}$

8. $\displaystyle\int \frac{x \, dx}{(ax + b)^n} = \frac{1}{a^2} \left[\frac{b}{(n - 1)(ax + b)^{n-1}} - \frac{1}{(n - 2)(ax + b)^{n-2}} \right]$

$$(n \neq 1, 2)$$

---

* Adapted, in part, from I. Bronstein and K. Semendjajev, *Pocketbook of Mathematics*, 6th ed., published by the Soviet Government, Moscow, 1956.

9. $\int \dfrac{x^2\,dx}{ax+b} = \dfrac{1}{a^3}\left[\dfrac{1}{2}(ax+b)^2 - 2b(ax+b) + b^2\log_e(ax+b)\right]$

10. $\int \dfrac{x^2\,dx}{(ax+b)^2} = \dfrac{1}{a^3}\left[(ax+b) - 2b\log_e(ax+b) - \dfrac{b^2}{ax+b}\right]$

11. $\int \dfrac{x^2\,dx}{(ax+b)^3} = \dfrac{1}{a^3}\left[\log_e(ax+b) + \dfrac{2b}{ax+b} - \dfrac{b^2}{2(ax+b)^2}\right]$

12. $\int x^2(ax+b)^n\,dx$

$$= \dfrac{1}{a^3}\left[\dfrac{(ax+b)^{n+3}}{n+3} - 2b\dfrac{(ax+b)^{n+2}}{n+2} + b^2\dfrac{(ax+b)^{n+1}}{n+1}\right]$$

$$(n \neq -1, -2, -3)$$

13. $\int \dfrac{dx}{x(ax+b)} = \dfrac{1}{b}\log_e\dfrac{x}{ax+b}$

14. $\int \dfrac{dx}{x(ax+b)^2} = \dfrac{1}{b(ax+b)} - \dfrac{1}{b^2}\log_e\dfrac{ax+b}{x}$

15. $\int \dfrac{dx}{x(ax+b)^3} = \dfrac{1}{b^3}\left[\dfrac{1}{2}\left(\dfrac{ax+2b}{ax+b}\right)^2 + \log_e\dfrac{x}{ax+b}\right]$

16. $\int \dfrac{dx}{x^2(ax+b)} = -\dfrac{1}{bx} + \dfrac{a}{b^2}\log_e\dfrac{ax+b}{x}$

17. $\int \dfrac{dx}{x^2(ax+b)^2} = -\dfrac{b+2ax}{b^2x(ax+b)} + \dfrac{2a}{b^3}\log_e\dfrac{ax+b}{x}$

18. $\int \dfrac{dx}{x^3(ax+b)} = \dfrac{2ax-b}{2b^2x^2} + \dfrac{a^2}{b^3}\log_e\dfrac{x}{ax+b}$

Let $ax+b \equiv X$ $(a \neq 0)$. Then

19. $\int \dfrac{x^3\,dx}{X} = \dfrac{1}{a^4}\left(\dfrac{X^3}{3} - \dfrac{3bX^2}{2} + 3b^2X - b^3\log_e X\right)$

20. $\int \dfrac{x^3\,dx}{X^2} = \dfrac{1}{a^4}\left(\dfrac{X^2}{2} - 3bX + 3b^2\log_e X + \dfrac{b^3}{X}\right)$

21. $\int \dfrac{x^3\,dx}{X^3} = \dfrac{1}{a^4}\left(X - 3b\log_e X - \dfrac{3b^2}{X} + \dfrac{b^3}{2X^2}\right)$

22. $\displaystyle\int \frac{x^3\,dx}{X^4} = \frac{1}{a^4}\left(\log_e X + \frac{3b}{X} - \frac{3b^2}{2X^2} + \frac{b^3}{3X^3}\right)$

23. $\displaystyle\int \frac{x^3\,dx}{X^n}$

$$= \frac{1}{a^4}\left[\frac{-1}{(n-4)X^{n-4}} + \frac{3b}{(n-3)X^{n-3}} - \frac{3b^2}{(n-2)X^{n-2}} + \frac{b^3}{(n-1)X^{n-1}}\right]$$

$$(n \neq 1, 2, 3, 4)$$

24. $\displaystyle\int \frac{dx}{xX^n} = -\frac{1}{b^n}\left[\log_e \frac{X}{x} - \sum_{k=1}^{n-1}\binom{n-1}{k}\frac{(-a)^k x^k}{kX^k}\right] \qquad (n \geq 1)$

25. $\displaystyle\int \frac{dx}{x^2 X^3} = -a\left[\frac{1}{2b^2 X^2} + \frac{2}{b^3 X} + \frac{1}{ab^3 x} - \frac{3}{b^4}\log_e \frac{X}{x}\right]$

26. $\displaystyle\int \frac{dx}{x^2 X^n} = -\frac{1}{b^{n+1}}\left[-\sum_{k=2}^{n}\binom{n}{k}\frac{(-a)^k x^{k-1}}{(k-1)X^{k-1}} + \frac{X}{x} - na\log_e \frac{X}{x}\right]$

$$(n \geq 2)$$

27. $\displaystyle\int \frac{dx}{x^3 X^2} = -\frac{1}{b^4}\left[3a^2\log_e \frac{X}{x} + \frac{a^3 x}{X} + \frac{X^2}{2x^2} - \frac{3aX}{x}\right]$

28. $\displaystyle\int \frac{dx}{x^3 X^3} = -\frac{1}{b^5}\left[6a^2\log_e \frac{X}{x} + \frac{4a^3 x}{X} - \frac{a^4 x^2}{2X^2} + \frac{X^2}{2x^2} - \frac{4aX}{x}\right]$

29. $\displaystyle\int \frac{dx}{x^3 X^n} = -\frac{1}{b^{n+2}}\left[-\sum_{k=3}^{n+1}\binom{n+1}{k}\frac{(-a)^k x^{k-2}}{(k-2)X^{k-2}} + \frac{a^2 X^2}{2x^2}\right.$

$$\left. - \frac{(n+1)aX}{x} + \frac{n(n+1)a^2}{2}\log_e \frac{X}{x}\right] \qquad (n \geq 3)$$

30. $\displaystyle\int \frac{dx}{x^m X^n} = -\frac{1}{b^{m+n-1}}\sum_{k=0}^{m+n-2}\binom{m+n-2}{k}\frac{X^{m-k-1}(-a)^k}{(m-k-1)x^{m-k-1}}$

$$\left[\text{terms with } (m-k-1)=0 \text{ are replaced by}\right.$$

$$\left.\binom{m+n-2}{m-1}(-a)^{m-1}\log_e \frac{X}{x}\right]$$

(b) Integrals containing $ax+b$ **and** $cx+d$ $\qquad (a \neq 0, c \neq 0)$

31. $\displaystyle\int \frac{ax+b}{cx+d}\,dx = \frac{a}{c}x + \frac{bc-ad}{c^2}\log_e (cx+d)$

32. $\displaystyle\int \frac{dx}{(ax+b)(cx+d)} = \frac{1}{bc-ad} \log_e \frac{cx+d}{ax+b}$ $(bc-ad \neq 0)$

33. $\displaystyle\int \frac{x\,dx}{(ax+b)(cx+d)}$

$$= \frac{1}{bc-ad}\left[\frac{b}{a}\log (ax+b) - \frac{d}{c}\log_e (cx+d)\right] \quad (bc-ad \neq 0)$$

34. $\displaystyle\int \frac{dx}{(ax+b)^2(cx+d)}$

$$= \frac{1}{bc-ad}\left[\frac{1}{ax+b} + \frac{c}{bc-ad}\log_e \frac{cx+d}{ax+b}\right] \quad (bc-ad \neq 0)$$

(c) Integrals containing $a+x$ and $b+x$ $(a \neq b)$

35. $\displaystyle\int \frac{x\,dx}{(a+x)(b+x)^2} = \frac{b}{(a-b)(b+x)} - \frac{a}{(a-b)^2}\log_e \frac{a+x}{b+x}$

36. $\displaystyle\int \frac{x^2\,dx}{(a+x)(b+x)^2} = \frac{b^2}{(b-a)(b+x)} + \frac{a^2}{(b-a)^2}\log_e (a+x)$

$$+ \frac{b^2-2ab}{(b-a)^2}\log_e (b+x)$$

37. $\displaystyle\int \frac{dx}{(a+x)^2(b+x)^2}$

$$= \frac{-1}{(a-b)^2}\left(\frac{1}{a+x} + \frac{1}{b+x}\right) + \frac{2}{(a-b)^3}\log_e \frac{a+x}{b+x}$$

38. $\displaystyle\int \frac{x\,dx}{(a+x)^2(b+x)^2}$

$$= \frac{1}{(a-b)^2}\left(\frac{a}{a+x} + \frac{b}{b+x}\right) + \frac{a+b}{(a-b)^3}\log_e \frac{a+x}{b+x}$$

39. $\displaystyle\int \frac{x^2\,dx}{(a+x)^2(b+x)^2}$

$$= \frac{-1}{(a-b)^2}\left(\frac{a^2}{a+x} + \frac{b^2}{b+x}\right) + \frac{2ab}{(a-b)^3}\log_e \frac{a+x}{b+x}$$

(d) *Integrals containing* $ax^2 + bx + c$ $(a \neq 0)$

40. $\displaystyle \int \frac{dx}{ax^2 + bx + c}$

$$= \begin{cases} \dfrac{1}{\sqrt{b^2 - 4ac}} \log_e \dfrac{2ax + b - \sqrt{b^2 - 4ac}}{2ax + b + \sqrt{b^2 - 4ac}} & (b^2 > 4ac) \\[3mm] \dfrac{2}{\sqrt{4ac - b^2}} \arctan \dfrac{2ax + b}{\sqrt{4ac - b^2}} & (b^2 < 4ac) \\[3mm] -\dfrac{2}{2ax + b} & (b^2 = 4ac) \end{cases}$$

In numbers 41 through 47, let $b^2 - 4ac \neq 0$.

41. $\displaystyle \int \frac{dx}{(ax^2 + bx + c)^2} = \frac{2ax + b}{(4ac - b^2)(ax^2 + bx + c)}$

$$+ \frac{2a}{(4ac - b^2)} \int \frac{dx}{ax^2 + bx + c}$$

42. $\displaystyle \int \frac{dx}{(ax^2 + bx + c)^{n+1}} = \frac{2ax + b}{n(4ac - b^2)(ax^2 + bx + c)^n}$

$$+ \frac{2(2n - 1)a}{n(4ac - b^2)} \int \frac{dx}{(ax^2 + bx + c)^n}$$

43. $\displaystyle \int \frac{x\,dx}{ax^2 + bx + c} = \frac{1}{2a} \log_e (ax^2 + bx + c) - \frac{b}{2a} \int \frac{dx}{ax^2 + bx + c}$

44. $\displaystyle \int \frac{x^2\,dx}{ax^2 + bx + c} = \frac{x}{a} - \frac{b}{2a^2} \log_e (ax^2 + bx + c)$

$$+ \frac{b^2 - 2ac}{2a^2} \int \frac{dx}{ax^2 + bx + c}$$

45. $\displaystyle \int \frac{x^n\,dx}{ax^2 + bx + c} = \frac{x^{n-1}}{(n - 1)a} - \frac{c}{a} \int \frac{x^{n-2}\,dx}{ax^2 + bx + c}$

$$- \frac{b}{a} \int \frac{x^{n-1}\,dx}{ax^2 + bx + c} \qquad (n \neq 1)$$

46. $\displaystyle \int \frac{x\,dx}{(ax^2 + bx + c)^{n+1}} = \frac{-(2c + bx)}{n(4ac - b^2)(ax^2 + bx + c)^n}$

$$- \frac{b(2n - 1)}{n(4ac - b^2)} \int \frac{dx}{(ax^2 + bx + c)^n}$$

47. $\displaystyle\int \frac{x^m\,dx}{(ax^2 + bx + c)^{n+1}} = -\,\frac{x^{m-1}}{a(2n - m + 1)(ax^2 + bx + c)^n}$

$\qquad\qquad -\,\dfrac{n - m + 1}{2n - m + 1}\cdot\dfrac{b}{a}\displaystyle\int \frac{x^{m-1}\,dx}{(ax^2 + bx + c)^{n+1}}$

$\qquad\qquad +\,\dfrac{m - 1}{2n - m + 1}\cdot\dfrac{c}{a}\displaystyle\int \frac{x^{m-2}\,dx}{(ax^2 + bx + c)^{n+1}} \qquad (m \neq 2n + 1)$

Let $ax^2 + bx + c \equiv X\ (a \neq 0)$.   Then

48. $\displaystyle\int \frac{x^{2n-1}\,dx}{X^n} = \frac{1}{a}\int \frac{x^{2n-3}\,dx}{X^{n-1}} - \frac{c}{a}\int \frac{x^{2n-3}\,dx}{X^n} - \frac{b}{a}\int \frac{x^{2n-2}\,dx}{X^n}$

49. $\displaystyle\int \frac{dx}{xX} = \frac{1}{2c}\log_e \frac{x^2}{X} - \frac{b}{2c}\int \frac{dx}{X}$

50. $\displaystyle\int \frac{dx}{xX^n} = \frac{1}{2c(n - 1)X^{n-1}} - \frac{b}{2c}\int \frac{dx}{X^n} + \frac{1}{c}\int \frac{dx}{xX^{n-1}}$

51. $\displaystyle\int \frac{dx}{x^2X} = \frac{b}{2c^2}\log_e \frac{X}{x^2} - \frac{1}{cx} + \left(\frac{b^2}{2c^2} - \frac{a}{c}\right)\int \frac{dx}{X}$

52. $\displaystyle\int \frac{dx}{x^mX^n} = -\,\frac{1}{(m - 1)cx^{m-1}X^{n-1}} - \frac{(2n + m - 3)a}{(m - 1)c}\int \frac{dx}{x^{m-2}X^n}$

$\qquad\qquad -\,\dfrac{(n + m - 2)b}{(m - 1)c}\displaystyle\int \frac{dx}{x^{m-1}X^n} \qquad (m > 1)$

53. $\displaystyle\int \frac{dx}{(fx + g)X} = \frac{1}{2(cf^2 - gbf + g^2a)}\left[f\log_e \frac{(fx + g)^2}{X}\right]$

$\qquad\qquad +\,\dfrac{2ga - bf}{2(cf^2 - gbf + g^2a)}\displaystyle\int \frac{dx}{X}$

(e) Integrals containing $a^2 \pm x^2$, with

$$X \equiv a^2 + x^2 \qquad Y \equiv \arctan \frac{x}{a}$$

or

$$X \equiv a^2 - x^2 \qquad Y \equiv \tanh^{-1}\frac{x}{a} \equiv \begin{cases} \dfrac{1}{2}\log_e \dfrac{a + x}{a - x} & (|x| < a) \\[2mm] \dfrac{1}{2}\log_e \dfrac{x + a}{x - a} & (|x| > a) \end{cases}$$

Where $\pm$ or $\mp$ appears in a formula, the upper sign refers to $X \equiv a^2 + x^2$ and the lower sign to $X \equiv a^2 - x^2$ $(a \neq 0)$.

54. $\displaystyle\int \frac{dx}{X} = \frac{1}{a} Y$

55. $\displaystyle\int \frac{dx}{X^2} = \frac{x}{2a^2 X} + \frac{1}{2a^3} Y$

56. $\displaystyle\int \frac{dx}{X^3} = \frac{x}{4a^2 X^2} + \frac{3x}{8a^4 X} + \frac{3}{8a^5} Y$

57. $\displaystyle\int \frac{dx}{X^{n+1}} = \frac{x}{2na^2 X^n} + \frac{2n-1}{2na^2} \int \frac{dx}{X^n}$

58. $\displaystyle\int \frac{x\,dx}{X} = \pm \frac{1}{2} \log_e X$

59. $\displaystyle\int \frac{x\,dx}{X^2} = \mp \frac{1}{2X}$

60. $\displaystyle\int \frac{x\,dx}{X^3} = \mp \frac{1}{4X^2}$

61. $\displaystyle\int \frac{x\,dx}{X^{n+1}} = \mp \frac{1}{2nX^n}$ $(n \neq 0)$

62. $\displaystyle\int \frac{x^2\,dx}{X} = \pm x \mp aY$

63. $\displaystyle\int \frac{x^2\,dx}{X^2} = \mp \frac{x}{2X} \pm \frac{1}{2a} Y$

64. $\displaystyle\int \frac{x^2\,dx}{X^3} = \mp \frac{x}{4X^2} \pm \frac{x}{8a^2 X} \pm \frac{1}{8a^3} Y$

65. $\displaystyle\int \frac{x^2\,dx}{X^{n+1}} = \mp \frac{x}{2nX^n} \pm \frac{1}{2n} \int \frac{dx}{X^n}$ $(n \neq 0)$

66. $\displaystyle\int \frac{x^3\,dx}{X} = \pm \frac{x^2}{2} - \frac{a^2}{2} \log_e X$

67. $\displaystyle\int \frac{x^3\,dx}{X^2} = \frac{a^2}{2X} + \frac{1}{2} \log_e X$

68. $\displaystyle\int \frac{x^3\,dx}{X^3} = -\frac{1}{2X} + \frac{a^2}{4X^2}$

69. $\int \dfrac{x^3\,dx}{X^{n+1}} = -\dfrac{1}{2(n-1)X^{n-1}} + \dfrac{a^2}{2nX^n}$ $\quad (n > 1)$

70. $\int \dfrac{dx}{xX} = \dfrac{1}{2a^2} \log_e \dfrac{x^2}{X}$

71. $\int \dfrac{dx}{xX^2} = \dfrac{1}{2a^2X} + \dfrac{1}{2a^4} \log_e \dfrac{x^2}{X}$

72. $\int \dfrac{dx}{xX^3} = \dfrac{1}{4a^2X^2} + \dfrac{1}{2a^4X} + \dfrac{1}{2a^6} \log_e \dfrac{x^2}{X}$

73. $\int \dfrac{dx}{x^2X} = -\dfrac{1}{a^2x} \mp \dfrac{1}{a^3} Y$

74. $\int \dfrac{dx}{x^2X^2} = -\dfrac{1}{a^4x} \mp \dfrac{x}{2a^4X} \mp \dfrac{3}{2a^5} Y$

75. $\int \dfrac{dx}{x^2X^3} = -\dfrac{1}{a^6x} \mp \dfrac{x}{4a^4X^2} \mp \dfrac{7x}{8a^6X} \mp \dfrac{15}{8a^7} Y$

76. $\int \dfrac{dx}{x^3X} = -\dfrac{1}{2a^2x^2} \mp \dfrac{1}{2a^4} \log_e \dfrac{x^2}{X}$

77. $\int \dfrac{dx}{x^3X^2} = -\dfrac{1}{2a^4x^2} \mp \dfrac{1}{2a^4X} \mp \dfrac{1}{a^6} \log_e \dfrac{x^2}{X}$

78. $\int \dfrac{dx}{x^3X^3} = -\dfrac{1}{2a^6x^2} \mp \dfrac{1}{a^6X} \mp \dfrac{1}{4a^4X^2} \mp \dfrac{3}{2a^8} \log_e \dfrac{x^2}{X}$

79. $\int \dfrac{dx}{(b+cx)X} = \dfrac{1}{a^2c^2 \pm b^2} \left[c \log_e (b + cx) - \dfrac{c}{2} \log_e X \pm \dfrac{b}{a} Y \right]$

(f) Integrals containing $a^3 \pm x^3$, with

$$X \equiv a^3 \pm x^3 \quad (a \neq 0)$$

Where $\pm$ or $\mp$ appears in a formula, the upper sign refers to $X \equiv a^3 + x^3$ and the lower sign to $X \equiv a^3 - x^3$.

80. $\int \dfrac{dx}{X} = \pm \dfrac{1}{6a^2} \log_e \dfrac{(a \pm x)^2}{a^2 \mp ax + x^2} + \dfrac{1}{a^2\sqrt{3}} \arctan \dfrac{2x \mp a}{a\sqrt{3}}$

81. $\int \dfrac{dx}{X^2} = \dfrac{x}{3a^3X} + \dfrac{2}{3a^3} \int \dfrac{dx}{X}$

82. $\displaystyle \int \frac{x\,dx}{X} = \frac{1}{6a} \log_e \frac{a^2 \mp ax + x^2}{(a \pm x)^2} \pm \frac{1}{a\sqrt{3}} \arctan \frac{2x \mp a}{a\sqrt{3}}$

83. $\displaystyle \int \frac{x\,dx}{X^2} = \frac{x^2}{3a^3X} + \frac{1}{3a^3} \int \frac{x\,dx}{X}$

84. $\displaystyle \int \frac{x^2\,dx}{X} = \pm \frac{1}{3} \log_e X$

85. $\displaystyle \int \frac{x^2\,dx}{X^2} = \mp \frac{1}{3X}$

86. $\displaystyle \int \frac{x^3\,dx}{X} = \pm x \mp a^3 \int \frac{dx}{X}$

87. $\displaystyle \int \frac{x^3\,dx}{X^2} = \mp \frac{x}{3X} \pm \frac{1}{3} \int \frac{dx}{X}$

88. $\displaystyle \int \frac{dx}{xX} = \frac{1}{3a^3} \log_e \frac{x^3}{X}$

89. $\displaystyle \int \frac{dx}{xX^2} = \frac{1}{3a^3X} + \frac{1}{3a^6} \log_e \frac{x^3}{X}$

90. $\displaystyle \int \frac{dx}{x^2X} = -\frac{1}{a^3x} \mp \frac{1}{a^3} \int \frac{x\,dx}{X}$

91. $\displaystyle \int \frac{dx}{x^2X^2} = -\frac{1}{a^6x} \mp \frac{x^2}{3a^6X} \mp \frac{4}{3a^6} \int \frac{x\,dx}{X}$

92. $\displaystyle \int \frac{dx}{x^3X} = -\frac{1}{2a^3x^2} \mp \frac{1}{a^3} \int \frac{dx}{X}$

93. $\displaystyle \int \frac{dx}{x^3X^2} = -\frac{1}{2a^6x^2} \mp \frac{x}{3a^6X} \mp \frac{5}{3a^6} \int \frac{dx}{X}$

(g) Integrals containing $a^4 \pm x^4$　　　$(a \neq 0)$

94. $\displaystyle \int \frac{dx}{a^4 + x^4} = \frac{1}{4a^3\sqrt{2}} \log_e \frac{x^2 + ax\sqrt{2} + a^2}{x^2 - ax\sqrt{2} + a^2} + \frac{1}{2a^3\sqrt{2}} \arctan \frac{ax\sqrt{2}}{a^2 - x^2}$

95. $\displaystyle \int \frac{x\,dx}{a^4 + x^4} = \frac{1}{2a^2} \arctan \frac{x^2}{a^2}$

96. $\displaystyle \int \frac{x^2\,dx}{a^4 + x^4} = -\frac{1}{4a\sqrt{2}} \log_e \frac{x^2 + ax\sqrt{2} + a^2}{x^2 - ax\sqrt{2} + a^2} + \frac{1}{2a\sqrt{2}} \arctan \frac{ax\sqrt{2}}{a^2 - x^2}$

97. $\displaystyle\int \frac{x^3\,dx}{a^4 + x^4} = \frac{1}{4}\log_e (a^4 + x^4)$

98. $\displaystyle\int \frac{dx}{a^4 - x^4} = \frac{1}{4a^3}\log_e \frac{a + x}{a - x} + \frac{1}{2a^3}\arctan\frac{x}{a}$

99. $\displaystyle\int \frac{x\,dx}{a^4 - x^4} = \frac{1}{4a^3}\log_e \frac{a^2 + x^2}{a^2 - x^2}$

100. $\displaystyle\int \frac{x^2\,dx}{a^4 - x^4} = \frac{1}{4a}\log_e \frac{a + x}{a - x} - \frac{1}{2a}\arctan\frac{x}{a}$

101. $\displaystyle\int \frac{x^3\,dx}{a^4 - x^4} = -\frac{1}{4}\log_e (a^4 - x^4)$

(h) Integrals containing $\sqrt{x}$ and $a^2 + b^2x$ $(a, b \neq 0)$

102. $\displaystyle\int \frac{\sqrt{x}\,dx}{a^2 + b^2x} = \frac{2\sqrt{x}}{b^2} - \frac{2a}{b^3}\arctan\frac{b\sqrt{x}}{a}$

103. $\displaystyle\int \frac{x\sqrt{x}\,dx}{a^2 + b^2x} = \frac{2x\sqrt{x}}{3b^2} - \frac{2a^2\sqrt{x}}{b^4} + \frac{2a^3}{b^5}\arctan\frac{b\sqrt{x}}{a}$

104. $\displaystyle\int \frac{\sqrt{x}\,dx}{(a^2 + b^2x)^2} = -\frac{\sqrt{x}}{b^2(a^2 + b^2x)} + \frac{1}{ab^3}\arctan\frac{b\sqrt{x}}{a}$

105. $\displaystyle\int \frac{x\sqrt{x}\,dx}{(a^2 + b^2x)^2} = \frac{2b^2x\sqrt{x} + 3a^2\sqrt{x}}{b^4(a^2 + b^2x)} - \frac{3a}{b^5}\arctan\frac{b\sqrt{x}}{a}$

106. $\displaystyle\int \frac{dx}{(a^2 + b^2x)\sqrt{x}} = \frac{2}{ab}\arctan\frac{b\sqrt{x}}{a}$

107. $\displaystyle\int \frac{dx}{(a^2 + b^2x)x\sqrt{x}} = -\frac{2}{a^2\sqrt{x}} - \frac{2b}{a^3}\arctan\frac{b\sqrt{x}}{a}$

108. $\displaystyle\int \frac{dx}{(a^2 + b^2x)^2\sqrt{x}} = \frac{\sqrt{x}}{a^2(a^2 + b^2x)} + \frac{1}{a^3b}\arctan\frac{b\sqrt{x}}{a}$

(i) Integrals containing $\sqrt{x}$ and $a^2 - b^2x > 0$ $(a, b \neq 0)$

109. $\displaystyle\int \frac{\sqrt{x}\,dx}{a^2 - b^2x} = -\frac{2\sqrt{x}}{b^2} + \frac{a}{b^3}\log_e \frac{a + b\sqrt{x}}{a - b\sqrt{x}}$

110. $\displaystyle\int \frac{x\sqrt{x}\,dx}{a^2 - b^2x} = -\frac{2x\sqrt{x}}{3b^2} - \frac{2a^2\sqrt{x}}{b^4} + \frac{a^3}{b^5}\log_e \frac{a + b\sqrt{x}}{a - b\sqrt{x}}$

111. $\int \dfrac{\sqrt{x}\,dx}{(a^2 - b^2 x)^2} = \dfrac{\sqrt{x}}{b^2(a^2 - b^2 x)} - \dfrac{1}{2ab^3} \log_e \dfrac{a + b\sqrt{x}}{a - b\sqrt{x}}$

112. $\int \dfrac{x\sqrt{x}\,dx}{(a^2 - b^2 x)^2} = \dfrac{-2b^2 x\sqrt{x} + 3a^2\sqrt{x}}{b^4(a^2 - b^2 x)} - \dfrac{3a}{2b^5} \log_e \dfrac{a + b\sqrt{x}}{a - b\sqrt{x}}$

113. $\int \dfrac{dx}{(a^2 - b^2 x)\sqrt{x}} = \dfrac{1}{ab} \log_e \dfrac{a + b\sqrt{x}}{a - b\sqrt{x}}$

114. $\int \dfrac{dx}{(a^2 - b^2 x)x\sqrt{x}} = -\dfrac{2}{a^2\sqrt{x}} + \dfrac{b}{a^3} \log_e \dfrac{a + b\sqrt{x}}{a - b\sqrt{x}}$

115. $\int \dfrac{dx}{(a^2 - b^2 x)^2\sqrt{x}} = \dfrac{\sqrt{x}}{a^2(a^2 - b^2 x)} + \dfrac{1}{2a^3 b} \log_e \dfrac{a + b\sqrt{x}}{a - b\sqrt{x}}$

116. $\int \dfrac{dx}{(a^2 - b^2 x)^2 x\sqrt{x}} = -\dfrac{2}{a^2(a^2 - b^2 x)\sqrt{x}} + \dfrac{3b^2\sqrt{x}}{a^4(a^2 - b^2 x)}$

$$+ \dfrac{3b}{2a^5} \log_e \dfrac{a + b\sqrt{x}}{a - b\sqrt{x}}$$

(j) *Other integrals containing* $\sqrt{x}$ $\quad$ $(a > \sqrt{x} > 0)$

117. $\int \dfrac{\sqrt{x}\,dx}{a^4 + x^2} = -\dfrac{1}{2a\sqrt{2}} \log_e \dfrac{x + a\sqrt{2x} + a^2}{x - a\sqrt{2x} + a^2} + \dfrac{1}{a\sqrt{2}} \arctan \dfrac{a\sqrt{2x}}{a^2 - x}$

118. $\int \dfrac{dx}{(a^4 + x^2)\sqrt{x}} = \dfrac{1}{2a^3\sqrt{2}} \log_e \dfrac{x + a\sqrt{2x} + a^2}{x - a\sqrt{2x} + a^2}$

$$+ \dfrac{1}{a^3\sqrt{2}} \arctan \dfrac{a\sqrt{2x}}{a^2 - x}$$

119. $\int \dfrac{\sqrt{x}\,dx}{a^4 - x^2} = \dfrac{1}{2a} \log_e \dfrac{a + \sqrt{x}}{a - \sqrt{x}} - \dfrac{1}{a} \arctan \dfrac{\sqrt{x}}{a}$

120. $\int \dfrac{dx}{(a^4 - x^2)\sqrt{x}} = \dfrac{1}{2a^3} \log_e \dfrac{a + \sqrt{x}}{a - \sqrt{x}} + \dfrac{1}{a^3} \arctan \dfrac{\sqrt{x}}{a}$

(k) *Integrals containing* $\sqrt{ax + b}$*, with*

$$X \equiv ax + b \qquad Y \equiv fx + g \qquad \Delta \equiv bf - ag \qquad (a \neq 0)$$

121. $\displaystyle\int \sqrt{X}\,dx = \frac{2}{3a}\sqrt{X^3}$

122. $\displaystyle\int x\sqrt{X}\,dx = \frac{2(3ax-2b)\sqrt{X^3}}{15a^2}$

123. $\displaystyle\int x^2\sqrt{X}\,dx = \frac{2(15a^2x^2-12abx+8b^2)\sqrt{X^3}}{105a^3}$

124. $\displaystyle\int \frac{dx}{\sqrt{X}} = \frac{2\sqrt{X}}{a}$

125. $\displaystyle\int \frac{x\,dx}{\sqrt{X}} = \frac{2(ax-2b)}{3a^2}\sqrt{X}$

126. $\displaystyle\int \frac{x^2\,dx}{\sqrt{X}} = \frac{2(3a^2x^2-4abx+8b^2)\sqrt{X}}{15a^3}$

127. $\displaystyle\int \frac{dx}{x\sqrt{X}} = \begin{cases} -\dfrac{2}{\sqrt{b}}\tanh^{-1}\sqrt{\dfrac{X}{b}} = \dfrac{1}{\sqrt{b}}\log_e \dfrac{\sqrt{X}-\sqrt{b}}{\sqrt{X}+\sqrt{b}} & (b>0) \\[3mm] \dfrac{2}{\sqrt{-b}}\arctan\sqrt{\dfrac{X}{-b}} & (b<0) \end{cases}$

128. $\displaystyle\int \frac{\sqrt{X}}{x}\,dx = 2\sqrt{X} + b\int \frac{dx}{x\sqrt{X}}$

129. $\displaystyle\int \frac{dx}{x^2\sqrt{X}} = -\frac{\sqrt{X}}{bx} - \frac{a}{2b}\int \frac{dx}{x\sqrt{X}}$

130. $\displaystyle\int \frac{\sqrt{X}}{x^2}\,dx = -\frac{\sqrt{X}}{x} + \frac{a}{2}\int \frac{dx}{x\sqrt{X}}$

131. $\displaystyle\int \frac{dx}{x^n\sqrt{X}} = -\frac{\sqrt{X}}{(n-1)bx^{n-1}} - \frac{(2n-3)a}{(2n-2)b}\int \frac{dx}{x^{n-1}\sqrt{X}} \qquad (n\neq 1)$

132. $\displaystyle\int \sqrt{X^3}\,dx = \frac{2\sqrt{X^5}}{5a}$

133. $\displaystyle\int x\sqrt{X^3}\,dx = \frac{2}{35a^2}\left(5\sqrt{X^7} - 7b\sqrt{X^5}\right)$

134. $\displaystyle\int x^2\sqrt{X^3}\,dx = \frac{2}{a^3}\left(\frac{\sqrt{X^9}}{9} - \frac{2b\sqrt{X^7}}{7} + \frac{b^2\sqrt{X^5}}{5}\right)$

135. $\int \dfrac{\sqrt{X^3}}{x}\,dx = \dfrac{2\sqrt{X^3}}{3} + 2b\sqrt{X} + b^2 \int \dfrac{dx}{x\sqrt{X}}$

136. $\int \dfrac{x\,dx}{\sqrt{X^3}} = \dfrac{2}{a^2}\left(\sqrt{X} + \dfrac{b}{\sqrt{X}}\right)$

137. $\int \dfrac{x^2\,dx}{\sqrt{X^3}} = \dfrac{2}{a^3}\left(\dfrac{\sqrt{X^3}}{3} - 2b\sqrt{X} - \dfrac{b^2}{\sqrt{X}}\right)$

138. $\int \dfrac{dx}{x\sqrt{X^3}} = \dfrac{2}{b\sqrt{X}} + \dfrac{1}{b}\int \dfrac{dx}{x\sqrt{X}}$ $(b \neq 0)$

139. $\int \dfrac{dx}{x^2\sqrt{X^3}} = -\dfrac{1}{bx\sqrt{X}} - \dfrac{3a}{b^2\sqrt{X}} - \dfrac{3a}{2b^2}\int \dfrac{dx}{x\sqrt{X}}$ $(b \neq 0)$

140. $\int X^{\pm n/2}\,dx = \dfrac{2X^{(2\pm n)/2}}{a(2 \pm n)}$ $(n \neq \mp 2)$

141. $\int xX^{\pm n/2}\,dx = \dfrac{2}{a^2}\left(\dfrac{X^{(4\pm n)/2}}{4 \pm n} - \dfrac{bX^{(2\pm n)/2}}{2 \pm n}\right)$ $(n \neq \mp 2, \mp 4)$

142. $\int x^2X^{\pm n/2}\,dx = \dfrac{2}{a^3}\left(\dfrac{X^{(6\pm n)/2}}{6 \pm n} - \dfrac{2bX^{(4\pm n)/2}}{4 \pm n} + \dfrac{b^2X^{(2\pm n)/2}}{2 \pm n}\right)$

$(n \neq \mp 2, \mp 4, \mp 6)$

143. $\int \dfrac{X^{n/2}\,dx}{x} = \dfrac{2X^{n/2}}{n} + b\int \dfrac{X^{(n-2)/2}}{x}\,dx$ $(n \neq 0)$

144. $\int \dfrac{dx}{xX^{n/2}} = \dfrac{2}{(n-2)bX^{(n-2)/2}} + \dfrac{1}{b}\int \dfrac{dx}{xX^{(n-2)/2}}$ $(n \neq 2,\, b \neq 0)$

145. $\int \dfrac{dx}{x^2X^{n/2}} = -\dfrac{1}{bxX^{(n-2)/2}} - \dfrac{na}{2b}\int \dfrac{dx}{xX^{n/2}}$ $(b \neq 0)$

146. $\int \dfrac{dx}{\sqrt{XY}} = \begin{cases} \dfrac{2}{\sqrt{-af}}\arctan\sqrt{-\dfrac{fX}{aY}} & (af < 0) \\[4mm] \dfrac{2}{\sqrt{af}}\tanh^{-1}\sqrt{\dfrac{fX}{aY}} = \dfrac{2}{\sqrt{af}}\log_e\left(\sqrt{aY} + \sqrt{fX}\right) + C_1 \end{cases}$

$(af > 0)$

147. $\int \dfrac{x\,dx}{\sqrt{XY}} = \dfrac{\sqrt{XY}}{af} - \dfrac{ag + bf}{2af}\int \dfrac{dx}{\sqrt{XY}}$

148. $\displaystyle\int \frac{dx}{\sqrt{X}\sqrt{Y^3}} = -\frac{2\sqrt{X}}{\Delta\sqrt{Y}}$

149. $\displaystyle\int \frac{dx}{Y\sqrt{X}} = \begin{cases} \dfrac{2}{\sqrt{-f\Delta}} \arctan \dfrac{f\sqrt{X}}{\sqrt{-f\Delta}} & (f\Delta < 0) \\[3ex] \dfrac{1}{\sqrt{f\Delta}} \log_e \dfrac{f\sqrt{X} - \sqrt{f\Delta}}{f\sqrt{X} + \sqrt{f\Delta}} & (f\Delta > 0) \end{cases}$

150. $\displaystyle\int \sqrt{XY}\, dx = \frac{\Delta + 2aY}{4af} \sqrt{XY} - \frac{\Delta^2}{8af} \int \frac{dx}{\sqrt{XY}}$

151. $\displaystyle\int \sqrt{\frac{Y}{X}}\, dx = \frac{1}{a} \sqrt{XY} - \frac{\Delta}{2a} \int \frac{dx}{\sqrt{XY}}$

152. $\displaystyle\int \frac{\sqrt{X}\, dx}{Y} = \frac{2\sqrt{X}}{f} + \frac{\Delta}{f} \int \frac{dx}{Y\sqrt{X}} \qquad (f \neq 0)$

153. $\displaystyle\int \frac{Y^n\, dx}{\sqrt{X}} = \frac{2}{(2n+1)a} \left(\sqrt{X}Y^n - n\Delta \int \frac{Y^{n-1}\, dx}{\sqrt{X}} \right)$

154. $\displaystyle\int \frac{dx}{\sqrt{X}Y^n} = -\frac{1}{(n-1)\Delta} \left\{ \frac{\sqrt{X}}{Y^{n-1}} + \left(n - \frac{3}{2}\right) a \int \frac{dx}{\sqrt{X}Y^{n-1}} \right\}$

$$(\Delta \neq 0, n \neq 1)$$

155. $\displaystyle\int \sqrt{X}Y^n\, dx = \frac{1}{(2n+3)f} \left(2\sqrt{X}Y^{n+1} + \Delta \int \frac{Y^n\, dx}{\sqrt{X}} \right) \qquad (f \neq 0)$

156. $\displaystyle\int \frac{\sqrt{X}\, dx}{Y^n} = \frac{1}{(n-1)f} \left(-\frac{\sqrt{X}}{Y^{n-1}} + \frac{a}{2} \int \frac{dx}{\sqrt{X}Y^{n-1}} \right) \qquad (f \neq 0, n \neq 1)$

(l) Integrals containing $\sqrt{a^2 - x^2}$, with

$$\boxed{X \equiv a^2 - x^2 \qquad (a > 0)}$$

157. $\displaystyle\int \sqrt{X}\, dx = \frac{1}{2} \left(x\sqrt{X} + a^2 \arcsin \frac{x}{a} \right)$

158. $\displaystyle\int x\sqrt{X}\, dx = -\frac{1}{3}\sqrt{X^3}$

159. $\int x^2\sqrt{X}\,dx = -\dfrac{x}{4}\sqrt{X^3} + \dfrac{a^2}{8}\left(x\sqrt{X} + a^2\arcsin\dfrac{x}{a}\right)$

160. $\int x^3\sqrt{X}\,dx = \dfrac{\sqrt{X^5}}{5} - a^2\dfrac{\sqrt{X^3}}{3}$

161. $\int \dfrac{\sqrt{X}}{x}\,dx = \sqrt{X} - a\log_e\dfrac{a + \sqrt{X}}{x}$

162. $\int \dfrac{\sqrt{X}}{x^2}\,dx = -\dfrac{\sqrt{X}}{x} - \arcsin\dfrac{x}{a}$

163. $\int \dfrac{\sqrt{X}}{x^3}\,dx = -\dfrac{\sqrt{X}}{2x^2} + \dfrac{1}{2a}\log_e\dfrac{a + \sqrt{X}}{x}$

164. $\int \dfrac{dx}{\sqrt{X}} = \arcsin\dfrac{x}{a}$

165. $\int \dfrac{x\,dx}{\sqrt{X}} = -\sqrt{X}$

166. $\int \dfrac{x^2\,dx}{\sqrt{X}} = -\dfrac{x}{2}\sqrt{X} + \dfrac{a^2}{2}\arcsin\dfrac{x}{a}$

167. $\int \dfrac{x^3\,dx}{\sqrt{X}} = \dfrac{\sqrt{X^3}}{3} - a^2\sqrt{X}$

168. $\int \dfrac{dx}{x\sqrt{X}} = -\dfrac{1}{a}\log_e\dfrac{a + \sqrt{X}}{x}$

169. $\int \dfrac{dx}{x^2\sqrt{X}} = -\dfrac{\sqrt{X}}{a^2x}$

170. $\int \dfrac{dx}{x^3\sqrt{X}} = -\dfrac{\sqrt{X}}{2a^2x^2} - \dfrac{1}{2a^3}\log_e\dfrac{a + \sqrt{X}}{x}$

171. $\int \sqrt{X^3}\,dx = \dfrac{1}{4}\left(x\sqrt{X^3} + \dfrac{3a^2x}{2}\sqrt{X} + \dfrac{3a^4}{2}\arcsin\dfrac{x}{a}\right)$

172. $\int x\sqrt{X^3}\,dx = -\dfrac{1}{5}\sqrt{X^5}$

173. $\int x^2\sqrt{X^3}\,dx = -\dfrac{x\sqrt{X^5}}{6} + \dfrac{a^2x\sqrt{X^3}}{24} + \dfrac{a^4x\sqrt{X}}{16} + \dfrac{a^6}{16}\arcsin\dfrac{x}{a}$

174. $\displaystyle\int x^3 \sqrt{X^3}\, dx = \frac{\sqrt{X^7}}{7} - \frac{a^2\sqrt{X^5}}{5}$

175. $\displaystyle\int \frac{\sqrt{X^3}}{x}\, dx = \frac{\sqrt{X^3}}{3} + a^2\sqrt{X} - a^3 \log_e \frac{a + \sqrt{X}}{x}$

176. $\displaystyle\int \frac{\sqrt{X^3}}{x^2}\, dx = -\frac{\sqrt{X^3}}{x} - \frac{3}{2}x\sqrt{X} - \frac{3}{2}a^2 \arcsin \frac{x}{a}$

177. $\displaystyle\int \frac{\sqrt{X^3}}{x^3}\, dx = -\frac{\sqrt{X^3}}{2x^2} - \frac{3\sqrt{X}}{2} + \frac{3a}{2} \log_e \frac{a + \sqrt{X}}{x}$

178. $\displaystyle\int \frac{dx}{\sqrt{X^3}} = \frac{x}{a^2\sqrt{X}}$

179. $\displaystyle\int \frac{x\, dx}{\sqrt{X^3}} = \frac{1}{\sqrt{X}}$

180. $\displaystyle\int \frac{x^2\, dx}{\sqrt{X^3}} = \frac{x}{\sqrt{X}} - \arcsin \frac{x}{a}$

181. $\displaystyle\int \frac{x^3\, dx}{\sqrt{X^3}} = \sqrt{X} + \frac{a^2}{\sqrt{X}}$

182. $\displaystyle\int \frac{dx}{x\sqrt{X^3}} = \frac{1}{a^2\sqrt{X}} - \frac{1}{a^3} \log_e \frac{a + \sqrt{X}}{x}$

183. $\displaystyle\int \frac{dx}{x^2\sqrt{X^3}} = \frac{1}{a^4}\left(-\frac{\sqrt{X}}{x} + \frac{x}{\sqrt{X}}\right)$

184. $\displaystyle\int \frac{dx}{x^3\sqrt{X^3}} = -\frac{1}{2a^2x^2\sqrt{X}} + \frac{3}{2a^4\sqrt{X}} - \frac{3}{2a^5} \log_e \frac{a + \sqrt{X}}{x}$

(m) Integrals containing $\sqrt{x^2 + a^2}$, with

$$X \equiv x^2 + a^2 \qquad (a > 0)$$

185. $\displaystyle\int \sqrt{X}\, dx = \frac{1}{2}\left(x\sqrt{X} + a^2 \sinh^{-1}\frac{x}{a}\right)$

$$= \frac{1}{2}\left[x\sqrt{X} + a^2 \log_e (x + \sqrt{X})\right] + C_1$$

186. $\displaystyle\int x\sqrt{X}\,dx = \frac{1}{3}\sqrt{X^3}$

187. $\displaystyle\int x^2\sqrt{X}\,dx = \frac{x}{4}\sqrt{X^3} - \frac{a^2}{8}\left(x\sqrt{X} + a^2\sinh^{-1}\frac{x}{a}\right)$

$$= \frac{x}{4}\sqrt{X^3} - \frac{a^2}{8}[x\sqrt{X} + a^2\log_e(x+\sqrt{X})] + C_1$$

188. $\displaystyle\int x^3\sqrt{X}\,dx = \frac{\sqrt{X^5}}{5} - \frac{a^2\sqrt{X^3}}{3}$

189. $\displaystyle\int \frac{\sqrt{X}}{x}\,dx = \sqrt{X} - a\log_e\frac{a+\sqrt{X}}{x}$

190. $\displaystyle\int \frac{\sqrt{X}}{x^2}\,dx = -\frac{\sqrt{X}}{x} + \sinh^{-1}\frac{x}{a}$

$$= -\frac{\sqrt{X}}{x} + \log_e(x+\sqrt{X}) + C_1$$

191. $\displaystyle\int \frac{\sqrt{X}}{x^3}\,dx = -\frac{\sqrt{X}}{2x^2} - \frac{1}{2a}\log_e\frac{a+\sqrt{X}}{x}$

192. $\displaystyle\int \frac{dx}{\sqrt{X}} = \sinh^{-1}\frac{x}{a} = \log_e(x+\sqrt{X}) + C_1$

193. $\displaystyle\int \frac{x\,dx}{\sqrt{X}} = \sqrt{X}$

194. $\displaystyle\int \frac{x^2\,dx}{\sqrt{X}} = \frac{x}{2}\sqrt{X} - \frac{a^2}{2}\sinh^{-1}\frac{x}{a}$

$$= \frac{x}{2}\sqrt{X} - \frac{a^2}{2}\log_e(x+\sqrt{X}) + C_1$$

195. $\displaystyle\int \frac{x^3\,dx}{\sqrt{X}} = \frac{\sqrt{X^3}}{3} - a^2\sqrt{X}$

196. $\displaystyle\int \frac{dx}{x\sqrt{X}} = -\frac{1}{a}\log_e\frac{a+\sqrt{X}}{x}$

197. $\displaystyle\int \frac{dx}{x^2\sqrt{X}} = -\frac{\sqrt{X}}{a^2x}$

198. $\displaystyle\int \frac{dx}{x^3\sqrt{X}} = -\frac{\sqrt{X}}{2a^2x^2} + \frac{1}{2a^3}\log_e \frac{a+\sqrt{X}}{x}$

199. $\displaystyle\int \sqrt{X^3}\,dx = \frac{1}{4}\left(x\sqrt{X^3} + \frac{3a^2x}{2}\sqrt{X} + \frac{3a^4}{2}\sinh^{-1}\frac{x}{a}\right)$

$\displaystyle\qquad = \frac{1}{4}\left[x\sqrt{X^3} + \frac{3a^2x}{2}\sqrt{X} + \frac{3a^4}{2}\log_e(x+\sqrt{X})\right] + C_1$

200. $\displaystyle\int x\sqrt{X^3}\,dx = \frac{1}{5}\sqrt{X^5}$

201. $\displaystyle\int x^2\sqrt{X^3}\,dx = \frac{x\sqrt{X^5}}{6} - \frac{a^2x\sqrt{X^3}}{24} - \frac{a^4x\sqrt{X}}{16} - \frac{a^6}{16}\sinh^{-1}\frac{x}{a}$

$\displaystyle\qquad = \frac{x\sqrt{X^5}}{6} - \frac{a^2x\sqrt{X^3}}{24} - \frac{a^4x\sqrt{X}}{16}$

$\displaystyle\qquad\qquad\qquad\qquad - \frac{a^6}{16}\log_e(x+\sqrt{X}) + C_1$

202. $\displaystyle\int x^3\sqrt{X^3}\,dx = \frac{\sqrt{X^7}}{7} - \frac{a^2\sqrt{X^5}}{5}$

203. $\displaystyle\int \frac{\sqrt{X^3}}{x}\,dx = \frac{\sqrt{X^3}}{3} + a^2\sqrt{X} - a^3\log_e\frac{a+\sqrt{X}}{x}$

204. $\displaystyle\int \frac{\sqrt{X^3}}{x^2}\,dx = -\frac{\sqrt{X^3}}{x} + \frac{3}{2}x\sqrt{X} + \frac{3}{2}a^2\sinh^{-1}\frac{x}{a}$

$\displaystyle\qquad = -\frac{\sqrt{X^3}}{x} + \frac{3}{2}x\sqrt{X} + \frac{3}{2}a^2\log_e(x+\sqrt{X}) + C_1$

205. $\displaystyle\int \frac{\sqrt{X^3}}{x^3}\,dx = -\frac{\sqrt{X^3}}{2x^2} + \frac{3}{2}\sqrt{X} - \frac{3}{2}a\log_e\left(\frac{a+\sqrt{X}}{x}\right)$

206. $\displaystyle\int \frac{dx}{\sqrt{X^3}} = \frac{x}{a^2\sqrt{X}}$

207. $\displaystyle\int \frac{x\,dx}{\sqrt{X^3}} = -\frac{1}{\sqrt{X}}$

208. $\displaystyle\int \frac{x^2\,dx}{\sqrt{X^3}} = -\frac{x}{\sqrt{X}} + \sinh^{-1}\frac{x}{a}$

$\displaystyle\qquad = -\frac{x}{\sqrt{X}} + \log_e(x+\sqrt{X}) + C_1$

209. $\int \dfrac{x^3\,dx}{\sqrt{X^3}} = \sqrt{X} + \dfrac{a^2}{\sqrt{X}}$

210. $\int \dfrac{dx}{x\sqrt{X^3}} = \dfrac{1}{a^2\sqrt{X}} - \dfrac{1}{a^3}\log_e \dfrac{a + \sqrt{X}}{x}$

211. $\int \dfrac{dx}{x^2\sqrt{X^3}} = -\dfrac{1}{a^4}\left(\dfrac{\sqrt{X}}{x} + \dfrac{x}{\sqrt{X}}\right)$

212. $\int \dfrac{dx}{x^3\sqrt{X^3}} = -\dfrac{1}{2a^2x^2\sqrt{X}} - \dfrac{3}{2a^4\sqrt{X}} + \dfrac{3}{2a^5}\log_e \dfrac{a + \sqrt{X}}{x}$

(n) Integrals containing $\sqrt{x^2 - a^2}$, with

$$X \equiv x^2 - a^2 \qquad (a > 0)$$

213. $\int \sqrt{X}\,dx = \dfrac{1}{2}\left(x\sqrt{X} - a^2\cosh^{-1}\dfrac{x}{a}\right)$

$$= \dfrac{1}{2}[x\sqrt{X} - a^2\log_e(x + \sqrt{X})] + C_1$$

214. $\int x\sqrt{X}\,dx = \dfrac{1}{3}\sqrt{X^3}$

215. $\int x^2\sqrt{X}\,dx = \dfrac{x}{4}\sqrt{X^3} + \dfrac{a^2}{8}\left(x\sqrt{X} - a^2\cosh^{-1}\dfrac{x}{a}\right)$

$$= \dfrac{x}{4}\sqrt{X^3} + \dfrac{a^2}{8}[x\sqrt{X} - a^2\log_e(x + \sqrt{X})] + C_1$$

216. $\int x^3\sqrt{X}\,dx = \dfrac{\sqrt{X^5}}{5} + \dfrac{a^2\sqrt{X^3}}{3}$

217. $\int \dfrac{\sqrt{X}}{x}\,dx = \sqrt{X} - a\arccos\dfrac{a}{x}$

218. $\int \dfrac{\sqrt{X}}{x^2}\,dx = -\dfrac{\sqrt{X}}{x} + \cosh^{-1}\dfrac{x}{a}$

$$= -\dfrac{\sqrt{X}}{x} + \log_e(x + \sqrt{X}) + C_1$$

219. $\displaystyle\int \frac{\sqrt{X}}{x^3}\, dx = -\frac{\sqrt{X}}{2x^2} + \frac{1}{2a}\arccos\frac{a}{x}$

220. $\displaystyle\int \frac{dx}{\sqrt{X}} = \cosh^{-1}\frac{x}{a} = \log_e\left(x + \sqrt{X}\right) + C_1$

221. $\displaystyle\int \frac{x\, dx}{\sqrt{X}} = \sqrt{X}$

222. $\displaystyle\int \frac{x^2\, dx}{\sqrt{X}} = \frac{x}{2}\sqrt{X} + \frac{a^2}{2}\cosh^{-1}\frac{x}{a}$

$\displaystyle\qquad = \frac{x}{2}\sqrt{X} + \frac{a^2}{2}\log_e\left(x + \sqrt{X}\right) + C_1$

223. $\displaystyle\int \frac{x^3\, dx}{\sqrt{X}} = \frac{\sqrt{X^3}}{3} + a^2\sqrt{X}$

224. $\displaystyle\int \frac{dx}{x\sqrt{X}} = \frac{1}{a}\arccos\frac{a}{x}$

225. $\displaystyle\int \frac{dx}{x^2\sqrt{X}} = \frac{\sqrt{X}}{a^2 x}$

226. $\displaystyle\int \frac{dx}{x^3\sqrt{X}} = \frac{\sqrt{X}}{2a^2 x^2} + \frac{1}{2a^3}\arccos\frac{a}{x}$

227. $\displaystyle\int \sqrt{X^3}\, dx = \frac{1}{4}\left(x\sqrt{X^3} - \frac{3a^2 x}{2}\sqrt{X} + \frac{3a^4}{2}\cosh^{-1}\frac{x}{a}\right)$

$\displaystyle\qquad = \frac{1}{4}\left[x\sqrt{X^3} - \frac{3a^2 x}{2}\sqrt{X} + \frac{3a^4}{2}\log_e\left(x + \sqrt{X}\right)\right] + C_1$

228. $\displaystyle\int x\sqrt{X^3}\, dx = \frac{1}{5}\sqrt{X^5}$

229. $\displaystyle\int x^2\sqrt{X^3}\, dx = \frac{x\sqrt{X^5}}{6} + \frac{a^2 x\sqrt{X^3}}{24} - \frac{a^4 x\sqrt{X}}{16} + \frac{a^6}{16}\cosh^{-1}\frac{x}{a}$

$\displaystyle\qquad = \frac{x\sqrt{X^5}}{6} + \frac{a^2 x\sqrt{X^3}}{24} - \frac{a^4 x\sqrt{X}}{16}$

$\displaystyle\qquad\qquad\qquad + \frac{a^6}{16}\log_e\left(x + \sqrt{X}\right) + C_1$

230. $\int x^3 \sqrt{X^3}\, dx \quad \dfrac{\sqrt{X^7}}{7} + \dfrac{a^2 \sqrt{X^5}}{5}$

231. $\int \dfrac{\sqrt{X^3}}{x}\, dx = \dfrac{\sqrt{X^3}}{3} - a^2\sqrt{X} + a^3 \arccos \dfrac{a}{x}$

232. $\int \dfrac{\sqrt{X^3}}{x^2}\, dx = -\dfrac{\sqrt{X^3}}{2} + \dfrac{3}{2}x\sqrt{X} - \dfrac{3}{2}a^2 \cosh^{-1} \dfrac{x}{a}$

$$= -\dfrac{\sqrt{X^3}}{2} + \dfrac{3}{2}x\sqrt{X} - \dfrac{3}{2}a^2 \log_e (x + \sqrt{X}) + C_1$$

233. $\int \dfrac{\sqrt{X^3}}{x^3}\, dx = -\dfrac{\sqrt{X^3}}{2x^2} + \dfrac{3\sqrt{X}}{2} - \dfrac{3}{2}a \arccos \dfrac{a}{x}$

234. $\int \dfrac{dx}{\sqrt{X^3}} = -\dfrac{x}{a^2\sqrt{X}}$

235. $\int \dfrac{x\, dx}{\sqrt{X^3}} = -\dfrac{1}{\sqrt{X}}$

236. $\int \dfrac{x^2\, dx}{\sqrt{X^3}} = -\dfrac{x}{\sqrt{X}} + \cosh^{-1} \dfrac{x}{a}$

$$= -\dfrac{x}{\sqrt{X}} + \log_e (x + \sqrt{X}) + C_1$$

237. $\int \dfrac{x^3\, dx}{\sqrt{X^3}} = \sqrt{X} - \dfrac{a^2}{\sqrt{X}}$

238. $\int \dfrac{dx}{x\sqrt{X^3}} = -\dfrac{1}{a^2\sqrt{X}} - \dfrac{1}{a^3} \arccos \dfrac{a}{x}$

239. $\int \dfrac{dx}{x^2\sqrt{X^3}} = -\dfrac{1}{a^4}\left(\dfrac{\sqrt{X}}{x} + \dfrac{x}{\sqrt{X}} \right)$

240. $\int \dfrac{dx}{x^3\sqrt{X^3}} = \dfrac{1}{2a^2 x^2 \sqrt{X}} - \dfrac{3}{2a^4\sqrt{X}} - \dfrac{3}{2a^5} \arccos \dfrac{a}{x}$

(o) Integrals containing $\sqrt{ax^2 + bx + c}$, with

$$X \equiv ax^2 + bx + c$$

$$\Delta = 4ac - b^2 \qquad k = \dfrac{4a}{4ac - b^2} \qquad\qquad (a \neq 0)$$

241. $\displaystyle \int \frac{dx}{\sqrt{X}} = \begin{cases} \dfrac{1}{\sqrt{a}} \log_e (2\sqrt{aX} + 2ax + b) + C & (a > 0) \\[3mm] \dfrac{1}{\sqrt{a}} \sinh^{-1} \dfrac{2ax + b}{\sqrt{\Delta}} + C_1 & (a > 0, \Delta > 0) \\[3mm] \dfrac{1}{\sqrt{a}} \log_e (2ax + b) & (a > 0, \Delta = 0) \\[3mm] -\dfrac{1}{\sqrt{-a}} \arcsin \dfrac{2ax + b}{\sqrt{-\Delta}} & (a < 0, \Delta < 0) \end{cases}$

242. $\displaystyle \int \frac{dx}{X\sqrt{X}} = \frac{2(2ax + b)}{\Delta\sqrt{X}} \qquad (\Delta \neq 0)$

243. $\displaystyle \int \frac{dx}{X^2\sqrt{X}} = \frac{2(2ax + b)}{3\Delta\sqrt{X}} \left(\frac{1}{X} + 2k \right) \qquad (\Delta \neq 0)$

244. $\displaystyle \int \frac{dx}{X^{(2n+1)/2}} = \frac{2(2ax + b)}{(2n - 1)\Delta X^{(2n-1)/2}} + \frac{2k(n - 1)}{2n - 1} \int \frac{dx}{X^{(2n-1)/2}}$

$$(\Delta \neq 0)$$

245. $\displaystyle \int \sqrt{X}\, dx = \frac{(2ax + b)\sqrt{X}}{4a} + \frac{1}{2k} \int \frac{dx}{\sqrt{X}}$

246. $\displaystyle \int X\sqrt{X}\, dx = \frac{(2ax + b)\sqrt{X}}{8a} \left(X + \frac{3}{2k} \right) + \frac{3}{8k^2} \int \frac{dx}{\sqrt{X}}$

247. $\displaystyle \int X^2\sqrt{X}\, dx = \frac{(2ax + b)\sqrt{X}}{12a} \left(X^2 + \frac{5X}{4k} + \frac{15}{8k^2} \right) + \frac{5}{16k^3} \int \frac{dx}{\sqrt{X}}$

248. $\displaystyle \int X^{(2n+1)/2}\, dx = \frac{(2ax + b)X^{(2n+1)/2}}{4a(n + 1)} + \frac{2n + 1}{2k(n + 1)} \int X^{(2n-1)/2}\, dx$

249. $\displaystyle \int \frac{x\, dx}{\sqrt{X}} = \frac{\sqrt{X}}{a} - \frac{b}{2a} \int \frac{dx}{\sqrt{X}}$

250. $\displaystyle \int \frac{x\, dx}{X\sqrt{X}} = -\frac{2(bx + 2c)}{\Delta\sqrt{X}} \qquad (\Delta \neq 0)$

251. $\displaystyle \int \frac{x\, dx}{X^{(2n+1)/2}} = -\frac{1}{(2n - 1)aX^{(2n-1)/2}} - \frac{b}{2a} \int \frac{dx}{X^{(2n+1)/2}}$

252. $\int \dfrac{x^2 \, dx}{\sqrt{X}} = \left(\dfrac{x}{2a} - \dfrac{3b}{4a^2}\right)\sqrt{X} + \dfrac{3b^2 - 4ac}{8a^2}\int \dfrac{dx}{\sqrt{X}}$

253. $\int \dfrac{x^2 \, dx}{X\sqrt{X}} = \dfrac{(2b^2 - 4ac)x + 2bc}{a\Delta\sqrt{X}} + \dfrac{1}{a}\int \dfrac{dx}{\sqrt{X}} \qquad (\Delta \neq 0)$

254. $\int x\sqrt{X} \, dx = \dfrac{X\sqrt{X}}{3a} - \dfrac{b(2ax + b)}{8a^2}\sqrt{X} - \dfrac{b}{4ak}\int \dfrac{dx}{\sqrt{X}}$

255. $\int xX\sqrt{X} \, dx = \dfrac{X^2\sqrt{X}}{5a} - \dfrac{b}{2a}\int X\sqrt{X} \, dx$

256. $\int xX^{(2n+1)/2} \, dx = \dfrac{X^{(2n+3)/2}}{(2n + 3)a} - \dfrac{b}{2a}\int X^{(2n+1)/2} \, dx$

257. $\int x^2\sqrt{X} \, dx = \left(x - \dfrac{5b}{6a}\right)\dfrac{X\sqrt{X}}{4a} + \dfrac{5b^2 - 4ac}{16a^2}\int \sqrt{X} \, dx$

258. $\int \dfrac{dx}{x\sqrt{X}} = \begin{cases} -\dfrac{1}{\sqrt{c}}\log_e\left(\dfrac{2\sqrt{cX}}{x} + \dfrac{2c}{x} + b\right) + C & (c > 0) \\[3mm] -\dfrac{1}{\sqrt{c}}\sinh^{-1}\dfrac{bx + 2c}{x\sqrt{\Delta}} + C_1 & (c > 0, \Delta > 0) \\[3mm] -\dfrac{1}{\sqrt{c}}\log_e\dfrac{bx + 2c}{x} & (c > 0, \Delta = 0) \\[3mm] \dfrac{1}{\sqrt{-c}}\arcsin\dfrac{bx + 2c}{x\sqrt{-\Delta}} & (c < 0, \Delta < 0) \end{cases}$

259. $\int \dfrac{dx}{x^2\sqrt{X}} = -\dfrac{\sqrt{X}}{cx} - \dfrac{b}{2c}\int \dfrac{dx}{x\sqrt{X}}$

260. $\int \dfrac{\sqrt{X} \, dx}{x} = \sqrt{X} + \dfrac{b}{2}\int \dfrac{dx}{\sqrt{X}} + c\int \dfrac{dx}{x\sqrt{X}}$

261. $\int \dfrac{\sqrt{X} \, dx}{x^2} = -\dfrac{\sqrt{X}}{x} + a\int \dfrac{dx}{\sqrt{X}} + \dfrac{b}{2}\int \dfrac{dx}{x\sqrt{X}}$

262. $\int \dfrac{X^{(2n+1)/2}}{x} \, dx = \dfrac{X^{(2n+1)/2}}{2n + 1} + \dfrac{b}{2}\int X^{(2n-1)/2} \, dx + c\int \dfrac{X^{(2n-1)/2}}{x} \, dx$

(p) Other irrational forms $(a > 0, b \neq 0)$

263. $\displaystyle \int \frac{dx}{x\sqrt{ax^2 + bx}} = -\frac{2}{bx}\sqrt{ax^2 + bx}$

264. $\displaystyle \int \frac{dx}{\sqrt{2ax - x^2}} = \arcsin \frac{x - a}{a}$

265. $\displaystyle \int \frac{x\,dx}{\sqrt{2ax - x^2}} = -\sqrt{2ax - x^2} + a \arcsin \frac{x - a}{a}$

266. $\displaystyle \int \sqrt{2ax - x^2}\,dx = \frac{x - a}{2}\sqrt{2ax - x^2} + \frac{a^2}{2}\arcsin \frac{x - a}{a}$

267. $\displaystyle \int \frac{dx}{(ax^2 + b)\sqrt{fx^2 + g}} = \frac{1}{\sqrt{b}\,\sqrt{ag - bf}}\arctan \frac{x\sqrt{ag - bf}}{\sqrt{b}\,\sqrt{fx^2 + g}}$

$$(ag - bf > 0)$$

$$= \frac{1}{2\sqrt{b}\,\sqrt{bf - ag}}\log_e \frac{\sqrt{b}\,\sqrt{fx^2 + g} + x\sqrt{bf - ag}}{\sqrt{b}\,\sqrt{fx^2 + g} - x\sqrt{bf - ag}}\quad (ag - bf < 0)$$

268. $\displaystyle \int \sqrt[n]{ax + b}\,dx = \frac{n(ax + b)}{(n + 1)a}\sqrt[n]{ax + b}$

269. $\displaystyle \int \frac{dx}{\sqrt[n]{ax + b}}\,dx = \frac{n(ax + b)}{(n - 1)a}\frac{1}{\sqrt[n]{ax + b}}$

270. $\displaystyle \int \frac{dx}{x\sqrt{x^n + a^2}} = -\frac{2}{na}\log_e \frac{a + \sqrt{x^n + a^2}}{\sqrt{x^n}}$

271. $\displaystyle \int \frac{dx}{x\sqrt{x^n - a^2}} = \frac{2}{na}\arccos \frac{a}{\sqrt{x^n}}$

272. $\displaystyle \int \frac{\sqrt{x}\,dx}{\sqrt{a^3 - x^3}} = \frac{2}{3}\arcsin \sqrt{\left(\frac{x}{a}\right)^3}$

(q) Recursion formulas *(m, n, p are integers)*

273. $\displaystyle \int x^m(ax^n + b)^p\,dx$

$$= \frac{1}{m + np + 1}\left[x^{m+1}(ax^n + b)^p + npb \int x^m(ax^n + b)^{p-1}\,dx \right]$$

$$= \frac{1}{bn(p+1)} \left[-x^{m+1}(ax^n + b)^{p+1} \right.$$
$$\left. + (m + n + np + 1) \int x^m (ax^n + b)^{p+1} \, dx \right]$$

$$= \frac{1}{(m+1)b} \left[x^{m+1}(ax^n + b)^{p+1} \right.$$
$$\left. - a(m + n + np + 1) \int x^{m+n} (ax^n + b)^p \, dx \right]$$

$$= \frac{1}{a(m+np+1)} \left[x^{m-n+1}(ax^n + b)^{p+1} \right.$$
$$\left. - (m - n + 1)b \int x^{m-n} (ax^n + b)^p \, dx \right]$$

(r) Integrals containing the sine function $(a \neq 0)$

274. $\displaystyle \int \sin ax \, dx = -\frac{1}{a} \cos ax$

275. $\displaystyle \int \sin^2 ax \, dx = \frac{1}{2}x - \frac{1}{4a} \sin 2ax$

276. $\displaystyle \int \sin^3 ax \, dx = -\frac{1}{a} \cos ax + \frac{1}{3a} \cos^3 ax$

277. $\displaystyle \int \sin^4 ax \, dx = \frac{3}{8}x - \frac{1}{4a} \sin 2ax + \frac{1}{32a} \sin 4ax$

278. $\displaystyle \int \sin^n ax \, dx = -\frac{\sin^{n-1} ax \cos ax}{na} + \frac{n-1}{n} \int \sin^{n-2} ax \, dx \quad (n > 0)$

279. $\displaystyle \int x \sin ax \, dx = \frac{\sin ax}{a^2} - \frac{x \cos ax}{a}$

280. $\displaystyle \int x^2 \sin ax \, dx = \frac{2x}{a^2} \sin ax - \left(\frac{x^2}{a} - \frac{2}{a^3} \right) \cos ax$

281. $\displaystyle \int x^3 \sin ax \, dx = \left(\frac{3x^2}{a^2} - \frac{6}{a^4} \right) \sin ax - \left(\frac{x^3}{a} - \frac{6x}{a^3} \right) \cos ax$

282. $\displaystyle \int x^n \sin ax \, dx = -\frac{x^n}{a} \cos ax + \frac{n}{a} \int x^{n-1} \cos ax \, dx$

283. $\displaystyle \int \frac{\sin ax}{x} \, dx = ax - \frac{(ax)^3}{3 \cdot 3!} + \frac{(ax)^5}{5 \cdot 5!} - \frac{(ax)^7}{7 \cdot 7!} + \cdots$

284. $\displaystyle\int \frac{\sin ax}{x^2}\, dx = -\frac{\sin ax}{x} + a \int \frac{\cos ax\, dx}{x}$

285. $\displaystyle\int \frac{\sin ax}{x^n}\, dx = -\frac{1}{n-1}\frac{\sin ax}{x^{n-1}} + \frac{a}{n-1}\int \frac{\cos ax}{x^{n-1}}\, dx$

286. $\displaystyle\int \frac{dx}{\sin ax} = \int \operatorname{cosec} ax\, dx = \frac{1}{a} \log_e \tan \frac{ax}{2}$

$$= \frac{1}{a} \log_e (\operatorname{cosec} ax - \cot ax)$$

287. $\displaystyle\int \frac{dx}{\sin^2 ax} = -\frac{1}{a} \cot ax$

288. $\displaystyle\int \frac{dx}{\sin^3 ax} = -\frac{\cos ax}{2a \sin^2 ax} + \frac{1}{2a} \log_e \tan \frac{ax}{2}$

289. $\displaystyle\int \frac{dx}{\sin^n ax} = -\frac{1}{a(n-1)}\frac{\cos ax}{\sin^{n-1} ax} + \frac{n-2}{n-1}\int \frac{dx}{\sin^{n-2} ax} \qquad (n > 1)$

290. $\displaystyle\int \frac{x\, dx}{\sin ax} = \frac{1}{a^2}\left[ax + \frac{(ax)^3}{3 \cdot 3!} + \frac{7(ax)^5}{3 \cdot 5 \cdot 5!} + \frac{31(ax)^7}{3 \cdot 7 \cdot 7!}\right.$

$$\left. + \frac{127(ax)^9}{3 \cdot 5 \cdot 9!} + \cdots \right]$$

291. $\displaystyle\int \frac{x\, dx}{\sin^2 ax} = -\frac{x}{a} \cot ax + \frac{1}{a^2} \log_e \sin ax$

292. $\displaystyle\int \frac{x\, dx}{\sin^n ax} = -\frac{x \cos ax}{(n-1)a \sin^{n-1} ax} - \frac{1}{(n-1)(n-2)a^2 \sin^{n-2} ax}$

$$+ \frac{n-2}{n-1}\int \frac{x\, dx}{\sin^{n-2} ax} \qquad (n > 2)$$

293. $\displaystyle\int \frac{dx}{1 + \sin ax} = -\frac{1}{a} \tan \left(\frac{\pi}{4} - \frac{ax}{2} \right)$

294. $\displaystyle\int \frac{dx}{1 - \sin ax} = \frac{1}{a} \tan \left(\frac{\pi}{4} + \frac{ax}{2} \right)$

295. $\displaystyle\int \frac{x\, dx}{1 + \sin ax} = -\frac{x}{a} \tan \left(\frac{\pi}{4} - \frac{ax}{2} \right) + \frac{2}{a^2} \log_e \cos \left(\frac{\pi}{4} - \frac{ax}{2} \right)$

296. $\displaystyle\int \frac{x\, dx}{1 - \sin ax} = \frac{x}{a} \cot \left(\frac{\pi}{4} - \frac{ax}{2} \right) + \frac{2}{a^2} \log_e \sin \left(\frac{\pi}{4} - \frac{ax}{2} \right)$

297. $\displaystyle\int \frac{\sin ax\, dx}{1 \pm \sin ax} = \pm x + \frac{1}{a} \tan\left(\frac{\pi}{4} \mp \frac{ax}{2}\right)$

298. $\displaystyle\int \frac{dx}{\sin ax\,(1 \pm \sin ax)} = \frac{1}{a} \tan\left(\frac{\pi}{4} \mp \frac{ax}{2}\right) + \frac{1}{a} \log_e \tan \frac{ax}{2}$

299. $\displaystyle\int \frac{dx}{(1 + \sin ax)^2} = -\frac{1}{2a} \tan\left(\frac{\pi}{4} - \frac{ax}{2}\right) - \frac{1}{6a} \tan^3\left(\frac{\pi}{4} - \frac{ax}{2}\right)$

300. $\displaystyle\int \frac{dx}{(1 - \sin ax)^2} = \frac{1}{2a} \cot\left(\frac{\pi}{4} - \frac{ax}{2}\right) + \frac{1}{6a} \cot^3\left(\frac{\pi}{4} - \frac{ax}{2}\right)$

301. $\displaystyle\int \frac{\sin ax\, dx}{(1 + \sin ax)^2} = -\frac{1}{2a} \tan\left(\frac{\pi}{4} - \frac{ax}{2}\right) + \frac{1}{6a} \tan^3\left(\frac{\pi}{4} - \frac{ax}{2}\right)$

302. $\displaystyle\int \frac{\sin ax\, dx}{(1 - \sin ax)^2} = -\frac{1}{2a} \cot\left(\frac{\pi}{4} - \frac{ax}{2}\right) + \frac{1}{6a} \cot^3\left(\frac{\pi}{4} - \frac{ax}{2}\right)$

303. $\displaystyle\int \frac{dx}{1 + \sin^2 ax} = \frac{1}{2\sqrt{2}\,a} \arcsin\left(\frac{3\sin^2 ax - 1}{\sin^2 ax + 1}\right)$

304. $\displaystyle\int \frac{dx}{1 - \sin^2 ax} = \int \frac{dx}{\cos^2 ax} = \frac{1}{a} \tan ax$

305. $\displaystyle\int \sin ax \sin bx\, dx = \frac{\sin (a - b)x}{2(a - b)} - \frac{\sin (a + b)x}{2(a + b)}$

$(|a| \neq |b|;$ for $|a| = |b|$ see 275)

306. $\displaystyle\int \frac{dx}{b + c \sin ax} = \frac{2}{a\sqrt{b^2 - c^2}} \arctan \frac{b \tan (ax/2) + c}{\sqrt{b^2 - c^2}}$ $\quad (b^2 > c^2)$

$\displaystyle\qquad\qquad = \frac{1}{a\sqrt{c^2 - b^2}} \log_e \frac{b \tan (ax/2) + c - \sqrt{c^2 - b^2}}{b \tan (ax/2) + c + \sqrt{c^2 - b^2}}$

$(b^2 < c^2)$

307. $\displaystyle\int \frac{\sin ax\, dx}{b + c \sin ax} = \frac{x}{c} - \frac{b}{c} \int \frac{dx}{b + c \sin ax}$

308. $\displaystyle\int \frac{dx}{\sin ax\,(b + c \sin ax)} = \frac{1}{ab} \log_e \tan \frac{ax}{2} - \frac{c}{b} \int \frac{dx}{b + c \sin ax}$

309. $\displaystyle\int \frac{dx}{(b + c \sin ax)^2} = \frac{c \cos ax}{a(b^2 - c^2)(b + c \sin ax)}$

$\displaystyle\qquad\qquad\qquad\qquad + \frac{b}{b^2 - c^2} \int \frac{dx}{b + c \sin ax}$

310. $\displaystyle \int \frac{\sin ax \, dx}{(b + c \sin ax)^2} = \frac{b \cos ax}{a(c^2 - b^2)(b + c \sin ax)}$

$$+ \frac{c}{c^2 - b^2} \int \frac{dx}{b + c \sin ax}$$

311. $\displaystyle \int \frac{dx}{b^2 + c^2 \sin^2 ax} = \frac{1}{ab\sqrt{b^2 + c^2}} \arctan \frac{\sqrt{b^2 + c^2} \tan ax}{b} \qquad (b > 0)$

312. $\displaystyle \int \frac{dx}{b^2 - c^2 \sin^2 ax} = \frac{1}{ab\sqrt{b^2 - c^2}} \arctan \frac{\sqrt{b^2 - c^2} \tan ax}{b}$

$$(b^2 > c^2, \, b > 0)$$

$$= \frac{1}{2ab\sqrt{c^2 - b^2}} \log_e \frac{\sqrt{c^2 - b^2} \tan ax + b}{\sqrt{c^2 - b^2} \tan ax - b}$$

$$(c^2 > b^2, \, b > 0)$$

(s) Integrals containing the cosine function $\qquad (a \neq 0)$

313. $\displaystyle \int \cos ax \, dx = \frac{1}{a} \sin ax$

314. $\displaystyle \int \cos^2 ax \, dx = \frac{1}{2}x + \frac{1}{4a} \sin 2ax$

315. $\displaystyle \int \cos^3 ax \, dx = \frac{1}{a} \sin ax - \frac{1}{3a} \sin^3 ax$

316. $\displaystyle \int \cos^4 ax \, dx = \frac{3}{8}x + \frac{1}{4a} \sin 2ax + \frac{1}{32a} \sin 4ax$

317. $\displaystyle \int \cos^n ax \, dx = \frac{\cos^{n-1} ax \sin ax}{na} + \frac{n-1}{n} \int \cos^{n-2} ax \, dx$

318. $\displaystyle \int x \cos ax \, dx = \frac{\cos ax}{a^2} + \frac{x \sin ax}{a}$

319. $\displaystyle \int x^2 \cos ax \, dx = \frac{2x}{a^2} \cos ax + \left(\frac{x^2}{a} - \frac{2}{a^3} \right) \sin ax$

320. $\displaystyle \int x^3 \cos ax \, dx = \left(\frac{3x^2}{a^2} - \frac{6}{a^4} \right) \cos ax + \left(\frac{x^3}{a} - \frac{6x}{a^3} \right) \sin ax$

321. $\displaystyle \int x^n \cos ax \, dx = \frac{x^n \sin ax}{a} - \frac{n}{a} \int x^{n-1} \sin ax \, dx \qquad (n > 0)$

322. $\displaystyle\int \frac{\cos ax}{x}\, dx = \log_e (ax) - \frac{(ax)^2}{2 \cdot 2!} + \frac{(ax)^4}{4 \cdot 4!} - \frac{(ax)^6}{6 \cdot 6!} + \cdots$

323. $\displaystyle\int \frac{\cos ax}{x^2}\, dx = -\frac{\cos ax}{x} - a \int \frac{\sin ax\, dx}{x}$

324. $\displaystyle\int \frac{\cos ax}{x^n}\, dx = -\frac{\cos ax}{(n-1)x^{n-1}} - \frac{a}{n-1} \int \frac{\sin ax\, dx}{x^{n-1}} \qquad (n \neq 1)$

325. $\displaystyle\int \frac{dx}{\cos ax} = \frac{1}{a} \log_e \tan \left(\frac{ax}{2} + \frac{\pi}{4}\right) = \frac{1}{a} \log_e (\sec ax + \tan ax)$

326. $\displaystyle\int \frac{dx}{\cos^2 ax} = \frac{1}{a} \tan ax$

327. $\displaystyle\int \frac{dx}{\cos^3 ax} = \frac{\sin ax}{2a \cos^2 ax} + \frac{1}{2a} \log_e \tan \left(\frac{\pi}{4} + \frac{ax}{2}\right)$

328. $\displaystyle\int \frac{dx}{\cos^n ax} = \frac{1}{a(n-1)} \frac{\sin ax}{\cos^{n-1} ax} + \frac{n-2}{n-1} \int \frac{dx}{\cos^{n-2} ax} \qquad (n > 1)$

329. $\displaystyle\int \frac{x\, dx}{\cos ax} = \frac{1}{a^2} \left[\frac{(ax)^2}{2} + \frac{(ax)^4}{4 \cdot 2!} + \frac{5(ax)^6}{6 \cdot 4!} + \frac{61(ax)^8}{8 \cdot 6!} \right.$
$$\left. + \frac{1{,}385(ax)^{10}}{10 \cdot 8!} + \cdots \right]$$

330. $\displaystyle\int \frac{x\, dx}{\cos^2 ax} = \frac{x}{a} \tan ax + \frac{1}{a^2} \log_e \cos ax$

331. $\displaystyle\int \frac{x\, dx}{\cos^n ax} = \frac{x \sin ax}{(n-1)a \cos^{n-1} ax} - \frac{1}{(n-1)(n-2)a^2 \cos^{n-2} ax}$
$$+ \frac{n-2}{n-1} \int \frac{x\, dx}{\cos^{n-2} ax} \qquad (n > 2)$$

332. $\displaystyle\int \frac{dx}{1 + \cos ax} = \frac{1}{a} \tan \frac{ax}{2}$

333. $\displaystyle\int \frac{dx}{1 - \cos ax} = -\frac{1}{a} \cot \frac{ax}{2}$

334. $\displaystyle\int \frac{x\, dx}{1 + \cos ax} = \frac{x}{a} \tan \frac{ax}{2} + \frac{2}{a^2} \log_e \cos \frac{ax}{2}$

335. $\displaystyle\int \frac{x\, dx}{1 - \cos ax} = -\frac{x}{a} \cot \frac{ax}{2} + \frac{2}{a^2} \log_e \sin \frac{ax}{2}$

336. $\displaystyle\int \frac{\cos ax\, dx}{1 + \cos ax} = x - \frac{1}{a}\tan\frac{ax}{2}$

337. $\displaystyle\int \frac{\cos ax\, dx}{1 - \cos ax} = -x - \frac{1}{a}\cot\frac{ax}{2}$

338. $\displaystyle\int \frac{dx}{\cos ax\,(1 + \cos ax)} = \frac{1}{a}\log_e \tan\left(\frac{\pi}{4} + \frac{ax}{2}\right) - \frac{1}{a}\tan\frac{ax}{2}$

339. $\displaystyle\int \frac{dx}{\cos ax\,(1 - \cos ax)} = \frac{1}{a}\log_e \tan\left(\frac{\pi}{4} + \frac{ax}{2}\right) - \frac{1}{a}\cot\frac{ax}{2}$

340. $\displaystyle\int \frac{dx}{(1 + \cos ax)^2} = \frac{1}{2a}\tan\frac{ax}{2} + \frac{1}{6a}\tan^3\frac{ax}{2}$

341. $\displaystyle\int \frac{dx}{(1 - \cos ax)^2} = -\frac{1}{2a}\cot\frac{ax}{2} - \frac{1}{6a}\cot^3\frac{ax}{2}$

342. $\displaystyle\int \frac{\cos ax\, dx}{(1 + \cos ax)^2} = \frac{1}{2a}\tan\frac{ax}{2} - \frac{1}{6a}\tan^3\frac{ax}{2}$

343. $\displaystyle\int \frac{\cos ax\, dx}{(1 - \cos ax)^2} = \frac{1}{2a}\cot\frac{ax}{2} - \frac{1}{6a}\cot^3\frac{ax}{2}$

344. $\displaystyle\int \frac{dx}{1 + \cos^2 ax} = \frac{1}{2\sqrt{2}\,a}\arcsin\left(\frac{1 - 3\cos^2 ax}{1 + \cos^2 ax}\right)$

345. $\displaystyle\int \frac{dx}{1 - \cos^2 ax} = \int \frac{dx}{\sin^2 ax} = -\frac{1}{a}\cot ax$

346. $\displaystyle\int \cos ax \cos bx\, dx = \frac{\sin(a - b)x}{2(a - b)} + \frac{\sin(a + b)x}{2(a + b)}$

$$(|a| \neq |b|;\ \text{for } |a| = |b|,\ \text{see } 314)$$

347. $\displaystyle\int \frac{dx}{b + c\cos ax} = \frac{2}{a\sqrt{b^2 - c^2}}\arctan\frac{(b - c)\tan(ax/2)}{\sqrt{b^2 - c^2}}\quad (b^2 > c^2)$

$$= \frac{1}{a\sqrt{c^2 - b^2}}\log_e \frac{(c - b)\tan(ax/2) + \sqrt{c^2 - b^2}}{(c - b)\tan(ax/2) - \sqrt{c^2 - b^2}}$$

$$(b^2 < c^2)$$

348. $\displaystyle\int \frac{\cos ax\, dx}{b + c\cos ax} = \frac{x}{c} - \frac{b}{c}\int \frac{dx}{b + c\cos ax}$

349. $\displaystyle\int \frac{dx}{\cos ax \, (b + c \cos ax)} = \frac{1}{ab} \log_e \tan\left(\frac{ax}{2} + \frac{\pi}{4}\right) - \frac{c}{b} \int \frac{dx}{b + c \cos ax}$

350. $\displaystyle\int \frac{dx}{(b + c \cos ax)^2} = \frac{c \sin ax}{a(c^2 - b^2)(b + c \cos ax)}$

$$- \frac{b}{c^2 - b^2} \int \frac{dx}{b + c \cos ax}$$

351. $\displaystyle\int \frac{\cos ax \, dx}{(b + c \cos ax)^2} = \frac{b \sin ax}{a(b^2 - c^2)(b + c \cos ax)}$

$$- \frac{c}{b^2 - c^2} \int \frac{dx}{b + c \cos ax}$$

352. $\displaystyle\int \frac{dx}{b^2 + c^2 \cos^2 ax} = \frac{1}{ab\sqrt{b^2 + c^2}} \arctan \frac{b \tan ax}{\sqrt{b^2 + c^2}} \qquad (b > 0)$

353. $\displaystyle\int \frac{dx}{b^2 - c^2 \cos^2 ax} = \frac{1}{ab\sqrt{b^2 - c^2}} \arctan \frac{b \tan ax}{\sqrt{b^2 - c^2}} \quad (b^2 > c^2, b > 0)$

$$= \frac{1}{2ab\sqrt{c^2 - b^2}} \log_e \frac{b \tan ax - \sqrt{c^2 - b^2}}{b \tan ax + \sqrt{c^2 - b^2}}$$

$$(c^2 > b^2, \, b > 0)$$

(t) Integrals containing both sine and cosine $\qquad (a \neq 0)$

354. $\displaystyle\int \sin ax \cos ax \, dx = \frac{1}{2a} \sin^2 ax$

355. $\displaystyle\int \sin^2 ax \cos^2 ax \, dx = \frac{x}{8} - \frac{\sin 4ax}{32a}$

356. $\displaystyle\int \sin^n ax \cos ax \, dx = \frac{1}{a(n + 1)} \sin^{n+1} ax \qquad (n \neq -1)$

357. $\displaystyle\int \sin ax \cos^n ax \, dx = -\frac{1}{a(n + 1)} \cos^{n+1} ax \qquad (n \neq -1)$

358. $\displaystyle\int \sin^n ax \cos^m ax \, dx$

$$= -\frac{\sin^{n-1} ax \cos^{m+1} ax}{a(n + m)} + \frac{n - 1}{n + m} \int \sin^{n-2} ax \cos^m ax \, dx$$

$$(m, \, n > 0)$$

$$= \frac{\sin^{n+1} ax \cos^{m-1} ax}{a(n + m)} + \frac{m - 1}{n + m} \int \sin^n ax \cos^{m-2} ax\, dx$$

$$(m, n > 0)$$

359. $\displaystyle\int \frac{dx}{\sin ax \cos ax} = \frac{1}{a} \log_e \tan ax$

360. $\displaystyle\int \frac{dx}{\sin^2 ax \cos ax} = \frac{1}{a}\left[\log_e \tan\left(\frac{\pi}{4} + \frac{ax}{2}\right) - \frac{1}{\sin ax}\right]$

361. $\displaystyle\int \frac{dx}{\sin ax \cos^2 ax} = \frac{1}{a}\left(\log_e \tan \frac{ax}{2} + \frac{1}{\cos ax}\right)$

362. $\displaystyle\int \frac{dx}{\sin^3 ax \cos ax} = \frac{1}{a}\left(\log_e \tan ax - \frac{1}{2\sin^2 ax}\right)$

363. $\displaystyle\int \frac{dx}{\sin ax \cos^3 ax} = \frac{1}{a}\left(\log_e \tan ax + \frac{1}{2\cos^2 ax}\right)$

364. $\displaystyle\int \frac{dx}{\sin^2 ax \cos^2 ax} = -\frac{2}{a}\cot 2ax$

365. $\displaystyle\int \frac{dx}{\sin^2 ax \cos^3 ax} = \frac{1}{a}\left[\frac{\sin ax}{2\cos^2 ax} - \frac{1}{\sin ax} + \frac{3}{2}\log_e \tan\left(\frac{\pi}{4} + \frac{ax}{2}\right)\right]$

366. $\displaystyle\int \frac{dx}{\sin^3 ax \cos^2 ax} = \frac{1}{a}\left(\frac{1}{\cos ax} - \frac{\cos ax}{2\sin^2 ax} + \frac{3}{2}\log_e \tan \frac{ax}{2}\right)$

367. $\displaystyle\int \frac{dx}{\sin ax \cos^n ax} = \frac{1}{a(n - 1)\cos^{n-1} ax} + \int \frac{dx}{\sin ax \cos^{n-2} ax}$

$$(n \neq 1); \text{ (see 361, 363)}$$

368. $\displaystyle\int \frac{dx}{\sin^n ax \cos ax} = -\frac{1}{a(n - 1)\sin^{n-1} ax} + \int \frac{dx}{\sin^{n-2} ax \cos ax}$

$$(n \neq 1); \text{ (see 360, 362)}$$

369. $\displaystyle\int \frac{dx}{\sin^n ax \cos^m ax}$

$$= -\frac{1}{a(n - 1)} \cdot \frac{1}{\sin^{n-1} ax \cos^{m-1} ax} + \frac{n + m - 2}{n - 1} \int \frac{dx}{\sin^{n-2} ax \cos^m ax}$$

$$(m > 0, n > 1)$$

$$= \frac{1}{a(m - 1)} \cdot \frac{1}{\sin^{n-1} ax \cos^{m-1} ax} + \frac{n + m - 2}{m - 1} \int \frac{dx}{\sin^n ax \cos^{m-2} ax}$$

$$(n > 0, m > 1)$$

370. $\displaystyle\int \frac{\sin ax\,dx}{\cos^2 ax} = \frac{1}{a\cos ax}$

371. $\displaystyle\int \frac{\sin ax\,dx}{\cos^3 ax} = \frac{1}{2a\cos^2 ax} = \frac{1}{2a}\tan^2 ax + C_1$

372. $\displaystyle\int \frac{\sin ax\,dx}{\cos^n ax} = \frac{1}{a(n-1)\cos^{n-1} ax}$

373. $\displaystyle\int \frac{\sin^2 ax\,dx}{\cos ax} = -\frac{1}{a}\sin ax + \frac{1}{a}\log_e \tan\left(\frac{\pi}{4} + \frac{ax}{2}\right)$

374. $\displaystyle\int \frac{\sin^2 ax\,dx}{\cos^3 ax} = \frac{1}{a}\left[\frac{\sin ax}{2\cos^2 ax} - \frac{1}{2}\log_e \tan\left(\frac{\pi}{4} + \frac{ax}{2}\right)\right]$

375. $\displaystyle\int \frac{\sin^2 ax\,dx}{\cos^n ax} = \frac{\sin ax}{a(n-1)\cos^{n-1} ax} - \frac{1}{n-1}\int \frac{dx}{\cos^{n-2} ax}$

$$(n \neq 1) \qquad \text{(see 325, 326, 328)}$$

376. $\displaystyle\int \frac{\sin^3 ax\,dx}{\cos ax} = -\frac{1}{a}\left(\frac{\sin^2 ax}{2} + \log_e \cos ax\right)$

377. $\displaystyle\int \frac{\sin^3 ax\,dx}{\cos^2 ax} = \frac{1}{a}\left(\cos ax + \frac{1}{\cos ax}\right)$

378. $\displaystyle\int \frac{\sin^3 ax\,dx}{\cos^n ax} = \frac{1}{a}\left[\frac{1}{(n-1)\cos^{n-1} ax} - \frac{1}{(n-3)\cos^{n-3} ax}\right]$

$$(n \neq 1,\ n \neq 3)$$

379. $\displaystyle\int \frac{\sin^n ax}{\cos ax}\,dx = -\frac{\sin^{n-1} ax}{a(n-1)} + \int \frac{\sin^{n-2} ax\,dx}{\cos ax} \qquad (n \neq 1)$

380. $\displaystyle\int \frac{\sin^n ax}{\cos^m ax}\,dx = \frac{\sin^{n+1} ax}{a(m-1)\cos^{m-1} ax} - \frac{n-m+2}{m-1}\int \frac{\sin^n ax}{\cos^{m-2} ax}\,dx$

$$(m \neq 1)$$

$$= -\frac{\sin^{n-1} ax}{a(n-m)\cos^{m-1} ax} + \frac{n-1}{n-m}\int \frac{\sin^{n-2} ax\,dx}{\cos^m ax}$$

$$(m \neq n)$$

$$= \frac{\sin^{n-1} ax}{a(m-1)\cos^{m-1} ax} - \frac{n-1}{m-1}\int \frac{\sin^{n-1} ax\,dx}{\cos^{m-2} ax}$$

$$(m \neq 1)$$

381. $\displaystyle\int \frac{\cos ax\, dx}{\sin^2 ax} = -\frac{1}{a \sin ax}$

382. $\displaystyle\int \frac{\cos ax\, dx}{\sin^3 ax} = -\frac{1}{2a \sin^2 ax}$

383. $\displaystyle\int \frac{\cos ax\, dx}{\sin^n ax} = -\frac{1}{a(n-1) \sin^{n-1} ax} \qquad (n \neq 1)$

384. $\displaystyle\int \frac{\cos^2 ax\, dx}{\sin ax} = \frac{1}{a}\left(\cos ax + \log_e \tan \frac{ax}{2} \right)$

385. $\displaystyle\int \frac{\cos^2 ax\, dx}{\sin^3 ax} = -\frac{1}{2a}\left(\frac{\cos ax}{\sin^2 ax} - \log_e \tan \frac{ax}{2} \right)$

386. $\displaystyle\int \frac{\cos^2 ax\, dx}{\sin^n ax} = -\frac{1}{n-1}\left(\frac{\cos ax}{a \sin^{n-1} ax} + \int \frac{dx}{\sin^{n-2} ax} \right)$

$$(n \neq 1);\ \text{(see 289)}$$

387. $\displaystyle\int \frac{\cos^3 ax\, dx}{\sin ax} = \frac{1}{a}\left(\frac{\cos^2 ax}{2} + \log_e \sin ax \right)$

388. $\displaystyle\int \frac{\cos^3 ax\, dx}{\sin^2 ax} = -\frac{1}{a}\left(\sin ax + \frac{1}{\sin ax} \right)$

389. $\displaystyle\int \frac{\cos^3 ax\, dx}{\sin^n ax} = \frac{1}{a}\left[\frac{1}{(n-3) \sin^{n-3} ax} - \frac{1}{(n-1) \sin^{n-1} ax} \right]$

$$(n \neq 1,\ n \neq 3)$$

390. $\displaystyle\int \frac{\cos^n ax}{\sin ax}\, dx = \frac{\cos^{n-1} ax}{a(n-1)} + \int \frac{\cos^{n-2} ax\, dx}{\sin ax} \qquad (n \neq 1)$

391. $\displaystyle\int \frac{\cos^n ax\, dx}{\sin^m ax} = -\frac{\cos^{n+1} ax}{a(m-1) \sin^{m-1} ax} - \frac{n-m+2}{m-1} \int \frac{\cos^n ax\, dx}{\sin^{m-2} ax}$

$$(m \neq 1)$$

$$= \frac{\cos^{n-1} ax}{a(n-m) \sin^{m-1} ax} + \frac{n-1}{n-m} \int \frac{\cos^{n-2} ax\, dx}{\sin^m ax}$$

$$(m \neq n)$$

$$= -\frac{\cos^{n-1} ax}{a(m-1) \sin^{m-1} ax} - \frac{n-1}{m-1} \int \frac{\cos^{n-2} ax\, dx}{\sin^{m-2} ax}$$

$$(m \neq 1)$$

392. $\displaystyle\int \frac{dx}{\sin ax \, (1 \pm \cos ax)} = \pm \frac{1}{2a(1 \pm \cos ax)} + \frac{1}{2a} \log_e \tan \frac{ax}{2}$

393. $\displaystyle\int \frac{dx}{\cos ax \, (1 \pm \sin ax)} = \mp \frac{1}{2a(1 \pm \sin ax)} + \frac{1}{2a} \log_e \tan \left(\frac{\pi}{4} + \frac{ax}{2} \right)$

394. $\displaystyle\int \frac{\sin ax \, dx}{\cos ax \, (1 \pm \cos ax)} = \frac{1}{a} \log_e \frac{1 \pm \cos ax}{\cos ax}$

395. $\displaystyle\int \frac{\cos ax \, dx}{\sin ax \, (1 \pm \sin ax)} = -\frac{1}{a} \log_e \frac{1 \pm \sin ax}{\sin ax}$

396. $\displaystyle\int \frac{\sin ax \, dx}{\cos ax \, (1 \pm \sin ax)} = \frac{1}{2a(1 \pm \sin ax)} \pm \frac{1}{2a} \log_e \tan \left(\frac{\pi}{4} + \frac{ax}{2} \right)$

397. $\displaystyle\int \frac{\cos ax \, dx}{\sin ax \, (1 \pm \cos ax)} = -\frac{1}{2a(1 \pm \cos ax)} \pm \frac{1}{2a} \log_e \tan \frac{ax}{2}$

398. $\displaystyle\int \frac{\sin ax \, dx}{\sin ax \pm \cos ax} = \frac{x}{2} \mp \frac{1}{2a} \log_e (\sin ax \pm \cos ax)$

399. $\displaystyle\int \frac{\cos ax \, dx}{\sin ax \pm \cos ax} = \pm \frac{x}{2} + \frac{1}{2a} \log_e (\sin ax \pm \cos ax)$

400. $\displaystyle\int \frac{dx}{\sin ax \pm \cos ax} = \frac{1}{a\sqrt{2}} \log_e \tan \left(\frac{ax}{2} \pm \frac{\pi}{8} \right)$

401. $\displaystyle\int \frac{dx}{1 + \cos ax \pm \sin ax} = \pm \frac{1}{a} \log_e \left(1 \pm \tan \frac{ax}{2} \right)$

402. $\displaystyle\int \frac{dx}{b \sin ax + c \cos ax} = \frac{1}{a\sqrt{b^2 + c^2}} \log_e \tan \frac{ax + \theta}{2}$

$$\sin \theta = \frac{c}{\sqrt{b^2 + c^2}} \qquad \tan \theta = \frac{c}{b}$$

403. $\displaystyle\int \frac{\sin ax \, dx}{b + c \cos ax} = -\frac{1}{ac} \log_e (b + c \cos ax)$

404. $\displaystyle\int \frac{\cos ax \, dx}{b + c \sin ax} = \frac{1}{ac} \log_e (b + c \sin ax)$

405. $\displaystyle\int \frac{\sin^2 ax \, dx}{b + c \cos^2 ax} = \frac{1}{ac} \sqrt{\frac{b + c}{b}} \arctan \left(\sqrt{\frac{b}{b + c}} \tan ax \right) - \frac{x}{c}$

406. $\displaystyle\int \frac{\sin ax \cos ax\, dx}{b \cos^2 ax + c \sin^2 ax} = \frac{1}{2a(c-b)} \log_e (b \cos^2 ax + c \sin^2 ax)$

$$(c \neq b)$$

407. $\displaystyle\int \frac{dx}{b^2 \cos^2 ax + c^2 \sin^2 ax} = \frac{1}{abc} \arctan\left(\frac{c}{b} \tan ax\right)$

408. $\displaystyle\int \frac{dx}{b^2 \cos^2 ax - c^2 \sin^2 ax} = \frac{1}{2abc} \log_e \frac{c \tan ax + b}{c \tan ax - b}$

409. $\displaystyle\int \sin ax \cos bx\, dx = -\frac{\cos (a+b)x}{2(a+b)} - \frac{\cos (a-b)x}{2(a-b)}$

$$(a^2 \neq b^2; \text{ for } a = b \text{ see } 354)$$

410. $\displaystyle\int \frac{dx}{b + c \cos ax + d \sin ax}$

$$= \begin{cases} \dfrac{-1}{a\sqrt{b^2 - c^2 - d^2}} \arcsin \dfrac{c^2 + d^2 + b(c \cos ax + d \sin ax)}{\sqrt{c^2 + d^2}(b + c \cos ax + d \sin ax)} \\ \qquad\qquad (b^2 > c^2 + d^2, |ax| < \pi) \\[4pt] \dfrac{1}{a\sqrt{c^2 + d^2 - b^2}} \\ \log_e \dfrac{\begin{array}{c} c^2 + d^2 + b(c \cos ax + d \sin ax) \\ + \sqrt{c^2 + d^2 - b^2}(c \sin ax - d \cos ax) \end{array}}{\sqrt{c^2 + d^2}(b + c \cos ax + d \sin ax)} \\ \qquad\qquad (b^2 < c^2 + d^2, |ax| < \pi) \\[4pt] \dfrac{1}{ab}\left[\dfrac{b - (c+d)\cos ax + (c-d)\sin ax}{b + (c-d)\cos ax + (c+d)\sin ax}\right] \quad (b^2 = c^2 + d^2) \end{cases}$$

(u) Integrals containing tangent and cotangent functions
$(a \neq 0)$

411. $\displaystyle\int \tan ax\, dx = -\frac{1}{a} \log_e \cos ax$

412. $\displaystyle\int \tan^2 ax\, dx = \frac{1}{a} \tan ax - x$

413. $\displaystyle\int \tan^3 ax\, dx = \frac{1}{2a} \tan^2 ax + \frac{1}{a} \log_e \cos ax$

414. $\displaystyle\int \tan^n ax\, dx = \frac{1}{a(n-1)} \tan^{n-1} ax - \int \tan^{n-2} ax\, dx \qquad (n > 1)$

415. $\int \dfrac{dx}{b + c \tan ax} = \int \dfrac{\cot ax \, dx}{b \cot ax + c}$

$$= \dfrac{1}{b^2 + c^2}\left[bx + \dfrac{c}{a}\log_e (b \cos ax + c \sin ax)\right]$$

416. $\int \dfrac{dx}{\sqrt{b + c \tan^2 ax}} = \dfrac{1}{a\sqrt{b - c}} \arcsin\left(\sqrt{\dfrac{b - c}{b}} \sin ax\right)$

$$(b > 0, \, b^2 > c^2)$$

417. $\int \dfrac{\tan^n ax}{\cos^2 ax} \, dx = \dfrac{\tan^{n+1} ax}{a(n + 1)} \qquad (n \neq -1)$

418. $\int \cot ax \, dx = \dfrac{1}{a}\log_e \sin ax$

419. $\int \cot^2 ax \, dx = \int \dfrac{dx}{\tan^2 ax} = -\dfrac{1}{a}\cot ax - x$

420. $\int \cot^3 ax \, dx = -\dfrac{1}{2a}\cot^2 ax - \dfrac{1}{a}\log_e \sin ax$

421. $\int \cot^n ax \, dx = \int \dfrac{dx}{\tan^n ax} = -\dfrac{1}{a(n - 1)}\cot^{n-1} ax$

$$- \int \cot^{n-2} ax \, dx \qquad (n > 1)$$

422. $\int \dfrac{dx}{b + c \cot ax} = \int \dfrac{\tan ax \, dx}{b \tan ax + c}$

$$= \dfrac{1}{b^2 + c^2}\left[bx - \dfrac{c}{a}\log_e (c \cos ax + b \sin ax)\right]$$

423. $\int \dfrac{\cot^n ax}{\sin^2 ax} \, dx = \dfrac{-\cot^{n+1} ax}{a(n + 1)} \qquad (n \neq -1)$

(v) Integrals containing hyperbolic functions $\qquad (a \neq 0)$

424. $\int \sinh x \, dx = \cosh x$

425. $\int \sinh^2 x \, dx = \dfrac{\sinh 2x}{4} - \dfrac{x}{2}$

426. $\int \dfrac{dx}{\sinh x} = \log_e \tanh\left(\dfrac{x}{2}\right)$

427. $\displaystyle\int \frac{dx}{\sinh^2 x} = -\coth x$

428. $\displaystyle\int \cosh x \, dx = \sinh x$

429. $\displaystyle\int \cosh^2 x \, dx = \frac{\sinh 2x}{4} + \frac{x}{2}$

430. $\displaystyle\int \frac{dx}{\cosh x} = 2 \arctan e^x = \arctan (\sinh x)$

431. $\displaystyle\int \frac{dx}{\cosh^2 x} = \tanh x$

432. $\displaystyle\int \frac{\sinh x}{\cosh^2 x} \, dx = -\frac{1}{\cosh x}$

433. $\displaystyle\int \frac{\cosh x}{\sinh^2 x} \, dx = -\frac{1}{\sinh x}$

434. $\displaystyle\int x \sinh x \, dx = x \cosh x - \sinh x$

435. $\displaystyle\int x \cosh x \, dx = x \sinh x - \cosh x$

436. $\displaystyle\int \tanh x \, dx = \log_e \cosh x$

437. $\displaystyle\int \tanh^2 x \, dx = x - \tanh x$

438. $\displaystyle\int \coth x \, dx = \log_e \sinh x$

439. $\displaystyle\int \coth^2 x \, dx = x - \coth x$

440. $\displaystyle\int \sinh^n ax \, dx$

$$= \begin{cases} \dfrac{1}{an} \sinh^{n-1} ax \cosh ax - \dfrac{n-1}{n} \displaystyle\int \sinh^{n-2} ax \, dx & (n > 0) \\[3ex] \dfrac{1}{a(n+1)} \sinh^{n+1} ax \cosh ax - \dfrac{n+2}{n+1} \displaystyle\int \sinh^{n+2} ax \, dx \\[2ex] \hfill (n < -1) \end{cases}$$

441. $\displaystyle\int \cosh^n ax \, dx$

$$= \begin{cases} \dfrac{1}{an} \sinh ax \cosh^{n-1} ax + \dfrac{n-1}{n} \displaystyle\int \cosh^{n-2} ax \, dx & (n > 0) \\[4mm] -\dfrac{1}{a(n+1)} \sinh ax \cosh^{n+1} ax + \dfrac{n+2}{n+1} \displaystyle\int \cosh^{n+2} ax \, dx \\[4mm] \hfill (n < -1) \end{cases}$$

442. $\displaystyle\int \sinh ax \sinh bx \, dx = \dfrac{\sinh (a+b)x}{2(a+b)} - \dfrac{\sinh (a-b)x}{2(a-b)}$

443. $\displaystyle\int \cosh ax \cosh bx \, dx = \dfrac{\sinh (a+b)x}{2(a+b)} + \dfrac{\sinh (a-b)x}{2(a-b)}$ $\left.\rule{0mm}{18mm}\right\}$ $(a^2 \neq b^2)$

444. $\displaystyle\int \sinh ax \cosh bx \, dx = \dfrac{\cosh (a+b)x}{2(a+b)} + \dfrac{\cosh (a-b)x}{2(a-b)}$

445. $\displaystyle\int \sinh ax \sin ax \, dx = \dfrac{1}{2a} (\cosh ax \sin ax - \sinh ax \cos ax)$

446. $\displaystyle\int \cosh ax \cos ax \, dx = \dfrac{1}{2a} (\sinh ax \cos ax + \cosh ax \sin ax)$

447. $\displaystyle\int \sinh ax \cos ax \, dx = \dfrac{1}{2a} (\cosh ax \cos ax + \sinh ax \sin ax)$

448. $\displaystyle\int \cosh ax \sin ax \, dx = \dfrac{1}{2a} (\sinh ax \sin ax - \cosh ax \cos ax)$

(w) Integrals containing exponential functions

449. $\displaystyle\int e^{ax} \, dx = \dfrac{1}{a} e^{ax}$

450. $\displaystyle\int xe^{ax} \, dx = \dfrac{e^{ax}}{a^2} (ax - 1)$

451. $\displaystyle\int x^2 e^{ax} \, dx = e^{ax} \left(\dfrac{x^2}{a} - \dfrac{2x}{a^2} + \dfrac{2}{a^3} \right)$

452. $\displaystyle\int x^n e^{ax} \, dx = \dfrac{1}{a} x^n e^{ax} - \dfrac{n}{a} \int x^{n-1} e^{ax} \, dx$ $(n > 0)$

453. $\displaystyle\int \dfrac{e^{ax}}{x} \, dx = \log_e x + \dfrac{ax}{1 \cdot 1!} + \dfrac{(ax)^2}{2 \cdot 2!} + \dfrac{(ax)^3}{3 \cdot 3!} + \cdots$

454. $\displaystyle\int \frac{e^{ax}}{x^n}\, dx = \frac{1}{n-1}\left(-\frac{e^{ax}}{x^{n-1}} + a\int \frac{e^{ax}}{x^{n-1}}\, dx\right) \qquad (n > 1)$

455. $\displaystyle\int \frac{dx}{1 + e^{ax}} = \frac{1}{a}\log_e \frac{e^{ax}}{1 + e^{ax}}$

456. $\displaystyle\int \frac{dx}{b + ce^{ax}} = \frac{x}{b} - \frac{1}{ab}\log_e (b + ce^{ax})$

457. $\displaystyle\int \frac{e^{ax}\, dx}{b + ce^{ax}} = \frac{1}{ac}\log_e (b + ce^{ax})$

458. $\displaystyle\int \frac{dx}{be^{ax} + ce^{-ax}} = \frac{1}{a\sqrt{bc}}\arctan\left(e^{ax}\sqrt{\frac{b}{c}}\right) \qquad (bc > 0)$

$\displaystyle\qquad\qquad\qquad = \frac{1}{2a\sqrt{-bc}}\log_e \frac{c + e^{ax}\sqrt{-bc}}{c - e^{ax}\sqrt{-bc}} \qquad (bc < 0)$

459. $\displaystyle\int \frac{xe^{ax}\, dx}{(1 + ax)^2} = \frac{e^{ax}}{a^2(1 + ax)}$

460. $\displaystyle\int e^{ax}\log_e x\, dx = \frac{1}{a}e^{ax}\log_e x - \frac{1}{a}\int \frac{e^{ax}}{x}\, dx$

461. $\displaystyle\int e^{ax}\sin bx\, dx = \frac{e^{ax}}{a^2 + b^2}(a\sin bx - b\cos bx)$

462. $\displaystyle\int e^{ax}\cos bx\, dx = \frac{e^{ax}}{a^2 + b^2}(a\cos bx + b\sin bx)$

463. $\displaystyle\int xe^{ax}\sin bx\, dx = \frac{xe^{ax}}{a^2 + b^2}(a\sin bx - b\cos bx)$

$\displaystyle\qquad\qquad - \frac{e^{ax}}{(a^2 + b^2)^2}[(a^2 - b^2)\sin bx - 2ab\cos bx]$

464. $\displaystyle\int xe^{ax}\cos bx\, dx = \frac{xe^{ax}}{a^2 + b^2}(a\cos bx + b\sin bx)$

$\displaystyle\qquad\qquad - \frac{e^{ax}}{(a^2 + b^2)^2}[(a^2 - b^2)\cos bx + 2ab\sin bx]$

465. $\displaystyle\int e^{ax}\sin bx\sin cx\, dx = \frac{e^{ax}[(b - c)\sin (b - c)x + a\cos (b - c)x]}{2[a^2 + (b - c)^2]}$

$\displaystyle\qquad\qquad - \frac{e^{ax}[(b + c)\sin (b + c)x + a\cos (b + c)x]}{2[a^2 + (b + c)^2]}$

466. $\displaystyle\int e^{ax}\cos bx \cos cx\, dx = \frac{e^{ax}[(b-c)\sin{(b-c)}x + a\cos{(b-c)}x]}{2[a^2 + (b-c)^2]}$

$$+ \frac{e^{ax}[(b+c)\sin{(b+c)}x + a\cos{(b+c)}x]}{2[a^2 + (b+c)^2]}$$

467. $\displaystyle\int e^{ax}\sin bx \cos cx\, dx = \frac{e^{ax}[a\sin{(b-c)}x - (b-c)\cos{(b-c)}x]}{2[a^2 + (b-c)^2]}$

$$+ \frac{e^{ax}[a\sin{(b+c)}x - (b+c)\cos{(b+c)}x]}{2[a^2 + (b+c)^2]}$$

468. $\displaystyle\int e^{ax}\sin bx \sin{(bx+c)}\, dx$

$$= \frac{e^{ax}\cos c}{2a} - \frac{e^{ax}[a\cos{(2bx+c)} + 2b\sin{(2bx+c)}]}{2(a^2 + 4b^2)}$$

469. $\displaystyle\int e^{ax}\cos bx \cos{(bx+c)}\, dx$

$$= \frac{e^{ax}\cos c}{2a} + \frac{e^{ax}[a\cos{(2bx+c)} + 2b\sin{(2bx+c)}]}{2(a^2 + 4b^2)}$$

470. $\displaystyle\int e^{ax}\sin bx \cos{(bx+c)}\, dx$

$$= -\frac{e^{ax}\sin c}{2a} + \frac{e^{ax}[a\sin{(2bx+c)} - 2b\cos{(2bx+c)}]}{2(a^2 + 4b^2)}$$

471. $\displaystyle\int e^{ax}\cos bx \sin{(bx+c)}\, dx$

$$= \frac{e^{ax}\sin c}{2a} + \frac{e^{ax}[a\sin{(2bx+c)} - 2b\cos{(2bx+c)}]}{2(a^2 + 4b^2)}$$

472. $\displaystyle\int e^{ax}\sin^n bx\, dx = \frac{e^{ax}\sin^{n-1} bx\,(a\sin bx - nb\cos bx)}{a^2 + n^2 b^2}$

$$+ \frac{n(n-1)b^2}{a^2 + n^2 b^2}\int e^{ax}\sin^{n-2} bx\, dx$$

473. $\displaystyle\int e^{ax}\cos^n bx\, dx = \frac{e^{ax}\cos^{n-1} bx\,(a\cos bx + nb\sin bx)}{a^2 + n^2 b^2}$

$$+ \frac{n(n-1)b^2}{a^2 + n^2 b^2}\int e^{ax}\cos^{n-2} bx\, dx$$

(x) Integrals containing logarithmic functions $\quad (a \neq 0)$

474. $\displaystyle\int \log_e ax \, dx = x \log_e ax - x$

475. $\displaystyle\int (\log_e ax)^2 \, dx = x(\log_e ax)^2 - 2x \log_e ax + 2x$

476. $\displaystyle\int (\log_e ax)^n \, dx = x(\log_e ax)^n - n \int (\log_e ax)^{n-1} \, dx \qquad (n \neq -1)$

477. $\displaystyle\int \frac{dx}{\log_e ax} = \frac{1}{a}\left[\log_e (\log_e ax) + \log_e ax + \frac{(\log_e ax)^2}{2 \cdot 2!} \right.$
$$\left. + \frac{(\log_e ax)^3}{3 \cdot 3!} + \cdots \right]$$

478. $\displaystyle\int x \log_e ax \, dx = \frac{x^2}{2} \log_e ax - \frac{x^2}{4}$

479. $\displaystyle\int x^2 \log_e ax \, dx = \frac{x^3}{3} \log_e ax - \frac{x^3}{9}$

480. $\displaystyle\int x^n \log_e ax \, dx = x^{n+1}\left[\frac{\log_e ax}{n+1} - \frac{1}{(n+1)^2} \right] \qquad (n \neq -1)$

481. $\displaystyle\int x^n (\log_e ax)^m \, dx = \frac{x^{n+1}}{n+1} (\log_e ax)^m - \frac{m}{n+1} \int x^n (\log_e ax)^{m-1} \, dx$
$$(m, n \neq -1)$$

482. $\displaystyle\int \frac{(\log_e ax)^n}{x} \, dx = \frac{(\log_e ax)^{n+1}}{n+1} \qquad (n \neq -1)$

483. $\displaystyle\int \frac{\log_e x}{x^n} \, dx = -\frac{\log_e x}{(n-1)x^{n-1}} - \frac{1}{(n-1)^2 x^{n-1}} \qquad (n \neq 1)$

484. $\displaystyle\int \frac{(\log_e x)^m}{x^n} \, dx = -\frac{(\log_e x)^m}{(n-1)x^{n-1}} + \frac{m}{n-1} \int \frac{(\log_e x)^{m-1}}{x^n} \, dx$
$$(n \neq 1)$$

485. $\displaystyle\int \frac{x^n \, dx}{\log_e ax} = \frac{1}{a^{n+1}}\left[\log_e (\log_e ax) + (n+1) \log_e ax \right.$
$$+ \frac{(n+1)^2(\log_e ax)^2}{2 \cdot 2!} + \frac{(n+1)^3(\log_e ax)^3}{3 \cdot 3!} + \cdots \right]$$
$$= \frac{1}{a^{n+1}} \int \frac{e^y \, dy}{y} \qquad [y = (n+1) \log_e ax]$$

486. $\displaystyle\int \frac{x^n \, dx}{(\log_e ax)^m} = \frac{-x^{n+1}}{(m-1)(\log_e ax)^{m-1}} + \frac{n+1}{m-1} \int \frac{x^n \, dx}{(\log_e ax)^{m-1}}$

$$(m \neq 1)$$

487. $\displaystyle\int \frac{dx}{x \log_e ax} = \log_e (\log_e ax)$

488. $\displaystyle\int \frac{dx}{x(\log_e ax)^n} = -\frac{1}{(n-1)(\log_e ax)^{n-1}}$

489. $\displaystyle\int \sin (\log_e ax) \, dx = \frac{x}{2} \left[\sin (\log_e ax) - \cos (\log_e ax) \right]$

490. $\displaystyle\int \cos (\log_e ax) \, dx = \frac{x}{2} \left[\sin (\log_e ax) + \cos (\log_e ax) \right]$

491. $\displaystyle\int e^{ax} \log_e bx \, dx = \frac{1}{a} e^{ax} \log_e bx - \frac{1}{a} \int \frac{e^{ax}}{x} \, dx$

(y) Integrals containing inverse trigonometric and hyperbolic functions $(a > 0)$

492. $\displaystyle\int \arcsin \frac{x}{a} \, dx = x \arcsin \frac{x}{a} + \sqrt{a^2 - x^2}$

493. $\displaystyle\int x \arcsin \frac{x}{a} \, dx = \left(\frac{x^2}{2} - \frac{a^2}{4} \right) \arcsin \frac{x}{a} + \frac{x}{4} \sqrt{a^2 - x^2}$

494. $\displaystyle\int x^2 \arcsin \frac{x}{a} \, dx = \frac{x^3}{3} \arcsin \frac{x}{a} + \frac{1}{9} (x^2 + 2a^2)\sqrt{a^2 - x^2}$

495. $\displaystyle\int x^n \arcsin \frac{x}{a} \, dx = \frac{x^{n+1}}{n+1} \arcsin \frac{x}{a} - \frac{1}{n+1} \int \frac{x^{n+1}}{\sqrt{a^2 - x^2}} \, dx$

$$(n \neq -1)$$

496. $\displaystyle\int \frac{\arcsin \dfrac{x}{a} \, dx}{x} = \frac{x}{a} + \frac{1}{2 \cdot 3 \cdot 3} \frac{x^3}{a^3}$

$$+ \frac{1 \cdot 3}{2 \cdot 4 \cdot 5 \cdot 5} \frac{x^5}{a^5} + \frac{1 \cdot 3 \cdot 5}{2 \cdot 4 \cdot 6 \cdot 7 \cdot 7} \frac{x^7}{a^7} + \cdots$$

$$(x^2 < a^2)$$

497. $\displaystyle\int \frac{\arcsin \dfrac{x}{a} \, dx}{x^2} = -\frac{1}{x} \arcsin \frac{x}{a} - \frac{1}{a} \log_e \frac{a + \sqrt{a^2 - x^2}}{x}$

498. $\int \left(\arcsin \dfrac{x}{a}\right)^2 dx = x \left(\arcsin \dfrac{x}{a}\right)^2 + 2 \left(\sqrt{a^2 - x^2} \arcsin \dfrac{x}{a} - x\right)$

499. $\int \arccos \dfrac{x}{a}\, dx = x \arccos \dfrac{x}{a} - \sqrt{a^2 - x^2}$

500. $\int x \arccos \dfrac{x}{a}\, dx = \left(\dfrac{x^2}{2} - \dfrac{a^2}{4}\right) \arccos \dfrac{x}{a} - \dfrac{x}{4} \sqrt{a^2 - x^2}$

501. $\int x^2 \arccos \dfrac{x}{a}\, dx = \dfrac{x^3}{3} \arccos \dfrac{x}{a} - \dfrac{1}{9} (x^2 + 2a^2)\sqrt{a^2 - x^2}$

502. $\int x^n \arccos \dfrac{x}{a}\, dx = \dfrac{x^{n+1}}{n+1} \arccos \dfrac{x}{a} + \dfrac{1}{n+1} \int \dfrac{x^{n+1}}{\sqrt{a^2 - x^2}}\, dx$

$$(n \neq -1)$$

503. $\int \dfrac{\arccos \dfrac{x}{a}\, dx}{x} = \dfrac{\pi}{2} \log_e x - \dfrac{x}{a}$

$$- \dfrac{1}{2 \cdot 3 \cdot 3} \dfrac{x^3}{a^3} - \dfrac{1 \cdot 3}{2 \cdot 4 \cdot 5 \cdot 5} \dfrac{x^5}{a^5} - \dfrac{1 \cdot 3 \cdot 5}{2 \cdot 4 \cdot 6 \cdot 7 \cdot 7} \dfrac{x^7}{a^7} - \cdots$$

$$(x^2 < a^2)$$

504. $\int \dfrac{\arccos \dfrac{x}{a}\, dx}{x^2} = -\dfrac{1}{x} \arccos \dfrac{x}{a} + \dfrac{1}{a} \log_e \dfrac{a + \sqrt{a^2 - x^2}}{x}$

505. $\int \left(\arccos \dfrac{x}{a}\right)^2 dx = x \left(\arccos \dfrac{x}{a}\right)^2 - 2 \left(\sqrt{a^2 - x^2} \arccos \dfrac{x}{a} + x\right)$

506. $\int \arctan \dfrac{x}{a}\, dx = x \arctan \dfrac{x}{a} - \dfrac{a}{2} \log_e (a^2 + x^2)$

507. $\int x \arctan \dfrac{x}{a}\, dx = \dfrac{1}{2} (x^2 + a^2) \arctan \dfrac{x}{a} - \dfrac{ax}{2}$

508. $\int x^2 \arctan \dfrac{x}{a}\, dx = \dfrac{x^3}{3} \arctan \dfrac{x}{a} - \dfrac{ax^2}{6} + \dfrac{a^3}{6} \log_e (a^2 + x^2)$

509. $\int x^n \arctan \dfrac{x}{a}\, dx = \dfrac{x^{n+1}}{n+1} \arctan \dfrac{x}{a} - \dfrac{a}{n+1} \int \dfrac{x^{n+1}\, dx}{a^2 + x^2}$

$$(n \neq -1)$$

510. $$\int \frac{\arctan \dfrac{x}{a} \, dx}{x} = \frac{x}{a} - \frac{x^3}{3^2 a^3} + \frac{x^5}{5^2 a^5} - \frac{x^7}{7^2 a^7} + \cdots \quad (|x| < |a|)$$

511. $$\int \frac{\arctan \dfrac{x}{a} \, dx}{x^2} = -\frac{1}{x} \arctan \frac{x}{a} - \frac{1}{2a} \log_e \frac{a^2 + x^2}{x^2}$$

512. $$\int \frac{\arctan \dfrac{x}{a} \, dx}{x^n} = -\frac{1}{(n-1)x^{n-1}} \arctan \frac{x}{a}$$
$$+ \frac{a}{n-1} \int \frac{dx}{x^{n-1}(a^2 + x^2)} \qquad (n \neq 1)$$

513. $$\int \operatorname{arccot} \frac{x}{a} \, dx = x \operatorname{arccot} \frac{x}{a} + \frac{a}{2} \log_e (a^2 + x^2)$$

514. $$\int x \operatorname{arccot} \frac{x}{a} \, dx = \frac{1}{2} (x^2 + a^2) \operatorname{arccot} \frac{x}{a} + \frac{ax}{2}$$

515. $$\int x^2 \operatorname{arccot} \frac{x}{a} \, dx = \frac{x^3}{3} \operatorname{arccot} \frac{x}{a} + \frac{ax^2}{6} - \frac{a^3}{6} \log_e (a^2 + x^2)$$

516. $$\int x^n \operatorname{arccot} \frac{x}{a} \, dx = \frac{x^{n+1}}{n+1} \operatorname{arccot} \frac{x}{a} + \frac{a}{n+1} \int \frac{x^{n+1} \, dx}{a^2 + x^2}$$
$$(n \neq -1)$$

517. $$\int \frac{\operatorname{arccot} \dfrac{x}{a} \, dx}{x} = \frac{\pi}{2} \log_e x - \frac{x}{a} + \frac{x^3}{3^2 a^3} - \frac{x^5}{5^2 a^5} + \frac{x^7}{7^2 a^7} - \cdots$$

518. $$\int \frac{\operatorname{arccot} \dfrac{x}{a} \, dx}{x^2} = -\frac{1}{x} \operatorname{arccot} \frac{x}{a} + \frac{1}{2a} \log_e \frac{a^2 + x^2}{x^2}$$

519. $$\int \frac{\operatorname{arccot} \dfrac{x}{a} \, dx}{x^n} = -\frac{1}{(n-1)x^{n-1}} \operatorname{arccot} \frac{x}{a}$$
$$- \frac{a}{n-1} \int \frac{dx}{x^{n-1}(a^2 + x^2)} \qquad (n \neq 1)$$

520. $\displaystyle\int \sinh^{-1}\frac{x}{a}\,dx = x\sinh^{-1}\frac{x}{a} - \sqrt{x^2 + a^2}$

521. $\displaystyle\int x\sinh^{-1}\frac{x}{a}\,dx = \frac{1}{2}\left(x^2 + \frac{a^2}{2}\right)\sinh^{-1}\frac{x}{a} - \frac{x}{4}\sqrt{x^2 + a^2}$

522. $\displaystyle\int \cosh^{-1}\frac{x}{a}\,dx = x\cosh^{-1}\frac{x}{a} \mp \sqrt{x^2 - a^2}$

$\left(\text{upper sign for } \cosh^{-1}\frac{x}{a} > 0\right)$

523. $\displaystyle\int \tanh^{-1}\frac{x}{a}\,dx = x\tanh^{-1}\frac{x}{a} + \frac{a}{2}\log_e(a^2 - x^2)$

524. $\displaystyle\int x\tanh^{-1}\frac{x}{a}\,dx = \frac{x^2 - a^2}{2}\tanh^{-1}\frac{x}{a} + \frac{ax}{2}$

525. $\displaystyle\int \coth^{-1}\frac{x}{a}\,dx = x\coth^{-1}\frac{x}{a} + \frac{a}{2}\log_e(x^2 - a^2)$

E-3. Definite Integrals (*see also Secs. 11.2-1 and 11.3-1 and Appendix D*). *m, n* are integers.

(a) Integrals containing algebraic functions

1. $\displaystyle\int_1^\infty \frac{dx}{x^n} = \frac{1}{n-1} \qquad (n > 1)$

2. $\displaystyle\int_0^\infty \frac{a\,dx}{a^2 + x^2} = \begin{cases} \dfrac{\pi}{2} & (a > 0) \\[2mm] 0 & (a = 0) \\[2mm] -\dfrac{\pi}{2} & (a < 0) \end{cases}$

3. $\displaystyle\int_0^1 x^\alpha(1-x)^\beta\,dx = 2\int_0^1 x^{2\alpha+1}(1-x^2)^\beta\,dx$

$\displaystyle\qquad = \int_0^\infty \frac{x^\alpha}{(1+x)^{\alpha+\beta+2}}\,dx$

$\displaystyle\qquad = \frac{\Gamma(\alpha+1)\Gamma(\beta+1)}{\Gamma(\alpha+\beta+2)} = B(\alpha+1,\,\beta+1)$

4. $\int_0^\infty \dfrac{dx}{(1+x)x^a} = \dfrac{\pi}{\sin a\pi}$ $(a < 1)$

5. $\int_0^\infty \dfrac{x^{a-1}\,dx}{1+x} = \dfrac{\pi}{\sin a\pi}$ $(0 < a < 1)$

6. $\int_0^\infty \dfrac{dx}{(1-x)x^a} = -\pi \cot a\pi$ $(a < 1)$

7. $\int_0^\infty \dfrac{x^{a-1}}{1+x^b}\,dx = \dfrac{\pi}{b \sin (a\pi/b)}$ $(0 < a < b)$

8. $\int_0^1 \dfrac{dx}{\sqrt{1 - x^a}} = \dfrac{\sqrt{\pi}\,\Gamma(1/a)}{a\Gamma\left(\dfrac{2+a}{2a}\right)}$

(b) Integrals containing trigonometric functions (*see also Secs. E-3c and d*)

9. $\int_0^\pi \sin mx \cos nx\,dx = \begin{cases} 0 & (m - n \text{ even}) \\[2mm] \dfrac{2m}{m^2 - n^2} & (m - n \text{ odd}) \end{cases}$

10. $\int_0^\pi \sin mx \sin (nx + \vartheta)\,dx = \int_0^\pi \cos mx \cos (nx + \vartheta)\,dx$

$$= \begin{cases} 0 & (m \neq n) \\[2mm] \dfrac{\pi}{2} \cos \vartheta & (m = n) \end{cases}$$

11. $\int_0^{\pi/2} \sin^a x\,dx = \int_0^{\pi/2} \cos^a x\,dx = \dfrac{1}{2}\sqrt{\pi}\,\dfrac{\Gamma\left(\dfrac{a+1}{2}\right)}{\Gamma\left(\dfrac{a}{2}+1\right)}$ $(a > -1)$

$$= \begin{cases} \dfrac{1 \cdot 3 \cdot 5 \cdots (a-1)}{2 \cdot 4 \cdot 6 \cdots a} \cdot \dfrac{\pi}{2} & (a = 2, 4, \ldots) \\[4mm] \dfrac{2 \cdot 4 \cdot 6 \cdots (a-1)}{1 \cdot 3 \cdot 5 \cdot 7 \cdots a} & (a = 3, 5, \ldots) \end{cases}$$

12. $\int_0^{\pi/2} \sin^{2\alpha+1} x \cos^{2\beta+1} x\,dx = \dfrac{\Gamma(\alpha + 1)\Gamma(\beta + 1)}{2\Gamma(\alpha + \beta + 2)}$

$$= \dfrac{1}{2} B(\alpha + 1, \beta + 1)\qquad (\alpha, \beta \neq -1)$$

$$= \dfrac{\alpha!\beta!}{2(\alpha + \beta + 1)!}\qquad (\alpha, \beta \text{ integers} > 0)$$

Note: Use formula (12) to obtain

$$\int_0^{\pi/2} \sqrt{\sin x}\, dx \qquad \int_0^{\pi/2} \sqrt[3]{\sin x}\, dx \qquad \int_0^{\pi/2} \frac{dx}{\sqrt[3]{\cos x}} \qquad \text{etc.}$$

13. $\displaystyle\int_0^\infty \frac{\sin ax}{x}\, dx = \begin{cases} \dfrac{\pi}{2} & (a > 0) \\[3mm] -\dfrac{\pi}{2} & (a < 0) \end{cases}$

14. $\displaystyle\int_0^\alpha \frac{\cos ax\, dx}{x} = \infty \qquad (\alpha \neq 0)$

15. $\displaystyle\int_0^\infty \frac{\tan ax\, dx}{x} = \begin{cases} \dfrac{\pi}{2} & (a > 0) \\[3mm] -\dfrac{\pi}{2} & (a < 0) \end{cases}$

16. $\displaystyle\int_0^\infty \frac{\cos ax - \cos bx}{x}\, dx = \log_e \frac{b}{a} \qquad (a, b \neq 0)$

17. $\displaystyle\int_0^\infty \frac{\sin x \cos ax}{x}\, dx = \begin{cases} \dfrac{\pi}{2} & (|a| < 1) \\[3mm] \dfrac{\pi}{4} & (|a| = 1) \\[3mm] 0 & (|a| > 1) \end{cases}$

18. $\displaystyle\int_0^\infty \frac{\sin x\, dx}{\sqrt{x}} = \int_0^\infty \frac{\cos x\, dx}{\sqrt{x}} = \sqrt{\frac{\pi}{2}}$

19. $\displaystyle\int_0^\infty \frac{x \sin bx}{a^2 + x^2}\, dx = \frac{\pi}{2} e^{-|ab|} \qquad (b > 0)$

20. $\displaystyle\int_0^\infty \frac{\cos ax}{1 + x^2}\, dx = \frac{\pi}{2} e^{-|a|}$

21. $\displaystyle\int_0^\infty \frac{\sin^2 ax}{x^2}\, dx = \frac{\pi}{2} |a|$

22. $\displaystyle\int_0^\infty \frac{\sin ax \sin bx}{x^2}\, dx = \frac{\pi a}{2} \qquad (a < b)$

23. $\displaystyle\int_0^\infty \cos(x^2)\, dx = \int_0^\infty \sin(x^2)\, dx = \frac{1}{2}\sqrt{\frac{\pi}{2}}$

24. $\displaystyle\int_0^{\pi} \sin^2 mx \, dx = \int_0^{\pi} \cos^2 mx \, dx = \frac{\pi}{2}$

25. $\displaystyle\int_0^{\pi} \frac{dx}{a + b \cos x} = \frac{\pi}{\sqrt{a^2 - b^2}} \qquad (a > b > 0)$

26. $\displaystyle\int_0^{\pi/2} \frac{dx}{a + b \cos x} = \frac{\arccos (b/a)}{\sqrt{a^2 - b^2}} \qquad (a > b)$

27. $\displaystyle\int_0^{\pi/2} \frac{dx}{a^2 \cos^2 x + b^2 \sin^2 x} = \frac{\pi}{2ab} \qquad (ab \neq 0)$

28. $\displaystyle\int_0^{\pi/2} \frac{dx}{(a^2 \cos^2 x + b^2 \sin^2 x)^2} = \frac{\pi(a^2 + b^2)}{4a^3 b^3}$

29. $\displaystyle\int_0^{\pi} \frac{(a - b \cos x) \, dx}{a^2 - 2ab \cos x + b^2} = \begin{cases} 0 & (a^2 < b^2) \\[2mm] \dfrac{\pi}{2a} & (a = b) \\[2mm] \dfrac{\pi}{a} & (a^2 > b^2) \end{cases}$

30. $\displaystyle\int_0^{\pi} \frac{\cos nx \, dx}{1 - 2b \cos x + b^2} = \frac{\pi b^n}{1 - b^2} \qquad (n \geq 0, \, |b| < 1)$

31. $\displaystyle\int_0^{1} \frac{dx}{1 + 2x \cos a + x^2} = \frac{a}{2 \sin a} \qquad \left(0 < a < \frac{\pi}{2}\right)$

32. $\displaystyle\int_0^{\infty} \frac{dx}{1 + 2x \cos a + x^2} = \frac{a}{\sin x} \qquad \left(0 < a < \frac{\pi}{2}\right)$

33. $\displaystyle\int_0^{\pi/2} \frac{\sin x \, dx}{\sqrt{1 - k^2 \sin^2 x}} = \frac{1}{2k} \log_e \frac{1 + k}{1 - k}$

34. $\displaystyle\int_0^{\pi/2} \frac{\cos x \, dx}{\sqrt{1 - k^2 \sin^2 x}} = \frac{1}{k} \arcsin k$

35. $\displaystyle\int_0^{\pi/2} \frac{\sin^2 x \, dx}{\sqrt{1 - k^2 \sin^2 x}} = \frac{1}{k^2} (\mathbf{K} - \mathbf{E})$

36. $\displaystyle\int_0^{\pi/2} \frac{\cos^2 x \, dx}{\sqrt{1 - k^2 \sin^2 x}} = \frac{1}{k^2} [\mathbf{E} - (1 - k^2)\mathbf{K}]$

$(|k| < 1)$

(c) Integrals containing exponential and hyperbolic functions $\quad (a > 0)$

37. $\displaystyle\int_0^\infty e^{-ax}\,dx = \frac{1}{a}$

38. $\displaystyle\int_0^\infty x^b e^{-ax}\,dx = \frac{\Gamma(b+1)}{a^{b+1}} \qquad (a > 0,\, b > -1)$

$$= \frac{b!}{a^{b+1}} \qquad (a > 0,\, b = 0, 1, 2, \ldots)$$

39. $\displaystyle\int_0^\infty x^b e^{-ax^2}\,dx = \frac{\Gamma\!\left(\dfrac{b+1}{2}\right)}{2a^{(b+1)/2}} \qquad (a > 0,\, b > -1)$

$$= \begin{cases} \dfrac{1 \cdot 3 \,\cdots\, (b-1)\sqrt{\pi}}{2^{(b/2)+1}a^{(b+1)/2}} & (a > 0,\, b = 0, 2, 4, \ldots) \\[4mm] \dfrac{\left(\dfrac{b-1}{2}\right)!}{2a^{(b+1)/2}} & (a > 0,\, b = 1, 3, 5, \ldots) \end{cases}$$

40. $\displaystyle\int_0^\infty e^{-a^2 x^2}\,dx = \frac{\sqrt{\pi}}{2a}$

41. $\displaystyle\int_0^\infty x e^{-x^2}\,dx = \frac{1}{2}$

42. $\displaystyle\int_0^\infty x^2 e^{-x^2}\,dx = \frac{\sqrt{\pi}}{4}$

43. $\displaystyle\int_0^\infty \sqrt{x}\, e^{-ax}\,dx = \frac{1}{2a}\sqrt{\frac{\pi}{a}}$

44. $\displaystyle\int_0^\infty \frac{e^{-ax}}{\sqrt{x}}\,dx = \sqrt{\frac{\pi}{a}}$

45. $\displaystyle\int_0^\infty e^{(-x^2 - a^2/x^2)}\,dx = \frac{1}{2}e^{-2a}\sqrt{\pi}$

46. $\displaystyle\int_0^\infty \frac{e^{-ax} - e^{-bx}}{x}\,dx = \log_e \frac{b}{a} \qquad (a,\, b > 0)$

47. $\displaystyle\int_0^\infty \frac{x\,dx}{e^x - 1} = \frac{\pi^2}{6}$

48. $\displaystyle\int_0^\infty \frac{x\,dx}{e^x + 1} = \frac{\pi^2}{12}$

49. $\displaystyle\int_0^\infty e^{-ax} \cos bx \, dx = \frac{a}{a^2 + b^2}$

50. $\displaystyle\int_0^\infty e^{-ax} \sin bx \, dx = \frac{b}{a^2 + b^2}$

51. $\displaystyle\int_0^\infty e^{-ax} \cosh bx \, dx = \frac{a}{a^2 - b^2} \qquad (a > b \geq 0)$

52. $\displaystyle\int_0^\infty e^{-ax} \sinh bx \, dx = \frac{b}{a^2 - b^2} \qquad (a > b \geq 0)$

53. $\displaystyle\int_0^\infty xe^{-ax} \sin bx \, dx = \frac{2ab}{(a^2 + b^2)^2}$

54. $\displaystyle\int_0^\infty xe^{-ax} \cos bx \, dx = \frac{a^2 - b^2}{(a^2 + b^2)^2}$

55. $\displaystyle\int_0^\infty e^{-a^2x^2} \cos bx \, dx = \frac{\sqrt{\pi} \cdot e^{-b^2/4a^2}}{2a}$

56. $\displaystyle\int_0^\infty x^2 e^{-ax} \sin bx \, dx = \frac{2b(3a^2 - b^2)}{(a^2 + b^2)^3}$

57. $\displaystyle\int_0^\infty x^2 e^{-ax} \cos bx \, dx = \frac{2a(a^2 - 3b^2)}{(a^2 + b^2)^3}$

58. $\displaystyle\int_0^\infty \frac{e^{-ax} \sin x}{x} \, dx = \arctan \frac{1}{a}$

59. $\displaystyle\int_0^\infty \frac{dx}{\cosh ax} = \frac{\pi}{2a}$

60. $\displaystyle\int_0^\infty \frac{x\,dx}{\sinh ax} = \frac{\pi^2}{4a^2}$

(d) Integrals containing logarithmic functions

61. $\displaystyle\int_0^1 \log_e |\log_e x| \, dx = \int_0^\infty e^{-x} \log_e x \, dx = -C = -0.577\,2157 \cdots$

62. $\displaystyle\int_0^1 \frac{\log_e x}{1 - x}\, dx = -\frac{\pi^2}{6}$

63. $\displaystyle\int_0^1 \frac{\log_e x}{1 + x}\, dx = -\frac{\pi^2}{12}$

64. $\displaystyle\int_0^1 \frac{\log_e x}{1 - x^2}\, dx = -\frac{\pi^2}{8}$

65. $\displaystyle\int_0^1 \log_e\left(\frac{1 + x}{1 - x}\right) \cdot \frac{dx}{x} = \int_0^\infty \log_e\left(\frac{e^x + 1}{e^x - 1}\right) dx = \frac{\pi^2}{4}$

66. $\displaystyle\int_0^1 \frac{\log_e x}{\sqrt{1 - x^2}}\, dx = -\frac{\pi}{2}\log_e 2$

67. $\displaystyle\int_0^1 x \log_e (1 - x)\, dx = -\frac{3}{4}$

68. $\displaystyle\int_0^1 x \log_e (1 + x)\, dx = \frac{1}{4}$

69. $\displaystyle\int_0^1 \frac{\log_e (1 + x)}{x}\, dx = \frac{\pi^2}{12}$

70. $\displaystyle\int_0^1 \frac{\log_e (1 + x)}{x^2 + 1}\, dx = \frac{\pi}{8}\log_e 2$

71. $\displaystyle\int_0^1 \frac{x^b - x^a}{\log_e x}\, dx = \log_e \frac{1 + b}{1 + a} \qquad (a, b > -1)$

72. $\displaystyle\int_0^1 \left(\log_e \frac{1}{x}\right)^{\frac{1}{2}} dx = \frac{\sqrt{\pi}}{2}$

73. $\displaystyle\int_0^1 \left(\log_e \frac{1}{x}\right)^{-\frac{1}{2}} dx = \sqrt{\pi}$

74. $\displaystyle\int_0^1 \left(\log_e \frac{1}{x}\right)^a dx = \Gamma(a + 1) \qquad (a > -1)$

75. $\displaystyle\int_0^1 (\log_e x)^n\, dx = (-1)^n \cdot n! \qquad (n = 1, 2, \dots)$

76. $\displaystyle\int_0^1 x^n \left(\log_e \frac{1}{x}\right)^a dx = \frac{\Gamma(a + 1)}{(n + 1)^{a+1}} \qquad (a, n > -1)$

77. $\displaystyle\int_0^{\pi/2} \log_e \sin x\, dx = \int_0^{\pi/2} \log_e \cos x\, dx = -\frac{\pi}{2}\log_e 2$

78. $\displaystyle\int_0^\pi x \log_e \sin x \, dx = -\frac{\pi^2}{2} \log_e 2$

79. $\displaystyle\int_0^\pi \log_e (a \pm b \cos x) \, dx = \pi \log_e \left(\frac{a + \sqrt{a^2 - b^2}}{2}\right)$ $(a \geq b)$

80. $\displaystyle\int_0^\pi \frac{\log_e (1 + \sin a \cos x)}{\cos x} \, dx = \pi a$

81. $\displaystyle\int_0^{\pi/2} \sin x \log_e \sin x \, dx = \log_e 2 - 1$

82. $\displaystyle\int_0^{\pi/2} \log_e \tan x \, dx = 0$

83. $\displaystyle\int_0^\pi \log_e (a^2 - 2ab \cos x + b^2) \, dx = \begin{cases} 2\pi \log_e a & (a \geq b > 0) \\ 2\pi \log_e b & (b \geq a > 0) \end{cases}$

84. $\displaystyle\int_0^{\pi/4} \log_e (1 + \tan x) \, dx = \frac{\pi}{8} \log_e 2$

F NUMERICAL TABLES

The following numerical tables are intended less for extensive numerical computations than as quantitative background material indicating the behavior of the most important transcendental functions.

The following *numerical constants* are frequently useful:

$$\pi = 3.1415927 \qquad \log_{10} \pi = 0.4971499$$

$$2\pi = 6.2831853 \qquad \log_{10} 2\pi = 0.7981799$$

$$\frac{1}{2\pi} = 0.1591549 \qquad \log_{10} \frac{1}{2\pi} = 9.2018201 - 10$$

$$\pi^2 = 9.8696044 \qquad \log_{10} \pi^2 = 0.9942997$$

$$e = 2.71828183 \qquad \log_{10} e = \frac{1}{\log_e 10} = 0.43429448$$

$$\log_e 10 = \frac{1}{\log_{10} e} = 2.302585093$$

Table F-1 Squares, cubes, square roots, and cube roots*

No.	Square	Cube	Sq. Root	Cu. Root	No.	Square	Cube	Sq. Root	Cu. Root
1	1	1	1.0000	1.0000	60	3,600	216,000	7.7460	3.9149
2	4	8	1.4142	1.2599	61	3,721	226,981	7.8102	3.9365
3	9	27	1.7321	1.4422	62	3,844	238,328	7.8740	3.9579
4	16	64	2.0000	1.5874	63	3,969	250,047	7.9373	3.9791
5	25	125	2.2361	1.7100	64	4,096	262,144	8.0000	4.0000
6	36	216	2.4495	1.8171	65	4,225	274,625	8.0623	4.0207
7	49	343	2.6458	1.9129	66	4,356	287,496	8.1240	4.0412
8	64	512	2.8284	2.0000	67	4,489	300,763	8.1854	4.0615
9	81	729	3.0000	2.0801	68	4,624	314,432	8.2462	4.0817
10	100	1,000	3.1623	2.1544	69	4,761	328,509	8.3066	4.1016
11	121	1,331	3.3166	2.2240	70	4,900	343,000	8.3666	4.1213
12	144	1,728	3.4641	2.2894	71	5,041	357,911	8.4261	4.1408
13	169	2,197	3.6056	2.3513	72	5,184	373,248	8.4853	4.1602
14	196	2,744	3.7417	2.4101	73	5,329	389,017	8.5440	4.1793
15	225	3,375	3.8730	2.4662	74	5,476	405,224	8.6023	4.1983
16	256	4,096	4.0000	2.5198	75	5,625	421,875	8.6603	4.2172
17	289	4,913	4.1231	2.5713	76	5,776	438,976	8.7178	4.2358
18	324	5,832	4.2426	2.6207	77	5,929	456,533	8.7750	4.2543
19	361	6,859	4.3589	2.6684	78	6,084	474,552	8.8318	4.2727
20	400	8,000	4.4721	2.7144	79	6,241	493,039	8.8882	4.2908
21	441	9,261	4.5826	2.7589	80	6,400	512,000	8.9443	4.3089
22	484	10,648	4.6904	2.8020	81	6,561	531,441	9.0000	4.3267
23	529	12,167	4.7958	2.8439	82	6,724	551,368	9.0554	4.3445
24	576	13,824	4.8990	2.8845	83	6,889	571,787	9.1104	4.3621
25	625	15,625	5.0000	2.9240	84	7,056	592,704	9.1652	4.3795
26	676	17,576	5.0990	2.9625	85	7,225	614,125	9.2195	4.3968
27	729	19,683	5.1962	3.0000	86	7,396	636,056	9.2736	4.4140
28	784	21,952	5.2915	3.0366	87	7,569	658,503	9.3274	4.4310
29	841	24,389	5.3852	3.0723	88	7,744	681,472	9.3808	4.4480
30	900	27,000	5.4772	3.1072	89	7,921	704,969	9.4340	4.4647
31	961	29,791	5.5678	3.1414	90	8,100	729,000	9.4868	4.4814
32	1,024	32,768	5.6569	3.1748	91	8,281	753,571	9.5394	4.4979
33	1,089	35,937	5.7446	3.2075	92	8,464	778,688	9.5917	4.5144
34	1,156	39,304	5.8310	3.2396	93	8,649	804,357	9.6437	4.5307
35	1,225	42,875	5.9161	3.2711	94	8,836	830,584	9.6954	4.5468
36	1,296	46,656	6.0000	3.3019	95	9,025	857,375	9.7468	4.5629
37	1,369	50,653	6.0828	3.3322	96	9,216	884,736	9.7980	4.5789
38	1,444	54,872	6.1644	3.3620	97	9,409	912,673	9.8489	4.5947
39	1,521	59,319	6.2450	3.3912	98	9,604	941,192	9.8995	4.6104
40	1,600	64,000	6.3246	3.4200	99	9,801	970,299	9.9499	4.6261
41	1,681	68,921	6.4031	3.4482	100	10,000	1,000,000	10.0000	4.6416
42	1,764	74,088	6.4807	3.4760	101	10,201	1,030,301	10.0499	4.6570
43	1,849	79,507	6.5574	3.5034	102	10,404	1,061,208	10.0995	4.6723
44	1,936	85,184	6.6332	3.5303	103	10,609	1,092,727	10.1489	4.6875
45	2,025	91,125	6.7082	3.5569	104	10,816	1,124,864	10.1980	4.7027
46	2,116	97,336	6.7823	3.5830	105	11,025	1,157,625	10.2470	4.7177
47	2,209	103,823	6.8557	3.6088	106	11,236	1,191,016	10.2956	4.7326
48	2,304	110,592	6.9282	3.6342	107	11,449	1,225,043	10.3441	4.7475
49	2,401	117,649	7.0000	3.6593	108	11,664	1,259,712	10.3923	4.7622
50	2,500	125,000	7.0711	3.6840	109	11,881	1,295,029	10.4403	4.7769
51	2,601	132,651	7.1414	3.7084	110	12,100	1,331,000	10.4881	4.7914
52	2,704	140,608	7.2111	3.7325	111	12,321	1,367,631	10.5357	4.8059
53	2,809	148,877	7.2801	3.7563	112	12,544	1,404,928	10.5830	4.8203
54	2,916	157,464	7.3485	3.7798	113	12,769	1,442,897	10.6301	4.8346
55	3,025	166,375	7.4162	3.8030	114	12,996	1,481,544	10.6771	4.8488
56	3,136	175,616	7.4833	3.8259	115	13,225	1,520,875	10.7238	4.8629
57	3,249	185,193	7.5498	3.8485	116	13,456	1,560,896	10.7703	4.8770
58	3,364	195,112	7.6158	3.8709	117	13,689	1,601,613	10.8167	4.8910
59	3,481	205,379	7.6811	3.8930	118	13,924	1,643,032	10.8628	4.9049

* From E. S. Allen, "Six-Place Tables," McGraw-Hill Book Company, New York, 1947.

Table F-1 Squares, cubes, square roots, and cube roots (*Continued*)

No.	Square	Cube	Sq. Root	Cu. Root	No.	Square	Cube	Sq. Root	Cu. Root
119	14,161	1,685,159	10.9087	4.9187	182	33,124	6,028,568	13.4907	5.6671
120	14,400	1,728,000	10.9545	4.9324	183	33,489	6,128,487	13.5277	5.6774
121	14,641	1,771,561	11.0000	4.9461	184	33,856	6,229,504	13.5647	5.6877
122	14,884	1,815,848	11.0454	4.9597	185	34,225	6,331,625	13.6015	5.6980
123	15,129	1,860,867	11.0905	4.9732	186	34,596	6,434,856	13.6382	5.7083
124	15,376	1,906,624	11.1355	4.9866	187	34,969	6,539,203	13.6748	5.7185
125	15,625	1,953,125	11.1803	5.0000	188	35,344	6,644,672	13.7113	5.7287
126	15,876	2,000,376	11.2250	5.0133	189	35,721	6,751,269	13.7477	5.7388
127	16,129	2,048,383	11.2694	5.0265	190	36,100	6,859,000	13.7840	5.7489
128	16,384	2,097,152	11.3137	5.0397	191	36,481	6,967,871	13.8203	5.7590
129	16,641	2,146,689	11.3578	5.0528	192	36,864	7,077,888	13.8564	5.7690
130	16,900	2,197,000	11.4018	5.0658	193	37,249	7,189,057	13.8924	5.7790
131	17,161	2,248,091	11.4455	5.0788	194	37,636	7,301,384	13.9284	5.7890
132	17,424	2,299,968	11.4891	5.0916	195	38,025	7,414,875	13.9642	5.7989
133	17,689	2,352,637	11.5326	5.1045	196	38,416	7,529,536	14.0000	5.8088
134	17,956	2,406,104	11.5758	5.1172	197	38,809	7,645,373	14.0357	5.8186
135	18,225	2,460,375	11.6190	5.1299	198	39,204	7,762,392	14.0712	5.8285
136	18,496	2,515,456	11.6619	5.1426	199	39,601	7,880,599	14.1067	5.8383
137	18,769	2,571,353	11.7047	5.1551	200	40,000	8,000,000	14.1421	5.8480
138	19,044	2,628,072	11.7473	5.1676	201	40,401	8,120,601	14.1774	5.8578
139	19,321	2,685,619	11.7898	5.1801	202	40,804	8,242,408	14.2127	5.8675
140	19,600	2,744,000	11.8322	5.1925	203	41,209	8,365,427	14.2478	5.8771
141	19,881	2,803,221	11.8743	5.2048	204	41,616	8,489,664	14.2829	5.8868
142	20,164	2,863,288	11.9164	5.2171	205	42,025	8,615,125	14.3178	5.8964
143	20,449	2,924,207	11.9583	5.2293	206	42,436	8,741,816	14.3527	5.9059
144	20,736	2,985,984	12.0000	5.2415	207	42,849	8,869,743	14.3875	5.9155
145	21,025	3,048,625	12.0416	5.2536	208	43,264	8,998,912	14.4222	5.9250
146	21,316	3,112,136	12.0830	5.2656	209	43,681	9,129,329	14.4568	5.9345
147	21,609	3,176,523	12.1244	5.2776	210	44,100	9,261,000	14.4914	5.9439
148	21,904	3,241,792	12.1655	5.2896	211	44,521	9,393,931	14.5258	5.9533
149	22,201	3,307,949	12.2066	5.3015	212	44,944	9,528,128	14.5602	5.9627
150	22,500	3,375,000	12.2474	5.3133	213	45,369	9,663,597	14.5945	5.9721
151	22,801	3,442,951	12.2882	5.3251	214	45,796	9,800,344	14.6287	5.9814
152	23,104	3,511,808	12.3288	5.3368	215	46,225	9,938,375	14.6629	5.9907
153	23,409	3,581,577	12.3693	5.3485	216	46,656	10,077,696	14.6969	6.0000
154	23,716	3,652,264	12.4097	5.3601	217	47,089	10,218,313	14.7309	6.0092
155	24,025	3,723,875	12.4499	5.3717	218	47,524	10,360,232	14.7648	6.0185
156	24,336	3,796,416	12.4900	5.3832	219	47,961	10,503,459	14.7986	6.0277
157	24,649	3,869,893	12.5300	5.3947	220	48,400	10,648,000	14.8324	6.0368
158	24,964	3,944,312	12.5698	5.4061	221	48,841	10,793,861	14.8661	6.0459
159	25,281	4,019,679	12.6095	5.4175	222	49,284	10,941,048	14.8997	6.0550
160	25,600	4,096,000	12.6491	5.4288	223	49,729	11,089,567	14.9332	6.0641
161	25,921	4,173,281	12.6886	5.4401	224	50,176	11,239,424	14.9666	6.0732
162	26,244	4,251,528	12.7279	5.4514	225	50,625	11,390,625	15.0000	6.0822
163	26,569	4,330,747	12.7671	5.4626	226	51,076	11,543,176	15.0333	6.0912
164	26,896	4,410,944	12.8062	5.4737	227	51,529	11,697,083	15.0665	6.1002
165	27,225	4,492,125	12.8452	5.4848	228	51,984	11,852,352	15.0997	6.1091
166	27,556	4,574,296	12.8841	5.4959	229	52,441	12,008,989	15.1327	6.1180
167	27,889	4,657,463	12.9228	5.5069	230	52,900	12,167,000	15.1658	6.1269
168	28,224	4,741,632	12.9615	5.5178	231	53,361	12,326,391	15.1987	6.1358
169	28,561	4,826,809	13.0000	5.5288	232	53,824	12,487,168	15.2315	6.1446
170	28,900	4,913,000	13.0384	5.5397	233	54,289	12,649,337	15.2643	6.1534
171	29,241	5,000,211	13.0767	5.5505	234	54,756	12,812,904	15.2971	6.1622
172	29,584	5,088,448	13.1149	5.5613	235	55,225	12,977,875	15.3297	6.1710
173	29,929	5,177,717	13.1529	5.5721	236	55,696	13,144,256	15.3623	6.1797
174	30,276	5,268,024	13.1909	5.5828	237	56,169	13,312,053	15.3948	6.1885
175	30,625	5,359,375	13.2288	5.5934	238	56,644	13,481,272	15.4272	6.1972
176	30,976	5,451,776	13.2665	5.6041	239	57,121	13,651,919	15.4596	6.2058
177	31,329	5,545,233	13.3041	5.6147	240	57,600	13,824,000	15.4919	6.2145
178	31,684	5,639,752	13.3417	5.6252	241	58,081	13,997,521	15.5242	6.2231
179	32,041	5,735,339	13.3791	5.6357	242	58,564	14,172,488	15.5563	6.2317
180	32,400	5,832,000	13.4164	5.6462	243	59,049	14,348,907	15.5885	6.2403
181	32,761	5,929,741	13.4536	5.6567	244	59,536	14,526,784	15.6205	6.2488

Table F-1 Squares, cubes, square roots, and cube roots (Continued)

No.	Square	Cube	Sq. Root	Cu. Root	No.	Square	Cube	Sq. Root	Cu. Root
245	60,025	14,706,125	15.6525	6.2573	308	94,864	29,218,112	17.5499	6.7533
246	60,516	14,886,936	15.6844	6.2658	309	95,481	29,503,629	17.5784	6.7606
247	61,009	15,069,223	15.7162	6.2743	310	96,100	29,791,000	17.6068	6.7679
248	61,504	15,252,992	15.7480	6.2828	311	96,721	30,080,231	17.6352	6.7752
249	62,001	15,438,249	15.7797	6.2912	312	97,344	30,371,328	17.6635	6.7824
250	62,500	15,625,000	15.8114	6.2996	313	97,969	30,664,297	17.6918	6.7897
251	63,001	15,813,251	15.8430	6.3080	314	98,596	30,959,144	17.7200	6.7969
252	63,504	16,003,008	15.8745	6.3164	315	99,225	31,255,875	17.7482	6.8041
253	64,009	16,194,277	15.9060	6.3247	316	99,856	31,554,496	17.7764	6.8113
254	64,516	16,387,064	15.9374	6.3330	317	100,489	31,855,013	17.8045	6.8185
255	65,025	16,581,375	15.9687	6.3413	318	101,124	32,157,432	17.8326	6.8256
256	65,536	16,777,216	16.0000	6.3496	319	101,761	32,461,759	17.8606	6.8328
257	66,049	16,974,593	16.0312	6.3579	320	102,400	32,768,000	17.8885	6.8399
258	66,564	17,173,512	16.0624	6.3661	321	103,041	33,076,161	17.9165	6.8470
259	67,081	17,373,979	16.0935	6.3743	322	103,684	33,386,248	17.9444	6.8541
260	67,600	17,576,000	16.1245	6.3825	323	104,329	33,698,267	17.9722	6.8612
261	68,121	17,779,581	16.1555	6.3907	324	104,976	34,012,224	18.0000	6.8683
262	68,644	17,984,728	16.1864	6.3988	325	105,625	34,328,125	18.0278	6.8753
263	69,169	18,191,447	16.2173	6.4070	326	106,276	34,645,976	18.0555	6.8824
264	69,696	18,399,744	16.2481	6.4151	327	106,929	34,965,783	18.0831	6.8894
265	70,225	18,609,625	16.2788	6.4232	328	107,584	35,287,552	18.1108	6.8964
266	70,756	18,821,096	16.3095	6.4312	329	108,241	35,611,289	18.1384	6.9034
267	71,289	19,034,163	16.3401	6.4393	330	108,900	35,937,000	18.1659	6.9104
268	71,824	19,248,832	16.3707	6.4473	331	109,561	36,264,691	18.1934	6.9174
269	72,361	19,465,109	16.4012	6.4553	332	110,224	36,594,368	18.2209	6.9244
270	72,900	19,683,000	16.4317	6.4633	333	110,889	36,926,037	18.2483	6.9313
271	73,441	19,902,511	16.4621	6.4713	334	111,556	37,259,704	18.2757	6.9382
272	73,984	20,123,648	16.4924	6.4792	335	112,225	37,595,375	18.3030	6.9451
273	74,529	20,346,417	16.5227	6.4872	336	112,896	37,933,056	18.3303	6.9521
274	75,076	20,570,824	16.5529	6.4951	337	113,569	38,272,753	18.3576	6.9589
275	75,625	20,796,875	16.5831	6.5030	338	114,244	38,614,472	18.3848	6.9658
276	76,176	21,024,576	16.6132	6.5108	339	114,921	38,958,219	18.4120	6.9727
277	76,729	21,253,933	16.6433	6.5187	340	115,600	39,304,000	18.4391	6.9795
278	77,284	21,484,952	16.6733	6.5265	341	116,281	39,651,821	18.4662	6.9864
279	77,841	21,717,639	16 7033	6.5343	342	116,964	40,001,688	18.4932	6.9932
280	78,400	21,952,000	16.7332	6.5421	343	117,649	40,353,607	18.5203	7.0000
281	78,961	22,188,041	16.7631	6.5499	344	118,336	40,707,584	18.5472	7.0068
282	79,524	22,425,768	16.7929	6.5577	345	119,025	41,063,625	18.5742	7.0136
283	80,089	22,665,187	16.8226	6.5654	346	119,716	41,421,736	18.6011	7.0203
284	80,656	22,906,304	16.8523	6.5731	347	120,409	41,781,923	18.6279	7.0271
285	81,225	23,149,125	16.8819	6.5808	348	121,104	42,144,192	18.6548	7.0338
286	81,796	23,393,656	16.9115	6.5885	349	121,801	42,508,549	18.6815	7.0406
287	82,369	23,639,903	16.9411	6.5962	350	122,500	42,875,000	18.7083	7.0473
288	82,944	23,887,872	16.9706	6.6039	351	123,201	43,243,551	18.7350	7.0540
289	83,521	24,137,569	17.0000	6.6115	352	123,904	43,614,208	18.7617	7.0607
290	84,100	24,389,000	17.0294	6.6191	353	124,609	43,986,977	18.7883	7.0674
291	84,681	24,642,171	17.0587	6.6267	354	125,316	44,361,864	18.8149	7.0740
292	85,264	24,897,088	17.0880	6.6343	355	126,025	44,738,875	18.8414	7.0807
293	85,849	25,153,757	17.1172	6.6419	356	126,736	45,118,016	18.8680	7.0873
294	86,436	25,412,184	17.1464	6.6494	357	127,449	45,499,293	18.8944	7.0940
295	87,025	25,672,375	17.1756	6.6569	358	128,164	45,882,712	18.9209	7.1006
296	87,616	25,934,336	17.2047	6.6644	359	128,881	46,268,279	18.9473	7.1072
297	88,209	26,198,073	17.2337	6.6719	360	129,600	46,656,000	18.9737	7.1138
298	88,804	26,463,592	17.2627	6.6794	361	130,321	47,045,881	19.0000	7.1204
299	89,401	26,730,899	17.2916	6.6869	362	131,044	47,437,928	19.0263	7.1269
300	90,000	27,000,000	17.3205	6.6943	363	131,769	47,832,147	19.0526	7.1335
301	90,601	27,270,901	17.3494	6.7018	364	132,496	48,228,544	19.0788	7.1400
302	91,204	27,543,608	17.3781	6.7092	365	133,225	48,627,125	19.1050	7.1466
303	91,809	27,818,127	17.4069	6.7166	366	133,956	49,027,896	19.1311	7.1531
304	92,416	28,094,464	17.4356	6.7240	367	134,689	49,430,863	19.1572	7.1596
305	93,025	28,372,625	17.4642	6.7313	368	135,424	49,836,032	19.1833	7.1661
306	93,636	28,652,616	17.4929	6.7387	369	136,161	50,243,409	19.2094	7.1726
307	94,249	28,934,443	17.5214	6.7460	870	136,900	50,653,000	19.2354	7.1791

Table F-1   Squares, cubes, square roots, and cube roots (*Continued*)

No.	Square	Cube	Sq. Root	Cu. Root	No.	Square	Cube	Sq. Root	Cu. Root
371	137,641	51,064,811	19.2614	7.1855	434	188,356	81,746,504	20.8327	7.5712
372	138,384	51,478,848	19.2873	7.1920	435	189,225	82,312,875	20.8567	7.5770
373	139,129	51,895,117	19.3132	7.1984	436	190,096	82,881,856	20.8806	7.5828
374	139,876	52,313,624	19.3391	7.2048	437	190,969	83,453,453	20.9045	7.5886
375	140,625	52,734,375	19.3649	7.2112	438	191,844	84,027,672	20.9284	7.5944
376	141,376	53,157,376	19.3907	7.2177	439	192,721	84,604,519	20.9523	7.6001
377	142,129	53,582,633	19.4165	7.2240	440	193,600	85,184,000	20.9762	7.6059
378	142,884	54,010,152	19.4422	7.2304	441	194,481	85,766,121	21.0000	7.6117
379	143,641	54,439,939	19.4679	7.2368	442	195,364	86,350,888	21.0238	7.6174
380	144,400	54,872,000	19.4936	7.2432	443	196,249	86,938,307	21.0476	7.6232
381	145,161	55,306,341	19.5192	7.2495	444	197,136	87,528,384	21.0713	7.6289
382	145,924	55,742,968	19.5448	7.2558	445	198,025	88,121,125	21.0950	7.6346
383	146,689	56,181,887	19.5704	7.2622	446	198,916	88,716,536	21.1187	7.6403
384	147,456	56,623,104	19.5959	7.2685	447	199,809	89,314,623	21.1424	7.6460
385	148,225	57,066,625	19.6214	7.2748	448	200,704	89,915,392	21.1660	7.6517
386	148,996	57,512,456	19.6469	7.2811	449	201,601	90,518,849	21.1896	7.6574
387	149,769	57,960,603	19.6723	7.2874	450	202,500	91,125,000	21.2132	7.6631
388	150,544	58,411,072	19.6977	7.2936	451	203,401	91,733,851	21.2368	7.6688
389	151,321	58,863,869	19.7231	7.2999	452	204,304	92,345,408	21.2603	7.6744
390	152,100	59,319,000	19.7484	7.3061	453	205,209	92,959,677	21.2838	7.6801
391	152,881	59,776,471	19.7737	7.3124	454	206,116	93,576,664	21.3073	7.6857
392	153,664	60,236,288	19.7990	7.3186	455	207,025	94,196,375	21.3307	7.6914
393	154,449	60,698,457	19.8242	7.3248	456	207,936	94,818,816	21.3542	7.6970
394	155,236	61,162,984	19.8494	7.3310	457	208,849	95,443,993	21.3776	7.7026
395	156,025	61,629,875	19.8746	7.3372	458	209,764	96,071,912	21.4009	7.7082
396	156,816	62,099,136	19.8997	7.3434	459	210,681	96,702,579	21.4213	7.7138
397	157,609	62,570,773	19.9249	7.3496	460	211,600	97,336,000	21.4476	7.7194
398	158,404	63,044,792	19.9499	7.3558	461	212,521	97,972,181	21.4709	7.7250
399	159,201	63,521,199	19.9750	7.3619	462	213,444	98,611,128	21.4942	7.7306
400	160,000	64,000,000	20.0000	7.3681	463	214,369	99,252,847	21.5174	7.7362
401	160.801	64,481,201	20.0250	7.3742	464	215,296	99,897,344	21.5407	7.7418
402	161,604	64,964,808	20.0499	7.3803	465	216,225	100,544,625	21.5639	7.7473
403	162,409	65,450,827	20.0749	7.3864	466	217,156	101,194,696	21.5870	7.7529
404	163,216	65,939,264	20.0998	7.3925	467	218,089	101,847,563	21.6102	7.7584
405	164,025	66,430,125	20.1246	7.3986	468	219,024	102,503,232	21.6333	7.7639
406	164,836	66,923,416	20.1494	7.4047	469	219,961	103,161,709	21.6564	7.7695
407	165,649	67,419,143	20.1742	7.4108	470	220,900	103,823,000	21.6795	7.7750
408	166,464	67,917,312	20.1990	7.4169	471	221,841	104,487,111	21.7025	7.7805
409	167,281	68,417,929	20.2237	7.4229	472	222,784	105,154,048	21.7256	7.7860
410	168,100	68,921,000	20.2485	7.4290	473	223,729	105,823,817	21.7486	7.7915
411	168,921	69,426,531	20.2731	7.4350	474	224,676	106,496,424	21.7715	7.7970
412	169,744	69,934,528	20.2978	7.4410	475	225,625	107,171,875	21.7945	7.8025
413	170,569	70,444,997	20.3224	7.4470	476	226,576	107,850,176	21.8174	7.8079
414	171,396	70,957,944	20.3470	7.4530	477	227,529	108,531,333	21.8403	7.8134
415	172,225	71,473,375	20.3715	7.4590	478	228,484	109,215,352	21.8632	7.8188
416	173,056	71,991,296	20.3961	7.4650	479	229,441	109,902,239	21.8861	7.8243
417	173,889	72,511,713	20.4206	7.4710	480	230,400	110,592,000	21.9089	7.8297
418	174,724	73,034,632	20.4450	7.4770	481	231,361	111,284,641	21.9317	7.8352
419	175,561	73,560,059	20.4695	7.4829	482	232,324	111,980,168	21.9545	7.8406
420	176,400	74,088,000	20.4939	7.4889	483	233,289	112,678,587	21.9773	7.8460
421	177,241	74,618,461	20.5183	7.4948	484	234,256	113,379,904	22.0000	7.8514
422	178,084	75,151,448	20.5426	7.5007	485	235,225	114,084,125	22.0227	7.8568
423	178,929	75,686,967	20.5670	7.5067	486	236,196	114,791,256	22.0454	7.8622
424	179,776	76,225,024	20.5913	7.5126	487	237,169	115,501,303	22.0681	7.8676
425	180,625	76,765,625	20.6155	7.5185	488	238,144	116,214,272	22.0907	7.8730
426	181,476	77,308,776	20.6398	7.5244	489	239,121	116,930,169	22.1133	7.8784
427	182,329	77,854,483	20.6640	7.5302	490	240,100	117,649,000	22.1359	7.8837
428	183,184	78,402,752	20.6882	7.5361	491	241,081	118,370,771	22.1585	7.8891
429	184,041	78,953,589	20.7123	7.5420	492	242,064	119,095,488	22.1811	7.8944
430	184,900	79,507,000	20.7364	7.5478	493	243,049	119,823,157	22.2036	7.8998
431	185,761	80,062,991	20.7605	7.5537	494	244,036	120,553,784	22.2261	7.9051
432	186,624	80,621,568	20.7846	7.5595	495	245,025	121,287,375	22.2486	7.9105
433	187,489	81,182,737	20.8087	7.5654	496	246,016	122,023,936	22.2711	7.9158

Table F-1 Squares, cubes, square roots, and cube roots (*Continued*)

No.	Square	Cube	Sq. Root	Cu. Root	No.	Square	Cube	Sq. Root	Cu. Root
497	247,009	122,763,473	22.2935	7.9211	560	313,600	175,616,000	23.6643	8.2426
498	248,004	123,505,992	22.3159	7.9264	561	314,721	176,558,481	23.6854	8.2475
499	249,001	124,251,499	22.3383	7.9317	562	315,844	177,504,328	23.7065	8.2524
500	250,000	125,000,000	22.3607	7.9370	563	316,969	178,453,547	23.7276	8.2573
501	251,001	125,751,501	22.3830	7.9423	564	318,096	179,406,144	23.7487	8.2621
502	252,004	126,506,008	22.4054	7.9476	565	319,225	180,362,125	23.7697	8.2670
503	253,009	127,263,527	22.4277	7.9528	566	320,356	181,321,496	23.7908	8.2719
504	254,016	128,024,064	22.4499	7.9581	567	321,489	182,284,263	23.8118	8.2768
505	255,025	128,787,625	22.4722	7.9634	568	322,624	183,250,432	23.8328	8.2816
506	256,036	129,554,216	22.4944	7.9686	569	323,761	184,220,009	23.8537	8.2865
507	257,049	130,323,843	22.5167	7.9739	570	324,900	185,193,000	23.8747	8.2913
508	258,064	131,096,512	22.5389	7.9791	571	326,041	186,169,411	23.8956	8.2962
509	259,081	131,872,229	22.5610	7.9843	572	327,184	187,149,248	23.9165	8.3010
510	260,100	132,651,000	22.5832	7.9896	573	328,329	188,132,517	23.9374	8.3059
511	261,121	133,432,831	22.6053	7.9948	574	329,476	189,119,224	23.9583	8.3107
512	262,144	134,217,728	22.6274	8.0000	575	330,625	190,109,375	23.9792	8.3155
513	263,169	135,005,697	22.6495	8.0052	576	331,776	191,102,976	24.0000	8.3203
514	264,196	135,796,744	22.6716	8.0104	577	332,929	192,100,033	24.0208	8.3251
515	265,225	136,590,875	22.6936	8.0156	578	334,084	193,100,552	24.0416	8.3300
516	266,256	137,388,096	22.7156	8.0208	579	335,241	194,104,539	24.0624	8.3348
517	267,289	138,188,413	22.7376	8.0260	580	336,400	195,112,000	24.0832	8.3396
518	268,324	138,991,832	22.7596	8.0311	581	337,561	196,122,941	24.1039	8.3443
519	269,361	139,798,359	22.7816	8.0363	582	338,724	197,137,368	24.1247	8.3491
520	270,400	140,608,000	22.8035	8.0415	583	339,889	198,155,287	24.1454	8.3539
521	271,441	141,420,761	22.8254	8.0466	584	341,056	199,176,704	24.1661	8.3587
522	272,484	142,236,648	22.8473	8.0517	585	342,225	200,201,625	24.1868	8.3634
523	273,529	143,055,667	22.8692	8.0569	586	343,396	201,230,056	24.2074	8.3682
524	274,576	143,877,824	22.8910	8.0620	587	344,569	202,262,003	24.2281	8.3730
525	275,625	144,703,125	22.9129	8.0671	588	345,744	203,297,472	24.2487	8.3777
526	276,676	145,531,576	22.9347	8.0723	589	346,921	204,336,469	24.2693	8.3825
527	277,729	146,363,183	22.9565	8.0774	590	348,100	205,379,000	24.2899	8.3872
528	278,784	147,197,952	22.9783	8.0825	591	349,281	206,425,071	24.3105	8.3919
529	279,841	148,035,889	23.0000	8.0876	592	350,464	207,474,688	24.3311	8.3967
530	280,900	148,877,000	23.0217	8.0927	593	351,649	208,527,857	24.3516	8.4014
531	281,961	149,721,291	23.0434	8.0978	594	352,836	209,584,584	24.3721	8.4061
532	283,024	150,568,768	23.0651	8.1028	595	354,025	210,644,875	24.3926	8.4108
533	284,089	151,419,437	23.0868	8.1079	596	355,216	211,708,736	24.4131	8.4155
534	285,156	152,273,304	23.1084	8.1130	597	356,409	212,776,173	24.4336	8.4202
535	286,225	153,130,375	23.1301	8.1180	598	357,604	213,847,192	24.4540	8.4249
536	287,296	153,990,656	23.1517	8.1231	599	358,801	214,921,799	24.4745	8.4296
537	288,369	154,854,153	23.1733	8.1281	600	360,000	216,000,000	24.4949	8.4343
538	289,444	155,720,872	23.1948	8.1332	601	361,201	217,081,801	24.5153	8.4390
539	290,521	156,590,819	23.2164	8.1382	602	362,404	218,167,208	24.5357	8.4437
540	291,600	157,464,000	23.2379	8.1433	603	363,609	219,256,227	24.5561	8.4484
541	292,681	158,340,421	23.2594	8.1483	604	364,816	220,348,864	24.5764	8.4530
542	293,764	159,220,088	23.2809	8.1533	605	366,025	221,445,125	24.5968	8.4577
543	294,849	160,103,007	23.3024	8.1583	606	367,236	222,545,016	24.6171	8.4623
544	295,936	160,989,184	23.3238	8.1633	607	368,449	223,648,543	24.6374	8.4670
545	297,025	161,878,625	23.3452	8.1683	608	369,664	224,755,712	24.6577	8.4716
546	298,116	162,771,336	23.3666	8.1733	609	370,881	225,866,529	24.6779	8.4763
547	299,209	163,667,323	23.3880	8.1783	610	372,100	226,981,000	24.6982	8.4809
548	300,304	164,566,592	23.4094	8.1833	611	373,321	228,099,131	24.7184	8.4856
549	301,401	165,469,149	23.4307	8.1882	612	374,544	229,220,928	24.7386	8.4902
550	302,500	166,375,000	23.4521	8.1932	613	375,769	230,346,397	24.7588	8.4948
551	303,601	167,284,151	23.4734	8.1982	614	376,996	231,475,544	24.7790	8.4994
552	304,704	168,196,608	23.4947	8.2031	615	378,225	232,608,375	24.7992	8.5040
553	305,809	169,112,377	23.5160	8.2081	616	379,456	233,744,896	24.8193	8.5086
554	306,916	170,031,464	23.5372	8.2130	617	380,689	234,885,113	24.8395	8.5132
555	308,025	170,953,875	23.5584	8.2180	618	381,924	236,029,032	24.8596	8.5178
556	309,136	171,879,616	23.5797	8.2229	619	383,161	237,176,659	24.8797	8.5224
557	310,249	172,808,693	23.6008	8.2278	620	384,400	238,328,000	24.8998	8.5270
558	311,364	173,741,112	23.6220	8.2327	621	385,641	239,483,061	24.9199	8.5316
559	312,481	174,676,879	23.6432	8.2377	622	386,884	240,641,848	24.9399	8.5362

Table F-1   Squares, cubes, square roots, and cube roots (Continued)

No.	Square	Cube	Sq. Root	Cu. Root	No.	Square	Cube	Sq. Root	Cu. Root
623	388,129	241,804,367	24.9600	8.5408	686	470,596	322,828,856	26.1916	8.8194
624	389,376	242,970,624	24.9800	8.5453	687	471,969	324,242,703	26.2107	8.8237
625	390,625	244,140,625	25.0000	8.5499	688	473,344	325,660,672	26.2298	8.8280
626	391,876	245,314,376	25.0200	8.5544	689	474,721	327,082,769	26.2488	8.8323
627	393,129	246,491,883	25.0400	8.5590	690	476,100	328,509,000	26.2679	8.8366
628	394,384	247,673,152	25.0599	8.5635	691	477,481	329,939,371	26.2869	8.8408
629	395,641	248,858,189	25.0799	8.5681	692	478,864	331,373,888	26.3059	8.8451
630	396,900	250,047,000	25.0998	8.5726	693	480,249	332,812,557	26.3249	8.8493
631	398,161	251,239,591	25.1197	8.5772	694	481,636	334,255,384	26.3439	8.8536
632	399,424	252,435,968	25.1396	8.5817	695	483,025	335,702,375	26.3629	8.8578
633	400,689	253,636,137	25.1595	8.5862	696	484,416	337,153,536	26.3818	8.8621
634	401,956	254,840,104	25.1794	8.5907	697	485,809	338,608,873	26.4008	8.8663
635	403,225	256,047,875	25.1992	8.5952	698	487,204	340,068,392	26.4197	8.8706
636	404,496	257,259,456	25.2190	8.5997	699	488,601	341,532,099	26.4386	8.8748
637	405,769	258,474,853	25.2389	8.6043	700	490,000	343,000,000	26.4575	8.8790
638	407,044	259,694,072	25.2587	8.6088	701	491,401	344,472,101	26.4764	8.8833
639	408,321	260,917,119	25.2784	8.6132	702	492,804	345,948,408	26.4953	8.8875
640	409,600	262,144,000	25.2982	8.6177	703	494,209	347,428,927	26.5141	8.8917
641	410,881	263,374,721	25.3180	8.6222	704	495,616	348,913,664	26.5330	8.8959
642	412,164	264,609,288	25.3377	8.6267	705	497,025	350,402,625	26.5518	8.9001
643	413,449	265,847,707	25.3574	8.6312	706	498,436	351,895,816	26.5707	8.9043
644	414,736	267,089,984	25.3772	8.6357	707	499,849	353,393,243	26.5895	8.9085
645	416,025	268,336,125	25.3969	8.6401	708	501,264	354,894,912	26.6083	8.9127
646	417,316	269,586,136	25.4165	8.6446	709	502,681	356,400,829	26.6271	8.9169
647	418,609	270,840,023	25.4362	8.6490	710	504,100	357,911,000	26.6458	8.9211
648	419,904	272,097,792	25.4558	8.6535	711	505,521	359,425,431	26.6646	8.9253
649	421,201	273,359,449	25.4755	8.6579	712	506,944	360,944,128	26.6833	8.9295
650	422,500	274,625,000	25.4951	8.6624	713	508,369	362,467,097	26.7021	8.9337
651	423,801	275,894,451	25.5147	8.6668	714	509,796	363,994,344	26.7208	8.9378
652	425,104	277,167,808	25.5343	8.6713	715	511,225	365,525,875	26.7395	8.9420
653	426,409	278,445,077	25.5539	8.6757	716	512,656	367,061,696	26.7582	8.9462
654	427,716	279,726,264	25.5734	8.6801	717	514,089	368,601,813	26.7769	8.9503
655	429,025	281,011,375	25.5930	8.6845	718	515,524	370,146,232	26.7955	8.9545
656	430,336	282,300,416	25.6125	8.6890	719	516,961	371,694,959	26.8142	8.9587
657	431,649	283,593,393	25.6320	8.6934	720	518,400	373,248,000	26.8328	8.9628
658	432,964	284,890,312	25.6515	8.6978	721	519,841	374,805,361	26.8514	8.9670
659	434,281	286,191,179	25.6710	8.7022	722	521,284	376,367,048	26.8701	8.9711
660	435,600	287,496,000	25.6905	8.7066	723	522,729	377,933,067	26.8887	8.9752
661	436,921	288,804,781	25.7099	8.7110	724	524,176	379,503,424	26.9072	8.9794
662	438,244	290,117,528	25.7294	8.7154	725	525,625	381,078,125	26.9258	8.9835
663	439,569	291,434.247	25.7488	8.7198	726	527,076	382,657,176	26.9444	8.9876
664	440,896	292,754,944	25.7682	8.7241	727	528,529	384,240,583	26.9629	8.9918
665	442,225	294,079,625	25.7876	8.7285	728	529,984	385,828,352	26.9815	8.9959
666	443,556	295,408,296	25.8070	8.7329	729	531,441	387,420,489	27.0000	9.0000
667	444,889	296,740,963	25.8263	8.7373	730	532,900	389,017,000	27.0185	9.0041
668	446,224	298,077,632	25.8457	8.7416	731	534,361	390,617,891	27.0370	9.0082
669	447,561	299,418,309	25.8650	8.7460	732	535,824	392,223,168	27.0555	9.0123
670	448,900	300,763,000	25.8844	8.7503	733	537,289	393,832,837	27.0740	9.0164
671	450,241	302,111,711	25.9037	8.7547	734	538,756	395,446,904	27.0924	9.0205
672	451,584	303,464,448	25.9230	8.7590	735	540,225	397,065,375	27.1109	9.0246
673	452,929	304,821,217	25.9422	8.7634	736	541,696	398,688,256	27.1293	9.0287
674	454,276	306,182,024	25.9615	8.7677	737	543,169	400,315,553	27.1477	9.0328
675	455,625	307,546,875	25.9808	8.7721	738	544,644	401,947,272	27.1662	9.0369
676	456,976	308,915,776	26.0000	8.7764	739	546,121	403,583,419	27.1846	9.0410
677	458,329	310,288,733	26.0192	8.7807	740	547,600	405,224,000	27.2029	9.0450
678	459,684	311,665,752	26.0384	8.7850	741	549,081	406,869,021	27.2213	9.0491
679	461,041	313,046,839	26.0576	8.7893	742	550,564	408,518,488	27.2397	9.0532
680	462,400	314,432,000	26.0768	8.7937	743	552,049	410,172,407	27.2580	9.0572
681	463,761	315,821,241	26.0960	8.7980	744	553,536	411,830,784	27.2764	9.0613
682	465,124	317,214,568	26.1151	8.8023	745	555,025	413,493,625	27.2947	9.0654
683	466,489	318,611,987	26.1343	8.8066	746	556,516	415,160,936	27.3130	9.0694
684	467,856	320,013,504	26.1534	8.8109	747	558,009	416,832,723	27.3313	9.0735
685	469,225	321,419,125	26.1725	8.8152	748	559,504	418,508,992	27.3496	9.0775

Table F-1 Squares, cubes, square roots, and cube roots (Continued)

No.	Square	Cube	Sq. Root	Cu. Root	No.	Square	Cube	Sq. Root	Cu. Root
749	561,001	420,189,749	27.3679	9.0816	812	659,344	535,387,328	28.4956	9.3294
750	562,500	421,875,000	27.3861	9.0856	813	660,969	537,367,797	28.5132	9.3332
751	564,001	423,564,751	27.4044	9.0896	814	662,596	539,353,144	28.5307	9.3370
752	565,504	425,259,008	27.4226	9.0937	815	664,225	541,343,375	28.5482	9.3408
753	567,009	426,957,777	27.4408	9.0977	816	665,856	543,338,496	28.5657	9.3447
754	568,516	428,661,064	27.4591	9.1017	817	667,489	545,338,513	28.5832	9.3485
755	570,025	430,368,875	27.4773	9.1057	818	669,124	547,343,432	28.6007	9.3523
756	571,536	432,081,216	27.4955	9.1098	819	670,761	549,353,259	28.6182	9.3561
757	573,049	433,798,093	27.5136	9.1138	820	672,400	551,368,000	28.6356	9.3599
758	574,564	435,519,512	27.5318	9.1178	821	674,041	553,387,661	28.6531	9.3637
759	576,081	437,245,479	27.5500	9.1218	822	675,684	555,412,248	28.6705	9.3675
760	577,600	438,976,000	27.5681	9.1258	823	677,329	557,441,767	28.6880	9.3713
761	579,121	440,711,081	27.5862	9.1298	824	678,976	559,476,224	28.7054	9.3751
762	580,644	442,450,728	27.6043	9.1338	825	680,625	561,515,625	28.7228	9.3789
763	582,169	444,194,947	27.6225	9.1378	826	682,276	563,559,976	28.7402	9.3827
764	583,696	445,943,744	27.6405	9.1418	827	683,929	565,609,283	28.7576	9.3865
765	585,225	447,697,125	27.6586	9.1458	828	685,584	567,663,552	28.7750	9.3902
766	586,756	449,455,096	27.6767	9.1498	829	687,241	569,722,789	28.7924	9.3940
767	588,289	451,217,663	27.6948	9.1537	830	688,900	571,787,000	28.8097	9.3978
768	589,824	452,984,832	27.7128	9.1577	831	690,561	573,856,191	28.8271	9.4016
769	591,361	454,756,609	27.7308	9.1617	832	692,224	575,930,368	28.8444	9.4053
770	592,900	456,533,000	27.7489	9.1657	833	693,889	578,009,537	28.8617	9.4091
771	594,441	458,314,011	27.7669	9.1696	834	695,556	580,093,704	28.8791	9.4129
772	595,984	460,099,648	27.7849	9.1736	835	697,225	582,182,875	28.8964	9.4166
773	597,529	461,889,917	27.8029	9.1775	836	698,896	584,277,056	28.9137	9.4204
774	599,076	463,684,824	27.8209	9.1815	837	700,569	586,376,253	28.9310	9.4241
775	600,625	465,484,375	27.8388	9.1855	838	702,244	588,480,472	28.9482	9.4279
776	602,176	467,288,576	27.8568	9.1894	839	703,921	590,589,719	28.9655	9.4316
777	603,729	469,097,433	27.8747	9.1933	840	705,600	592,704,000	28.9828	9.4354
778	605,284	470,910,952	27.8927	9.1973	841	707,281	594,823,321	29.0000	9.4391
779	606,841	472,729,139	27.9106	9.2012	842	708,964	596,947,688	29.0172	9.4429
780	608,400	474,552,000	27.9285	9.2052	843	710,649	599,077,107	29.0345	9.4466
781	609,961	476,379,541	27.9464	9.2091	844	712,336	601,211,584	29.0517	9.4503
782	611,524	478,211,768	27.9643	9.2130	845	714,025	603,351,125	29.0689	9.4541
783	613,089	480,048,687	27.9821	9.2170	846	715,716	605,495,736	29.0861	9.4578
784	614,656	481,890,304	28.0000	9.2209	847	717,409	607,645,423	29.1033	9.4615
785	616,225	483,736,625	28.0179	9.2248	848	719,104	609,800,192	29.1204	9.4652
786	617,796	485,587,656	28.0357	9.2287	849	720,801	611,960,049	29.1376	9.4690
787	619,369	487,443,403	28.0535	9.2326	850	722,500	614,125,000	29.1548	9.4727
788	620,944	489,303,872	28.0713	9.2365	851	724,201	616,295,051	29.1719	9.4764
789	622,521	491,169,069	28.0891	9.2404	852	725,904	618,470,208	29.1890	9.4801
790	624,100	493,039,000	28.1069	9.2443	853	727,609	620,650,477	29.2062	9.4838
791	625,681	494,913,671	28.1247	9.2482	854	729,316	622,835,864	29.2233	9.4875
792	627,264	496,793,088	28.1425	9.2521	855	731,025	625,026,375	29.2404	9.4912
793	628,849	498,677,257	28.1603	9.2560	856	732,736	627,222,016	29.2575	9.4949
794	630,436	500,566,184	28.1780	9.2599	857	734,449	629,422,793	29.2746	9.4986
795	632,025	502,459,875	28.1957	9.2638	858	736,164	631,628,712	29.2916	9.5023
796	633,616	504,358,336	28.2135	9.2677	859	737,881	633,839,779	29.3087	9.5060
797	635,209	506,261,573	28.2312	9.2716	860	739,600	636,056,000	29.3258	9.5097
798	636,804	508,169,592	28.2489	9.2754	861	741,321	638,277,381	29.3428	9.5134
799	638,401	510,082,399	28.2666	9.2793	862	743,044	640,503,928	29.3598	9.5171
800	640,000	512,000,000	28.2843	9.2832	863	744,769	642,735,647	29.3769	9.5207
801	641,601	513,922,401	28.3019	9.2870	864	746,496	644,972,544	29.3939	9.5244
802	643,204	515,849,608	28.3196	9.2909	865	748,225	647,214,625	29.4109	9.5281
803	644,809	517,781,627	28.3373	9.2948	866	749,956	649,461,896	29.4279	9.5317
804	646,416	519,718,464	28.3549	9.2986	867	751,689	651,714,363	29.4449	9.5354
805	648,025	521,660,125	28.3725	9.3025	868	753,424	653,972,032	29.4618	9.5391
806	649,636	523,606,616	28.3901	9.3063	869	755,161	656,234,909	29.4788	9.5427
807	651,249	525,557,943	28.4077	9.3102	870	756,900	658,503,000	29.4958	9.5464
808	652,864	527,514,112	28.4253	9.3140	871	758,641	660,776,311	29.5127	9.5501
809	654,481	529,475,129	28.4429	9.3179	872	760,384	663,054,848	29.5296	9.5537
810	656,100	531,441,000	28.4605	9.3217	873	762,129	665,338,617	29.5466	9.5574
811	657,721	533,411,731	28.4781	9.3255	874	763,876	667,627,624	29.5635	9.5610

Table F-1 Squares, cubes, square roots, and cube roots (Continued)

No.	Square	Cube	Sq. Root	Cu. Root	No.	Square	Cube	Sq. Root	Cu. Root
875	765,625	669,921,875	29.5804	9.5647	938	879,844	825,293,672	30.6268	9.7889
876	767,376	672,221,376	29.5973	9.5683	939	881,721	827,936,019	30.6431	9.7924
877	769,129	674,526,133	29.6142	9.5719	940	883,600	830,584,000	30.6594	9.7959
878	770,884	676,836,152	29.6311	9.5756	941	885,481	833,237,621	30.6757	9.7993
879	772,641	679,151,439	29.6479	9.5792	942	887,364	835,896,888	30.6920	9.8028
880	774,400	681,472,000	29.6648	9.5828	943	889,249	838,561,807	30.7083	9.8063
881	776,161	683,797.841	29.6816	9.5865	944	891,136	841,232,384	30.7246	9.8097
882	777,924	686,128,968	29.6985	9.5901	945	893,025	843,908,625	30.7409	9.8132
883	779.689	688,465,387	29.7153	9.5937	946	894,916	846,590,536	30.7571	9.8167
884	781,456	690,807,104	29.7321	9.5973	947	896,809	849,278,123	30.7734	9.8201
885	783,225	693,154.125	29.7489	9.6010	948	898,704	851,971,392	30.7896	9.8236
886	784,996	695,506,456	29.7658	9.6046	949	900,601	854,670,349	30.8058	9.8270
887	786,769	697,864,103	29.7825	9.6082	950	902,500	857,375,000	30.8221	9.8305
888	788,544	700,227,072	29.7993	9.6118	951	904,401	860,085,351	30.8383	9.8339
889	790,321	702,595,369	29.8161	9.6154	952	906,304	862,801,408	30.8545	9.8374
890	792,100	704,969,000	29.8329	9.6190	953	908,209	865,523,177	30.8707	9.8408
891	793,881	707,347,971	29.8496	9.6226	954	910,116	868,250,664	30.8869	9.8443
892	795,664	709,732,288	29.8664	9.6262	955	912,025	870,983,875	30.9031	9.8477
893	797,449	712,121,957	29.8831	9.6298	956	913,936	873,722,816	30.9192	9.8511
894	799,236	714,516,984	29.8998	9.6334	957	915,849	876,467,493	30.9354	9.8546
895	801,025	716,917,375	29.9166	9.6370	958	917,764	879,217,912	30.9516	9.8580
896	802,816	719,323,136	29.9333	9.6406	959	919,681	881,974,079	30.9677	9.8614
897	804,609	721,734,273	29.9500	9.6442	960	921,600	884,736,000	30.9839	9.8648
898	806,404	724,150,792	29.9666	9.6477	961	923,521	887,503,681	31.0000	9.8683
899	808,201	726,572,699	29.9833	9.6513	962	925,444	890,277,128	31.0161	9.8717
900	810,000	729,000,000	30.0000	9.6549	963	927,369	893,056,347	31.0322	9.8751
901	811,801	731,432,701	30.0167	9.6585	964	929,296	895,841,344	31.0483	9.8785
902	813,604	733,870,808	30.0333	9.6620	965	931,225	898,632,125	31.0644	9.8819
903	815,409	736,314,327	30.0500	9.6656	966	933,156	901,428,696	31.0805	9.8854
904	817,216	738,763,264	30.0666	9.6692	967	935,089	904,231,063	31.0966	9.8888
905	819,025	741,217,625	30.0832	9.6727	968	937,024	907,039,232	31.1127	9.8922
906	820,836	743,677,416	30.0998	9.6763	969	938,961	909,853.209	31.1288	9.8956
907	822,649	746,142,643	30.1164	9.6799	970	940,900	912,673,000	31.1448	9.8990
908	824.464	748,613,312	30.1330	9.6834	971	942,841	915,498,611	31.1609	9.9024
909	826,281	751,089,429	30.1496	9.6870	972	944,784	918,330.048	31.1769	9.9058
910	828.100	753,571,000	30.1662	9.6905	973	946,729	921,167,317	31.1929	9.9092
911	829,921	756,058,031	30.1828	9.6941	974	948,676	924,010,424	31.2090	9.9126
912	831,744	758,550,528	30.1993	9.6976	975	950,625	926,859,375	31.2250	9.9160
913	833,569	761,048,497	30.2159	9.7012	976	952,576	929,714,176	31.2410	9.9194
914	835,396	763,551,944	30.2324	9.7047	977	954,529	932,574,833	31.2570	9.9227
915	837,225	766,060,875	30.2490	9.7082	978	956,484	935,441,352	31.2730	9.9261
916	839,056	768,575,296	30.2655	9.7118	979	958,441	938,313,739	31.2890	9.9295
917	840,889	771,095,213	30.2820	9.7153	980	960,400	941,192,000	31.3050	9.9329
918	842,724	773,620,632	30.2985	9.7188	981	962,361	944,076,141	31.3209	9.9363
919	844,561	776,151,559	30.3150	9.7224	982	964,324	946,966,168	31.3369	9.9396
920	846,400	778,688,000	30.3315	9.7259	983	966,289	949,862,087	31.3528	9.9430
921	848,241	781,229,961	30.3480	9.7294	984	968,256	952,763,904	31.3688	9.9464
922	850,084	783,777,448	30.3645	9.7329	985	970,225	955,671,625	31.3847	9.9497
923	851,929	786,330,467	30.3809	9.7364	986	972,196	958,585,256	31.4006	9.9531
924	853,776	788,889,024	30.3974	9.7400	987	974,169	961,504,803	31.4166	9.9565
925	855,625	791,453,125	30.4138	9.7435	988	976,144	964,430,272	31.4325	9.9598
926	857,476	794.022,776	30.4302	9.7470	989	978,121	967,361,669	31.4484	9.9632
927	859,329	796,597,983	30.4467	9.7505	990	980,100	970,299,000	31.4643	9.9666
928	861,184	799,178,752	30.4631	9.7540	991	982,081	973,242,271	31.4802	9.9699
929	863.041	801,765,089	30.4795	9.7575	992	984,064	976,191,488	31.4960	9.9733
930	864.900	804,357,000	30.4959	9.7610	993	986,049	979,146,657	31.5119	9.9766
931	866,761	806,954,491	30.5123	9.7645	994	988,036	982,107,784	31.5278	9.9800
932	868,624	809.557,568	30.5287	9.7680	995	990,025	985,074,875	31.5436	9.9833
933	870,489	812,166.237	30.5450	9.7715	996	992,016	988,047,936	31.5595	9.9866
934	872,356	814,780.504	30.5614	9.7750	997	994.009	991,026,973	31.5753	9.9900
935	874,225	817,400,375	30.5778	9.7785	998	996,004	994,011,992	31.5911	9.9933
936	876,096	820,025,856	30.5941	9.7819	999	998.001	997,002,999	31.6070	9.9967
937	877,969	822,656,953	30.6105	9.7854	1000	1,000,000	1,000,000,000	31.6228	10.0000

Appendix F

Table F-2 Common logarithms of numbers*

Num-ber	0	1	2	3	4	5	6	7	8	9	Avg diff
1.0	0.0000	0043	0086	0128	0170	0212	0253	0294	0334	0374	
1.1	0414	0453	0492	0531	0569	0607	0645	0682	0719	0755	
1.2	0792	0828	0864	0899	0934	0969	1004	1038	1072	1106	
1.3	1139	1173	1206	1239	1271	1303	1335	1367	1399	1430	See pages 1-40 to 1-42
1.4	1461	1492	1523	1553	1584	1614	1644	1673	1703	1732	
1.5	1761	1790	1818	1847	1875	1903	1931	1959	1987	2014	
1.6	2041	2068	2095	2122	2148	2175	2201	2227	2253	2279	
1.7	2304	2330	2355	2380	2405	2430	2455	2480	2504	2529	
1.8	2553	2577	2601	2625	2648	2672	2695	2718	2742	2765	
1.9	2788	2810	2833	2856	2878	2900	2923	2945	2967	2989	
2.0	0.3010	3032	3054	3075	3096	3118	3139	3160	3181	3201	21
2.1	3222	3243	3263	3284	3304	3324	3345	3365	3385	3404	20
2.2	3424	3444	3464	3483	3502	3522	3541	3560	3579	3598	19
2.3	3617	3636	3655	3674	3692	3711	3729	3747	3766	3784	18
2.4	3802	3820	3838	3856	3874	3892	3909	3927	3945	3962	17
2.5	3979	3997	4014	4031	4048	4065	4082	4099	4116	4133	17
2.6	4150	4166	4183	4200	4216	4232	4249	4265	4281	4298	16
2.7	4314	4330	4346	4362	4378	4393	4409	4425	4440	4456	16
2.8	4472	4487	4502	4518	4533	4548	4564	4579	4594	4609	15
2.9	4624	4639	4654	4669	4683	4698	4713	4728	4742	4757	15
3.0	0.4771	4786	4800	4814	4829	4843	4857	4871	4886	4900	14
3.1	4914	4928	4942	4955	4969	4983	4997	5011	5024	5038	14
3.2	5051	5065	5079	5092	5105	5119	5132	5145	5159	5172	13
3.3	5185	5198	5211	5224	5237	5250	5263	5276	5289	5302	13
3.4	5315	5328	5340	5353	5366	5378	5391	5403	5416	5428	13
3.5	5441	5453	5465	5478	5490	5502	5514	5527	5539	5551	12
3.6	5563	5575	5587	5599	5611	5623	5635	5647	5658	5670	12
3.7	5682	5694	5705	5717	5729	5740	5752	5763	5775	5786	12
3.8	5798	5809	5821	5832	5843	5855	5866	5877	5888	5899	11
3.9	5911	5922	5933	5944	5955	5966	5977	5988	5999	6010	11
4.0	0.6021	6031	6042	6053	6064	6075	6085	6096	6107	6117	11
4.1	6128	6138	6149	6160	6170	6180	6191	6201	6212	6222	10
4.2	6232	6243	6253	6263	6274	6284	6294	6304	6314	6325	10
4.3	6335	6345	6355	6365	6375	6385	6395	6405	6415	6425	10
4.4	6435	6444	6454	6464	6474	6484	6493	6503	6513	6522	10
4.5	6532	6542	6551	6561	6571	6580	6590	6599	6609	6618	10
4.6	6628	6637	6646	6656	6665	6675	6684	6693	6702	6712	10
4.7	6721	6730	6739	6749	6758	6767	6776	6785	6794	6803	9
4.8	6812	6821	6830	6839	6848	6857	6866	6875	6884	6893	9
4.9	6902	6911	6920	6928	6937	6946	6955	6964	6972	6981	9

$\log \pi = 0.4971$ $\log \pi/2 = 0.1961$ $\log \pi^2 = 0.9943$ $\log \sqrt{\pi} = 0.2486$

$\log e = 0.4343$ $\log (0.4343) = 0.6378 - 1$

These two pages give the common logarithms of numbers between 1 and 10, correct to four places. Moving the decimal point n places to the right [or left] in the number is equivalent to adding n [or $-n$] to the logarithm. Thus, $\log 0.017453 = 0.2419 - 2$, which may also be written $\bar{2}.2419$ or $8.2419 - 10$.

$$\log (ab) = \log a + \log b \qquad \log (a^N) = N \log a$$

$$\log \left(\frac{a}{b}\right) = \log a - \log b \qquad \log \left(\sqrt[N]{a}\right) = \frac{1}{N} \log a$$

*L. S. Marks, "Mechanical Engineers' Handbook," McGraw-Hill Book Company, New York.

Table F-2 **Common logarithms of numbers** (*Continued*)

Num- ber	0	1	2	3	4	5	6	7	8	9	Avg. diff.
5.0	0.6990	6998	7007	7016	7024	7033	7042	7050	7059	7067	9
5.1	7076	7084	7093	7101	7110	7118	7126	7135	7143	7152	8
5.2	7160	7168	7177	7185	7193	7202	7210	7218	7226	7235	8
5.3	7243	7251	7259	7267	7275	7284	7292	7300	7308	7316	8
5.4	7324	7332	7340	7348	7356	7364	7372	7380	7388	7396	8
5.5	7404	7412	7419	7427	7435	7443	7451	7459	7466	7474	8
5.6	7482	7490	7497	7505	7513	7520	7528	7536	7543	7551	8
5.7	7559	7566	7574	7582	7589	7597	7604	7612	7619	7627	8
5.8	7634	7642	7649	7657	7664	7672	7679	7686	7694	7701	7
5.9	7709	7716	7723	7731	7738	7745	7752	7760	7767	7774	7
6.0	0.7782	7789	7796	7803	7810	7818	7825	7832	7839	7846	7
6.1	7853	7860	7868	7875	7882	7889	7896	7903	7910	7917	7
6.2	7924	7931	7938	7945	7952	7959	7966	7973	7980	7987	7
6.3	7993	8000	8007	8014	8021	8028	8035	8041	8048	8055	7
6.4	8062	8069	8075	8082	8089	8096	8102	8109	8116	8122	7
6.5	8129	8136	8142	8149	8156	8162	8169	8176	8182	8189	7
6.6	8195	8202	8209	8215	8222	8228	8235	8241	8248	8254	7
6.7	8261	8267	8274	8280	8287	8293	8299	8306	8312	8319	6
6.8	8325	8331	8338	8344	8351	8357	8363	8370	8376	8382	6
6.9	8388	8395	8401	8407	8414	8420	8426	8432	8439	8445	6
7.0	0.8451	8457	8463	8470	8476	8482	8488	8494	8500	8506	6
7.1	8513	8519	8525	8531	8537	8543	8549	8555	8561	8567	6
7.2	8573	8579	8585	8591	8597	8603	8609	8615	8621	8627	6
7.3	8633	8639	8645	8651	8657	8663	8669	8675	8681	8686	6
7.4	8692	8698	8704	8710	8716	8722	8727	8733	8739	8745	6
7.5	8751	8756	8762	8768	8774	8779	8785	8791	8797	8802	6
7.6	8808	8814	8820	8825	8831	8837	8842	8848	8854	8859	6
7.7	8865	8871	8876	8882	8887	8893	8899	8904	8910	8915	6
7.8	8921	8927	8932	8938	8943	8949	8954	8960	8965	8971	6
7.9	8976	8982	8987	8993	8998	9004	9009	9015	9020	9025	5
8.0	0.9031	9036	9042	9047	9053	9058	9063	9069	9074	9079	5
8.1	9085	9090	9096	9101	9106	9112	9117	9122	9128	9133	5
8.2	9138	9143	9149	9154	9159	9165	9170	9175	9180	9186	5
8.3	9191	9196	9201	9206	9212	9217	9222	9227	9232	9238	5
8.4	9243	9248	9253	9258	9263	9269	9274	9279	9284	9289	5
8.5	9294	9299	9304	9309	9315	9320	9325	9330	9335	9340	5
8.6	9345	9350	9355	9360	9365	9370	9375	9380	9385	9390	5
8.7	9395	9400	9405	9410	9415	9420	9425	9430	9435	9440	5
8.8	9445	9450	9455	9460	9465	9469	9474	9479	9484	9489	5
8.9	9494	9499	9504	9509	9513	9518	9523	9528	9533	9538	5
9.0	0.9542	9547	9552	9557	9562	9566	9571	9576	9581	9586	5
9.1	9590	9595	9600	9605	9609	9614	9619	9624	9628	9633	5
9.2	9638	9643	9647	9652	9657	9661	9666	9671	9675	9680	5
9.3	9685	9689	9694	9699	9703	9708	9713	9717	9722	9727	5
9.4	9731	9736	9741	9745	9750	9754	9759	9763	9768	9773	5
9.5	9777	9782	9786	9791	9795	9800	9805	9809	9814	9818	5
9.6	9823	9827	9832	9836	9841	9845	9850	9854	9859	9863	4
9.7	9868	9872	9877	9881	9886	9890	9894	9899	9903	9908	4
9.8	9912	9917	9921	9926	9930	9934	9939	9943	9948	9952	4
9.9	9956	9961	9965	9969	9974	9978	9983	9987	9991	9996	4

*Table F-3 Natural trigonometric functions and their logarithms**

Deg	Radians	Nat sin	Log sin	Nat cos	Log cos	Nat tan	Log tan	Nat cot	Log cot	Radians	Deg
0° 00'	0.0000	0.0000		1.0000	0.0000	0.0000				1.5708	90° 00'
10	.0029	.0029	7.4637	1.0000	0.0000	.0029	7.4637	343.77	2.5363	1.5679	50
20	.0058	.0058	7.7648	1.0000	0.0000	.0058	7.7648	171.89	2.2352	1.5650	40
30	.0087	.0087	7.9408	1.0000	0.0000	.0087	7.9409	114.59	2.0591	1.5621	30
40	.0116	.0116	8.0658	0.9999	0.0000	.0116	8.0658	85.940	1.9342	1.5592	20
50	.0145	.0145	8.1627	.9999	0.0000	.0146	8.1627	68.750	1.8373	1.5563	10
1° 00'	.0175	.0175	8.2419	.9999	9.9999	.0175	8.2419	57.290	1.7581	1.5533	89° 00'
10	.0204	.0204	8.3088	.9998	9.9999	.0204	8.3089	49.104	1.6911	1.5504	50
20	.0233	.0233	8.3668	.9997	9.9999	.0233	8.3668	42.964	1.6331	1.5475	40
30	.0262	.0262	8.4179	.9997	9.9999	.0262	8.4181	38.188	1.5819	1.5446	30
40	.0291	.0291	8.4637	.9996	9.9998	.0291	8.4639	34.368	1.5362	1.5417	20
50	.0320	.0320	8.5050	.9995	9.9998	.0320	8.5053	31.242	1.4947	1.5388	10
2° 00'	.0349	.0349	8.5428	.9994	9.9997	.0349	8.5431	28.636	1.4569	1.5359	88° 00'
10	.0378	.0378	8.5776	.9993	9.9997	.0378	8.5779	26.432	1.4221	1.5330	50
20	.0407	.0407	8.6097	.9992	9.9996	.0408	8.6101	24.542	1.3899	1.5301	40
30	.0436	.0436	8.6397	.9991	9.9996	.0437	8.6401	22.904	1.3599	1.5272	30
40	.0465	.0465	8.6677	.9989	9.9995	.0466	8.6682	21.470	1.3318	1.5243	20
50	.0495	.0494	8.6940	.9988	9.9995	.0495	8.6945	20.206	1.3055	1.5213	10
3° 00'	.0524	.0523	8.7188	.9986	9.9994	.0524	8.7194	19.081	1.2806	1.5184	87° 00'
10	.0553	.0552	8.7423	.9985	9.9993	.0553	8.7429	18.075	1.2571	1.5155	50
20	.0582	.0581	8.7645	.9983	9.9993	.0582	8.7653	17.169	1.2348	1.5126	40
30	.0611	.0611	8.7857	.9981	9.9992	.0612	8.7865	16.350	1.2135	1.5097	30
40	.0640	.0640	8.8059	.9980	9.9991	.0641	8.8067	15.605	1.1933	1.5068	20
50	.0669	.0669	8.8251	.9978	9.9990	.0670	8.8261	14.924	1.1739	1.5039	10
4° 00'	.0698	.0698	8.8436	.9976	9.9989	.0699	8.8446	14.301	1.1554	1.5010	86° 00'
10	.0727	.0727	8.8613	.9974	9.9989	.0729	8.8624	13.727	1.1376	1.4981	50
20	.0756	.0756	8.8783	.9971	9.9988	.0758	8.8795	13.197	1.1205	1.4952	40
30	.0785	.0785	8.8946	.9969	9.9987	.0787	8.8960	12.706	1.1040	1.4923	30
40	.0814	.0814	8.9104	.9967	9.9986	.0816	8.9119	12.251	1.0882	1.4893	20
50	.0844	.0843	8.9256	.9964	9.9985	.0846	8.9272	11.826	1.0728	1.4864	10
5° 00'	.0873	.0872	8.9403	.9962	9.9983	.0875	8.9420	11.430	1.0581	1.4835	85° 00'
10	.0902	.0901	8.9545	.9959	9.9982	.0904	8.9563	11.059	1.0437	1.4806	50
20	.0931	.0930	8.9682	.9957	9.9981	.0934	8.9701	10.712	1.0299	1.4777	40
30	.0960	.0959	8.9816	.9954	9.9980	.0963	8.9836	10.385	1.0164	1.4748	30
40	.0989	.0987	8.9945	.9951	9.9979	.0992	8.9966	10.078	1.0034	1.4719	20
50	.1018	.1016	9.0070	.9948	9.9978	.1022	9.0093	9.7882	0.9907	1.4690	10

Deg	Radians	Log tan	Nat tan	Log cot	Nat cot	Log sin	Nat sin	Log cos	Nat cos	Radians	Deg
84° 00'	1.4661	.9784	9.5144	9.0216	.1051	9.9976	.9945	9.0192	.1045	.1047	6° 00'
50	1.4632	.9664	9.2553	9.0336	.1081	9.9975	.9942	9.0311	.1074	.1076	10
40	1.4603	.9547	9.0098	9.0453	.1110	9.9973	.9939	9.0426	.1103	.1105	20
30	1.4573	.9433	8.7769	9.0567	.1139	9.9972	.9936	9.0539	.1132	.1134	30
20	1.4544	.9323	8.5556	9.0678	.1169	9.9971	.9932	9.0648	.1161	.1164	40
10	1.4515	.9214	8.3450	9.0786	.1198	9.9969	.9929	9.0755	.1190	.1193	50
83° 00'	1.4486	.9109	8.1443	9.0891	.1228	9.9968	.9926	9.0859	.1219	.1222	7° 00'
50	1.4457	.9005	7.9530	9.0995	.1257	9.9966	.9922	9.0961	.1248	.1251	10
40	1.4428	.8904	7.7704	9.1096	.1287	9.9964	.9918	9.1060	.1276	.1280	20
30	1.4399	.8806	7.5958	9.1194	.1317	9.9963	.9914	9.1157	.1305	.1309	30
20	1.4370	.8709	7.4287	9.1291	.1346	9.9961	.9911	9.1252	.1334	.1338	40
10	1.4341	.8615	7.2687	9.1385	.1376	9.9959	.9907	9.1345	.1363	.1367	50
82° 00'	1.4312	.8522	7.1154	9.1478	.1405	9.9958	.9903	9.1436	.1392	.1396	8° 00'
50	1.4283	.8431	6.9682	9.1569	.1435	9.9956	.9899	9.1525	.1421	.1425	10
40	1.4254	.8342	6.8269	9.1658	.1465	9.9954	.9894	9.1612	.1449	.1454	20
30	1.4224	.8255	6.6912	9.1745	.1495	9.9952	.9890	9.1697	.1478	.1484	30
20	1.4195	.8169	6.5606	9.1831	.1524	9.9950	.9886	9.1781	.1507	.1513	40
10	1.4166	.8085	6.4348	9.1915	.1554	9.9948	.9881	9.1863	.1536	.1542	50
81° 00'	1.4137	.8003	6.3138	9.1997	.1584	9.9946	.9877	9.1943	.1564	.1571	9° 00'
50	1.4108	.7922	6.1970	9.2078	.1614	9.9944	.9872	9.2022	.1593	.1600	10
40	1.4079	.7842	6.0844	9.2158	.1644	9.9942	.9868	9.2100	.1622	.1629	20
30	1.4050	.7764	5.9758	9.2236	.1673	9.9940	.9863	9.2176	.1651	.1658	30
20	1.4021	.7687	5.8708	9.2313	.1703	9.9938	.9858	9.2251	.1679	.1687	40
10	1.3992	.7611	5.7694	9.2389	.1733	9.9936	.9853	9.2324	.1708	.1716	50
80° 00'	1.3963	.7537	5.6713	9.2463	.1763	9.9934	.9848	9.2397	.1737	.1745	10° 00'
50	1.3934	.7464	5.5764	9.2536	.1793	9.9931	.9843	9.2468	.1765	.1774	10
40	1.3904	.7391	5.4845	9.2609	.1823	9.9929	.9838	9.2538	.1794	.1804	20
30	1.3875	.7320	5.3955	9.2680	.1853	9.9927	.9833	9.2606	.1822	.1833	30
20	1.3846	.7250	5.3093	9.2750	.1884	9.9924	.9827	9.2674	.1851	.1862	40
10	1.3817	.7181	5.2257	9.2819	.1914	9.9922	.9822	9.2741	.1880	.1891	50
79° 00'	1.3788	.7114	5.1446	9.2887	.1944	9.9920	.9816	9.2806	.1908	.1920	11° 00'
50	1.3759	.7047	5.0658	9.2954	.1974	9.9917	.9811	9.2871	.1937	.1949	10
40	1.3730	.6981	4.9894	9.3020	.2004	9.9915	.9805	9.2934	.1965	.1978	20
30	1.3701	.6915	4.9152	9.3085	.2035	9.9912	.9799	9.2997	.1994	.2007	30
20	1.3672	.6851	4.8430	9.3149	.2065	9.9909	.9793	9.3058	.2022	.2036	40
10	1.3643	.6788	4.7729	9.3212	.2095	9.9907	.9788	9.3119	.2051	.2065	50
78° 00'	1.3614	.6725	4.7046	9.3275	.2126	9.9904	.9782	9.3179	.2079	.2094	12° 00'
Deg	Radians	Log tan	Nat tan	Log cot	Nat cot	Log sin	Nat sin	Log cos	Nat cos	Radians	Deg

* From R. H. Perry, *Engineering Manual*, McGraw-Hill, New York, 1959.

Table F-3   *Natural trigonometric functions and their logarithms (Continued)*

Deg	Radians	Nat sin	Log sin	Nat cos	Log cos	Nat tan	Log tan	Nat cot	Log cot	Radians	Deg
12° 00'	.2094	0.2079	9.3179	0.9782	9.9904	0.2126	9.3275	4.7046	0.6725	1.3614	78° 00'
10	.2123	.2108	9.3238	.9775	9.9901	.2156	9.3337	4.6383	.6664	1.3584	50
20	.2153	.2136	9.3296	.9769	9.9899	.2186	9.3397	4.5736	.6603	1.3555	40
30	.2182	.2164	9.3353	.9763	9.9896	.2217	9.3458	4.5107	.6542	1.3526	30
40	.2211	.2193	9.3410	.9757	9.9893	.2248	9.3517	4.4494	.6483	1.3497	20
50	.2240	.2221	9.3466	.9750	9.9890	.2278	9.3576	4.3897	.6424	1.3468	10
13° 00'	.2269	.2250	9.3521	.9744	9.9887	.2309	9.3634	4.3315	.6366	1.3439	77° 00'
10	.2298	.2278	9.3575	.9737	9.9884	.2339	9.3691	4.2747	.6309	1.3410	50
20	.2327	.2306	9.3629	.9730	9.9881	.2370	9.3748	4.2193	.6252	1.3381	40
30	.2356	.2335	9.3682	.9724	9.9878	.2401	9.3804	4.1653	.6197	1.3352	30
40	.2385	.2363	9.3734	.9717	9.9875	.2432	9.3859	4.1126	.6141	1.3323	20
50	.2414	.2391	9.3786	.9710	9.9872	.2462	9.3914	4.0611	.6086	1.3294	10
14° 00'	.2443	.2419	9.3837	.9703	9.9869	.2493	9.3968	4.0108	.6032	1.3265	76° 00'
10	.2473	.2447	9.3887	.9696	9.9866	.2524	9.4021	3.9617	.5979	1.3235	50
20	.2502	.2476	9.3937	.9689	9.9863	.2555	9.4074	3.9136	.5926	1.3206	40
30	.2531	.2504	9.3986	.9682	9.9859	.2586	9.4127	3.8667	.5873	1.3177	30
40	.2560	.2532	9.4035	.9674	9.9856	.2617	9.4178	3.8208	.5822	1.3148	20
50	.2589	.2560	9.4083	.9667	9.9853	.2648	9.4230	3.7760	.5770	1.3119	10
15° 00'	.2618	.2588	9.4130	.9659	9.9849	.2680	9.4281	3.7321	.5720	1.3090	75° 00'
10	.2647	.2616	9.4177	.9652	9.9846	.2711	9.4331	3.6891	.5669	1.3061	50
20	.2676	.2644	9.4223	.9644	9.9843	.2742	9.4381	3.6471	.5619	1.3032	40
30	.2705	.2672	9.4269	.9636	9.9839	.2773	9.4430	3.6059	.5570	1.3003	30
40	.2734	.2700	9.4314	.9629	9.9836	.2805	9.4479	3.5656	.5521	1.2974	20
50	.2763	.2728	9.4359	.9621	9.9832	.2836	9.4527	3.5261	.5473	1.2945	10
16° 00'	.2793	.2756	9.4403	.9613	9.9828	.2868	9.4575	3.4874	.5425	1.2915	74° 00'
10	.2822	.2784	9.4447	.9605	9.9825	.2899	9.4622	3.4495	.5378	1.2886	50
20	.2851	.2812	9.4491	.9596	9.9821	.2931	9.4669	3.4124	.5331	1.2857	40
30	.2880	.2840	9.4533	.9588	9.9817	.2962	9.4716	3.3759	.5284	1.2828	30
40	.2909	.2868	9.4576	.9580	9.9814	.2994	9.4762	3.3402	.5238	1.2799	20
50	.2938	.2896	9.4618	.9572	9.9810	.3026	9.4808	3.3052	.5192	1.2770	10
17° 00'	.2967	.2924	9.4659	.9563	9.9806	.3057	9.4853	3.2709	.5147	1.2741	73° 00'
10	.2996	.2952	9.4701	.9555	9.9802	.3089	9.4898	3.2371	.5102	1.2712	50
20	.3025	.2979	9.4741	.9546	9.9798	.3121	9.4943	3.2041	.5057	1.2683	40
30	.3054	.3007	9.4781	.9537	9.9794	.3153	9.4987	3.1716	.5013	1.2654	30
40	.3083	.3035	9.4821	.9528	9.9790	.3185	9.5031	3.1397	.4969	1.2625	20
50	.3113	.3063	9.4861	.9520	9.9786	.3217	9.5075	3.1084	.4925	1.2595	10

Deg	Radians	Log tan	Nat tan	Log cot	Nat cot	Log sin	Nat sin	Log cos	Nat cos	Radians	Deg
72° 00'	1.2566	.4882	3.0777	9.5118	.3249	9.9782	.9511	9.4900	.5090	.3142	18° 00'
50	1.2537	.4839	3.0475	9.5161	.3281	9.9778	.9502	9.4939	.5118	.3171	10
40	1.2508	.4797	3.0178	9.5203	.3314	9.9774	.9492	9.4977	.5145	.3200	20
30	1.2479	.4755	2.9887	9.5245	.3346	9.9770	.9483	9.5015	.5173	.3229	30
20	1.2450	.4713	2.9600	9.5287	.3378	9.9765	.9474	9.5052	.5201	.3258	40
10	1.2421	.4672	2.9319	9.5329	.3411	9.9761	.9465	9.5090	.5228	.3287	50
71° 00'	1.2392	.4630	2.9042	9.5370	.3443	9.9757	.9455	9.5126	.5256	.3316	19° 00'
50	1.2363	.4589	2.8770	9.5411	.3476	9.9752	.9446	9.5163	.5283	.3345	10
40	1.2334	.4549	2.8502	9.5451	.3509	9.9748	.9436	9.5199	.5311	.3374	20
30	1.2305	.4509	2.8239	9.5492	.3541	9.9744	.9426	9.5235	.5338	.3403	30
20	1.2275	.4469	2.7980	9.5532	.3574	9.9739	.9417	9.5271	.5366	.3432	40
10	1.2246	.4429	2.7725	9.5571	.3607	9.9734	.9407	9.5306	.5393	.3462	50
70° 00'	1.2217	.4389	2.7475	9.5611	.3640	9.9730	.9397	9.5341	.3420	.3491	20° 00'
50	1.2188	.4350	2.7228	9.5650	.3673	9.9725	.9387	9.5375	.3448	.3520	10
40	1.2159	.4311	2.6985	9.5689	.3706	9.9721	.9377	9.5409	.3475	.3549	20
30	1.2130	.4273	2.6746	9.5727	.3739	9.9716	.9367	9.5443	.3502	.3578	30
20	1.2101	.4234	2.6511	9.5766	.3772	9.9711	.9357	9.5477	.3529	.3607	40
10	1.2072	.4196	2.6279	9.5804	.3805	9.9706	.9346	9.5510	.3557	.3636	50
69° 00'	1.2043	.4158	2.6051	9.5842	.3839	9.9702	.9336	9.5543	.3584	.3665	21° 00'
50	1.2014	.4121	2.5826	9.5879	.3872	9.9697	.9325	9.5576	.3611	.3694	10
40	1.1985	.4083	2.5605	9.5917	.3906	9.9692	.9315	9.5609	.3638	.3723	20
30	1.1956	.4046	2.5387	9.5954	.3939	9.9687	.9304	9.5641	.3665	.3752	30
20	1.1926	.4009	2.5172	9.5991	.3973	9.9682	.9294	9.5673	.3692	.3782	40
10	1.1897	.3972	2.4960	9.6028	.4007	9.9677	.9283	9.5704	.3719	.3811	50
68° 00'	1.1868	.3936	2.4751	9.6064	.4040	9.9672	.9272	9.5736	.3746	.3840	22° 00'
50	1.1839	.3900	2.4545	9.6100	.4074	9.9667	.9261	9.5767	.3773	.3869	10
40	1.1810	.3864	2.4342	9.6136	.4108	9.9661	.9250	9.5798	.3800	.3898	20
30	1.1781	.3828	2.4142	9.6172	.4142	9.9656	.9239	9.5828	.3827	.3927	30
20	1.1752	.3792	2.3945	9.6208	.4176	9.9651	.9228	9.5859	.3854	.3956	40
10	1.1723	.3757	2.3750	9.6243	.4211	9.9646	.9216	9.5889	.3881	.3985	50
67° 00'	1.1694	.3722	2.3559	9.6279	.4245	9.9640	.9205	9.5919	.3907	.4014	23° 00'
50	1.1665	.3687	2.3369	9.6314	.4279	9.9635	.9194	9.5948	.3934	.4043	10
40	1.1636	.3652	2.3183	9.6348	.4314	9.9629	.9182	9.5978	.3961	.4072	20
30	1.1606	.3617	2.2998	9.6383	.4348	9.9624	.9171	9.6007	.3988	.4102	30
20	1.1577	.3583	2.2817	9.6418	.4383	9.9619	.9159	9.6036	.4014	.4131	40
10	1.1548	.3548	2.2637	9.6452	.4418	9.9613	.9147	9.6065	.4041	.4160	50
66° 00'	1.1519	.3514	2.2460	9.6486	.4452	9.9607	.9136	9.6093	.4067	.4189	24° 00'
Deg	Radians	Log tan	Nat tan	Log cot	Nat cot	Log sin	Nat sin	Log cos	Nat cos	Radians	Deg

Table F-3   Natural trigonometric functions and their logarithms (Continued)

Deg	Radians	Nat sin	Log sin	Nat cos	Log cos	Nat tan	Log tan	Nat cot	Log cot	Radians	Deg
24° 00'	0.4189	0.4067	9.6093	0.9136	9.9607	0.4452	9.6486	2.2460	0.3514	1.1519	66° 00'
10	.4218	.4094	.6121	.9124	.9602	.4487	.6520	2.2286	.3480	.1490	50
20	.4247	.4120	.6149	.9112	.9596	.4522	.6554	2.2113	.3447	.1461	40
30	.4276	.4147	.6177	.9100	.9590	.4557	.6587	2.1943	.3413	.1432	30
40	.4305	.4173	.6205	.9088	.9584	.4592	.6620	2.1775	.3380	.1403	20
50	.4334	.4200	.6232	.9075	.9579	.4628	.6654	2.1609	.3346	.1374	10
25° 00'	.4363	.4226	9.6260	.9063	9.9573	.4663	9.6687	2.1445	.3313	1.1345	65° 00'
10	.4392	.4253	.6287	.9051	.9567	.4699	.6720	2.1283	.3280	.1316	50
20	.4422	.4279	.6313	.9038	.9561	.4734	.6752	2.1123	.3248	.1286	40
30	.4451	.4305	.6340	.9026	.9555	.4770	.6785	2.0965	.3215	.1257	30
40	.4480	.4331	.6366	.9013	.9549	.4806	.6817	2.0809	.3183	.1228	20
50	.4509	.4358	.6392	.9001	.9543	.4841	.6850	2.0655	.3150	.1199	10
26° 00'	.4538	.4384	9.6418	.8988	9.9537	.4877	9.6882	2.0503	.3118	1.1170	64° 00'
10	.4567	.4410	.6444	.8975	.9530	.4913	.6914	2.0353	.3086	.1141	50
20	.4596	.4436	.6470	.8962	.9524	.4950	.6946	2.0204	.3054	.1112	40
30	.4625	.4462	.6495	.8949	.9518	.4986	.6977	2.0057	.3023	.1083	30
40	.4654	.4488	.6521	.8936	.9512	.5022	.7009	1.9912	.2991	.1054	20
50	.4683	.4514	.6546	.8923	.9505	.5059	.7040	1.9768	.2960	.1025	10
27° 00'	.4712	.4540	9.6571	.8910	9.9499	.5095	9.7072	1.9626	.2928	1.0996	63° 00'
10	.4741	.4566	.6595	.8897	.9492	.5132	.7103	1.9486	.2897	.0966	50
20	.4771	.4592	.6620	.8884	.9486	.5169	.7134	1.9347	.2866	.0937	40
30	.4800	.4618	.6644	.8870	.9479	.5206	.7165	1.9210	.2835	.0908	30
40	.4829	.4643	.6668	.8857	.9473	.5243	.7196	1.9074	.2805	.0879	20
50	.4858	.4669	.6692	.8843	.9466	.5280	.7226	1.8940	.2774	.0850	10
28° 00'	.4887	.4695	9.6716	.8830	9.9459	.5317	9.7257	1.8807	.2743	1.0821	62° 00'
10	.4916	.4720	.6740	.8816	.9453	.5355	.7287	1.8676	.2713	.0792	50
20	.4945	.4746	.6763	.8802	.9446	.5392	.7318	1.8546	.2683	.0763	40
30	.4974	.4772	.6787	.8788	.9439	.5430	.7348	1.8418	.2652	.0734	30
40	.5003	.4797	.6810	.8774	.9432	.5467	.7378	1.8291	.2622	.0705	20
50	.5032	.4823	.6833	.8760	.9425	.5505	.7408	1.8165	.2592	.0676	10
29° 00'	.5061	.4848	9.6856	.8746	9.9418	.5543	9.7438	1.8041	.2563	1.0647	61° 00'
10	.5091	.4874	.6878	.8732	.9411	.5581	.7467	1.7917	.2533	.0617	50
20	.5120	.4899	.6901	.8718	.9404	.5619	.7497	1.7796	.2503	.0588	40
30	.5149	.4924	.6923	.8704	.9397	.5658	.7526	1.7675	.2474	.0559	30
40	.5178	.4950	.6946	.8689	.9390	.5696	.7556	1.7556	.2444	.0530	20
50	.5207	.4975	.6968	.8675	.9383	.5735	.7585	1.7438	.2415	.0501	10

Deg	Radians	Log tan	Nat tan	Log cot	Nat cot	Log sin	Nat sin	Log cos	Nat cos	Radians	Deg
60° 00'	1.0472	.2386	1.7321	9.7614	.5774	9.9375	.8660	9.6990	.5000	.5236	30° 00'
50	1.0443	.2357	1.7205	9.7644	.5812	9.9368	.8646	9.7012	.5025	.5265	10
40	1.0414	.2328	1.7090	9.7673	.5851	9.9361	.8631	9.7033	.5050	.5294	20
30	1.0385	.2299	1.6977	9.7702	.5891	9.9353	.8616	9.7055	.5075	.5323	30
20	1.0356	.2270	1.6864	9.7730	.5930	9.9346	.8602	9.7076	.5100	.5352	40
10	1.0327	.2241	1.6753	9.7759	.5969	9.9338	.8587	9.7097	.5125	.5381	50
59° 00'	1.0297	.2212	1.6643	9.7788	.6009	9.9331	.8572	9.7118	.5150	.5411	31° 00'
50	1.0268	.2184	1.6534	9.7816	.6048	9.9323	.8557	9.7139	.5175	.5440	10
40	1.0239	.2155	1.6426	9.7845	.6088	9.9315	.8542	9.7160	.5200	.5469	20
30	1.0210	.2127	1.6319	9.7873	.6128	9.9308	.8526	9.7181	.5225	.5498	30
20	1.0181	.2099	1.6213	9.7902	.6168	9.9300	.8511	9.7201	.5250	.5527	40
10	1.0152	.2070	1.6107	9.7930	.6208	9.9292	.8496	9.7222	.5275	.5556	50
58° 00'	1.0123	.2042	1.6003	9.7958	.6249	9.9284	.8481	9.7242	.5299	.5585	32° 00'
50	1.0094	.2014	1.5900	9.7986	.6289	9.9276	.8465	9.7262	.5324	.5614	10
40	1.0065	.1986	1.5798	9.8014	.6330	9.9268	.8450	9.7282	.5348	.5643	20
30	1.0036	.1958	1.5697	9.8042	.6371	9.9260	.8434	9.7302	.5373	.5672	30
20	1.0007	.1930	1.5597	9.8070	.6412	9.9252	.8418	9.7322	.5398	.5701	40
10	0.9977	.1903	1.5497	9.8098	.6453	9.9244	.8403	9.7342	.5422	.5730	50
57° 00'	.9948	.1875	1.5399	9.8125	.6494	9.9236	.8387	9.7361	.5446	.5760	33° 00'
50	.9919	.1847	1.5301	9.8153	.6536	9.9228	.8371	9.7381	.5471	.5789	10
40	.9890	.1820	1.5204	9.8180	.6577	9.9219	.8355	9.7400	.5495	.5818	20
30	.9861	.1792	1.5108	9.8208	.6619	9.9211	.8339	9.7419	.5519	.5847	30
20	.9832	.1765	1.5013	9.8235	.6661	9.9203	.8323	9.7438	.5544	.5876	40
10	.9803	.1737	1.4919	9.8263	.6703	9.9194	.8307	9.7457	.5568	.5905	50
56° 00'	.9774	.1710	1.4826	9.8290	.6745	9.9186	.8290	9.7476	.5592	.5934	34° 00'
50	.9745	.1683	1.4733	9.8317	.6788	9.9177	.8274	9.7494	.5616	.5963	10
40	.9716	.1656	1.4641	9.8344	.6830	9.9169	.8258	9.7513	.5640	.5992	20
30	.9687	.1629	1.4550	9.8371	.6873	9.9160	.8241	9.7531	.5664	.6021	30
20	.9657	.1602	1.4460	9.8398	.6916	9.9151	.8225	9.7550	.5688	.6050	40
10	.9628	.1575	1.4370	9.8425	.6959	9.9143	.8208	9.7568	.5712	.6080	50
55° 00'	.9599	.1548	1.4282	9.8452	.7002	9.9134	.8192	9.7586	.5736	.6109	35° 00'
50	.9570	.1521	1.4193	9.8479	.7046	9.9125	.8175	9.7604	.5760	.6138	10
40	.9541	.1494	1.4106	9.8506	.7089	9.9116	.8158	9.7622	.5783	.6167	20
30	.9512	.1467	1.4020	9.8533	.7133	9.9107	.8141	9.7640	.5807	.6196	30
20	.9483	.1441	1.3934	9.8559	.7177	9.9098	.8124	9.7657	.5831	.6225	40
10	.9454	.1414	1.3848	9.8586	.7221	9.9089	.8107	9.7675	.5854	.6254	50
54° 00'	.9425	.1387	1.3764	9.8613	.7265	9.9080	.8090	9.7692	.5878	.6283	36° 00'
Deg	Radians	Log tan	Nat tan	Log cot	Nat cot	Log sin	Nat sin	Log cos	Nat cos	Radians	Deg

Table F-3   *Natural trigonometric functions and their logarithms (Continued)*

Deg	Radians	Nat sin	Log sin	Nat cos	Log cos	Nat tan	Log tan	Nat cot	Log cot	Radians	Deg
36° 00'	0.6283	0.5878	9.7692	0.8090	9.9080	0.7265	9.8613	1.3764	0.1387	0.9425	54° 00'
10	.6312	.5901	9.7710	.8073	9.9070	.7310	9.8639	1.3680	.1361	.9396	50
20	.6341	.5925	9.7727	.8056	9.9061	.7355	9.8666	1.3597	.1334	.9367	40
30	.6370	.5948	9.7744	.8039	9.9052	.7400	9.8692	1.3514	.1308	.9338	30
40	.6400	.5972	9.7761	.8021	9.9042	.7445	9.8719	1.3432	.1282	.9308	20
50	.6429	.5995	9.7778	.8004	9.9033	.7490	9.8745	1.3351	.1255	.9279	10
37° 00'	.6458	.6018	9.7795	.7986	9.9024	.7536	9.8771	1.3270	.1229	.9250	53° 00'
10	.6487	.6041	9.7811	.7969	9.9014	.7581	9.8797	1.3190	.1203	.9221	50
20	.6516	.6065	9.7828	.7951	9.9004	.7627	9.8824	1.3111	.1176	.9192	40
30	.6545	.6088	9.7845	.7934	9.8995	.7673	9.8850	1.3032	.1150	.9163	30
40	.6574	.6111	9.7861	.7916	9.8985	.7720	9.8876	1.2954	.1124	.9134	20
50	.6603	.6134	9.7877	.7898	9.8975	.7766	9.8902	1.2876	.1098	.9105	10
38° 00'	.6632	.6157	9.7893	.7880	9.8965	.7813	9.8928	1.2799	.1072	.9076	52° 00'
10	.6661	.6180	9.7910	.7862	9.8955	.7860	9.8954	1.2723	.1046	.9047	50
20	.6690	.6202	9.7926	.7844	9.8946	.7907	9.8980	1.2647	.1020	.9018	40
30	.6720	.6225	9.7942	.7826	9.8935	.7954	9.9006	1.2572	.0994	.8988	30
40	.6749	.6248	9.7957	.7808	9.8925	.8002	9.9032	1.2497	.0968	.8959	20
50	.6778	.6271	9.7973	.7790	9.8915	.8050	9.9058	1.2423	.0942	.8930	10
39° 00'	.6807	.6293	9.7989	.7772	9.8905	.8098	9.9084	1.2349	.0916	.8901	51° 00'
10	.6836	.6316	9.8004	.7753	9.8895	.8146	9.9110	1.2276	.0891	.8872	50
20	.6865	.6338	9.8020	.7735	9.8884	.8195	9.9135	1.2203	.0865	.8843	40
30	.6894	.6361	9.8035	.7716	9.8874	.8243	9.9161	1.2131	.0839	.8814	30
40	.6923	.6383	9.8050	.7698	9.8864	.8292	9.9187	1.2059	.0813	.8785	20
50	.6952	.6406	9.8066	.7679	9.8853	.8342	9.9213	1.1988	.0788	.8756	10
40° 00'	.6981	.6428	9.8081	.7660	9.8843	.8391	9.9238	1.1918	.0762	.8727	50° 00'
10	.7010	.6450	9.8096	.7642	9.8832	.8441	9.9264	1.1847	.0736	.8698	50
20	.7039	.6472	9.8111	.7623	9.8821	.8491	9.9289	1.1778	.0711	.8668	40
30	.7069	.6495	9.8125	.7604	9.8810	.8541	9.9315	1.1709	.0685	.8639	30
40	.7098	.6517	9.8140	.7585	9.8800	.8591	9.9341	1.1640	.0659	.8610	20
50	.7127	.6539	9.8155	.7566	9.8789	.8642	9.9366	1.1572	.0634	.8581	10
41° 00'	.7156	.6561	9.8169	.7547	9.8778	.8693	9.9392	1.1504	.0608	.8552	49° 00'
10	.7185	.6583	9.8184	.7528	9.8767	.8744	9.9417	1.1436	.0583	.8523	50
20	.7214	.6604	9.8198	.7509	9.8756	.8796	9.9443	1.1369	.0557	.8494	40
30	.7243	.6626	9.8213	.7490	9.8745	.8847	9.9468	1.1303	.0532	.8465	30
40	.7272	.6648	9.8227	.7470	9.8733	.8899	9.9494	1.1237	.0507	.8436	20
50	.7301	.6670	9.8241	.7451	9.8722	.8952	9.9519	1.1171	.0481	.8407	10

Deg	Radians	Log tan	Nat tan	Log cot	Nat cot	Log sin	Nat sin	Log cos	Nat cos	Radians	Deg
48° 00'	.8378	.0456	1.1106	9.9544	.9004	9.8711	.7431	9.8255	.6691	.7330	42° 00'
50	.8348	.0430	1.1041	9.9570	.9057	9.8699	.7412	9.8269	.6713	.7359	10
40	.8319	.0405	1.0977	9.9595	.9110	9.8688	.7392	9.8283	.6734	.7389	20
30	.8290	.0380	1.0913	9.9621	.9163	9.8676	.7373	9.8297	.6756	.7418	30
20	.8261	.0354	1.0850	9.9646	.9217	9.8665	.7353	9.8311	.6777	.7447	40
10	.8232	.0329	1.0786	9.9671	.9271	9.8653	.7333	9.8324	.6799	.7476	50
47° 00'	.8203	.0303	1.0724	9.9697	.9325	9.8641	.7314	9.8338	.6820	.7505	43° 00'
50	.8174	.0278	1.0661	9.9722	.9380	9.8630	.7294	9.8351	.6841	.7534	10
40	.8145	.0253	1.0599	9.9747	.9435	9.8618	.7274	9.8365	.6862	.7563	20
30	.8116	.0228	1.0538	9.9773	.9490	9.8606	.7254	9.8378	.6884	.7592	30
20	.8087	.0202	1.0477	9.9798	.9545	9.8594	.7234	9.8391	.6905	.7621	40
10	.8058	.0177	1.0416	9.9823	.9601	9.8582	.7214	9.8405	.6926	.7650	50
46° 00'	.8029	.0152	1.0355	9.9848	.9657	9.8569	.7193	9.8418	.6947	.7679	44° 00'
50	.7999	.0126	1.0295	9.9874	.9713	9.8557	.7173	9.8431	.6968	.7709	10
40	.7970	.0101	1.0236	9.9899	.9770	9.8545	.7153	9.8444	.6988	.7738	20
30	.7941	.0076	1.0176	9.9924	.9827	9.8532	.7133	9.8457	.7009	.7767	30
20	.7912	.0051	1.0117	9.9950	.9884	9.8520	.7112	9.8469	.7030	.7796	40
10	.7883	.0025	1.0058	9.9975	.9942	9.8507	.7092	9.8482	.7051	.7825	50
45° 00'	.7854	.0000	1.0000	0.0000	1.0000	9.8495	.7071	9.8495	.7071	.7854	45° 00'
Deg	Radians	Nat cot	Log cot	Nat tan	Log tan	Nat cos	Log cos	Nat sin	Log sin	Radians	Deg

Table F-4 Values and logarithms of exponential and hyperbolic functions*

x	e^x Value	e^x log₁₀	e^{-x} (value)	sinh x Value	sinh x log₁₀	cosh x Value	cosh x log₁₀	tanh x (value)
0.00	1.0000	0.00000	1.00000	0.0000	$-\infty$	1.0000	0.00000	0.00000
0.01	1.0101	.00434	0.99005	.0100	$\bar{2}$.00001	1.0001	.00002	.01000
0.02	1.0202	.00869	.98020	.0200	$\bar{2}$.30106	1.0002	.00009	.02000
0.03	1.0305	.01303	.97045	.0300	$\bar{2}$.47719	1.0005	.03020	.02999
0.04	1.0408	.01737	.96079	.0400	$\bar{2}$.60218	1.0008	.00035	.03998
0.05	1.0513	.02171	.95123	.0500	$\bar{2}$.69915	1.0013	.00054	.04996
0.06	1.0618	.02606	.94176	.0600	$\bar{2}$.77841	1.0018	.00078	.05993
0.07	1.0725	.03040	.93239	.0701	$\bar{2}$.84545	1.0025	.00106	.06989
0.08	1.0833	.03474	.92312	.0801	$\bar{2}$.90355	1.0032	.00139	.07983
0.09	1.0942	.03909	.91393	.0901	$\bar{2}$.95483	1.0041	.00176	.08976
0.10	1.1052	.04343	.90484	.1002	$\bar{1}$.00072	1.0050	.00217	.09967
0.11	1.1163	.04777	.89583	.1102	$\bar{1}$.04227	1.0061	.00262	.10956
0.12	1.1275	.05212	.88692	.1203	$\bar{1}$.08022	1.0072	.00312	.11943
0.13	1.1388	.05646	.87809	.1304	$\bar{1}$.11517	1.0085	.00366	.12927
0.14	1.1503	.06080	.86936	.1405	$\bar{1}$.14755	1.0098	.00424	.13909
0.15	1.1618	.06514	.86071	.1506	$\bar{1}$.17772	1.0113	.00487	.14889
0.16	1.1735	.06949	.85214	.1607	$\bar{1}$.20597	1.0128	.00554	.15865
0.17	1.1853	.07383	.84366	.1708	$\bar{1}$.23254	1.0145	.00625	.16838
0.18	1.1972	.07817	.83527	.1810	$\bar{1}$.25762	1.0162	.00700	.17808
0.19	1.2092	.08252	.82696	.1911	$\bar{1}$.28136	1.0181	.00779	.18775
0.20	1.2214	.08686	.81873	.2013	$\bar{1}$.30392	1.0201	.00863	.19738
0.21	1.2337	.09120	.81058	.2115	$\bar{1}$.32541	1.0221	.00951	.20697
0.22	1.2461	.09554	.80252	.2218	$\bar{1}$.34592	1.0243	.01043	.21652
0.23	1.2586	.09989	.79453	.2320	$\bar{1}$.36555	1.0266	.01139	.22603
0.24	1.2712	.10423	.78663	.2423	$\bar{1}$.38437	1.0289	.01239	.23550
0.25	1.2840	.10857	.77880	.2526	$\bar{1}$.40245	1.0314	.01343	.24492
0.26	1.2969	.11292	.77105	.2629	$\bar{1}$.41986	1.0340	.01452	.25430
0.27	1.3100	.11726	.76338	.2733	$\bar{1}$.43663	1.0367	.01564	.26362
0.28	1.3231	.12160	.75578	.2837	$\bar{1}$.45282	1.0395	.01681	.27291
0.29	1.3364	12595	.74826	.2941	$\bar{1}$.46847	1.0423	.01801	.28213
0.30	1.3499	.13029	.74082	.3045	$\bar{1}$.48362	1.0453	.01926	.29131
0.31	1.3634	.13463	.73345	.3150	$\bar{1}$.49830	1.0484	.02054	.30044
0.32	1.3771	.13897	.72615	.3255	$\bar{1}$.51254	1.0516	.02187	.30951
0.33	1.3910	.14332	.71892	.3360	$\bar{1}$.52637	1.0549	.02323	.31852
0.34	1.4049	.14766	.71177	.3466	$\bar{1}$.53981	1.0584	.02463	.32748
0.35	1.4191	.15200	.70469	.3572	$\bar{1}$.55290	1.0619	.02607	.33638
0.36	1.4333	.15635	.69768	.3678	$\bar{1}$.56564	1.0655	.02755	.34521
0.37	1.4477	.16069	.69073	.3785	$\bar{1}$.57807	1.0692	.02907	.35399
0.38	1.4623	.16503	.68386	.3892	$\bar{1}$.59019	1.0731	.03063	.36271
0.39	1.4770	.16937	.67706	.4000	$\bar{1}$.60202	1.0770	.03222	.37136
0.40	1.4918	.17372	.67032	.4108	$\bar{1}$.61358	1.0811	.03385	.37995
0.41	1.5068	.17806	.66365	.4216	$\bar{1}$.62488	1.0852	.03552	.38847
0.42	1.5220	.18240	.65705	.4325	$\bar{1}$.63594	1.0895	.03723	.39693
0.43	1.5373	.18675	.65051	.4434	$\bar{1}$.64677	1.0939	.03897	.40532
0.44	1.5527	.19109	.64404	.4543	$\bar{1}$.65738	1.0984	.04075	.41364
0.45	1.5683	.19543	.63763	.4653	$\bar{1}$.66777	1.1030	.04256	.42190
0.46	1.5841	.19978	.63128	.4764	$\bar{1}$.67797	1.1077	.04441	.43008
0.47	1.6000	.20412	.62500	.4875	$\bar{1}$.68797	1.1125	.04630	.43820
0.48	1.6161	.20846	.61878	.4986	$\bar{1}$.69779	1.1174	.04822	.44624
0.49	1.6323	.21280	.61263	.5098	$\bar{1}$.70744	1.1225	.05018	.45422
0.50	1.6487	.21715	.60653	.5211	$\bar{1}$.71692	1.1276	.05217	.46212

* From R. H. Perry, *Engineering Manual*, McGraw-Hill, New York, 1959.

Table F-4 Values and logarithms of exponential and hyperbolic functions *(Continued)*

x	e^x Value	e^x log₁₀	e^{-x} (value)	sinh x Value	sinh x log₁₀	cosh x Value	cosh x log₁₀	tanh x (value)
0.50	1.6487	0.21715	0.60653	0.5211	$\bar{1}$.71692	1.1276	0.05217	0.46212
0.51	1.6653	.22149	.60050	0.5324	$\bar{1}$.72624	1.1329	.05419	.46995
0.52	1.6820	.22583	.59452	0.5438	$\bar{1}$.73540	1.1383	.05625	.47770
0.53	1.6989	.23018	.58860	0.5552	$\bar{1}$.74442	1.1438	.05834	.48538
0.54	1.7160	.23452	.58275	0.5666	$\bar{1}$.75330	1.1494	.06046	.49299
0.55	1.7333	.23886	.57695	0.5782	$\bar{1}$.76204	1.1551	.06262	.50052
0.56	1.7507	.24320	.57121	0.5897	$\bar{1}$.77065	1.1609	.06481	.50798
0.57	1.7683	.24755	.56553	0.6014	$\bar{1}$.77914	1.1669	.06703	.51536
0.58	1.7860	.25189	.55990	0.6131	$\bar{1}$.78751	1.1730	.06929	.52267
0.59	1.8040	.25623	.55433	0.6248	$\bar{1}$.79576	1.1792	.07157	.52990
0.60	1.8221	.26058	.54881	0.6367	$\bar{1}$.80390	1.1855	.07389	.53705
0.61	1.8404	.26492	.54335	0.6485	$\bar{1}$.81194	1.1919	.07624	.54413
0.62	1.8589	.26926	.53794	0.6605	$\bar{1}$.81987	1.1984	.07861	.55113
0.63	1.8776	.27361	.53259	0.6725	$\bar{1}$.82770	1.2051	.08102	.55805
0.64	1.8965	.27795	.52729	0.6846	$\bar{1}$.83543	1.2119	.08346	.56490
0.65	1.9155	.28229	.52205	0.6967	$\bar{1}$.84308	1.2188	.08593	.57167
0.66	1.9348	.28664	.51685	0.7090	$\bar{1}$.85063	1.2258	.08843	.57836
0.67	1.9542	.29098	.51171	0.7213	$\bar{1}$.85809	1.2330	.09095	.58498
0.68	1.9739	.29532	.50662	0.7336	$\bar{1}$.86548	1.2402	.09351	.59152
0.69	1.9937	.29966	.50158	0.7461	$\bar{1}$.87278	1.2476	.09609	.59798
0.70	2.0138	.30401	.49659	0.7586	$\bar{1}$.88000	1.2552	.09870	.60437
0.71	2.0340	.30835	.49164	0.7712	$\bar{1}$.88715	1.2628	.10134	.61068
0.72	2.0544	.31269	.48675	0.7838	$\bar{1}$.89423	1.2706	.10401	.61691
0.73	2.0751	.31703	.48191	0.7966	$\bar{1}$.90123	1.2785	.10670	.62307
0.74	2.0959	.32138	.47711	0.8094	$\bar{1}$.90817	1.2865	.10942	.62915
0.75	2.1170	.32572	.47237	0.8223	$\bar{1}$.91504	1.2947	.11216	.63515
0.76	2.1383	.33006	.46767	0.8353	$\bar{1}$.92185	1.3030	.11493	.64108
0.77	2.1598	.33441	.46301	0.8484	$\bar{1}$.92859	1.3114	.11773	.64693
0.78	2.1815	.33875	.45841	0.8615	$\bar{1}$.93527	1.3199	.12055	.65271
0.79	2.2034	.34309	.45384	0.8748	$\bar{1}$.94190	1.3286	.12340	.65841
0.80	2.2255	.34744	.44933	0.8881	$\bar{1}$.94846	1.3374	.12627	.66404
0.81	2.2479	.35178	.44486	0.9015	$\bar{1}$.95498	1.3464	.12917	.66959
0.82	2.2705	.35612	.44043	0.9150	$\bar{1}$.96144	1.3555	.13209	.67507
0.83	2.2933	.36046	.43605	0.9286	$\bar{1}$.96784	1.3647	.13503	.68048
0.84	2.3164	.36481	.43171	0.9423	$\bar{1}$.97420	1.3740	.13800	.68581
0.85	2.3396	.36915	.42741	0.9561	$\bar{1}$.98051	1.3835	.14099	.69107
0.86	2.3632	.37349	.42316	0.9700	$\bar{1}$.98677	1.3932	.14400	.69626
0.87	2.3869	.37784	.41895	0.9840	$\bar{1}$.99299	1.4029	.14704	.70137
0.88	2.4109	.38218	.41478	0.9981	$\bar{1}$.99916	1.4128	.15009	.70642
0.89	2.4351	.38652	.41066	1.0122	0.00528	1.4229	.15317	.71139
0.90	2.4596	.39087	.40657	1.0265	.01137	1.4331	.15627	.71630
0.91	2.4843	.39521	.40252	1.0409	.01741	1.4434	.15939	.72113
0.92	2.5093	.39955	.39852	1.0554	.02341	1.4539	.16254	.72590
0.93	2.5345	.40389	.39455	1.0700	.02937	1.4645	.16570	.73059
0.94	2.5600	.40824	.39063	1.0847	.03530	1.4753	.16888	.73522
0.95	2.5857	.41258	.38674	1.0995	.04119	1.4862	.17208	.73978
0.96	2.6117	.41692	.38289	1.1144	.04704	1.4973	.17531	.74428
0.97	2.6379	.42127	.37908	1.1294	.05286	1.5085	.17855	.74870
0.98	2.6645	.42561	.37531	1.1446	.05864	1.5199	.18181	.75307
0.99	2.6912	.42995	.37158	1.1598	.06439	1.5314	.18509	.75736
1.00	2.7183	.43429	.36788	1.1752	.07011	1.5431	.18839	.76159

Table F-4 Values and logarithms of exponential and hyperbolic functions (*Continued*)

x	e^x Value	e^x log₁₀	e^{-x} (value)	sinh x Value	sinh x log₁₀	cosh x Value	cosh x log₁₀	tanh x (value)
1.00	2.7183	0.43429	0.36788	1.1752	0.07011	1.5431	0.18839	0.76159
1.01	2.7456	.43864	.36422	1.1907	.07580	1.5549	.19171	.76576
1.02	2.7732	.44298	.36060	1.2063	.08146	1.5669	.19504	.76987
1.03	2.8011	.44732	.35701	1.2220	.08708	1.5790	.19839	.77391
1.04	2.8292	.45167	.35345	1.2379	.09268	1.5913	.20176	.77789
1.05	2.8577	.45601	.34994	1.2539	.09825	1.6038	.20515	.78181
1.06	2.8864	.46035	.34646	1.2700	.10379	1.6164	.20855	.78566
1.07	2.9154	.46470	.34301	1.2862	.10930	1.6292	.21197	.78946
1.08	2.9447	.46904	.33960	1.3025	.11479	1.6421	.21541	.79320
1.09	2.9743	.47338	.33622	1.3190	.12025	1.6552	.21886	.79688
1.10	3.0042	.47772	.33287	1.3356	.12569	1.6685	.22233	.80050
1.11	3.0344	.48207	.32956	1.3524	.13111	1.6820	.22582	.80406
1.12	3.0649	.48641	.32628	1.3693	.13649	1.6956	.22931	.80757
1.13	3.0957	.49075	.32303	1.3863	.14186	1.7093	.23283	.81102
1.14	3.1268	.49510	.31982	1.4035	.14720	1.7233	.23636	.81441
1.15	3.1582	.49944	.31664	1.4208	.15253	1.7374	.23990	.81775
1.16	3.1899	.50378	.31349	1.4382	.15783	1.7517	.24346	.82104
1.17	3.2220	.50812	.31037	1.4558	.16311	1.7662	.24703	.82427
1.18	3.2544	.51247	.30728	1.4735	.16836	1.7808	.25062	.82745
1.19	3.2871	.51681	.30422	1.4914	.17360	1.7957	.25422	.83058
1.20	3.3201	.52115	.30119	1.5095	.17882	1.8107	.25784	.83365
1.21	3.3535	.52550	.29820	1.5276	.18402	1.8258	.26146	.83668
1.22	3.3872	.52984	.29523	1.5460	.18920	1.8412	.26510	.83965
1.23	3.4212	.53418	.29229	1.5645	.19437	1.8568	.26876	.84258
1.24	3.4556	.53853	.28938	1.5831	.19951	1.8725	.27242	.84546
1.25	3.4903	.54287	.28650	1.6019	.20464	1.8884	.27610	.84828
1.26	3.5254	.54721	.28365	1.6209	.20975	1.9045	.27979	.85106
1.27	3.5609	.55155	.28083	1.6400	.21485	1.9208	.28349	.85380
1.28	3.5966	.55590	.27804	1.6593	.21993	1.9373	.28721	.85648
1.29	3.6328	.56024	.27527	1.6788	.22499	1.9540	.29093	.85913
1.30	3.6693	.56458	.27253	1.6984	.23004	1.9709	.29467	.86172
1.31	3.7062	.56893	.26982	1.7182	.23507	1.9880	.29842	.86428
1.32	3.7434	.57327	.26714	1.7381	.24009	2.0053	.30217	.86678
1.33	3.7810	.57761	.26448	1.7583	.24509	2.0228	.30594	.86925
1.34	3.8190	.58195	.26185	1.7786	.25008	2.0404	.30972	.87167
1.35	3.8574	.58630	.25924	1.7991	.25505	2.0583	.31352	.87405
1.36	3.8962	.59064	.25666	1.8198	.26002	2.0764	.31732	.87639
1.37	3.9354	.59498	.25411	1.8406	.26496	2.0947	.32113	.87869
1.38	3.9749	.59933	.25158	1.8617	.26990	2.1132	.32495	.88095
1.39	4.0149	.60367	.24908	1.8829	.27482	2.1320	.32878	.88317
1.40	4.0552	.60801	.24660	1.9043	.27974	2.1509	.33262	.88535
1.41	4.0960	.61236	.24414	1.9259	.28464	2.1700	.33647	.88749
1.42	4.1371	.61670	.24171	1.9477	.28952	2.1894	.34033	.88960
1.43	4.1787	.62104	.23931	1.9697	.29440	2.2090	.34420	.89167
1.44	4.2207	.62538	.23693	1.9919	.29926	2.2288	.34807	.89370
1.45	4.2631	.62973	.23457	2.0143	.30412	2.2488	.35196	.89569
1.46	4.3060	.63407	.23224	2.0369	.30896	2.2691	.35585	.89765
1.47	4.3492	.63841	.22993	2.0597	.31379	2.2896	.35976	.89958
1.48	4.3929	.64276	.22764	2.0827	.31862	2.3103	.36367	.90147
1.49	4.4371	.64710	.22537	2.1059	.32343	2.3312	.36759	.90332
1.50	4.4817	.65144	.22313	2.1293	.32823	2.3524	.37151	.90515

Table F-4 Values and logarithms of exponential and hyperbolic functions (*Continued*)

x	e^x Value	e^x log₁₀	e^{-x} (value)	sinh x Value	sinh x log₁₀	cosh x Value	cosh x log₁₀	tanh x (value)
1.50	4.4817	0.65144	0.22313	2.1293	0.32823	2.3524	0.37151	0.90515
1.51	4.5267	.65578	.22091	2.1529	.33303	2.3738	.37545	.90694
1.52	4.5722	.66013	.21871	2.1768	.33781	2.3955	.37939	.90870
1.53	4.6182	.66447	.21654	2.2008	.34258	2.4174	.38334	.91042
1.54	4.6646	.66881	.21438	2.2251	.34735	2.4395	.38730	.91212
1.55	4.7115	.67316	.21225	2.2496	.35211	2.4619	.39126	.91379
1.56	4.7588	.67750	.21014	2.2743	.35686	2.4845	.39524	.91542
1.57	4.8066	.68184	.20805	2.2993	.36160	2.5073	.39921	.91703
1.58	4.8550	.68619	.20598	2.3245	.36633	2.5305	.40320	.91860
1.59	4.9037	.69053	.20393	2.3499	.37105	2.5538	.40719	.92015
1.60	4.9530	.69487	.20190	2.3756	.37577	2.5775	.41119	.92167
1.61	5.0028	.69921	.19989	2.4015	.38048	2.6013	.41520	.92316
1.62	5.0531	.70356	.19790	2.4276	.38518	2.6255	.41921	.92462
1.63	5.1039	.70790	.19593	2.4540	.38987	2.6499	.42323	.92606
1.64	5.1552	.71224	.19398	2.4806	.39456	2.6746	.42725	.92747
1.65	5.2070	.71659	.19205	2.5075	.39923	2.6995	.43129	.92886
1.66	5.2593	.72093	.19014	2.5346	.40391	2.7247	.43532	.93022
1.67	5.3122	.72527	.18825	2.5620	.40857	2.7502	.43937	.93155
1.68	5.3656	.72961	.18637	2.5896	.41323	2.7760	.44341	.93286
1.69	5.4195	.73396	.18452	2.6175	.41788	2.8020	.44747	.93415
1.70	5.4739	.73830	.18268	2.6456	.42253	2.8283	.45153	.93541
1.71	5.5290	.74264	.18087	2.6740	.42717	2.8549	.45559	.93665
1.72	5.5845	.74699	.17907	2.7027	.43180	2.8818	.45966	.93786
1.73	5.6407	.75133	.17728	2.7317	.43643	2.9090	.46374	.93906
1.74	5.6973	.75567	.17552	2.7609	.44105	2.9364	.46782	.94023
1.75	5.7546	.76002	.17377	2.7904	.44567	2.9642	.47191	.94138
1.76	5.8124	.76436	.17204	2.8202	.45028	2.9922	.47600	.94250
1.77	5.8709	.76870	.17033	2.8503	.45488	3.0206	.48009	.94361
1.78	5.9299	.77304	.16864	2.8806	.45948	3.0492	.48419	.94470
1.79	5.9895	.77739	.16696	2.9112	.46408	3.0782	.48830	.94576
1.80	6.0496	.78173	.16530	2.9422	.46867	3.1075	.49241	.94681
1.81	6.1104	.78607	.16365	2.9734	.47325	3.1371	.49652	.94783
1.82	6.1719	.79042	.16203	3.0049	.47783	3.1669	.50064	.94884
1.83	6.2339	.79476	.16041	3.0367	.48241	3.1972	.50476	.94983
1.84	6.2965	.79910	.15882	3.0689	.48698	3.2277	.50889	.95080
1.85	6.3598	.80344	.15724	3.1013	.49154	3.2585	.51302	.95175
1.86	6.4237	.80779	.15567	3.1340	.49610	3.2897	.51716	.95268
1.87	6.4883	.81213	.15412	3.1671	.50066	3.3212	.52130	.95359
1.88	6.5535	.81647	.15259	3.2005	.50521	3.3530	.52544	.95449
1.89	6.6194	.82082	.15107	3.2341	.50976	3.3852	.52959	.95537
1.90	6.6859	.82516	.14957	3.2682	.51430	3.4177	.53374	.95624
1.91	6.7531	.82950	.14808	3.3025	.51884	3.4506	.53789	.95709
1.92	6.8210	.83385	.14661	3.3372	.52338	3.4838	.54205	.95792
1.93	6.8895	.83819	.14515	3.3722	.52791	3.5173	.54621	.95873
1.94	6.9588	.84253	.14370	3.4075	.53244	3.5512	.55038	.95953
1.95	7.0287	.84687	.14227	3.4432	.53696	3.5855	.55455	.96032
1.96	7.0993	.85122	.14086	3.4792	.54148	3.6201	.55872	.96109
1.97	7.1707	.85556	.13946	3.5156	.54600	3.6551	.56290	.96185
1.98	7.2427	.85990	.13807	3.5523	.55051	3.6904	.56707	.96259
1.99	7.3155	.86425	.13670	3.5894	.55502	3.7261	.57126	.96331
2.00	7.3891	.86859	.13534	3.6269	.55953	3.7622	.57544	.96403

Table F-4 Values and logarithms of exponential and hyperbolic functions (*Continued*)

x	e^x Value	e^x log₁₀	e^{-x} (value)	sinh x Value	sinh x log₁₀	cosh x Value	cosh x log₁₀	tanh x (value)
2.00	7.3891	0.86859	0.13534	3.6269	0.55953	3.7622	0.57544	0.96403
2.01	7.4633	0.87293	.13399	3.6647	.56403	3.7987	.57963	.96473
2.02	7.5383	0.87727	.13266	3.7028	.56853	3.8355	.58382	.96541
2.03	7.6141	0.88162	.13134	3.7414	.57303	3.8727	.58802	.96609
2.04	7.6906	0.88596	.13003	3.7803	.57753	3.9103	.59221	.96675
2.05	7.7679	0.89030	.12873	3.8196	.58202	3.9483	.59641	.96740
2.06	7.8460	0.89465	.12745	3.8593	.58650	3.9867	.60061	.96803
2.07	7.9248	0.89899	.12619	3.8993	.59099	4.0255	.60482	.96865
2.08	8.0045	0.90333	.12493	3.9398	.59547	4.0647	.60903	.96926
2.09	8.0849	0.90768	.12369	3.9806	.59995	4.1043	.61324	.96986
2.10	8.1662	0.91202	.12246	4.0219	.60443	4.1443	.61745	.97045
2.11	8.2482	0.91636	.12124	4.0635	.60890	4.1847	.62167	.97103
2.12	8.3311	0.92070	.12003	4.1056	.61337	4.2256	.62589	.97159
2.13	8.4149	0.92505	.11884	4.1480	.61784	4.2669	.63011	.97215
2.14	8.4994	0.92939	.11765	4.1909	.62231	4.3085	.63433	.97269
2.15	8.5849	0.93373	.11648	4.2342	.62677	4.3507	.63856	.97323
2.16	8.6711	0.93808	.11533	4.2779	.63123	4.3932	.64278	.97375
2.17	8.7583	0.94242	.11418	4.3221	.63569	4.4362	.64701	.97426
2.18	8.8463	0.94676	.11304	4.3666	.64015	4.4797	.65125	.97477
2.19	8.9352	0.95110	.11192	4.4116	.64460	4.5236	.65548	.97526
2.20	9.0250	0.95545	.11080	4.4571	.64905	4.5679	.65972	.97574
2.21	9.1157	0.95979	.10970	4.5030	.65350	4.6127	.66396	.97622
2.22	9.2073	0.96413	.10861	4.5494	.65795	4.6580	.66820	.97668
2.23	9.2999	0.96848	.10753	4.5962	.66240	4.7037	.67244	.97714
2.24	9.3933	0.97282	.10646	4.6434	.66684	4.7499	.67668	.97759
2.25	9.4877	0.97716	.10540	4.6912	.67128	4.7966	.68093	.97803
2.26	9.5831	0.98151	.10435	4.7394	.67572	4.8437	.68518	.97846
2.27	9.6794	0.98585	.10331	4.7880	.68016	4.8914	.68943	.97888
2.28	9.7767	0.99019	.10228	4.8372	.68459	4.9395	.69368	.97929
2.29	9.8749	0.99453	.10127	4.8868	.68903	4.9881	.69794	.97970
2.30	9.9742	0.99888	.10026	4.9370	.69346	5.0372	.70219	.98010
2.31	10.074	1.00322	.09926	4.9876	.69789	5.0868	.70645	.98049
2.32	10.176	1.00756	.09827	5.0387	.70232	5.1370	.71071	.98087
2.33	10.278	1.01191	.09730	5.0903	.70675	5.1876	.71497	.98124
2.34	10.381	1.01625	.09633	5.1425	.71117	5.2388	.71923	.98161
2.35	10.486	1.02059	.09537	5.1951	.71559	5.2905	.72349	.98197
2.36	10.591	1.02493	.09442	5.2483	.72002	5.3427	.72776	.98233
2.37	10.697	1.02928	.09348	5.3020	.72444	5.3954	.73203	.98267
2.38	10.805	1.03362	.09255	5.3562	.72885	5.4487	.73630	.98301
2.39	10.913	1.03796	.09163	5.4109	.73327	5.5026	.74056	.98335
2.40	11.023	1.04231	.09072	5.4662	.73769	5.5569	.74484	.98367
2.41	11.134	1.04665	.08982	5.5221	.74210	5.6119	.74911	.98400
2.42	11.246	1.05099	.08892	5.5785	.74652	5.6674	.75338	.98431
2.43	11.359	1.05534	.08804	5.6354	.75093	5.7235	.75766	.98462
2.44	11.473	1.05968	.08716	5.6929	.75534	5.7801	.76194	.98492
2.45	11.588	1.06402	.08629	5.7510	.75975	5.8373	.76621	.98522
2.46	11.705	1.06836	.08543	5.8097	.76415	5.8951	.77049	.98551
2.47	11.822	1.07271	.08458	5.8689	.76856	5.9535	.77477	.98579
2.48	11.941	1.07705	.08374	5.9288	.77296	6.0125	.77906	.98607
2.49	12.061	1.08139	.08291	5.9892	.77737	6.0721	.78334	.98635
2.50	12.182	1.08574	.08208	6.0502	.78177	6.1323	.78762	.98661

Table F-4 Values and logarithms of exponential and hyperbolic functions (*Continued*)

x	e^x Value	e^x log₁₀	e^{-x} (value)	sinh x Value	sinh x log₁₀	cosh x Value	cosh x log₁₀	tanh x (value)
2.50	12.182	1.08574	0.08208	6.0502	0.78177	6.1323	0.78762	0.98661
2.51	12.305	1.09008	.08127	6.1118	.78617	6.1931	.79191	.98688
2.52	12.429	1.09442	.08046	6.1741	.79057	6.2545	.79619	.98714
2.53	12.554	1.09877	.07966	6.2369	.79497	6.3166	.80048	.98739
2.54	12.680	1.10311	.07887	6.3004	.79937	6.3793	.80477	.98764
2.55	12.807	1.10745	.07808	6.3645	.80377	6.4426	.80906	.98788
2.56	12.936	1.11179	.07730	6.4293	.80816	6.5066	.81335	.98812
2.57	13.066	1.11614	.07654	6.4946	.81256	6.5712	.81764	.98835
2.58	13.197	1.12048	.07577	6.5607	.81695	6.6365	.82194	.98858
2.59	13.330	1.12482	.07502	6.6274	.82134	6.7024	.82623	.98881
2.60	13.464	1.12917	.07427	6.6947	.82573	6.7690	.83052	.98903
2.61	13.599	1.13351	.07353	6.7628	.83012	6.8363	.83482	.98924
2.62	13.736	1.13785	.07280	6.8315	.83451	6.9043	.83912	.98946
2.63	13.874	1.14219	.07208	6.9008	.83890	6.9729	.84341	.98966
2.64	14.013	1.14654	.07136	6.9709	.84329	7.0423	.84771	.98987
2.65	14.154	1.15088	.07065	7.0417	.84768	7.1123	.85201	.99007
2.66	14.296	1.15522	.06995	7.1132	.85206	7.1831	.85631	.99026
2.67	14.440	1.15957	.06925	7.1854	.85645	7.2546	.86061	.99045
2.68	14.585	1.16391	.06856	7.2583	.86083	7.3268	.86492	.99064
2.69	14.732	1.16825	.06788	7.3319	.86522	7.3998	.86922	.99083
2.70	14.880	1.17260	.06721	7.4063	.86960	7.4735	.87352	.99101
2.71	15.029	1.17694	.06654	7.4814	.87398	7.5479	.87783	.99118
2.72	15.180	1.18128	.06587	7.5572	.87836	7.6231	.88213	.99136
2.73	15.333	1.18562	.06522	7.6338	.88274	7.6991	.88644	.99153
2.74	15.487	1.18997	.06457	7.7112	.88712	7.7758	.89074	.99170
2.75	15.643	1.19431	.06393	7.7894	.89150	7.8533	.89505	.99186
2.76	15.800	1.19865	.06329	7.8683	.89588	7.9316	.89936	.99202
2.77	15.959	1.20300	.06266	7.9480	.90026	8.0106	.90367	.99218
2.78	16.119	1.20734	.06204	8.0285	.90463	8.0905	.90798	.99233
2.79	16.281	1.21168	.06142	8.1098	.90901	8.1712	.91229	.99248
2.80	16.445	1.21602	.06081	8.1919	.91339	8.2527	.91660	.99263
2.81	16.610	1.22037	.06020	8.2749	.91776	8.3351	.92091	.99278
2.82	16.777	1.22471	.05961	8.3586	.92213	8.4182	.92522	.99292
2.83	16.945	1.22905	.05901	8.4432	.92651	8.5022	.92953	.99306
2.84	17.116	1.23340	.05843	8.5287	.93088	8.5871	.93385	.99320
2.85	17.288	1.23774	.05784	8.6150	.93525	8.6728	.93816	.99333
2.86	17.462	1.24208	.05727	8.7021	.93963	8.7594	.94247	.99346
2.87	17.637	1.24643	.05670	8.7902	.94400	8.8469	.94679	.99359
2.88	17.814	1.25077	.05613	8.8791	.94837	8.9352	.95110	.99372
2.89	17.993	1.25511	.05558	8.9689	.95274	9.0244	.95542	.99384
2.90	18.174	1.25945	.05502	9.0596	.95711	9.1146	.95974	.99396
2.91	18.357	1.26380	.05448	9.1512	.96148	9.2056	.96405	.99408
2.92	18.541	1.26814	.05393	9.2437	.96584	9.2976	.96837	.99420
2.93	18.728	1.27248	.05340	9.3371	.97021	9.3905	.97269	.99431
2.94	18.916	1.27683	.05287	9.4315	.97458	9.4844	.97701	.99443
2.95	19.106	1.28117	.05234	9.5268	.97895	9.5791	.98133	.99454
2.96	19.298	1.28551	.05182	9.6231	.98331	9.6749	.98565	.99464
2.97	19.492	1.28985	.05130	9.7203	.98768	9.7716	.98997	.99475
2.98	19.688	1.29420	.05079	9.8185	.99205	9.8693	.99429	.99485
2.99	19.886	1.29854	.05029	9.9177	.99641	9.9680	.99861	.99496
3.00	20.086	1.30288	.04979	10.018	1.00078	10.068	1.00293	.99505

Table F-4 Values and logarithms of exponential and hyperbolic functions (*Continued*)

x	e^x Value	e^x log₁₀	e^{-x} (value)	sinh x Value	sinh x log₁₀	cosh x Value	cosh x log₁₀	tanh x (value)
3.00	20.086	1.30288	0.04979	10.018	1.00078	10.068	1.00293	0.99505
3.05	21.115	1.32460	.04736	10.534	1.02259	10.581	1.02454	0.99552
3.10	22.198	1.34631	.04505	11.076	1.04440	11.122	1.04616	0.99595
3.15	23.336	1.36803	.04285	11.647	1.06620	11.690	1.06779	0.99633
3.20	24.533	1.38974	.04076	12.246	1.08799	12.287	1.08943	0.99668
3.25	25.790	1.41146	.03877	12.876	1.10977	12.915	1.11108	0.99700
3.30	27.113	1.43317	.03688	13.538	1.13155	13.575	1.13273	0.99728
3.35	28.503	1.45489	.03508	14.234	1.15332	14.269	1.15439	0 99754
3.40	29.964	1.47660	.03337	14.965	1.17509	14.999	1.17605	0.99777
3.45	31.500	1.49832	.03175	15.734	1.19685	15.766	1.19772	0.99799
3.50	33.115	1.52003	.03020	16.543	1.21860	16.573	1.21940	0.99818
3.55	34.813	1.54175	.02872	17.392	1.24036	17.421	1.24107	0.99835
3.60	36.598	1.56346	.02732	18.286	1.26211	18.313	1.26275	0.99851
3.65	38.475	1.58517	.02599	19.224	1.28385	19.250	1.28444	0.99865
3.70	40.447	1.60689	.02472	20.211	1.30559	20.236	1.30612	0.99878
3.75	42.521	1.62860	.02352	21.249	1.32733	21.272	1.32781	0.99889
3.80	44.701	1.65032	.02237	22.339	1.34907	22.362	1.34951	0.99900
3.85	46.993	1.67203	.02128	23.486	1.37081	23.507	1.37120	0.99909
3.90	49.402	1.69375	.02024	24.691	1.39254	24.711	1.39290	0.99918
3.95	51.935	1.71546	.01925	25.958	1.41427	25.977	1.41459	0.99926
4.00	54.598	1.73718	.01832	27.290	1.43600	27.308	1.43629	0.99933
4.10	60.340	1.78061	.01657	30.162	1.47946	30.178	1.47970	0.99945
4.20	66.686	1.82404	.01500	33.336	1.52291	33.351	1.52310	0.99955
4.30	73.700	1.86747	.01357	36.843	1.56636	36.857	1.56652	0.99963
4.40	81.451	1.91090	.01227	40.719	1.60980	40.732	1.60993	0.99970
4.50	90.017	1.95433	.01111	45.003	1.65324	45.014	1.65335	0.99975
4.60	99.484	1.99775	.01005	49.737	1.69668	49.747	1.69677	0.99980
4.70	109.95	2.04118	.00910	54.969	1.74012	54.978	1.74019	0.99983
4.80	121.51	2.08461	.00823	60.751	1.78355	60.759	1.78361	0.99986
4.90	134.29	2.12804	.00745	67.141	1.82699	67.149	1.82704	0.99989
5.00	148.41	2.17147	.00674	74.203	1.87042	74.210	1.87046	0.99991
5.10	164.02	2.21490	.00610	82.008	1.91389	82.014	1.91389	0.99993
5.20	181.27	2.25833	.00552	90.633	1.95729	90.639	1.95731	0.99994
5.30	200.34	2.30176	.00499	100.17	2.00074	100.17	2.00074	0.99995
5.40	221.41	2.34519	.00452	110.70	2.04415	110.71	2.04417	0.99996
5.50	244.69	2.38862	.00409	122.34	2.08758	122.35	2.08760	0.99997
5.60	270.43	2.43205	.00370	135.21	2.13101	135.22	2.13103	0.99997
5.70	298.87	2.47548	.00335	149.43	2.17444	149.44	2.17445	0.99998
5.80	330.30	2.51891	.00303	165.15	2.21787	165.15	2.21788	0.99998
5.90	365.04	2.56234	.00274	182.52	2.26130	182.52	2.26131	0.99998
6.00	403.43	2.60577	.00248	201.71	2.30473	201.72	2.30474	0.99999
6.25	518.01	2.71434	.00193	259.01	2.41331	259.01	2.41331	0.99999
6.50	665.14	2.82291	.00150	332.57	2.52188	332.57	2.52189	1.00000
6.75	854.06	2.93149	.00117	427.03	2.63046	427.03	2.63046	1.00000
7.00	1096.6	3.04006	.00091	548.32	2.73903	548.32	2.73903	1.00000
7.50	1808.0	3.25721	.00055	904.02	2.95618	904.02	2.95618	1.00000
8.00	2981.0	3.47436	.00034	1490.5	3.17333	1490.5	3.17333	1.00000
8.50	4914.8	3.69150	.00020	2457.4	3.39047	2457.4	3.39047	1.00000
9.00	8103.1	3.90865	.00012	4051.5	3.60762	4051.5	3.60762	1.00000
9.50	13360.	4.12580	.00007	6679.9	3.82477	6679.9	3.82477	1.00000
10.00	22026.	4.34294	.00005	11013.	4.04191	11013.	4.04191	1.00000

Table F-5 Natural, napierian, or hyperbolic logarithms*

N	0	1	2	3	4	5	6	7	8	9
0	— ∞	0.0000	0.6931	1.0986	1.3863	1.6094	1.7918	1.9459	2.0794	2.1972
10	2.3026	2.3979	2.4849	2.5649	2.6391	2.7081	2.7726	2.8332	2.8904	2.9444
20	2.9957	3.0445	3.0910	3.1355	3.1781	3.2189	3.2581	3.2958	3.3322	3.3673
30	3.4012	3.4340	3.4657	3.4965	3.5264	3.5553	3.5835	3.6109	3.6376	3.6636
40	3.6889	3.7136	3.7377	3.7612	3.7842	3.8067	3.8286	3.8501	3.8712	3.8918
50	3.9120	3.9318	3.9512	3.9703	3.9890	4.0073	4.0254	4.0431	4.0604	4.0775
60	4.0943	4.1109	4.1271	4.1431	4.1589	4.1744	4.1897	4.2047	4.2195	4.2341
70	4.2485	4.2627	4.2767	4.2905	4.3041	4.3175	4.3307	4.3438	4.3567	4.3694
80	4.3820	4.3944	4.4067	4.4188	4.4308	4.4427	4.4543	4.4659	4.4773	4.4886
90	4.4998	4.5109	4.5218	4.5326	4.5433	4.5539	4.5643	4.5747	4.5850	4.5951
100	4.6052	4.6151	4.6250	4.6347	4.6444	4.6540	4.6634	4.6728	4.6821	4.6913
110	4.7005	4.7095	4.7185	4.7274	4.7362	4.7449	4.7536	4.7622	4.7707	4.7791
120	4.7875	4.7958	4.8040	4.8122	4.8203	4.8283	4.8363	4.8442	4.8520	4.8598
130	4.8675	4.8752	4.8828	4.8903	4.8978	4.9053	4.9127	4.9200	4.9273	4.9345
140	4.9416	4.9488	4.9558	4.9628	4.9698	4.9767	4.9836	4.9904	4.9972	5.0039
150	5.0106	5.0173	5.0239	5.0304	5.0370	5.0434	5.0499	5.0562	5.0626	5.0689
160	5.0752	5.0814	5.0876	5.0938	5.0999	5.1059	5.1120	5.1180	5.1240	5.1299
170	5.1358	5.1417	5.1475	5.1533	5.1591	5.1648	5.1705	5.1761	5.1818	5.1874
180	5.1930	5.1985	5.2040	5.2095	5.2149	5.2204	5.2257	5.2311	5.2364	5.2417
190	5.2470	5.2523	5.2575	5.2627	5.2679	5.2730	5.2781	5.2832	5.2883	5.2933
200	5.2983	5.3033	5.3083	5.3132	5.3181	5.3230	5.3279	5.3327	5.3375	5.3423
210	5.3471	5.3519	5.3566	5.3613	5.3660	5.3706	5.3753	5.3799	5.3845	5.3891
220	5.3936	5.3982	5.4027	5.4072	5.4116	5.4161	5.4205	5.4250	5.4293	5.4337
230	5.4381	5.4424	5.4467	5.4510	5.4553	5.4596	5.4638	5.4681	5.4723	5.4765
240	5.4806	5.4848	5.4889	5.4931	5.4972	5.5013	5.5053	5.5094	5.5134	5.5175
250	5.5215	5.5255	5.5294	5.5334	5.5373	5.5413	5.5452	5.5491	5.5530	5.5568
260	5.5607	5.5645	5.5683	5.5722	5.5759	5.5797	5.5835	5.5872	5.5910	5.5947
270	5.5984	5.6021	5.6058	5.6095	5.6131	5.6168	5.6204	5.6240	5.6276	5.6312
280	5.6348	5.6384	5.6419	5.6454	5.6490	5.6525	5.6560	5.6595	5.6630	5.6664
290	5.6699	5.6733	5.6768	5.6802	5.6836	5.6870	5.6904	5.6937	5.6971	5.7004
300	5.7038	5.7071	5.7104	5.7137	5.7170	5.7203	5.7236	5.7268	5.7301	5.7333
310	5.7366	5.7398	5.7430	5.7462	5.7494	5.7526	5.7557	5.7589	5.7621	5.7652
320	5.7683	5.7714	5.7746	5.7777	5.7807	5.7838	5.7869	5.7900	5.7930	5.7961
330	5.7991	5.8021	5.8051	5.8081	5.8111	5.8141	5.8171	5.8201	5.8230	5.8260
340	5.8289	5.8319	5.8348	5.8377	5.8406	5.8435	5.8464	5.8493	5.8522	5.8551
350	5.8579	5.8608	5.8636	5.8665	5.8693	5.8721	5.8749	5.8777	5.8805	5.8833
360	5.8861	5.8889	5.8916	5.8944	5.8972	5.8999	5.9026	5.9054	5.9081	5.9108
370	5.9135	5.9162	5.9189	5.9216	5.9243	5.9269	5.9296	5.9322	5.9349	5.9375
380	5.9402	5.9428	5.9454	5.9480	5.9506	5.9532	5.9558	5.9584	5.9610	5.9636
390	5.9661	5.9687	5.9713	5.9738	5.9764	5.9789	5.9814	5.9839	5.9865	5.9890
400	5.9915	5.9940	5.9965	5.9989	6.0014	6.0039	6.0064	6.0088	6.0113	6.0137
410	6.0162	6.0186	6.0210	6.0234	6.0259	6.0283	6.0307	6.0331	6.0355	6.0379
420	6.0403	6.0426	6.0450	6.0474	6.0497	6.0521	6.0544	6.0568	6.0591	6.0615
430	6.0638	6.0661	6.0684	6.0707	6.0730	6.0753	6.0776	6.0799	6.0822	6.0845
440	6.0868	6.0890	6.0913	6.0936	6.0958	6.0981	6.1003	6.1026	6.1048	6.1070
450	6.1092	6.1115	6.1137	6.1159	6.1181	6.1203	6.1225	6.1247	6.1269	6.1291
460	6.1312	6.1334	6.1356	6.1377	6.1399	6.1420	6.1442	6.1463	6.1485	6.1506
470	6.1527	6.1549	6.1570	6.1591	6.1612	6.1633	6.1654	6.1675	6.1696	6.1717
480	6.1738	6.1759	6.1779	6.1800	6.1821	6.1841	6.1862	6.1883	6.1903	6.1924
490	6.1944	6.1964	6.1985	6.2005	6.2025	6.2046	6.2066	6.2086	6.2106	6.2126

		n	$n \times 2.3026$
NOTE 1: Moving the decimal point n places to the right (or left) in the number is equivalent to adding (or subtracting) n times 2.3026.		1	$2.3026 = 0.6974\text{-}3$
		2	$4.6052 = 0.3948\text{-}5$
		3	$6.9078 = 0.0922\text{-}7$
NOTE 2:		4	$9.2103 = 0.7897\text{-}10$
$\log_e x = 2.3026 \log_{10} x$		5	$11.5129 = 0.4871\text{-}12$
$\log_{10} x = 0.4343 \log_e x$		6	$13.8155 = 0.1845\text{-}14$
$\log_e 10 = 2.3026$		7	$16.1181 = 0.8819\text{-}17$
$\log_{10} e = 0.4343$		8	$18.4207 = 0.5793\text{-}19$
		9	$20.7233 = 0.2767\text{-}21$

* From A. E. Knowlton, *Standard Handbook for Electrical Engineers*, 9th ed., McGraw-Hill, New York, 1957.

Table F-5   Natural, napierian, or hyperbolic logarithms (*Continued*)

N	0	1	2	3	4	5	6	7	8	9
500	6.2146	6.2166	6.2186	6.2206	6.2226	6.2246	6.2265	6.2285	6.2305	6.2324
510	6.2344	6.2364	6.2383	6.2403	6.2422	6.2442	6.2461	6.2480	6.2500	6.2519
520	6.2538	6.2558	6.2577	6.2596	6.2615	6.2634	6.2653	6.2672	6.2691	6.2710
530	6.2729	6.2748	6.2766	6.2785	6.2804	6.2823	6.2841	6.2860	6.2879	6.2897
540	6.2916	6.2934	6.2953	6.2971	6.2989	6.3008	6.3026	6.3044	6.3063	6.3081
550	6.3099	6.3117	6.3135	6.3154	6.3172	6.3190	6.3208	6.3226	6.3244	6.3261
560	6.3279	6.3297	6.3315	6.3333	6.3351	6.3368	6.3386	6.3404	6.3421	6.3439
570	6.3456	6.3474	6.3491	6.3509	6.3256	6.3544	6.3561	6.3578	6.3596	6.3613
580	6.3630	6.3648	6.3665	6.3682	6.3699	6.3716	6.3733	6.3750	6.3767	6.3784
590	6.3801	6.3818	6.3835	6.3852	6.3869	6.3886	6.3902	6.3919	6.3936	6.3953
600	6.3969	6.3986	6.4003	6.4019	6.4036	6.4052	6.4069	6.4085	6.4102	6.4118
610	6.4135	6.4151	6.4167	6.4184	6.4200	6.4216	6.4232	6.4249	6.4265	6.4281
620	6.4297	6.4313	6.4329	6.4345	6.4362	6.4378	6.4394	6.4409	6.4425	6.4441
630	6.4457	6.4473	6.4489	6.4505	6.4520	6.4536	6.4552	6.4568	6.4583	6.4599
640	6.4615	6.4630	6.4646	6.4661	6.4677	6.4693	6.4708	6.4723	6.4739	6.4754
650	6.4770	6.4785	6.4800	6.4816	6.4831	6.4846	6.4862	6.4877	6.4892	6.4907
660	6.4922	6.4938	6.4953	6.4968	6.4983	6.4998	6.5013	6.5028	6.5043	6.5058
670	6.5073	6.5088	6.5103	6.5117	6.5132	6.5147	6.5162	6.5177	6.5191	6.5206
680	6.5221	6.5236	6.5250	6.5265	6.5280	6.5294	6.5309	6.5323	6.5338	6.5352
690	6.5367	6.5381	6.5396	6.5410	6.5425	6.5439	6.5453	6.5468	6.5482	6.5497
700	6.5511	6.5525	6.5539	6.5554	6.5568	6.5582	6.5596	6.5610	6.5624	6.5639
710	6.5653	6.5667	6.5681	6.5695	6.5709	6.5723	6.5737	6.5751	6.5765	6.5779
720	6.5793	6.5806	6.5820	6.5834	6.5848	6.5862	6.5876	6.5889	6.5903	6.5917
730	6.5930	6.5944	6.5958	6.5971	6.5985	6.5999	6.6012	6.6026	6.6039	6.6053
740	6.6067	6.6080	6.6093	6.6107	6.6120	6.6134	6.6147	6.6161	6.6174	6.6187
750	6.6201	6.6214	6.6227	6.6241	6.6254	6.6267	6.6280	6.6294	6.6307	6.6320
760	6.6333	6.6346	6.6359	6.6373	6.6386	6.6399	6.6412	6.6425	6.6438	6.6451
770	6.6464	6.6477	6.6490	6.6503	6.6516	6.6529	6.6542	6.6554	6.6567	6.6580
780	6.6593	6.6606	6.6619	6.6631	6.6644	6.6657	6.6670	6.6682	6.6695	6.6708
790	6.6720	6.6733	6.6746	6.6758	6.6771	6.6783	6.6796	6.6809	6.6821	6.6834
800	6.6846	6.6859	6.6871	6.6884	6.6896	6.6908	6.6921	6.6933	6.6946	6.6958
810	6.6970	6.6983	6.6995	6.7007	6.7020	6.7032	6.7044	6.7056	6.7069	6.7081
820	6.7093	6.7105	6.7117	6.7130	6.7142	6.7154	6.7166	6.7178	6.7190	6.7202
830	6.7214	6.7226	6.7238	6.7250	6.7262	6.7274	6.7286	6.7298	6.7310	6.7322
840	6.7334	6.7346	6.7358	6.7370	6.7382	6.7393	6.7405	6.7417	6.6429	6.7441
850	6.7452	6.7464	6.7476	6.7488	6.7499	6.7511	6.7523	6.7534	6.7546	6.7558
860	6.7569	6.7581	6.7593	6.7604	6.7616	6.7627	6.7639	6.7650	6.7662	6.7673
870	6.7685	6.7696	6.7708	6.7719	6.7731	6.7742	6.7754	6.7765	6.7776	6.7788
880	6.7799	6.7811	6.7822	6.7833	6.7845	6.7856	6.7867	6.7867	5.7878	6.7890	6.7901
890	6.7912	6.7923	6.7935	6.7946	6.7957	6.7968	6.7979	6.7991	6.8002	6.8013
900	6.8024	6.8035	6.8046	6.8057	6.8068	6.8079	6.8090	6.8101	6.8112	6.8123
910	6.8134	6.8145	6.8156	6.8167	6.8178	6.8189	6.8200	6.8211	6.8222	6.8233
920	6.8244	6.8255	6.8265	6.8276	6.8287	6.8298	6.8309	6.8320	6.8330	6.8341
930	6.8352	6.8363	6.8373	6.8384	6.8395	6.8405	6.8416	6.8427	6.8437	6.8448
940	6.8459	5.8469	6.8480	6.8491	6.8501	6.8512	6.8522	6.8533	6.8544	6.8554
950	6.8565	6.8575	6.8586	6.8596	6.8607	6.8617	6.8628	6.8638	6.8648	6.8659
960	6.8669	6.8680	6.8690	6.8701	6.8711	6.8721	6.8732	6.8742	6.8752	6.8763
970	6.8773	6.8783	6.8794	6.8804	6.8814	6.8824	6.8835	6.8845	6.8855	6.8865
980	6.8876	6.8886	6.8896	6.8906	6.8916	6.8926	6.8937	6.8947	6.8957	6.8967
990	6.8977	6.8987	6.8997	6.9007	6.9017	6.9027	6.9037	6.9047	6.9057	6.9068

Table F-6a   Factorials and their reciprocals*

x	1	2	3	4	5	6	7	8	9	10
$x!$	1	2	6	24	120	720	5,040	40,320	362,880	3,628,800
$\dfrac{1}{x!}$	1	0.5	1.666667 $\times 10^{-1}$	4.166667 $\times 10^{-2}$	8.333333 $\times 10^{-3}$	1.388889 $\times 10^{-3}$	1.984127 $\times 10^{-4}$	2.480159 $\times 10^{-5}$	2.755732 $\times 10^{-6}$	2.755732 $\times 10^{-7}$

Table F-6b   Coefficients of the binomial expansion*

n	0	1	2	3	4	5	6	7	8	9	10
1	1	1									
2	1	2	1								
3	1	3	3	1							
4	1	4	6	4	1						
5	1	5	10	10	5	1					
6	1	6	15	20	15	6	1				
7	1	7	21	35	35	21	7	1			
8	1	8	28	56	70	56	28	8	1		
9	1	9	36	84	126	126	84	36	9	1	
10	1	10	45	120	210	252	210	120	45	10	1

Example: $(1 + x)^6 = 1 + 6x + 15x^2 + 20x^3 + 15x^4 + 6x^5 + x^6$

Each number in the table is the sum of the number above it and the number to the left of that number (see box: $36 + 84 = 120$). The table can be extended indefinitely in this way.

*From H. E. Etherington, *Nuclear Engineering Handbook*, McGraw-Hill, New York, 1958.

Table F-7 Probability function or error integral: erf x*

x	0	1	2	3	4	5	6	7	8	9
0.00	0.0000	0011	0023	0034	0045	0056	0068	0079	0090	0102
1	0113	0124	0135	0147	0158	0169	0181	0192	0203	0214
2	0226	0237	0248	0260	0271	0282	0293	0305	0316	0327
3	0338	0350	0361	0372	0384	0395	0406	0417	0429	0440
4	0451	0462	0474	0485	0496	0507	0519	0530	0541	0553
5	0564	0575	0586	0598	0609	0620	0631	0643	0654	0665
6	0676	0688	0699	0710	0721	0732	0744	0755	0766	0777
7	0789	0800	0811	0822	0834	0845	0856	0867	0878	0890
8	0901	0912	0923	0934	0946	0957	0968	0979	0990	1002
9	1013	1024	1035	1046	1058	1069	1080	1091	1102	1113
10	1125	1136	1147	1158	1169	1180	1192	1203	1214	1225
1	1236	1247	1259	1270	1281	1292	1303	1314	1325	1336
2	1348	1359	1370	1381	1392	1403	1414	1425	1436	1448
3	1459	1470	1481	1492	1503	1514	1525	1536	1547	1558
4	1569	1581	1592	1603	1614	1625	1636	1647	1658	1669
5	1680	1691	1702	1713	1724	1735	1746	1757	1768	1779
6	1790	1801	1812	1823	1834	1845	1856	1867	1878	1889
7	1900	1911	1922	1933	1944	1955	1966	1977	1988	1998
8	2009	2020	2031	2042	2053	2064	2075	2086	2097	2108
9	2118	2129	2140	2151	2162	2173	2184	2194	2205	2216
20	2227	2238	2249	2260	2270	2281	2292	2303	2314	2324
1	2335	2346	2357	2368	2378	2389	2400	2411	2421	2432
2	2443	2454	2464	2475	2486	2497	2507	2518	2529	2540
3	2550	2561	2572	2582	2593	2604	2614	2625	2636	2646
4	2657	2668	2678	2689	2700	2710	2721	2731	2742	2753
5	2763	2774	2784	2795	2806	2816	2827	2837	2848	2858
6	2869	2880	2890	2901	2911	2922	2932	2943	2953	2964
7	2974	2985	2995	3006	3016	3027	3037	3047	3058	3068
8	3079	3089	3100	3110	3120	3131	3141	3152	3162	3172
9	3183	3193	3204	3214	3224	3235	3245	3255	3266	3276
30	3286	3297	3307	3317	3327	3338	3348	3358	3369	3379
1	3389	3399	3410	3420	3430	3440	3450	3461	3471	3481
2	3491	3501	3512	3522	3532	3542	3552	3562	3573	3583
3	3593	3603	3613	3623	3633	3643	3653	3663	3674	3684
4	3694	3704	3714	3724	3734	3744	3754	3764	3774	3784
5	3794	3804	3814	3824	3834	3844	3854	3864	3873	3883
6	3893	3903	3913	3923	3933	3943	3953	3963	3972	3982
7	3992	4002	4012	4022	4031	4041	4051	4061	4071	4080
8	4090	4100	4110	4119	4129	4139	4149	4158	4168	4178
9	4187	4197	4207	4216	4226	4236	4245	4255	4265	4274
40	4284	4294	4303	4313	4322	4332	4341	4351	4361	4370
1	4380	4389	4399	4408	4418	4427	4437	4446	4456	4465
2	4475	4484	4494	4503	4512	4522	4531	4541	4550	4359
3	4569	4578	4588	4597	4606	4616	4625	4634	4644	4653
4	4662	4672	4681	4690	4699	4709	4718	4727	4736	4746
5	4755	4764	4773	4782	4792	4801	4810	4819	4828	4837
6	4847	4856	4865	4874	4883	4892	4901	4910	4919	4928
7	4937	4946	4956	4965	4974	4983	4992	5001	5010	5019
8	5027	5036	5045	5054	5063	5072	5081	5090	5099	5108
9	5117	5126	5134	5143	5152	5161	5170	5179	5187	5196
50	5205	5214	5223	5231	5240	5249	5258	5266	5275	5284

$$\operatorname{erf} x = H(x) = \frac{2}{\sqrt{\pi}} \int_0^x e^{-t^2}\, dt$$

* From H. E. Etherington, *Nuclear Engineering Handbook*, McGraw-Hill, New York, 1958.

Table F-8   Normal-distribution areas*

Fractional parts of the total area (1.000) under the normal curve between the mean and a perpendicular erected at various numbers of standard deviations (x/σ) from the mean.   To illustrate the use of the table, 39.065 per cent of the total area under the curve will lie between the mean and a perpendicular erected at a distance of 1.23σ from the mean.

Each figure in the body of the table is preceded by a decimal point.

x/σ	0.00	0.01	0.02	0.03	0.04	0.05	0.06	0.07	0.08	0.09
0.0	00000	00399	00798	01197	01595	01994	02392	02790	03188	03586
0.1	03983	04380	04776	05172	05567	05962	06356	06749	07142	07535
0.2	07926	08317	08706	09095	09483	09871	10257	10642	11026	11409
0.3	11791	12172	12552	12930	13307	13683	14058	14431	14803	15173
0.4	15554	15910	16276	16640	17003	17364	17724	18082	18439	18793
0.5	19146	19497	19847	20194	20450	20884	21226	21566	21904	22240
0.6	22575	22907	23237	23565	23891	24215	24537	24857	25175	25490
0.7	25804	26115	26424	26730	27035	27337	27637	27935	28230	28524
0.8	28814	29103	29389	29673	29955	30234	30511	30785	31057	31327
0.9	31594	31859	32121	32381	32639	32894	33147	33398	33646	33891
1.0	34134	34375	34614	34850	35083	35313	35543	35769	35993	36214
1.1	36433	36650	36864	37076	37286	37493	37698	37900	38100	38298
1.2	38493	38686	38877	39065	39251	39435	39617	39796	39973	40147
1.3	40320	40490	40658	40824	40988	41149	41308	41466	41621	41774
1.4	41924	42073	42220	42364	42507	42647	42786	42922	43056	43189
1.5	43319	43448	43574	43699	43822	43943	44062	44179	44295	44408
1.6	44520	44630	44738	44845	44950	45053	45154	45254	45352	45449
1.7	45543	45637	45728	45818	45907	45994	46080	46164	46246	46327
1.8	46407	46485	46562	46638	46712	46784	46856	46926	46995	47062
1.9	47128	47193	47257	47320	47381	47441	47500	47558	47615	47670
2.0	47725	47778	47831	47882	47932	47982	48030	48077	48124	48169
2.1	48214	48257	48300	48341	48382	48422	48461	48500	48537	48574
2.2	48610	48645	48679	48713	48745	48778	48809	48840	48870	48899
2.3	48928	48956	48983	49010	49036	49061	49086	49111	49134	49158
2.4	49180	49202	49224	49245	49266	49286	49305	49324	49343	49361
2.5	49379	49396	49413	49430	49446	49461	49477	49492	49506	49520
2.6	49534	49547	49560	49573	49585	49598	49609	49621	49632	49643
2.7	49653	49664	49674	49683	49693	49702	49711	49720	49728	49736
2.8	49744	49752	49760	49767	49774	49781	49788	49795	49801	49807
2.9	49813	49819	49825	49831	49836	49841	49846	49851	49856	49861
3.0	49865									
3.5	4997674									
4.0	4999683									
4.5	4999966									
5.0	4999997133									

* This table was adapted, by permission, from F. C. Kent, *Elements of Statistics*, McGraw-Hill, New York, 1924.

Appendix F

Table F-9 Normal-curve ordinates*

Ordinates (heights) of the unit normal curve. The height (y) at any number of standard deviations $\frac{x}{\sigma}$ from the mean is

$$y = 0.3989e^{-\frac{1}{2}\left(\frac{x}{\sigma}\right)^2}$$

To obtain answers in units of particular problems, multiply these ordinates by $\frac{Ni}{\sigma}$ where N is the number of cases, i the class interval, and σ the standard deviation.

Each figure in the body of the table is preceded by a decimal point.

x/σ	0.00	0.01	0.02	0.03	0.04	0.05	0.06	0.07	0.08	0.09
0.0	39894	39892	39886	39876	39862	39844	39822	39797	39767	39733
0.1	39695	39654	39608	39559	39505	39448	39387	39322	39253	39181
0.2	39104	39024	38940	38853	38762	38667	38568	38466	38361	38251
0.3	38139	38023	37903	37780	37654	37524	37391	37255	37115	36973
0.4	36827	36678	36526	36371	36213	36053	35889	35723	35553	35381
0.5	35207	35029	34849	34667	34482	34294	34105	33912	33718	33521
0.6	33322	33121	32918	32713	32506	32297	32086	31874	31659	31443
0.7	31225	31006	30785	30563	30339	30114	29887	29658	29430	29200
0.8	28969	28737	28504	28269	28034	27798	27562	27324	27086	26848
0.9	26609	26369	26129	25888	25647	25406	25164	24923	24681	24439
1.0	24197	23955	23713	23471	23230	22988	22747	22506	22265	22025
1.1	21785	21546	21307	21069	20831	20594	20357	20121	19886	19652
1.2	19419	19186	18954	18724	18494	18265	18037	17810	17585	17360
1.3	17137	16915	16694	16474	16256	16038	15822	15608	15395	15183
1.4	14973	14764	14556	14350	14146	13943	13742	13542	13344	13147
1.5	12952	12758	12566	12376	12188	12001	11816	11632	11450	11270
1.6	11092	10915	10741	10567	10396	10226	10059	09893	09728	09566
1.7	09405	09246	09089	08933	08780	08628	08478	08329	08183	08038
1.8	07895	07754	07614	07477	07341	07206	07074	06943	06814	06687
1.9	06562	06438	06316	06195	06077	05959	05844	05730	05618	05508
2.0	05399	05292	05186	05082	04980	04879	04780	04682	04586	04491
2.1	04398	04307	04217	04128	04041	03955	03871	03788	03706	03626
2.2	03547	03470	03394	03319	03246	03174	03103	03034	02965	02898
2.3	02833	02768	02705	02643	02582	02522	02463	02406	02349	02294
2.4	02239	02186	02134	02083	02033	01984	01936	01888	01842	01797
2.5	01753	01709	01667	01625	01585	01545	01506	01468	01431	01394
2.6	01358	01323	01289	01256	01223	01191	01160	01130	01100	01071
2.7	01042	01014	00987	00961	00935	00909	00885	00861	00837	00814
2.8	00792	00770	00748	00727	00707	00687	00668	00649	00631	00613
2.9	00595	00578	00562	00545	00530	00514	00499	00485	00470	00457
3.0	00443									
3.5	0008727									
4.0	0001338									
4.5	0000160									
5.0	000001487									

* This table was adapted, by permission, from F. C. Kent, *Elements of Statistics*, McGraw-Hill, New York, 1924.

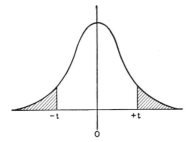

Table F-10   Distribution of t *

Values of t corresponding to certain selected probabilities (*i.e.*, tail areas under the curve). To illustrate: the probability is 0.05 that a sample with 20 degrees of freedom would have $t = 2.086$ or larger.

DF	Probability							
	0.80	0.40	0.20	0.10	0.05	0.02	0.01	0.001
1	0.325	1.376	3.078	6.314	12.706	31.821	63.657	636.619
2	0.289	1.061	1.886	2.920	4.303	6.965	9.925	31.598
3	0.277	0.978	1.638	2.353	3.182	4.541	5.841	12.941
4	0.271	0.941	1.533	2.132	2.776	3.747	4.604	8.610
5	0.267	0.920	1.476	2.015	2.571	3.365	4.032	6.859
6	0.265	0.906	1.440	1.943	2.447	3.143	3.707	5.959
7	0.263	0.896	1.415	1.895	2.365	2.998	3.499	5.405
8	0.262	0.889	1.397	1.860	2.306	2.896	3.355	5.041
9	0.261	0.883	1.383	1.833	2.262	2.821	3.250	4.781
10	0.260	0.879	1.372	1.812	2.228	2.764	3.169	4.587
11	0.260	0.876	1.363	1.796	2.201	2.718	3.106	4.437
12	0.259	0.873	1.356	1.782	2.179	2.681	3.055	4.318
13	0.259	0.870	1.350	1.771	2.160	2.650	3.012	4.221
14	0.258	0.868	1.345	1.761	2.145	2.624	2.977	4.140
15	0.258	0.866	1.341	1.753	2.131	2.602	2.947	4.073
16	0.258	0.865	1.337	1.746	2.120	2.583	2.921	4.015
17	0.257	0.863	1.333	1.740	2.110	2.567	2.898	3.965
18	0.257	0.862	1.330	1.734	2.101	2.552	2.878	3.922
19	0.257	0.861	1.328	1.729	2.093	2.539	2.861	3.883
20	0.257	0.860	1.325	1.725	2.086	2.528	2.845	3.850
21	0.257	0.859	1.323	1.721	2.080	2.518	2.831	3.819
22	0.256	0.858	1.321	1.717	2.074	2.508	2.819	3.792
23	0.256	0.858	1.319	1.714	2.069	2.500	2.807	3.767
24	0.256	0.857	1.318	1.711	2.064	2.492	2.797	3.745
25	0.256	0.856	1.316	1.708	2.060	2.485	2.787	3.725
26	0.256	0.856	1.315	1.706	2.056	2.479	2.779	3.707
27	0.256	0.855	1.314	1.703	2.052	2.473	2.771	3.690
28	0.256	0.855	1.313	1.701	2.048	2.467	2.763	3.674
29	0.256	0.854	1.311	1.699	2.045	2.462	2.756	3.659
30	0.256	0.854	1.310	1.697	2.042	2.457	2.750	3.646
40	0.255	0.851	1.303	1.684	2.021	2.423	2.704	3.551
60	0.254	0.848	1.296	1.671	2.000	2.390	2.660	3.460
120	0.254	0.845	1.289	1.658	1.980	2.358	2.617	3.373
∞	0.253	0.842	1.282	1.645	1.960	2.326	2.576	3.291

* This table is reproduced in abridged form from Table III of Fisher and Yates, *Statistical Tables for Biological, Agricultural, and Medical Research*, published by Oliver & Boyd, Ltd., Edinburgh, by permission of the authors and publishers.

Appendix F

Table F-11 Distribution of χ^2 *

Values of χ^2 corresponding to certain selected probabilities (*i.e.*, tail areas under the curve). To illustrate: the probability is 0.05 that a sample with 20 degrees of freedom, taken from a normal distribution, would have $\chi^2 = 31.410$ or larger.

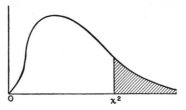

DF	Probability										
	0.99	0.98	0.95	0.90	0.80	0.20	0.10	0.05	0.02	0.01	0.001
1	0.0³157	0.0³628	0.00393	0.0158	0.0642	1.642	2.706	3.841	5.412	6.635	10.827
2	0.0201	0.0404	0.103	0.211	0.446	3.219	4.605	5.991	7.824	9.210	13.815
3	0.115	0.185	0.352	0.584	1.005	4.642	6.251	7.815	9.837	11.341	16.268
4	0.297	0.429	0.711	1.064	1.649	5.989	7.779	9.488	11.668	13.277	18.465
5	0.554	0.752	1.145	1.610	2.343	7.289	9.236	11.070	13.388	15.086	20.517
6	0.872	1.134	1.635	2.204	3.070	8.558	10.645	12.592	15.033	16.812	22.457
7	1.239	1.564	2.167	2.833	3.822	9.803	12.017	14.067	16.622	18.475	24.322
8	1.646	2.032	2.733	3.490	4.594	11.030	13.362	15.507	18.168	20.090	26.125
9	2.088	2.532	3.325	4.168	5.380	12.242	14.684	16.919	19.679	21.666	27.877
10	2.558	3.059	3.940	4.865	6.179	13.442	15.987	18.307	21.161	23.209	29.588
11	3.053	3.609	4.575	5.578	6.989	14.631	17.275	19.675	22.618	24.725	31.264
12	3.571	4.178	5.226	6.304	7.807	15.812	18.549	21.026	24.054	26.217	32.909
13	4.107	4.765	5.892	7.042	8.634	16.985	19.812	22.362	25.472	27.688	34.528
14	4.660	5.368	6.571	7.790	9.467	18.151	21.064	23.685	26.873	29.141	36.123
15	5.229	5.985	7.261	8.547	10.307	19.311	22.307	24.996	28.259	30.578	37.697
16	5.812	6.614	7.962	9.312	11.152	20.465	23.542	26.296	29.633	32.000	39.252
17	6.408	7.255	8.672	10.085	12.002	21.615	24.769	27.587	30.995	33.409	40.790
18	7.015	7.906	9.390	10.865	12.857	22.760	25.989	28.869	32.346	34.805	42.312
19	7.633	8.567	10.117	11.651	13.716	23.900	27.204	30.144	33.687	36.191	43.820
20	8.260	9.237	10.851	12.443	14.578	25.038	28.412	31.410	35.020	37.566	45.315
21	8.897	9.915	11.591	13.240	15.445	26.171	29.615	32.671	36.343	38.932	46.797
22	9.542	10.600	12.338	14.041	16.314	27.301	30.813	33.924	37.659	40.289	48.268
23	10.196	11.293	13.091	14.848	17.187	28.429	32.007	35.172	38.968	41.638	49.728
24	10.856	11.992	13.848	15.659	18.062	29.553	33.196	36.415	40.270	42.980	51.179
25	11.524	12.697	14.611	16.473	18.940	30.675	34.382	37.652	41.566	44.314	52.620
26	12.198	13.409	15.379	17.292	19.820	31.795	35.563	38.885	42.856	45.642	54.052
27	12.879	14.125	16.151	18.114	20.703	32.912	36.741	40.113	44.140	46.963	55.476
28	13.565	14.847	16.928	18.939	21.588	34.027	37.916	41.337	45.419	48.278	56.893
29	14.256	15.574	17.708	19.768	22.475	35.139	39.087	42.557	46.693	49.588	58.302
30	14.953	16.306	18.493	20.599	23.364	36.250	40.256	43.773	47.962	50.892	59.703

* This table is reproduced in abridged form from Table IV of Fisher and Yates, *Statistical Tables for Biological, Agricultural, and Medical Research,* published by Oliver & Boyd, Ltd., Edinburgh, by permission of the authors and publishers.

Table F-12 Units, conversion factors, and physical constants*

Length

1 meter = 39.3700 in. = 3.280833 ft = 1.093611 yd
1 kilometer = 0.62137 mile = 0.53996 nautical mile (International)
1 micron (μ) = 10^{-6} meter = 10^{-4} cm = 10^4 angstrom units = 39.3700×10^{-6} in.
1 angstrom unit = 10^{-8} cm = 10^{-10} meter = 10^{-4} micron = 3.937×10^{-9} in.
1 inch = 1,000 mils = 2.540005 cm
1 foot = 30.48006 cm = 1.89394×10^{-4} mile
1 yard = 0.91440183 meter
1 fathom = 6 ft = 1.828804 meters
1 chain (Gunter's) = 4 rods = 66 ft = 100 links = 0.1 furlong = 20.1168 meters
1 statute mile = 1,760 yd = 5,280 ft = 6.3360×10^4 in. = 1.60935 km = 0.868979
  nautical mile (International)
1 light year = 5.8804×10^{12} miles = 9.4637×10^{12} km = 0.307 parsec
1 nautical mile (International) = 1,852 meters = 6,076.10333 ft = 1.15078 miles

Area

1 sq cm = 10^{-4} sq meter = 10.764×10^{-4} sq ft = 0.15500 sq in.
1 sq km = 0.3861006 sq mile = 247.1044 acres
1 cir mil = area of circle 1 mil in diameter = 0.78540 sq mil = 10^{-6} cir in.
1 sq in. = 6.4516258 sq cm = 1.27324×10^6 cir mils
1 sq yd = 9 sq ft = 0.83613 sq meter
1 sq mile = 3.0976×10^6 sq yd = 640 acres = 2.589998×10^6 sq meters
1 acre = 43,560 sq ft = 10 sq chains = 4,046.873 sq meters

Volume

1 cu cm = 0.061023 cu in. = 0.03381 fl oz
1 liter = 1,000.027 cu cm = 33.8147 fl oz = 1.05671 qt (liq) = 0.26418 gal
1 cu ft = 1,728 cu in. = 28.317 liters = 7.481 gal = 0.80357 bushel
1 gal = 231 cu in. = 0.13368 cu ft = 3.78533 liters
1 qt = 32 fl oz = 946.33 ml
1 pt (liq) = 0.5 qt = 28.875 cu in. = 1.042 lb water at 62°F
1 fl oz = 1.042 oz (avdp) water at 62°F

Time

1 week = 7 days = 168 hr = 10,080 min = 604,800 sec
1 mean solar day = 1,440 min = 86,400 sec
1 calendar year = 365 days = 8,760 hr = 5.256×10^5 min = 3.1536×10^7 sec
1 sidereal year = 365.256 days (mean solar) = 8,766.14 hr (mean solar)

Velocity

1 meter/sec = 2.2369 mph
1 mph = 1.4667 ft/sec = 0.8690 knot = 1.6093 km/hr = 0.447041 meter/sec
1 knot = 1 nautical mile (International)/hr = 1.1508 statute miles/hr = 1.6878 ft/sec

---

* By A. H. Canada, et al. from William D. Cockrell, "Industrial Electronics Handbook," McGraw-Hill Book Company, New York, 1958.

Table F-12 Units, conversion factors, and physical constants
(*Continued*)

Angular velocity

1 radian/sec = 0.1592 rps = 9.549 rpm = 57.296 deg/sec
1 rpm = 0.01667 rps = 0.10472 radian/sec = 6 deg/sec

Acceleration

1 ft/sec^2 = 30.4801 cm/sec^2 = 0.6818 mile/hr-sec

Angle

1 radian = 360°/2π = 57.29578 deg = 10^3 angular mils
1 deg = 60 min = 0.01745 radian
1 min = 60 sec = 2.90888 $\times$ 10^{-4} radian
1 military mil = 360/6,400 deg = 0.05625 deg
1 sec slope = 4.848 μ in./in. = 0.001 in./17.19 ft
1 solid angle = 4 π steradians = 12.566 steradians = 1 sphere
1 steradian = 0.079580 solid angle

Mass

1 gram = 2.20462 $\times$ 10^{-3} lb (avdp) = 0.03527 oz (avdp) = 15.4324 grains
1 lb (avdp) = 16 oz (avdp) = 7,000 grains = 256 drams (avdp) = 453.5924 grams
1 oz (avdp) = 16 drams (avdp) = 437.5 grains = 28.34953 grams
1 short ton = 2,000 lb (avdp) = 907.185 kg = 20 cwt (short)
1 long ton = 2,240 lb (avdp) = 1,016.0470 kg = 20 cwt (long)

Density

1 lb/cu ft = 5.787 $\times$ 10^{-4} lb/cu in. = 16.018 kg/cu meter = 1.6018 $\times$ 10^{-2} grams/cu cm
1 gram/cu cm = 0.03613 lb/cu in. = 62.43 lb/cu ft

Pressure

1 atmosphere (atm) = 1.0133 bars = 14.696 lb/sq in. = 1.013246 $\times$ 10^6 dynes/sq cm
= 1,033.2 grams/sq cm (0°C) = 760 mm Hg (0°C) = 29.921 in. Hg (0°C) = 33.903
ft water (0°C)
1 dyne/sq cm = 1.01971 $\times$ 10^{-3} grams/sq cm = 1.4504 $\times$ 10^{-5} lb/sq in.
1 bar = 1.0 $\times$ 10^6 dynes/sq cm = 0.98692 atm
1 lb wt/sq in. = 70.307 grams/sq cm = 68,947 dynes/sq cm

Temperature

Temperature differences: Δ1° centigrade (C) = Δ1.8° Fahrenheit (F)
= Δ1.8° Rankine = Δ1° Kelvin (K) = Δ0.8° Reaumur (R)
0°C = 273°K = 32°F = 492° Rankine = 0°R
100°C = 373°K = 212°F = 672° Rankine = 125°R
0°K = − 273.16°C = − 459.72°F

Force

1 newton = 1 $\times$ 10^5 dynes = 0.22481 lb wt
1 dyne = 2.2481 $\times$ 10^{-6} lb wt = 7.2330 $\times$ 10^{-5} poundal = 0.0010197 gram wt
1 gram wt = 0.07932 poundal = 980.665 dynes = 2.2046 $\times$ 10^{-3} lb wt
1 lb wt = 32.174 poundals = 453.59 gram wt = 4.4482 newtons
1 poundal = 0.031081 lb wt = 14.098 gram wt = 1.3825 $\times$ 10^4 dynes

Table F-12   Units, conversion factors, and physical constants
(*Continued*)

Work and energy

1 absolute (abs) joule = 1 newton-meter = 1×10^7 ergs = 1×10^7 dyne-cm
   = 1 watt-sec = 1 volt-coulomb = 0.73756 ft-lb = 2.3889×10^{-4} kg-cal (mean)
   = 9.4805×10^{-4} Btu (mean) = 23.730 ft-poundal = 2.778×10^{-7} kwhr
   = 3.725×10^{-7} hp-hr
1 gram-cal (mean) = 4.186 joules (abs)
1 gram-cal (15°C) = 4.1855 joules (abs) = 0.003968 Btu
1 joule (International) = 1.000165 joules (abs)
1 kwhr = 3413.0 Btu (mean) = 2.6552×10^6 ft-lb = 1.3410 hp-hr
1 liter atm (normal) = 3.7745×10^{-5} hp-hr = 24.206 g-cal (mean) = 101.328
   joules (abs)
1 atomic mass unit (amu) = 931.16 Mev = 1.65983×10^{-24} gram mass
   (energy equiv)
1 electron volt = 1.60207×10^{-19} joule (abs)

Power

1 Btu (mean)/min = 0.023575 hp = 17.580 watts (abs) = 778.0 ft-lb/min
1 erg/sec = 10^{-10} kw = 1.3412×10^{-10} hp = 1×10^{-7} watt = 5.688×10^{-9}
   Btu (mean)/min = 1.4333×10^{-9} kg-cal (mean)/min = 7.3756×10^{-8} ft-lb/sec
1 hp (mech) = 0.70696 Btu (mean)/sec = 550 ft-lb/sec = 745.70 watts
   = 10.688 kg-cal (mean)/min
1 hp (elec) = 746.00 watts

Torque

1 dyne-cm = 1.0197×10^{-8} kg-meter = 7.3757×10^{-8} lb-ft = 8.8511×10^{-7} lb-in.
   = 2.3731×10^{-6} poundal-ft
1 kg-meter = 9.8066×10^7 dyne-cm
1 lb-ft = 1.3558×10^7 dyne-cm
1 poundal-ft = 4.2140×10^5 dyne-cm
1 lb-in. = 1.1298×10^6 dyne-cm

Physical constants

h = Planck constant = $(6.6252 \pm 0.0005) \times 10^{-27}$ erg-sec
R_0 = gas constant per mole = $(8.31662 \pm 0.00038) \times 10^7$ erg/°K-mole (physical scale)
   = $(8.20545 + 0.00037) \times 10^{-2}$ liter atm/°K-mole (chem scale)
k = Boltzmann constant = $(1.38042 \pm 0.00010) \times 10^{-16}$ erg/°K
σ = Stefan-Boltzmann constant (for black body) = $(5.6686 \pm 0.0005) \times 10^{-3}$
   erg/(sq cm)-(sec)(°K)^4
C = velocity of light = $(2.99793 \pm 0.00001) \times 10^{10}$ cm/sec = 186,284 miles/sec
$\mathfrak{F}$ = Faraday constant = $(96,520 \pm 3)$ abs coulombs/gram equivalent (physical scale)
e = electronic charge = $(1.60207 \pm 0.00007) \times 10^{-19}$ abs coulombs
   = $(4.80288 \pm 0.00021) \times 10^{-10}$ esu
e/m = specific electronic charge = $(1.75888 \pm 0.00005) \times 10^{11}$ abs coulombs/kg
N_0 = Avogadro's number = $(6.02472 \pm 0.00036) \times 10^{23}$ molecules/gram mole
   (physical scale) = $(6.02308 \pm 0.00040) \times 10^{23}$ molecules/gram mole
   (chemical scale)
α_0 = $h^2/4\pi \, me^2$ = first Bohr radius = $(5.29171 \pm 0.00006) \times 10^{-9}$ cm
ϵ_0 = $1/\mu_0 \, C^2$ = permittivity of free space = $(8.8542 \pm 0.0001) \times 10^{-12}$ farad/meter
μ_0 = permeability of free space = $4\pi \times 10^{-7}$ henry/meter = 12.5664×10^{-7}
   henry/meter
Z_0 = $(\mu_0/\epsilon_0)^{1/2}$ = impedance of free space = (376.731 ± 0.001) ohm
G = Newton's gravity constant = $(6.670 \pm 0.005) \times 10^{-8}$ cu cm/gram sec

Table F-12 **Units,** **conversion** **factors,** **and** **physical** **constants** (*Continued*)

---

g = acceleration due to gravity (standard) = 32.174 ft/sec^2 = 980.665 cm/sec^2
 = 386.09 in./sec^2 = 21.94 miles/hr-sec
Rest energy of the electron = 0.51098 Mev
Electron mass = $(9.1085 \pm 0.0006) \times 10^{-28}$ gram = 0.51098 Mev = 5.48760×10^{-4} amu
Proton mass = $(1.67243 \pm 0.00010) \times 10^{-24}$ gram = 938.232 Mev = 1.007593 amu
Neutron mass = $(1.67474 \pm 0.00010) \times 10^{-24}$ gram = 939.526 Mev = 1.008982 amu
$\propto$ particle mass = $(6.6442 \pm 0.0012) \times 10^{-24}$ gram = 3727.377 Mev = 4.00294 amu
H_1 atom mass = $(1.67335 \pm 0.00010) \times 10^{-24}$ gram = 938.743 Mev = 1.008142 amu

SOURCE: Atomic Constants: Dumond and Cohen, *Rev. Mod. Phys.*, **25**:691 (1953).

Electrical units

Absolute Practical	Electrostatic (esu)	Electromagnetic (emu)
1 coulomb	= 2.998×10^9 statcoulombs	= 10^{-1} abcoulomb
1 ampere (coulomb/sec)	= 2.998×10^9 statamp	= 10^{-1} abamp
1 volt	= 3.335×10^{-3} statvolt	= 10^8 abvolts
1 farad	= 8.988×10^{11} statfarads	= 10^{-9} abfarad
1 weber/sq meter	= $1/(3 \times 10^6)$	= 10^4 gauss
1 ampere turn/meter	= $12\pi \times 10^7$	= 1.257×10^{-2} oersted
1 ampere turn	= $12\pi \times 10^9$	= 1.257 gilberts
1 henry	= 1.112×10^{-12} stathenry	= 10^9 abhenrys
1 ohm	= 1.112×10^{-12} statohm	= 10^9 abohms

Miscellaneous constants and conversions

Density of water at 3.98°C, 760 mm Hg = 0.03613 lb/cu in. = 62.43 lb/cu ft
 = 1 gram/ml = 0.999973 gram/cu cm
Density of air (stp) = 1.293×10^{-3} gram/cu cm
stp = standard temperature and pressure = 0°C and 760 mm Hg
Water heat of fusion (0°C) = 79.71 g-cal (15°C)/gram
Water heat of vaporization (100°C) = 539.55 g-cal (15°C)/gram
Molar volume (stp) = 359 cu ft/lb mole = (22.4207 ± 0.0006) liters/gram mole
 (physical scale)
Velocity of sound: in air (stp) = 331.7 meters/sec = 1,088 ft/sec
 in water (20°C) = 1,470 meters/sec = 4,823 ft/sec
 in pine wood = 3,320 meters/sec = 10,900 ft/sec
 in soft steel = 5,000 meters/sec = 16,410 ft/sec
Attenuation of sound in air (stp, 37% rh) = $\delta \cong 6 \times 10^{-14}$ db (kc)^2/ft
Viscosity of water (20°C) = 1.002 centipoises = 0.01002 dyne-sec/sq cm
1 curie activity = 3.7×10^{10} disintegrations/sec = 3.7×10^4 rutherfords
1 roentgen (r) radiation damage = ionization by X or γ rays producing 1 esu of
 charge in 1 cu cm air (stp)
1 barn cross section = 10^{-24} sq cm
Ratio physical (O^{16} = 16) to chemical scale (O = 16) of atomic weights
 = 1.000272 ± 0.000005
M = mass of earth = 5.983×10^{24} kg = 6.595×10^{21} tons
Interference fringe = 11.6μ in./fringe (He line: 5,875.6 angstrom units)
π = 3.1415926535+
e = 2.7182818284+
Log$_e$ N = log$_e$ 10 $\times$ log$_{10}$ N = 2.3026 log$_{10}$ N
1 kwhr $\cong 4.2 \times 10^{-5}$ gram U^{235} in fission
$ \cong 6.4 \times 10^{-6}$ gram H^3 in H^3 (d,n), He^4 reaction
$ \cong$ average noon insolation in 1 hr on a horizontal plane of 1 sq meter
$ \cong 0.74$ lb (highest modern power station efficiency on 12,500 Btu/lb coal)

G GLOSSARY OF SYMBOLS AND NOTATIONS

The symbols and notations used in this handbook were chosen so as to permit reference to most standard textbooks while still maintaining consistency throughout the handbook. This glossary lists generally useful symbols whose definitions may not appear in their immediate context; each entry gives the handbook section or sections in which the symbol is defined.

Scalars and matrices

α, β, . . . represent scalar (numerical) quantities, Chaps. 4 and 8. α^* is the complex conjugate of α, and $|\alpha|$ is the absolute value of α, **1.2-4.**

In Chap. 8, A, B, . . . represent matrices, most frequently square matrices, with $A \equiv [a_{ik}]$; and

$$x \equiv \{\xi_i\} \equiv \begin{bmatrix} \xi_1 \\ \xi_2 \\ \cdot\ \cdot\ \cdot \end{bmatrix} \quad \text{column matrix}$$

$$\tilde{x} \equiv (\xi_i) \equiv (\xi_1, \xi_2, \ .\ .\ .) \quad \text{row matrix}$$

Vectors and vector components

a, b, . . . and **x, y,** . . . represent vectors **4.1-1, 8.1-5**
u, unit vector **4.2-4**
i, j, k, right-handed rectangular cartesian base vectors **4.2-3**

$\mathbf{e}_i$, base vectors **4.2-2**

$\mathbf{r} \equiv x\mathbf{i} + y\mathbf{j} + z\mathbf{k}$ } position vectors in three-
$\boldsymbol{\varrho} \equiv \xi\mathbf{i} + \eta\mathbf{j} + \zeta\mathbf{k}$ } dimensional euclidean space **Chaps. 2, 3, 4**

$\mathbf{a} \cdot \mathbf{b}$, scalar product of vectors $\mathbf{a}$, $\mathbf{b}$ **4.2-5**

$|\mathbf{a}| \equiv (\mathbf{a} \cdot \mathbf{a})^{1/2}$, absolute value (norm) of $\mathbf{a}$ **4.2-4**

$\mathbf{a} \times \mathbf{b}$, vector product of three-dimensional vectors $\mathbf{a}$, $\mathbf{b}$ **4.2-6**

$[\mathbf{abc}]$, scalar triple product **4.2-7**

∇ (del or nabla), vector differential operator **4.5-2**

$\nabla^2 \equiv \nabla \cdot \nabla$, Laplacian operator **4.5-4**

Expected values (mean values) and averages

$E\{x\} = \xi$ expected value, ensemble average **9.1-6**

$\bar{x} = \dfrac{1}{n}(x_1 + x_2 + \cdots + x_n)$ statistical sample average (a random variable) **9.2-6**

$\arcsin z$, $\arccos z$, $\arctan z$	inverse trigonometric functions **11.1-4**
$\arg z$	argument of z **1.2-7**
$\operatorname{cn} z$	(cosinus amplitudinis), elliptic function **11.3-2**
$\cos z$	cosine function **11.1-1**
$\cosh z$	hyperbolic cosine **11.1-5**
$\cosh^{-1} z$	inverse hyperbolic cosine **11.1-9**
dn	(delta amplitudinis), elliptic function **11.3-2**
$\det [a_{ik}]$	determinant **1.3-1**
$\operatorname{erf} x$	error function **9.1-10**
$E(k, \varphi)$	Legendre's normal elliptic integral of the second kind **11.3-1**
$\mathbf{E}(k)$	Legendre's complete normal elliptic integral of the second kind **11.3-1**
$F(\hbar, \varphi)$	Legendre's normal elliptic integral of the first kind **11.3-1**
$H_m^{(1)}(z)$, $H_m^{(2)}(z)$	Hankel functions **11.3-3**
$i = \sqrt{-1}$	unit imaginary number **1.2-7**
$\operatorname{Im} z$	imaginary part of z **1.2-7**
$\inf x$	greatest lower bound **3.3-3**
$J_m(z)$	Bessel function of the first kind **11.3-3**
$\mathbf{K}(k)$	Legendre's complete elliptic integral of the first kind **11.3-1**
$\lim z$	limit **3.4-1**
$\log_a z$	logarithm **1.2-6**
$\max x$, $\min x$	maximum and minimum values **3.3-3**
$N_m(z)$	Neumann's Bessel function of the second kind **11.3-3**
$o[g(x)]$, $O[g(x)]$	asymptotic relations **3.4-3**
$P_n(z)$	Legendre's polynomial of the first kind **11.3-4**
$P_j{}^m(z)$	associated Legendre "polynomial" of the first kind **11.3-4**
$\operatorname{Re} z$	real part of z **1.2-7**

$\text{Res}_f a$	residue of $f(z)$ at $z = a$	**5.3-4**
sinc (t)	sampling function	**Table D-1**
$\sin z$	sine function	**11.1-1**
$\sinh z$	hyperbolic sine	**11.1-5**
$\sinh^{-1} z$	inverse hyperbolic sine	**11.1-9**
$\sup x$	least upper bound	**3.3-3**
$T_n(z)$	Chebyshev polynomial of the first kind	**11.3-4**
$\tan z$	tangent function	**11.1-1**
$\tanh z$	hyperbolic tangent	**11.1-5**
$\tanh^{-1} z$	inverse hyperbolic tangent	**11.1-9**
$\text{Tr} [a_{ik}]$	trace	**8.2-6**
$Y_j(\vartheta, \varphi)$	spherical surface harmonic	**11.3-4**

$[N_m(z)$ rather than $Y_m(z)$ is used for Neumann functions **11.3-3**]

$Z_m(z)$	cylinder function	**11.3-3**
Δy_k	forward difference	**10.2-1**
∇y_k	backward difference	**10.2-1**
δy_k	central difference	**10.2-1**
$\mathfrak{F}[f(t)] \equiv \mathfrak{F}[f(t); \nu]$	Fourier transform	**3.11-2**
$\mathfrak{F}_C[f(t)], \mathfrak{F}_S[f(t)]$	Fourier cosine and sine transforms	**3.11-2**
$\mathfrak{L}[f(t)] \equiv \mathfrak{L}[f(t); s] \equiv F(s)$	Laplace transform	**5.4-2**
$\mathcal{V}$	a vector space	**8.1-5**
$n!$	factorial	**1.2-8**
$\begin{pmatrix} x \\ n \end{pmatrix}$	binomial coefficient	**1.2-8**
$\dfrac{\partial(y_1, y_2, \ldots, y_n)}{\partial(x_1, x_2, \ldots, x_n)}$	Jacobian	**3.5-4**
$\cap$	cap	**3.3-2**
$\cup$	cup	**3.3-2, 8.3-4**
$*$	convolution symbol	**3.11-3, 5.4-6**
$\displaystyle\sum_{k=m}^{n}$	summation	
$\displaystyle\prod_{k=m}^{n}$	product	
$=$	equality symbol	**1.2-3**
$\equiv$	identity symbol	**1.2-3**
$\triangleq$	identity by definition	
$\approx$	approximate equality	
$\simeq$	asymptotically equal	**3.4-3**
$\sim$	asymptotically proportional	**3.4-3**
$<, >, \leq, \geq$	inequality, inclusion	
$\subset, \supset$	inclusion	**3.3-2**
$\in$	element of	**3.3-1**
$\ni$	such that	

D, V	domain, region
S	surface, boundary surface or hypersurface
C	curve, boundary curve
$ds, d\mathbf{r}$	scalar and vector path elements (see index)
$dA, d\mathbf{A}$	scalar and vector surface elements (see index)

INDEX

INDEX

References to essential definitions in this index make it useful as a mathematical dictionary. The following style is used for references: 5.4-2 and B-4. 5.4-2, for example, refers to Chapter 5, Section 4, Subsection 2, while all references that begin with a letter refer to the appendixes.